Telecommunications Transmission Engineering

Telecommunications Transmission Engineering is published in three volumes:

Volume 1 — *Principles*
Volume 2 — *Facilities*
Volume 3 — *Networks and Services*

Telecommunications Transmission Engineering

Third Edition

**Technical Personnel
Bellcore and
Bell Operating Companies**

**Volume 2
Facilities**

Operating and regional company employees may obtain copies of this volume, order the Bellcore Technical References cited in this volume, as well as subscribe to Bellcore's DIGEST of Technical Information by contacting their company documentation coordinators.

All others may obtain the same copies as well as subscribe to the DIGEST by calling Bellcore's documentation hotline 1–800–521–CORE or (201) 699–5802.

Order each *Telecommunications Transmission Engineering* volume by the ST number as follows.

Volume 1, *Principles*	ST–TEC–000051
Volume 2, *Facilities*	ST–TEC–000052
Volume 3, *Networks and Services*	ST–TEC–000053

Prepared for publication by
Bellcore Technical Publications.

This is the third edition of the *Telecommunications Transmission Engineering* three–volume series previously copyrighted by AT&T and AT&T Bell Laboratories.

ISBN 1–878108–02–6 (Volume 2)
ISBN 1–878108–04–2 (three–volume set)

Library of Congress Catalog Card Number: 90–62180

Telecommunications Transmission Engineering

Introduction

Telecommunications engineering is concerned with the planning, engineering, design, implementation, operation, and maintenance of the network of facilities, channels, switching equipment, and user devices required to provide voice and data communications between various locations. Transmission engineering is that part of telecommunications engineering that deals with the channels, the transmission facilities or systems that carry the channels or circuits, and the combinations of the many types of channels and facilities that help form a network. It is a discipline that combines skills and knowledge from science and technology with an understanding of economics, human factors, and system operations.

This three–volume reference book is written for the practicing transmission engineer and for the student of transmission engineering in an undergraduate curriculum. However, the material was planned and organized to make it useful to anyone concerned with the many facets of telecommunications engineering. Of necessity, it represents only the current status of communications technology being used and deployed today by the Bell operating companies in their intraLATA (local access and transport area) networks, which provide exchange telecommunications and exchange access services, as well as their official networks. The reader should be aware of the dynamic nature of the subject.

Volume 1, *Principles*, covers the transmission engineering principles that apply to communications systems. It defines the characteristics of various types of signal, describes signal impairments arising in practical channels, provides the basis for understanding the relationships between a communication network and its components, and provides an appreciation of how transmission objectives and achievable performance are interrelated.

Volume 2, *Facilities*, emphasizes the application of the principles of Volume 1 to the design, implementation, and operation of the transmission systems and facilities that are used to form the public networks.

Volume 3, *Networks and Services*, builds on the principles and facilities discussed in Volumes 1 and 2 and shows how the principles are applied to facilities to form networks that are used by the exchange carriers to provide services for various users.

The authors use a generic approach throughout all three volumes. However, they often use specific examples and illustrations that are most familiar to them to help clarify a concept. These examples are not intended to recommend any equipment or to imply that there is only one solution to a given problem.

The material has been written, edited, prepared, and reviewed by a large number of technical personnel from the Bell operating companies and Bellcore. Thus the book represents the cooperative efforts and views of many people.

As a point of reference for the reader, a brief description of these organizations follows. At divestiture, on January 1, 1984, 22 Bell operating companies were transferred from AT&T to seven newly formed regional companies: Ameritech, Bell Atlantic, BellSouth, NYNEX, Pacific Telesis, Southwestern Bell Corporation, and U S WEST. These regional companies, through their operating telephone companies, were empowered to provide local exchange telecommunications and exchange access services. They were also called upon to provide a common central point to meet the requirements of national security and emergency preparedness. Finally, they were allowed to create and support a centralized organization for the provision of engineering, administrative, and other services. This *central point* and organization is Bellcore.

The regional companies are both the owners and the clients of Bellcore. Bellcore's mission—to provide research, technical support, generic requirements, technical analyses, and other services to the Bell operating companies—allows them to provide modern, high-quality yet low-priced services to their customers. Bellcore provides neither manufacturing nor supplier recommendations, as procurement is a function of the regional companies.

Irwin Dorros
Executive Vice President –
Technical Services
Bellcore

Volume 2—Facilities

Preface

The telecommunications facilities network is made up of a large number of transmission systems, media, terminal units, and apparatus that have been designed and constructed to operate efficiently as an integrated communications system. The network has grown rapidly in recent years and has changed remarkably with the increasingly sophisticated technological designs and processes that have emerged over the same period.

The network has evolved as one capable of providing high-quality telecommunications services economically. In addition, its facilities and equipment give it flexibility and adaptability in the face of a wide range of environmental factors that include rural and metropolitan areas, residential and business communities, and many more. Furthermore, the entire network has proven to be adaptable to transmitting signals of constantly changing character, the result of providing new and expanded services.

Volume 2 describes the major facilities, systems, circuits, and equipment designed and used by exchange and interexchange carriers to provide the required wide range of communications services. The text is organized in seven sections covering (1) the network and its principal transmission media, (2) local plant facilities, (3) analog carrier systems on wire lines, (4) digital systems, (5) radio systems, (6) transmission maintenance systems and equipment, and (7) how all these elements are integrated to form a communications system that serves this nation and interconnects with the facilities network of the world.

Section 1 provides a general description of the facility network and discusses briefly the way it has evolved. A summary is also given of the characteristics of transmission media. Section 2 describes loops, voice frequency trunk facilities and circuit equipment, and voiceband data and wideband facilities. The section also covers the transmission characteristics of central office equipment as well as customer–premises equipment generically called Business Communications Systems.

Section 3 describes analog carrier systems on wire lines. The section begins with a chapter that describes frequency division multiplex equipment. Next is a discussion of basic design features of analog transmission systems followed by descriptions of systems based on wire–pair and coaxial cable. Section 4 covers digital transmission systems. The section begins with a description of pulse code modulation transmission systems and continues with a discussion of fiber optic technology. In addition, the section covers digital and optical bit rate hierarchies, formats, multiplexers and channel banks. The section ends with a description of digital transmission on metallic lines.

Section 5 contains descriptions of radio systems. Basic design features of terrestrial microwave systems, systems engineering, and protection switching systems are first described. These general discussions are followed by descriptions of the features of analog and digital microwave radio systems. Domestic satellite transmission and miscellaneous radio systems and services, principally cellular mobile communications, are also covered.

Section 6 discusses transmission maintenance. Maintenance systems, which play a prominent role in the field of transmission maintenance, are computer–controlled and are used to fulfill significant functions in record keeping, operations control, and force management. Descriptions of types of test equipment and their importance in transmission maintenance are also presented.

An overall view of the facilities network and how the parts fit together is presented in Section 7. It describes some of the limitations imposed on system use by the interferences introduced into one system by another. The section also covers how the parts are interconnected to ensure compatibility and synchronized to avoid transmission deterioration.

Contents

Contents

Contents

Contents

Section 3   Analog Carrier Systems on Wire Lines 211

Contents

Contents

Contents

Contents

Contents

Contents

Figures

Figures

Figures

Tables

Tables

Telecommunications Transmission Engineering

Section 1

The Facility Network

The public switched message network and the many special–services circuits share a nationwide array of telecommunications facilities. These facilities include transmission media, voice–frequency equipment, channelizing equipment, signalling and switching equipment, power supplies, and outside plant items of many descriptions. In short, the facility network comprises the telecommunications plant.

High–quality transmission is provided over this network by careful design of all of these facilities and by paying particular attention to the interactions at the interfaces. Each of the categories of facility mentioned above has some effect on transmission. However, those having the largest and most direct effects are transmission systems and transmission media.

Chapter 1 briefly reviews the evolution of transmission systems from single–wire, ground–return circuits that were initially leased from telegraph companies, through the alphabetically designated analog cable carrier systems and microwave radio facilities, to the modern digital transmission systems. Video signal transmission is also covered. The rapidly changing fields of maintenance and reliability are discussed. All of these factors are then related to deriving maximum benefit from dynamic network changes by adequate planning and by the application of engineering principles.

Every connection established for electrical communications between two points requires some transmission medium. Chapter 2 describes the media most commonly used. These include loaded and nonloaded multipair cables, optical fiber, coaxial cables, and the atmosphere, which is the medium for radio transmission systems.

1

Chapter 1

The Evolution of the Facility Network

Transmission facilities include transmission media, assemblies of equipment that make up transmission systems, and the channels derived from these systems. A network of such facilities exists to provide a wide variety of telecommunications services. Included are many types of transmission system and subsystem that have evolved with advancing technology and with demands for different types of service.

As it becomes necessary to expand facilities and to replace obsolete portions, criteria must be used to accomplish an orderly and economic expansion. The selection and application of new facilities depend on many factors. The growth and development rate of a geographic area, population shifts and business activities, and the influence of such factors on the community of interest must be taken into account while meeting state regulatory requirements. These factors must be considered separately for urban, suburban, and rural environments. Accurate forecasts of loop and trunk facility needs must also be made.

In all these aspects of facility–network evolution, engineering control must be exercised so that new plant is compatible with the existing plant. Engineering–economy studies are made to assure that use of capital is efficient and that short– and long–range objectives are satisfied wherever possible. New technology and innovations must be carefully evaluated and applied to ensure that customer demands for improved performance and new services are satisfied.

1-1 VOICE-FREQUENCY TRANSMISSION FACILITIES

The transmission media used during the years immediately following the invention of the telephone were single, iron–wire conductors rented from telegraph companies. These circuits operated on the principle of ground return and, as a result, were subject to noise and crosstalk. The advantages of paired copper conductors, primarily lower transmission loss and reduced susceptibility to noise, were recognized very early. By 1900, virtually all interoffice telephone communication was over paired copper conductors. The transition from iron to copper was accelerated by the development during the late nineteenth century of the hard–drawing process for copper wire. Also, by 1900, some cables had been manufactured and the technique of inductive loading had been invented and was being used. These advances permitted telephone communication over longer and longer distances: Boston to New York, 1884; New York to Chicago, 1892; and Denver to New York, 1911. All these distances were covered without the use of electronics.

With the introduction of electron–tube amplifiers, transmission of telephone signals from coast to coast was accomplished in 1915. All transcontinental circuits during those early years were open–wire lines. These were used for long–distance telephony because large–gauge conductors (typically 165–mil, or slightly thicker than No. 6 AWG) were necessary to obtain the required low loss.

As the toll plant grew in size and complexity, issues were recognized and solved one by one. In terms of transmission performance, these issues included the need to reduce circuit loss and noise and, as circuits increased in length, to control or suppress echoes. Losses were first reduced by increasing the size of conductors. Later, inductive loading was applied and, with the invention of the electron tube, amplification was provided. Noise performance was improved by using balanced pairs, transposed pairs, staggered twisting of cable conductors, and quadded cable. Four–wire transmission, four–wire switching, impedance matching, controlled losses, and echo suppressors improved echo performance of the network. In addition, economics and operational considerations led to the adoption of common–battery operation, the development of multichannel carrier systems, and the introduction of machine switching of local and toll traffic.

In the local plant, the transition from open–wire lines to cable and the application of inductive loading cut the costs of

4

subscriber loops and local trunks. Central–office equipment expanded from simple manual switchboards to large cord–type switchboards with A–board and B–board arrangements, the A–board for outgoing calls and the B–board for incoming traffic. This was followed by the first switching machines such as step–by–step and panel. In the manual and early machine switching systems, the state of telephone set development and signalling requirements limited wire–gauge selection in the loop and trunk plant to large sizes (e.g., 16–, 19–, and 22–gauge).

The use of smaller wire gauges in local facilities was initially made possible by the application of inductive loading. Later, the improvement of electron tubes, solid–state devices, and circuit components provided further advances in voice–frequency (VF) transmission performance. These new devices made possible the development of a wide range of amplifiers, repeaters, bridge lifters, hybrid transformers, impedance converters, noise–balancing circuits, and filters. They also led to improvements in frequency response, antisidetone features, and loop–current equalization of telephone station sets. These advances, together with the development of circuits to increase loop signalling ranges, made possible the use of smaller wire gauges in the loop plant, particularly the wide use of 26–gauge.

1–2 CARRIER TRANSMISSION FACILITIES

The history of carrier systems begins in the early years of the twentieth century. Carrier modes of transmission increase the efficiency of transmission media by combining (multiplexing) a large number of message signals into a single composite signal. Nearly all types of carrier modulation have been used, but three are now predominant. Single– and double–sideband *amplitude modulation* (AM) with frequency–division multiplexing (FDM) of signals, now vanishing rapidly, was once commonly used to form a broadband signal for transmission over analog cable carrier systems. *Frequency modulation* (FM) of a microwave carrier is used to transmit this broadband signal over microwave radio systems. *Pulse code modulation* (PCM) is used with time–division multiplex (TDM) techniques for transmitting signals over digital (regenerative–repeater) facilities and has effectively captured the field. Combinations of these techniques are possible and some

5

have been developed commercially, e.g., multilevel amplitude modulation in digital radio.

Analog Cable Carrier Systems

The maturing of electron tubes and solid–state devices and continuing improvements in passive components made it possible to develop carrier systems providing ever–wider bandwidths, substantially reducing the per–circuit cost of line mileage. Before the advent of digital switching, the cost of multiplex terminals affected the distance at which the use of electronics became more attractive than VF cable circuits.

In addition to the economic advantages of carrier, a number of performance improvements are realized. The velocity of propagation at carrier frequencies in any wire cable is substantially higher than at voice frequencies. This is especially true when carrier circuits are compared with loaded cable pairs. The higher velocity offers advantages in controlling echoes and is essential for transmission of a few types of signal where absolute delay is important. Four–wire transmission is inherent in carrier systems; as a result, impedances are better controlled, permitting the operation of circuits at lower losses yet with satisfactory stability and echo performance.

The development of the A–type system in 1917 was followed by a succession of carrier systems identified by alphabetical designations. These systems were at first developed for use on open–wire transmission lines. Most of these early systems, designated A through J, provided four–wire or equivalent–four–wire transmission in a frequency band above a VF channel that was simultaneously provided on the open–wire pair. One exception was the G1 system, first placed in service in 1935. It provided a single channel above a VF channel on a single pair of wires in a double–sideband transmitted–carrier mode and actually employed true two–wire transmission.

The J–type system provided 12 single–sideband suppressed–carrier channels on an open–wire pair in the equivalent four–wire mode. A VF channel and a C–type carrier system, which had a frequency allocation between the voiceband and the J–carrier band, could operate simultaneously on the same pair. A number of different frequency allocations were used for J carrier but all involved a first step of modulation into a group band covering the spectrum from 60 to 108 kHz. Thus, the *basic group* was formed to become the foundation of the entire FDM system during the 1930s. The K–carrier systems, developed at about the same time as the J–type, provided twelve single–sideband message channels for four–wire transmission on cable pairs rather than on open–wire lines. This was the first system in which the transmission medium was not shared with a VF channel or with another type of carrier system. To avoid crosstalk effects, separate cables were normally used for the two directions of transmission. Both J– and K–type systems were installed in quantity before, during, and after World War II. They are no longer in use.

While the J– and K–type systems filled long–haul needs, short–haul analog systems were also developed. In 1950, the first N–type system was placed in service to provide twelve double-sideband transmitted–carrier channels over nonloaded cable pairs for distances up to about 200 miles. The initial designs used electron tubes. However, the system was redesigned during the 1960s to exploit solid–state technology. The terminal equipment was later redesigned to permit the transmission of 24 single-sideband channels, and once again to adopt the use of integrated circuits and newest–vintage components.

The N–type systems were originally designed for four–wire transmission in two frequency bands that were alternated in succeeding repeater sections by a modulation process at each repeater (frequency frogging). This technique partially equalized the attenuation/frequency characteristic and minimized the crosstalk coupling between the two directions of transmission. A special–purpose line design also alternated frequency positions at each repeater but employed the equivalent–four–wire mode of transmission.

The O–type systems, made available during the same era and similar in many aspects to the N–type, provided short–haul carrier transmission on open–wire facilities. The equivalent–four–wire mode of transmission was used and frequency frogging was employed at each repeater. In addition, the open–wire pairs were transposed in accordance with a plan developed for carrier frequencies. These systems are rarely used today.

The O–type system provided a maximum of 16 4–kHz single-sideband channels multiplexed in groups of four. Each of the two pairs of channels in a four–channel group was transmitted on a common carrier frequency, one channel as an upper sideband and the other as a lower sideband. This arrangement was called twin–channel operation.

Certain O–type terminal arrangements were adapted for N–type lines. This combination was called an ON system and provided up to 24 channels. ON systems could be multiplexed to provide 96 channels on light–route microwave radio systems.

In 1929, the initial patent for a coaxial cable transmission system was granted. Cable and system development work continued from that time until 1941 when the L1 coaxial system was placed in service. L1 provided transmission for 480 4–kHz message channels (later expanded to 600) using separate coaxial units for each direction of transmission. The continuing development of coaxial systems produced the 1860–channel L3 system (1953), the 3600–channel L4 (1967), the 10,800–channel L5 (1974), and finally the L5E, expanded to a capacity of 13,200 channels.

Improvements in active devices, components, and systems have been paralleled by improvements in the performance and capabilities of the transmission media. From open wire, progress has been made in conductor, insulation, and sheath designs of cables and numerous advances were made in all aspects of coaxial cable design.

Radio Transmission Systems

In 1915, significant experimentation in voice communication by radio was started. One of its principal objectives was to provide a means for voice communications between the United States and Europe. By 1923, the basic feasibility had been established and intensive work was underway [1]. The first transatlantic commercial telephone service was established in 1927 when a long–wave (57–kHz) system was put into service between the

United States and Great Britain. This system employed single-sideband transmission with suppressed carrier. In 1928, short-wave systems were installed to operate in the 3–to–30–MHz range and service was expanded to all parts of the world. In the 1950s, overseas service was largely taken over by submarine cable transmission systems, and, in the 1960s, was supplemented heavily by satellite facilities.

During this period, radio transmission was also developed for a number of mobile services. These included high–seas ship–to–shore communication, coastal–harbor service (ship–to–ship and ship–to–shore), and mobile radio telephony to moving vehicles including automobiles, trains, and aircraft. Most important, from the standpoint of modern communications, was the development of microwave radio systems.

Microwave system development was stimulated significantly by World War II developments of radar and microwave components. There was some microwave transmission system work done for military applications and in preparation for the tremendous growth in communications services anticipated for the early post–war years. This growth quickly materialized; it was stimulated by the pent–up demand for service that could not be satisfied during the war and by the rapid growth of television. An experimental microwave radio system, called TDX, was installed between New York and Boston; service was begun in May 1948. This system was refined considerably and manufactured commercially as the TD–2 system [2].

Many microwave systems have been developed to fill service needs in long–haul and short–haul applications. These have been designed to operate in a number of frequency bands specified for common–carrier use. Since the medium must be shared by many users of communication services, the allocation of frequency bands and the design and use of radio transmission equipment in the United States are subject to licensing and control by the Federal Communications Commission (FCC). The frequency bands allocated for various types of service must conform to agreements made by member nations of the International Telecommunications Union through its World Administrative Radio Conferences. Figure 1–1 shows the principal bands and some of the services allocated to portions of the bands [3,4].

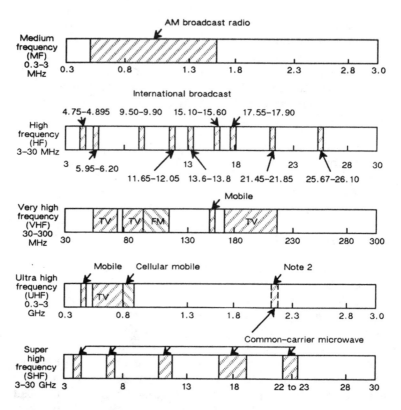

Notes:
1. The very low (VLF), low (LF), and extremely high frequency (EHF) allocations are not shown.

2. Common-carrier microwave and space telecommand signals share the bands from 2.11 to 2.13 and from 2.16 to 2.18 GHz.

Figure 1-1. Some radio-frequency spectrum allocations.

Microwave radio systems have filled a growing need for telecommunications circuits. In the early 1970s, they carried all of the interurban broadcast network television signals, but now satellite is the primary carrier of television while terrestrial microwave still carries a large proportion of the telephone, data, and other signals in the long-haul toll plant. Long repeater spacing, typically 25 miles, and ease of growth gave such systems substantial economic advantages over other types. Some limitation on this form of communication came from crowding of the radio–frequency spectrum but, as will be seen in subsequent chapters, some further growth of microwave radio may still be expected through improved techniques and more efficient use of the medium.

As telecommunication services and systems become more digitized, the development of digital radio systems was a natural evolution. This resulted in digital conversion of analog radios or outright replacement, and the near–exclusive use of digital for new installations. Digital systems with capacities of 2016 voice circuits per transmitter–receiver pair are now common. Digital radio is discussed further in Chapters 17, 18, and 20.

Pulse Transmission Systems

Some of the earliest attempts to transmit speech and music signals electrically involved efforts to code the signals into a pulse format and then to transmit the signal by telegraph [5]. These attempts were thwarted by the primitive technology of the times. Furthermore, devices were not available to facilitate experimentation with advanced coding techniques. Digital modes of transmission and digital processing of analog signals were delayed until more recent times, although digital data (telegraph) signals were often transmitted over analog systems.

While the evolving electron–tube technology permitted some advances in digital techniques [6], the most significant event leading to the application of PCM was the invention of the transistor in 1948. The small size, low power dissipation, high reliability, and low cost of transistors and other solid–state devices facilitated the design of practical circuits for digital transmission.

Progress in PCM and regenerative repeatered line operation advanced steadily. During the late 1950s, an experimental 1.544–Mb/s system was designed [7]. This system, later designated the T1 Carrier System, transmitted simultaneously 24 voice signals that had been processed by pulse coding and TDM [8]. It was put into first service in 1961, became commercially available in 1962, and shortly provided most of the circuit growth in metropolitan areas. As system costs fell, T1 proved to be economical at shorter and shorter trunk lengths relative to other types of facility, until the wide use of digital switching made the issue of distance moot.

Work on digital modes of transmission expanded to higher–capacity systems capable of transmitting over longer distances. In 1972, the T2 carrier system was introduced and provided 96 channels of toll quality on a 6.3–Mb/s pulse stream [9]. In the middle 1970s, the T4M and Canadian LD4 systems were installed as high–speed systems operating on coaxial cable. The T4M, designed for use in metropolitan areas, could carry 168 T1 line signals, thus providing 4032 voice–grade channels. Various "conversion" systems (T1C and T148 at 48 channels; T1D at 96 channels) were introduced for lower–cost metropolitan trunking, and were widely installed until fiber became economical.

The development of coding and multiplexing equipment for use with multimegabit transmission systems kept pace with development of the line equipment. One example is that of the D4 channel bank, which processes 48 voiceband signals into two 1.544–Mb/s bit streams [10]. These signals, designated DS1 in the digital hierarchy, may be transmitted separately over two T1–type lines or one T1C line. In addition, a combination of four DS1 signals from two banks used together may be combined by an internal multiplexer into a single 6.3–Mb/s bit stream to form a DS2 signal.

Digital transmission systems have proven to be highly effective for the transmission of analog signals that have been converted to a digital format. The noise level is controlled by the terminals and is thus virtually independent of line length; hence, PCM idle–circuit noise is almost universally lower than that of analog FDM circuits. This has been especially beneficial in the noisy long–haul plant environment. Regenerative repeatered lines are also more efficient for transmitting all forms of digital data signal.

Fiber Optics

In 1880, Alexander Graham Bell invented the "photophone," which transmitted voice signals using beams of light sent through the air. However, signal fluctuations caused by atmospheric disturbances and other technical problems prevented the device from becoming a workable communications medium.

Scientists continued to explore the idea of using light to transport information, but it was not until after 1960, when the laser was invented, that fiber optic telecommunications started to become a reality. Early efforts were limited in range because the light transmitted was rapidly attenuated in the optical fiber. But in 1966, Dr. Charles Kao of Standard Telecommunications Laboratory in England reported that optical fibers transparent enough for fiber optic communications links were technically feasible.

In the early research on optical fibers, attenuation was dominated by absorption caused by impurities. Initial reductions in fiber loss were due to careful purification and processing of materials. Then, in 1970, Corning Glass Works demonstrated a fiber fabrication process called chemical vapor deposition. This process lowered the light attenuation rate to 20 decibels/kilometer (dB/km). By 1976, optical fibers with 1.6 dB/km of attenuation were being achieved. Further improvements have led to fiber with attenuation as low as 0.16 dB/km.

In 1977, a 44.736–Mb/s fiber optic system was trialed in Chicago, Illinois. The 1.5–mile system carried 672 voice circuits on fiber pairs among three office buildings. Today, single fibers carrying information at more than 13 Gb/s over 60 kilometers have been demonstrated. This bit rate is achieved by wavelength–division multiplexing (WDM) and corresponds to 193,536 voice circuits on a fiber pair.

1-3 VIDEO TRANSMISSION

Transmission of still pictorial matter by electrical means was the subject of research for many years before practical systems evolved. Proposed methods of converting picture information to electrical signals and electrical signals to pictures included a number of electromechanical and electrochemical processes. Much research was spent on light–sensitive materials that could be used in these processes as well as on the ink and photographic processes used in receiving equipment. Synchronization and scanning were recognized as important ingredients of the overall problem and solutions were sought in the applications of tuning forks and pendulums to these processes.

Many of the transmission means that were proposed in the early investigations were made to work, some of them quite well. However, development of the first economically feasible system for general commercial application had to await the invention and development of electronics. Telephotograph transmission of commercially acceptable still pictures was first demonstrated in the United States by transmitting pictures of the 1924 Democratic and Republican National Conventions. Large–scale demonstrations were given in early 1925 when pictures of President Coolidge's inauguration were transmitted successfully from Washington to New York, Chicago, and San Francisco. Commercial services followed.

As work progressed toward the successful transmission of still pictures, research was going forward to achieve true television transmission, that is, the direct conversion of a live action scene to an electrical signal and its reproduction at a remote location. A major public demonstration of television signal transmission took place in 1927. Success in these efforts came with the invention of the cathode ray tube but commercial possibilities did not emerge until 1939.

Continued development of this medium was essentially halted during the years of World War II but in the immediate post–war era, television came into its own. With improved cameras and receivers, the quality of received pictures became quite acceptable and new emphasis had to be placed on methods of signal transmission over long distances. Concurrently, picture standards had to be established and, particularly with the anticipated introduction of color signal transmission, an industrywide National Television System Committee (NTSC) was formed to define the evolving signal format.

Systems were developed for the transmission of baseband monochrome and color television signals over intracity wire facilities. These systems were initially designed to use electron tubes; they were redesigned to use solid–state components. Earlier shielded conductor pairs have been replaced by fiber cable and microwave radio. Portable microwave radio systems are also used for remote pickups.

Experimental long–distance service over microwave radio began in November 1947 on the New York–to–Boston TDX system. That service grew to a nationwide network of microwave systems. Baseband signals from the originating broadcaster were sent to the coast–to–coast microwave network and were then picked off at microwave repeater stations and distributed to the local broadcast stations by the then–named Long Lines Department of AT&T and the exchange carriers. The baseband signals were switched at a television operating center (TOC) where network configurations were changed to satisfy the broadcaster's needs or to use transmission facilities efficiently.

This arrangement continued until the advent of specialized common carriers and eventually of domestic satellites. Now local broadcast stations pick up the network signals directly from a satellite with their own microwave antennas.

The L1 and L3 coaxial transmission systems were initially designed to permit television signal transmission but were replaced by the microwave system for improved quality and reduced cost.

1-4　MAINTENANCE AND RELIABILITY

By modern standards, early transmission facilities were simple in concept. The problems of adequate maintenance and reliability were correspondingly straightforward. As the plant has become more complex, it has been necessary to think of maintenance and reliability in terms of the overall plant and the operation of specific systems. Growth alone had serious repercussions on maintenance and reliability in earlier years. Common troubles can affect great numbers of circuits. Because of complex system interrelationships, the effects of such troubles may become widespread. Machine switching and direct distance dialing to a large extent removed the operator, an important monitor of transmission performance, from the network. As a result, when performance is below par on a connection, it is difficult to determine the source of trouble since the connection is lost when the call is terminated. With many carriers providing the end–to–end connection, quality control of each company's transport path is essential. Thus, there is need for automated routine trunk testing until surveillance–based maintenance of digital transmission systems becomes common. Automated loop testing has also been introduced to reduce technician requirements.

As carrier systems have increased in capacity and design sophistication, the need for improved reliability and simplified maintenance has also increased. For example, a fully equipped 565–Mb fiber system may carry 6000 interswitch trunks, 600 voice–grade special services, one digital television signal, 500 digital data circuits, 25 1.5–Mb high–capacity services, a dozen synchronizing signals, several order wires, and a full set of performance–monitoring and protection–switching signals. These multiple maintenance and control features may interact in ways that would make manual methods of measurement and analysis difficult. Therefore, modern systems contain automatic equipment that aids maintenance personnel in identifying, isolating, and repairing troubles. Transmission system equipment is designed in the form of plug–in units. Test procedures and equipment are designed to identify defective units. Thus, new pretested units may be quickly and easily substituted in order to restore circuits to service quickly.

Dedicated bays and new designs of equipment have been developed to provide test access to switched–network and special-services circuits by switching arrangements or by electronically intercepting a digital bit stream. Among these special arrangements are emergency restoration centers that permit the interconnection of high–capacity carrier facilities in such a way that service from failed systems can be restored by patching or switching to protection–line facilities.

The entire field of maintenance operations and reliability procedures is supplemented by maintenance support systems and equipment. These include special systems for communications (speech or data) among maintenance personnel, and error–performance monitors for digital transmission system. Alarm functions are provided in all operating systems. Provision is made to transmit alarms from unattended stations to central maintenance locations for analysis and action.

1-5 FACILITY SELECTION AND APPLICATION

In planning for the introduction or installation of new transmission facilities, a choice must be made from a number of alternatives. As a general rule, the available choices have been designed for use in a particular field of application such as the loop
plant or the trunk plant. These fields of application tend to over-
lap, so the choice must be based on an analysis of many criteria.

One feature that often influences the choice of facilities is the
steady growth of the plant. Inevitably, when new installations are
under consideration, plant expansion and the resulting interactions between the new plant and the old must be considered. The
growth may be due to an increase in traffic caused by expansion
of population centers or industrial park areas. Growth may also
be strongly influenced by changes in technology, by new service
offerings, by rate reductions, or by shifts in the economic status
of an area. These factors all interact. It is virtually impossible to
consider any one without considering the impact of the others.

Growth Factors

Population density and distribution and related community-
of-interest factors have a major effect on how the telecommunications plant is organized and, therefore, on the selection of
transmission facilities. In addition to the geographical factors that
influence the organization and growth, other factors that affect
the facility network relate to the scope and diversity of services.

Population Effects. Figure 1-2 shows a medium-size city,
C_a, with a number of surrounding suburban towns, S_1 to S_8, all
located within a radius of about 25 miles. Each suburb is large
enough to be served by a separate switching machine. Examina-
tion shows that any of the suburban communities in this local
access and transport area (LATA) may be interconnected by no
more than two trunks in tandem as shown between S_1 and S_3,
S_2 and S_5, or S_4 and S_8.

In a highly developed area such as that in Figure 1-2, distances are short. Most of the trunks shown would be between five
and ten miles long with a few, like those between S_4 and C_a and

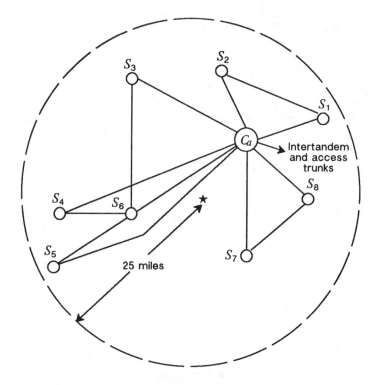

Figure 1-2. Illustrative city–suburban population distribution and telephone trunking.

S_5 and C_a, 25 to 30 miles long. It is likely that service in this area is provided by T1 systems and some residual VF trunks. As the area continues to grow, the problem might be that of deciding whether to fill out partially equipped T1 cable facilities or to concentrate growth on fiber systems. If it appears probable that anticipated growth of an industrial park area will create a demand for 45–Mb/s service, the option of paralleling one or more cables in the route with lightguide must be considered. Any such set of problems may be further complicated by the increasingly congested conditions in cable ducts, a major highway construction program, or public opinion pressure to convert pole–line cable to out–of–sight facilities.

The area depicted in Figure 1–3 and the problems encountered are quite different from those of Figure 1–2. In Figure 1–3,

C_b is a small city in a predominantly rural LATA. It is easy to imagine the rural towns and villages, r_1 through r_4, spread out over a considerable distance, perhaps along a river. Between r_2 and r_3 there may be a mountain range, which prevents the development of a strong community of interest and which makes direct trunking between the two communities uneconomical. Thus, calls between r_2 and r_3 are routed through C_b in spite of the longer distance involved.

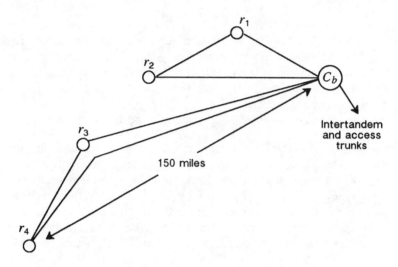

Figure 1-3. Illustrative population distribution and telephone trunking for small city and rural environs.

Facilities used in areas typified by Figure 1-3 would most likely be digital radio or T-type carrier systems. The trunks may be direct, tandem access, or intertandem depending on the specific conditions in the area and their relation to the network.

The simple examples discussed become considerably more complex when facility planning is undertaken on a larger scale. The congested area of Figure 1-2 may be expanded, for example, to represent a densely populated LATA and the geography of Figure 1-3 could be expanded to represent a sparsely populated LATA, such as those found in the mountainous areas of the west. Urban, suburban, and rural areas present different problems when planning and implementing facility networks.

Compromises must be made in providing trunks between switching machines and in choosing the type of transmission facilities for the outside plant. Equally complex problems arise when the facility choices must be made for feeder and distribution cables in the loop plant. As new cables and loop carrier systems are required, the cable type, size, and design plan must be selected to provide the most economical solution to the current problem, while considering emerging service requirements such as integrated services digital network (ISDN) and high–capacity channels.

Service Effects. In addition to creating demand for more service and more facilities, population growth brings other related effects. The nature of the growth may bring significant changes in community relationships that require different trunking patterns between central offices. The trunking pattern must also be changed when a new switching machine is added to the network.

Another effect related to facility growth is an increase in the amount and kind of services provided in an area. With an increase in overall standard of living and the spread of modem-equipped personal computers, many people upgrade their service from two–party to individual lines and even multiple lines. Such upgrades require additional loop facilities. The accompanying increase in calling rate may make added trunk facilities necessary.

As areas grow and business becomes more diverse, the demand emerges for a greater variety of services. Some of these services have stringent transmission requirements, particularly in the field of data communications. This diversity demands the provision of more sophisticated switching machines and improved transmission facilities that can meet modern requirements for both the message network and for a variety of special services.

Facility Forecasts

The process of providing new and expanded facilities is based on spare facilities in place, availability of new types of facility, and forecasts of needs. While the plant is administratively divided into loop and trunk, many special services share both parts. Thus, forecasts must include special services needs in addition to loop and trunk needs. The special–services market itself has undergone a remarkable change in the past few years, away from large groups of individual circuits toward a fast–rising number of 1.5–Mb/s and even 45–Mb/s high–capacity services.

The loop plant is under constant scrutiny to determine when it is necessary and timely to install new facilities in response to growth or other changes. Regular forecasts are made of new demands. They are based on information obtained from many sources such as building permits issued by local communities, plans announced by builders and developers, and the types of new building construction anticipated. In newly developed areas, the latter information affects the types of anticipated service such as residence, business, ISDN, etc. The forecasts and proposed facility construction must be associated with the type of central office and related plans to use digital loop carrier. The condition of existing facilities and related underground and overhead structures and the level of fill must also be taken into account.

The statistics of trunk and trunk–facility growth are under continuous study. As the switched network expands, traffic engineering studies are made to determine how and when new switching facilities are to be installed. Special–services circuit forecasts, which take into consideration the effects of new service offerings and changes in applicable tariffs, must also be included in the facility studies. From combinations of such studies of traffic network and special–services circuit growth, forecasts are made of trunk and trunk–facility needs.

Newly installed trunk facilities must be compatible with existing central offices and with planned installations. The capacity of existing plant and the expected date of exhaustion of spare capacity must be taken into account.

1-6 ENGINEERING CONSIDERATIONS

The selection of facilities to replace or augment existing plant must be based on the results of thorough studies and sound judgment. The decisions are influenced by economic and technological factors.

Economics

Before new facilities are provided, studies must be made to determine which of several alternatives is most economical.

When new loop or trunk facilities are under consideration, the question of augmenting metallic–pair carrier lines or adding fiber along a route previously served only by cable span–line facilities must be examined. In general, the fiber systems make more efficient use of transmission media because a number of DS1 channels are provided simultaneously by multiplexing. The cost relationships involve the substitution of electronics for copper, i.e., multiplexers and terminal equipment for additional span–line pairs. Efficiency in using the transmission media can be achieved only at the expense of the increased terminal costs incurred by the use of multiplexing equipment. Improved maintenance techniques, added craft training, and increased service protection must also be introduced.

Cost relationships in such cases are quite complex but, in general, cost analyses favor high–capacity carrier systems when distances are great, growth is fast, and cross sections are large. Under these conditions, line costs are greater than terminal costs and emphasis is placed on using the medium most efficiently. When distances are short, demand is static, and cross sections are small, terminal costs may be dominant and the economic balance would favor metallic span–line facilities.

The operation, application, and maintenance of all types of system and their interactions with environmental conditions also carry economic implications. For example, some of the basic criteria of telephone building construction have changed in an effort to improve plant design. Most equipment designs in the past were based on a ceiling height of 14 feet; the standard equipment bay height was 11 feet, 6 inches. Recent technological advances have increased the density of components on these equipment bays. Growth of plant, in addition, created difficult problems of congestion of cabling between equipment units. These factors combined to make a seven–foot bay height much more attractive in new structures. Floor loading, cable and wire distribution, and maintenance requirements (narrower aisles and no need for ladders) were all made more manageable by the lower bay height.

In addition, efforts to improve the efficiency of plant design led to equipment arrangements that placed functionally related equipment units (e.g., test access plus VF equipment) on bays specifically designed for this purpose. The arrangements resulted in less office cabling, lower cable congestion, space savings, lower use of interfloor tie cables, improved maintenance capabilities, and lower overall costs [11].

Although economic analyses play an important role in decision-making when new facilities are required, some decisions are made in response to other forces. Plant integrity and survivability may suggest the use of multiple routes and facility types that provide diversity and increase overall reliability. Uniformity of plant might be sacrificed and a higher price might be paid in order to satisfy particular service reliability requirements. The pressure of public opinion led to wide use of out-of-sight plant in preference to new pole-line construction. In this instance, economic advantages might be marginal; the use of out-of-sight plant is generally more costly than the use of more conventional installations, but more reliable weather-wise.

The economic solutions to loop facility problems involve the optimum mix of carrier and wire for feeder cables. Depending on the geographical area, the design plan must be selected from among those available, i.e., wire, fiber-based carrier, or hubbed fiber carrier with T1 extensions. The choice must be consistent with long-range planning studies, including the prospects for high-definition television and fiber-to-the-home.

For trunk facilities, many of the same factors must be considered. In addition, the reuse or rearrangement of facilities often offers an attractive solution.

Technology

The continuing shift from analog to digital technology is an example of how new technology interacts with the facility provision process. Pressures for the application of new systems, innovative concepts of operation, and new services occur with evolving technology to create demands for new facility types.

Much of the growth of communications technology in this century can be traced to research in physics and chemistry. From this research have come the new devices and materials that have yielded dramatic advances in telecommunications. These advances made possible much wider bandwidths for analog transmission in its day. They have enabled much higher rates of digital signal transmission: 1.5 Mb/s was ordinary for growth facilities in 1965, 45 Mb/s in 1980, and 565 Mb/s today.

Digital transmission and time–division switching have made the combination of these two techniques routine. Research studies in this area culminated in the construction of a laboratory model of an experimental system in the late 1950s. While this experiment was deemed to be a successful demonstration of the feasibility of combining time–division switching and transmission, practical implementation in the field had to await additional experience in applying the concepts to each of the two fields separately. The techniques that helped to achieve these goals led directly to digital toll switching systems [12], local switches [13], private branch exchanges, automatic call distributors, cross–connection systems, and operator services systems.

With these advances, new modes of operating the network come into play. Time–division switching is four–wire; thus, as integrated systems come into use, transmission circuits routinely use four–wire transmission from switch to switch and finally from end to end. It is highly probable that the via net loss design of the network will be changed, with most trunks operating at zero loss in an integrated system and losses placed only at analog–to–digital conversion points.

Another interplay among technological and other forces may be called mutual stimulation. Significant improvement in performance leads to more frequent use of a service, which in turn stimulates the installation of new systems and facilities. For example, the natural affinity of digital services and digital systems has fostered rapid growth supported by advances in the technology.

The facilities used in the telecommunications industry are in a constant state of flux. Old systems become obsolete and must be replaced. New technology brings new systems and techniques such as digital switches with unprecedented capabilities [14]. The demands for more facilities at lower cost and the introduction of new services insistently leads to a demand for new systems, new procedures, and new ways of organizing networks.

Certain services have been provided for some years but are continually expanding. Examples are the growth of high–capacity services and the extension of equal interexchange–carrier access to small central offices. The demand for digital data services led to the success of the Digital Data System (DDS), a network of data transmission facilities integrated with existing facilities used for message network and special services, and, beyond DDS, to simplified "basic" digital services.

All these forces of growth, change, and replacement require the application of high expertise in building, operating, and managing the plant. A snapshot view of the systems and facilities available at any given time is certain to become outdated within a relatively short time. The evolutionary nature of the plant requires much planning for the future since all new systems must be integrated into the existing plant. Adequate responses to the pressures of change can only come about by careful planning.

References

1. Anderson, C. N., A. Bailey, and L. Espenschied. "Transatlantic Radio Transmission," *Bell System Tech. J.*, Vol. 4 (July 1925), pp. 459–507.

2. Dickieson, A. C. "The TD2 Story: From Research to Field Trial," *Bell Laboratories Record*, Vol. 45, No. 9 (Oct. 1967), pp. 282–289.

3. *Reference Data for Engineers: Radio, Electronics, Computer, and Communications*, Seventh Edition (Indianapolis, IN: Howard W. Sams and Company, Inc., 1985), pp. 1–6 to 1–15.

4. Hardeman, L. J. "Heavy Traffic Calls for Crowd Control in the Electromagnetic Spectrum," *Electronics* (Sept. 25, 1972), pp. 83–99.

5. Deloraine, E. M. and A. H. Reeves. "The 25th Anniversary of Pulse Code Modulation," *IEEE Spectrum* (May 1965), pp. 56–63.

6. Meacham, L. A. and E. Peterson. "An Experimental Multichannel Pulse Code Modulation System of Toll Quality," *Bell System Tech. J.*, Vol. 27 (Jan. 1948), pp. 1–43.

7. Davis, C. G. "An Experimental Pulse Code Modulation System for Short–Haul Trunks," *Bell System Tech. J.*, Vol. 41 (Jan. 1962), pp. 1–24.

8. Fultz, K. E. and D. B. Penick. "The T1 Carrier System," *Bell System Tech. J.*, Vol. 44 (Sept. 1965), pp. 1405–1451.

9. Davis, J. H. "T2, A 6.3 Mb/s Digital Repeatered Line," *Conference Record*, IEEE International Conference on Communications (1969), pp. 34–9 to 34–16.

10. Lang, J. J. "The D4 Digital Channel Bank and Family," *Bell System Tech. J.*, Vol. 61 (Nov. 1982), pp. 2607–2815.

11. Giguere, W. J. and F. G. Merrill. "Getting it All Together with Unitized Terminals," *Bell Laboratories Record*, Vol. 51 (Jan. 1973).

12. Vaughan, H. E. "An Introduction to No. 4ESS," *IEEE International Switching Symposium Record* (1972).

13. "Special DMS–10 Issue," *Telephone Engineer and Management* (Nov. 1, 1985), pp. 4–32.

14. Holcomb, J. E. "Frontiers in Switching Technology—Part One: The Next–Generation Switch," Bellcore EXCHANGE, Vol. 3, Iss. 5 (Sept./Oct. 1987), pp. 23–27.

Chapter 2

Transmission Media

The transmission of communications signals between two points involves an interconnecting medium. This medium may constrain and guide the signals or may transmit them in an unguided or semiguided manner. Examples of guided-wave media are pairs of wires, shielded and nonshielded, that are installed individually or combined in cables, coaxial conductors, waveguides, and optical fibers. The atmosphere and the void of space provide unguided media for the transmission of radio signals. These media may be used for broadcasting signals in all directions or, with directional antennas, for transmitting signals within a controlled narrow beam between the transmitting and receiving devices.

Individual pairs of conductors in the form of open-wire lines have been giving way to carrier systems, paired cable, and fiber facilities for many years. Thus, the treatment here of open-wire lines is brief to allow more thorough discussion of cable pairs, which also are subject to displacement by such media as fiber. The designs of cables in which such conductors are combined vary significantly according to the field of application.

Radio communication may use any portion of a wide spectrum of frequencies. Allocations of the spectrum to various uses are controlled in the United States by the Federal Communications Commission. Discussion here is confined to the characterization of the medium and its exploitation in the bands allocated to common-carrier services.

2-1 OPEN WIRE

The following is a brief summary of open-wire characteristics. A typical open-wire line, usually consisting of bare copper or copper–steel wires 0.165, 0.128, 0.104, or 0.080 inch in diameter, is supported on utility poles spaced 40 to the mile. Transmission loss is quite low: at 1000 Hz, the dry–weather attenuation is only 0.03 to 0.08 dB per mile.

All open–wire pairs are transposed in predetermined patterns to minimize their susceptibility to crosstalk from other pairs and to noise from nearby power lines. The transposition pattern provides, ideally, for each pair to have equal positive and negative exposures to power lines and to all other pairs. In practice, regularity in pole spacing and wire sag is important in achieving close balance of the two polarities of exposure.

Variations from the standard open–wire line are numerous: (1) long–span construction (saves poles and pole placement but requires steel or copper–clad steel wire), (2) use of galvanized steel wire, (3) close spacing of the wires of a pair, (4) wide separation of pairs on crossarms, (5) wide spacing of crossarms, and (6) the use of added transpositions. All except (1) and (2) were used to control crosstalk, which became increasingly important as carrier systems were applied to open–wire lines.

2-2 LOOP AND LOCAL TRUNK CABLES

Cables used for the provision of loops from central offices to subscriber locations are called loop cables. Cables used for trunks in the local area are called trunk cables. The types of trunk and their uses in the general switching plan are discussed in Volume 3. Most cables are used for carrier as well as voice–frequency (VF) trunks.

Physical Characteristics

Cable pairs are made up of copper wires twisted together, each wire insulated with strip or pulp paper or with plastic. (Aluminum wire has also been used, but never in quantity.) Groups of such pairs, twisted (stranded) into a ropelike form, are called *units*. The degree of pair twist in a unit is varied or staggered. The variation in twist reduces crosstalk coupling in much the same way as transpositions do in open–wire circuits. Several units are twisted together (cabled) to form a *cable core*.

Loop and local trunk cables are made in a number of sizes, designated by the number of pairs they contain. Table 2–1 shows the range of cable sizes for the several available gauges for poly-ethylene–insulated cable (PIC), filled PIC, and pulp–insulated conductors. The table includes 19–gauge pairs, but coarse–gauge cable like this is no longer installed in quantity and 22–gauge is fading from use. Screened PIC cables, with the units divided into two groups by a lengthwise shield, are in sizable use for interoffice T1 and T1C span lines.

Table 2–1. Typical Cable Sizes

Number of Pairs	Filled PIC				PIC					Pulp–Insulated		
	19	22	24	26	19	22	24	25	26	22	24	26
6	X				X							
11	X	X			X	X	X		X			
16	X	X			X	X	X		X			
25	X	X	X	X	X	X	X		X			
50	X	X	X	X	X	X	X		X			
75	X	X			X	X	X		X			
100	X	X	X	X	X	X	X		X			
150	X	X			X	X	X		X			
200	X	X	X	X	X	X	X		X			
300	X	X	X	X	X	X	X		X			
400		X	X	X		X	X	X	X			
600		X	X	X		X	X	X	X	X		
900			X	X				X		X	X	X
1200								X		X	X	X
1400								X				
1500											X	X
1800								X			X	X
2100												X
2400												X
2700												X
3000												X
3600												X

The number of pairs per unit varies from 12 to 100 depending on wire gauge and cable size. Units are usually subdivided into 25–pair binder groups. Although unit construction is the common type now used, layered construction may still be found.

In the layered design, pairs are configured in concentric layers, each of which spirals around the preceding layer.

Figure 2-1 shows the relative positions of the several units of a 600-pair 22-gauge cable in the cable cross section. (Note, however, that the outer units are not fixed in relation to the inner ones; they may rotate about the inner units. This has implications as to crosstalk exposures between units.) Different colors are used in wire insulation and binder strings are applied around individual units for identification. In cables using polyethylene insulation, every pair is color-coded and can be identified visually at any splice without recourse to electrical testing. Earlier forms of color coding, used in paper and pulp-insulated cables, did not provide for visual identification of specific pairs.

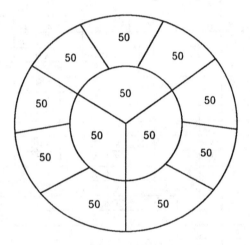

Figure 2-1.   Location and form of 50-pair units in a 600-pair cable.

Insulation resistance between each conductor in a cable and all other conductors grounded is required to be at least 500 megohm-miles (the product of the measured leakage resistance in megohms and the cable length in miles).

The basic requirements for wire-to-wire dielectric strength of pulp- and polyethylene-insulated conductors are given in Table 2-2. Insulation between cable core and sheath may be paper, polyethylene, rubber-polyester or combinations of these materials. Requirements for dielectric strength of core–to–sheath insulation range from 1.2 to 1.4 peak kV ac for paper core wrap to 20 kV dc for cables with an inner polyethylene jacket. The higher levels of core–to–sheath insulation are used, in particular, for providing service to locations like power substations where the local ground potential may rise to several kilovolts with respect to remote ground during power–line faults.

Table 2–2. Dielectric Strength Requirements

Type of Insulation	Voltage (kV)				
	19 GA	22 GA	24 GA	25 GA	26 GA
Pulp (peak ac)	0.7	0.5	0.5	NA	0.5
PIC (dc)	5	4	3	2	2.4

Other materials are used for physical and electrical protection of cables. The lead sheaths of the oldest cables provide both waterproofing and electrical protection against noise induction. However, they are also subject to electrolytic corrosion at points of stray earth–current leakage. Electrical drainage systems, installed to provide noncorrosive paths for such currents, reduce such damage, but it has not been economical to make such systems complex enough to be 100–percent effective. Some lead sheaths of underground cables, especially those in urban areas, ultimately admit moisture and require replacement.

Materials used outside the core insulation in newer cables include various combinations of (1) tacky waterproof coatings, (2) corrugated aluminum and steel shields, and (3) polyethylene jackets. The combination used depends on the cable application and on environmental conditions. The aluminum shields provide electrical protection against noise induction while the steel provides physical protection. Both shields are necessarily cut back at splice points but electrical continuity of the shields is bonded across splices. Most loop and local trunk cables have outer jackets of polyethylene and are not subject to electrolytic corrosion. Filled or waterproof PIC cables are common for buried use. In these, the space between pairs is packed with a jelly of petroleum and polyethylene particles or other compounds. Alternatively, nonfilled trunk cable is normally pressurized with dry air at 6 to

10 pounds per square inch. Thus, damage to the sheath does not necessarily result in impaired insulation.

Transmission Characteristics

The properties of a cable pair that must be known to calculate circuit performance are *characteristic impedance* and *propagation constant*. These secondary constants are derived from the four primary constants: series resistance, series inductance, shunt conductance, and shunt capacitance [1,2]. The constants are expressed in values per unit length of the pair. To permit accurate transmission engineering on the basis of secondary constants and cable length, the primary constants must be rigidly controlled during manufacture.

Primary and Secondary Constants. The relationships between the primary and secondary constants of a transmission line were developed in Chapter 5 of Volume 1. The constants are temperature– and frequency–dependent to some degree. The primary and secondary constants at any frequency depend on the medium alone and are not affected by sending– or receiving–end impedance. On the other hand, the actual transmission from a source to a termination depends on the source and termination impedances as well as on the properties of the medium.

For the case of 22–gauge cable pairs, Figure 2–2 shows the relation between attenuation and frequency, Figure 2–3 shows the dependence of delay on frequency, and Figure 2–4 shows the relation between characteristic impedance and frequency. The trends are similar for other gauges.

A special low–capacitance (LOCAP) cable has been used to provide reduced attenuation in cable pairs for the T2 digital system. These pairs have a nominal capacitance of 39 nF per mile (46 nF in filled cable) instead of the usual 83 nF per mile. The LOCAP cables were made up of 22–gauge copper conductors insulated with dual–expanded plastic. They were available with 26, 52, or 104 pairs.

Another LOCAP design, introduced for use in metropolitan areas, was designed to optimize transmission performance for

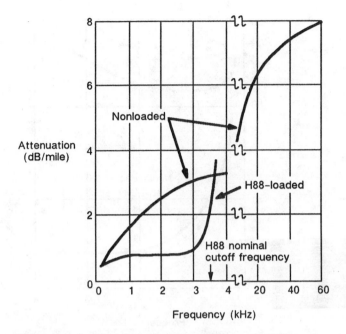

Figure 2-2. Attenuation/frequency   characteristic   of 22-gauge cable pair.

T1C carrier applications and minimize overall costs for all types of metropolitan area trunk (MAT). The MAT cable was designed for major metropolitan routes that could economically use 400- to 1800-pair complements. Cable pairs are 25-gauge copper with expanded plastic insulation. Their transmission characteristics make them approximately equivalent to 22-gauge pulp-insulated cable pairs for T1 or T1C spans. When loaded, the 25-gauge pairs are equivalent to 24H88 loaded pairs for VF circuits. The lighter-gauge conductors slightly reduce dc signalling range. The 25-gauge wire size was selected as a compromise for maximum compatibility with existing equipment that would, at the same time, yield a significant saving of copper. (A reduction of three gauge numbers implies a 50-percent reduction in copper.) This design produced characteristic impedances somewhat higher than those of earlier designs; as a result, different terminating impedances were used in the affected equipment. A similar LOCAP cable, but using 24-gauge pairs, has been used in nonmetropolitan areas.

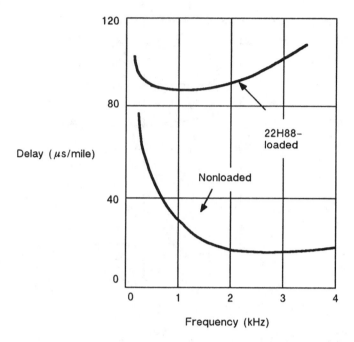

Figure 2-3. Delay/frequency characteristic of 22–gauge cable pair.

Crosstalk. Coupling between pairs in the same cable is unavoidable and results in the transfer of a small amount of signal power from each energized pair to other pairs. Although design and manufacture limit the coupling to acceptable values, crosstalk influences circuit design and system layout. For example, differences between signal amplitudes transmitted into a cable at a repeater point and the amplitudes received from the same cable at that point must be limited in order to control near-end crosstalk. This, in turn, limits the difference in amplitude from a repeater output to the next repeater input and thereby establishes a repeater–section loss limit.

Pulp–insulated loop and local trunk cables are designed with nine different lengths of pair–twist to guard against adjacent pairs having the same twist lengths. Each unit in a cable may be thought of as made up of several layers of pairs twisted around a common axis with a common length of layer twist. A different twist length is used for every pair, up to 25 pairs, in a PIC cable.

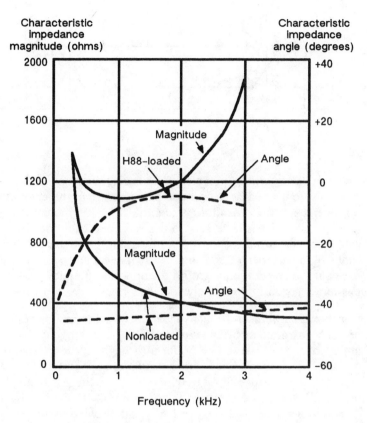

Figure 2-4.   Characteristic impedances for 22-gauge cable pair.

If normal circuit designs are followed, annoying crosstalk occurs only when cables are damaged or when significant unbalance exists between pair conductors and ground. Crosstalk also occurs when two adjacent pairs are inadvertently split during splicing operations along the cable route, as shown at point A in Figure 2-5. If the error is detected and corrected at a subsequent splice, point B, in an attempt to compensate for the split at A, high coupling remains in the length A–B. The usual dc tests made between the ends of the cable after splicing has been completed do not reveal the split. It is important, therefore, to avoid splitting pairs and, whenever split pairs are detected, to correct the error at the offending splice.

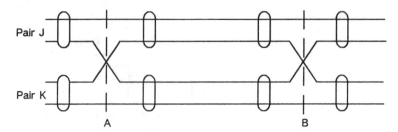

Figure 2-5. Split pairs.

Crosstalk couplings at voice frequencies in local cables are generally controlled by design and manufacture to the extent that no special splicing procedure is required. For T–type carrier systems, however, it is necessary to use screened cable or different cables for the two directions of transmission to obtain maximum cable fill and repeater spacing. With one–cable operation, it is necessary to select binder groups for opposite directions of transmission according to carefully specified rules.

Inductive Loading. Inductive loading of cable pairs is effective not only in reducing attenuation but also in making attenuation, impedance, and delay more uniform throughout the passband of the loading system. These transmission improvements are obtained at the sacrifice of all frequencies above the passband. Figures 2–2, 2–3, and 2–4 show the attenuation, delay, and characteristic impedance of 22–gauge H88–loaded pairs in comparison with the same characteristics of 22–gauge nonloaded pairs.

Load coils are made by winding two coils simultaneously on a core of high–permeability metal, one coil for each conductor of a pair. This bifilar method of winding ensures equal load inductances in the two wires of a pair and minimizes longitudinal unbalance. By cancellation effects, it also reduces the danger of damage to the coils that might result from longitudinal surge currents due to lightning or power system faults. The inductance of each winding alone is about one–fourth of the required total. The two windings are connected "series–aiding" in the circuit so that the total inductance is the sum of that of the two windings alone plus twice the mutual inductance. Since the total inductance depends slightly on the direct current flowing in the windings, allowance is made in design for the resulting decrease in inductance.

The bifilar method of winding load coils is illustrated in Figure 2-6. The complete coil has a volume of one to two cubic inches. Various quantities of coils, from 6 to 900, are housed in water-tight cases to serve different needs. Coil connections are provided to a stub cable, which is spliced into the cable to be loaded. The cases may be mounted aerially or underground. A typical aerial installation is shown in Figure 2-6(b).

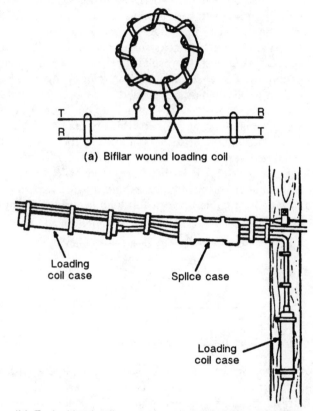

(a) Bifilar wound loading coil

(b) Typical load coil case arrangements for aerial cable

Figure 2-6. Typical loading coil and application.

Structural uniformity of a loaded cable pair is essential. Irregularities such as misplaced or omitted load coils can make the pair useless for a repeatered two-wire trunk by seriously reducing echo return loss. Uniformity of a loaded pair, however, can be no better than the uniformity of the capacitance, C, along the pair or of load–coil values. For that reason, the cost of attaining more accurate load–coil spacing than afforded by following specified rules would not be justified. Good factory control of capacitance and of load–coil inductance, plus good field control of load–coil spacing, provides adequate structural uniformity.

When it is necessary to locate a load point out of limits, the affected load section is made shorter than normal and then built out to the required length with a build–out capacitor (BOC) or a build–out lattice (BOL). The BOC is simply a capacitor shunted across the pair. Although it lacks series resistance, it is adequate for a short build–out and the resultant return loss is adequate for loop applications. For a trunk, a BOC may not provide adequate return loss and a BOL may be needed. The BOL is a balanced network of two resistors and two capacitors configured as in Figure 2–7. Close matching of the two resistors maintains longitudinal balance. The characteristic impedance is the same as if the total capacitance of the crisscrossed branches were evenly distributed along the resistors. It is therefore an excellent approximation to real cable at voice frequencies and may be used for simulating any length of cable up to a full load section with good return loss.

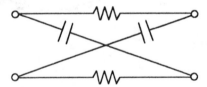

Figure 2–7. Build–out lattice.

Return Loss. Structural return loss is a convenient and sensitive measure of the structural quality of a loaded cable pair, that is, of the resemblance of the real pair to the ideal model in which load spacing, pair capacitance, and load–coil inductance all match the objectives perfectly in all load sections. Structural return loss is the ratio of the power of a signal sent into one end of a pair to the composite power reflected back to that end by all the small structural irregularities in the pair. The receiving end of the pair must be properly terminated (in a precision network that simulates the cable's characteristic impedance) to avoid mixing a reflection from that end with the structural reflections from within the pair. Since each reflection traverses a different distance, the components from the several reflections do not arrive in phase. Moreover, the relative phases and magnitudes change continuously with frequency. Thus, a measurement at a single frequency is not a reliable indication of structural regularity. To overcome this difficulty, a mixture of many frequencies in the voiceband (frequency–weighted noise) is used as a source and the structural return loss is measured directly with a return–loss measuring set.

Results of such measurements on loaded pairs are useful in judging the suitability of the pairs for service. If there is no irregularity, the return losses for a complement should cluster around a figure not more than 2 dB under the expected median value and none should fall more than 3 dB below the actual median. The source of return losses below the general distribution is usually located and corrected. Return losses higher than the general distribution do not signify irregularity.

The effect of load–spacing deviations on the structural return loss of normal 22–gauge H88–loaded pairs is illustrated in Figure 2–8. The return losses of polyethylene–insulated pairs are higher than those of paper–insulated pairs because it is practical to control their capacitance more closely as insulation is applied to the wires. The structural return losses expected for various wire gauges, load–spacing deviations, average splicing lengths, and pair insulations are tabulated for engineering use.

The cable between a central office and the first load coil is called an end section. To provide flexibility for connecting one loaded cable to another by way of cross–connection in a central office, end sections are usually made slightly less than half a load section in length (e.g., 2900 ft) so that the section including the path through the central office is a full load section.

Velocity of Propagation. The velocity of propagation over wire facilities is ω/β, where ω is the radian frequency and β is the phase constant. This velocity increases monotonically with frequency in nonloaded pairs, reaching about 129,000 miles per second at T1 frequencies. In H88–loaded pairs, it reaches a maximum within the passband of only about 13,000 mi/s and then decreases as shown in Figure 2–9. Since echo tolerance of

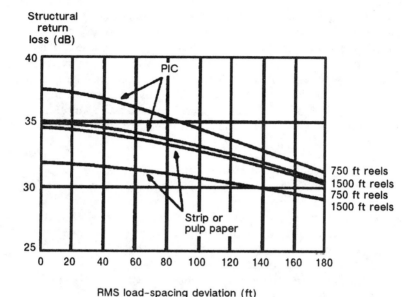

Figure 2-8. Expected median structural return losses in complements of 22-gauge H88-loaded pairs.

telephone users decreases as echo delay increases, velocity of propagation is an important factor, which historically favored carrier, in long–haul transmission system design.

2-3 TOLL TRUNK CABLES

Among other media, interoffice trunks may use cable pairs equipped with T– or N–type carrier systems. The trunks may also use cable pairs equipped as VF circuits, but to an ever–decreasing degree.

Cable Pairs

Physical Characteristics. Toll cable pairs are insulated with paper tape helically applied. Most of the pairs are twisted together, two pairs at a time, to form quads from which a phantom circuit (now rarely used) could be derived. In general, there are ten different quad types, as defined by the lengths of

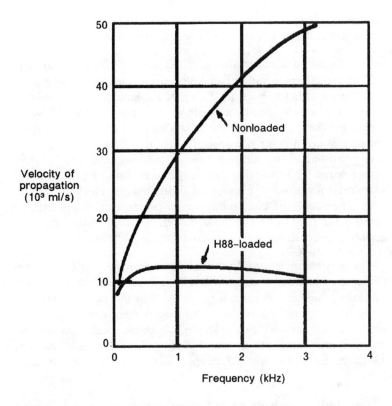

Figure 2-9. Velocity of propagation, 22-gauge cable pairs.

the pair twists and quad twists. Each type is keyed to a different combination of pair insulation colors.

A toll cable is formed of cylindrical layers of quads and pairs twisted helically around the cable axis. To keep the layers intact and the quads and pairs in order around the layers, adjacent layers are given opposite directions of rotation around the axis. This also prevents long adjacencies of pairs in different layers. All these design features were essential for control of crosstalk within and between quads and to reduce coupling to noise sources.

In the past, 16- and 19-gauge copper wire were the standard for VF toll, and 22-gauge wire was used for VF local facilities. These cables were loaded to reduce attenuation on long trunks.

As carrier systems replaced VF circuits, these cable pairs were deloaded and the use of 16-gauge wire became rare.

A number of sheaths are specified according to the physical and electrical environments in which the cables are to be placed and the hazards to which they may be subjected. Electrical insulation may be provided by a paper wrap or an inner polyethylene jacket on the core. Polyethylene is also used as an outer jacket for insulation and for physical protection. Physical protection is also provided by corrugated steel or lead sheaths and by steel armor wires for submarine cables. Lead or one or two layers of aluminum are used to provide shielding against electrical induction. Thermoplastic compounds or air pressurization are used to prevent the penetration of moisture. Problems of electrolytic corrosion of lead sheaths are similar to those in local cables.

Transmission Characteristics. The principal difference between the electrical characteristics of toll and local cable pairs is the lower capacitance of toll pairs. As a result of the lower capacitance, toll pairs have a higher cutoff frequency when both are identically loaded. For example, 22-gauge local cable with 83 nF per mile cuts off at about 3500 Hz when H88-loaded; 19-gauge toll cable with 62 nF per mile cuts off at about 4000 Hz.

The distinction between toll cable and local cable is not as clear as it was. The older 19-gauge cables, loaded for long-haul VF circuits, were widely deloaded for carrier systems. While nonloaded 22-gauge cable is used primarily for T-type carrier, cables of any gauge may be loaded or nonloaded for VF circuits where the use of carrier systems is not warranted.

Structural uniformity is especially important in toll cables for two-wire use since toll trunks are longer than local trunks and require more repeater gain. The capacitance is well controlled in the factory and when load-coil spacing in the field is controlled as well, structural return losses are a few dB higher than those in local cables. Build-out of quadded cables was accomplished by using finer-gauge quads in a calculated length of the main cable in order to increase the resistance, and then adding the required capacitance by connecting a calculated length of stub cable in parallel with the main cable.

Shielded Conductors. Some signals and systems are so sensitive to noise and crosstalk that the facilities used must be individually shielded. Video pairs of 16 gauge, once used widely for transmission of television signals in local areas, are a prime example.

The 16–gauge video pair consisted of two copper conductors insulated with expanded polyethylene and twisted together with two expanded plastic fillers. The pair and fillers were helically wrapped with polyethylene tape followed by a longitudinal copper shield and a helically wrapped copper shield. An outer longitudinal crepe–paper wrapping was bound with continuous strings of rayon or cotton, colored for identification. As with nonshielded conductors and to minimize crosstalk, pair twists ranging from 5.3 to 7.5 inches were used so that adjacent pairs in the same or adjacent layers had different twists.

These video pairs had a dc resistance of 42 ohms per loop mile at 68 degrees Fahrenheit and an attenuation of 17 dB per mile at 4.0 MHz. The characteristic impedance was 125.5 $\pm$ 3.5 ohms at 1.0 MHz. Manufacturing and splicing techniques were designed to preserve constant impedance, producing reflections of 38 dB or more below the amplitude of pulses used in measurement.

Coaxial Cables

Air–dielectric coaxial cables still carry a portion of long–haul circuits in the telecommunications network. In addition, this medium found some use for trunks in metropolitan networks. Although the cost of coaxial cable is high relative to paired cable, the adaptability of coaxial cable to very broad–band systems made it a contender for providing service where heavy cross sections of traffic existed. The per–channel–mile cost of these systems was relatively low. Some cables of this type were also used for cable television (CATV) systems before larger foam–insulated types became common.

Physical Characteristics. A coaxial cable is made up of 4 to 22 coaxial units with interstitial wire pairs and single wires, all wound helically around the cable axis. Sheath components perform the same functions as similar layers used in quadded toll cables. Because of the helical winding, or stranding, the coaxial units and some of the wire conductors are slightly longer than the cable. This extra length ranges from about 0.5 percent in four–unit cables to about 2.4 percent in one of the larger sizes.

The interstitial pairs and wires are used for maintenance functions such as order wires and alarms. The characteristics of the pairs are similar to those in toll cables. Pairs assigned to order–wire circuits in the L5 system (Chapter 12) are loaded at coaxial repeater points that are spaced about a mile apart but not nearly as uniformly as loading points usually are. This loading system, Q44, is satisfactory for these circuits because the four–wire design prevents reflections from structural irregularities from becoming echoes. The slight unevenness in transmission caused by the reflections is acceptable in an order–wire circuit.

The usual serrated–seam coaxial unit consists of a 0.1003–inch copper conductor centered within a 0.369–inch (inside diameter) copper tube by polyethylene insulating disks spaced about 1 inch apart. The tube is a strip of copper 0.012 inch thick formed into a cylinder around the disks. It is held closed by the interlocking of its serrated edges in a longitudinal seam and by two strips of steel tape wound helically around the copper tube with the outer tape overlapping the gap between turns of the inner one.

Transmission Characteristics. For coaxial cable units, primary and secondary constants are expressed the same as for cable pairs. The derived transmission characteristics are shown in Table 2–3. Note that, at carrier frequencies, the attenuation constant a is approximately proportional to the square root of frequency. This is primarily because of skin effect in the inner and outer conductors; as frequency increases, current flow is progressively restricted to the portions of the conductors near the surface. The phase constant β is nearly proportional to frequency, while delay and impedance Z_o are essentially constant. Propagation velocity is about 95 percent of the speed of light in air.

Because of the shielding effect of the outer coaxial conductors, the equal–level coupling loss between coaxial units is excellent above a few hundred kHz and increases with frequency. There is

44

no need for insulation between the outer conductors of the coaxial units.

Table 2-3.   Transmission Characteristics of Serrated-Seam Coaxials

Frequency (MHz)	α (dB/mi)	β (rad/mi)	Delay (μs/mi)	Z_o (ohms)
0.1	1.217	3.66	5.83	77.5
1.0	3.845	35.70	5.69	75.5
10.0	12.150	354	5.64	74.9
100.0	38.680	3533	5.62	74.7

As in loaded cable pairs, it is important to minimize reflections in coaxial conductors. Although transmission on each coaxial unit is in only one direction, double reflections can cause interference among signal components traveling in that direction. Reflections result from internal impedance variations caused by splices, sharp bends, dents, gas plugs, and terminations at equipment units. Factory measurements were made on each coaxial unit by a pulse technique to verify that internal reflections were sufficiently small. Random splicing lengths are used in the field to avoid in-phase buildup of reflections from regularly spaced splices; coaxial splicing techniques are designed to minimize the reflections at splices.

2-4   MICROWAVE RADIO TRANSMISSION

Microwave radio transmission media include propagation paths, antennas, and the waveguides used to couple the transmitters and receivers to the antennas. An understanding of radio propagation and the path losses encountered, antenna patterns and efficiencies, and waveguide transmission characteristics are essential to an application of these media. For microwave transmission, portions of the 2-to-40-GHz spectrum are available for fixed, common-carrier service. This range corresponds to wavelengths of 150 to 7.5 mm respectively, where it is practicable to direct the radiated energy in a narrow beam.

Propagation Paths

The principal propagation paths in the microwave range are the direct (free–space) wave and the ground–reflected wave as illustrated in Figure 2–10 [3]. If the antennas are located to provide a line–of–sight path with adequate clearance, the path loss for a large percentage of the time approximates the free–space loss. This loss obeys the inverse–square law.

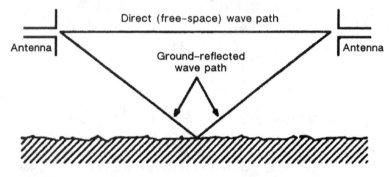

Figure 2–10. Microwave propagation paths between antennas.

Line–of–Sight Transmission. Imagine a radiated wave expanding as a spherical surface from a point source. The power density, in terms of power per square unit of that surface at distance d from the source radiating power p_T watts, is the radiated power divided by the area of the spherical surface at that distance, or $\frac{p_T}{4\pi d^2}$. If that radiated power is now concentrated in a narrow beam by means of a suitable antenna and accurately aimed at a receiving antenna, the latter receives many times the energy it received before the beam was concentrated. The actual power it receives before concentration is

$$p_R = \frac{p_T A_R}{4\pi d^2} \qquad (2-1)$$

where A_R is the effective area of the receiving antenna and p_T is the power transmitted at the transmitting antenna. It can be shown that the on–axis power gain of the transmitting antenna having its radiation concentrated in a narrow beam is $\frac{4\pi A_T}{\lambda^2}$, where λ is the wavelength and A_T is the effective area of the transmitting antenna.* When Equation 2-1 is modified to account for the transmitting antenna gain, the received power is

$$p_R = p_T \left(\frac{4\pi A_T}{\lambda^2} \right) \left(\frac{A_R}{4\pi d^2} \right). \qquad (2\text{-}2)$$

These factors may be regrouped so that the transmitting and receiving antenna gains are in the same form; thus,

$$p_R = p_T \left(\frac{4\pi A_T}{\lambda^2} \right) \left(\frac{4\pi A_R}{\lambda^2} \right) \left(\frac{\lambda}{4\pi d} \right)^2. \qquad (2\text{-}3)$$

Transmitting   Receiving   Free-space
antenna   antenna   pathloss
gain   gain

Note that the antenna gains are frequency-dependent and that the free-space path loss is both distance- and frequency-dependent as shown in Figure 2-11. In dB, the loss from the transmitter to the receiver is:

$$10 \ \log \ \frac{p_T}{p_R} - 10 \ \log \ \frac{4\pi A_T}{\lambda^2} - 10 \ \log \ \frac{4\pi A_R}{\lambda^2} + 20 \ \log \ \frac{4\pi d}{\lambda} \qquad (2\text{-}4)$$

where the units of length in A_T, A_R, λ, and d are all the same. The effective areas, A_T and A_R, are smaller than the physical areas because of power dissipation and reflections in the antennas.

Reflections. It is not enough that the line-of-sight path be unobstructed. It is also necessary to have adequate clearance all around that path to reduce the likelihood of reflections that may set up secondary paths longer than the direct path. Waves taking a longer path can arrive at the receiving antenna in any phase relationship with the direct wave. The phase relationship depends

---

* Antenna gain is defined as the ratio, in dB, of the signal amplitude received or transmitted by an antenna to the amplitude that would be received or transmitted by an isotropic (all-directional) antenna at the same location and fed with the same power.

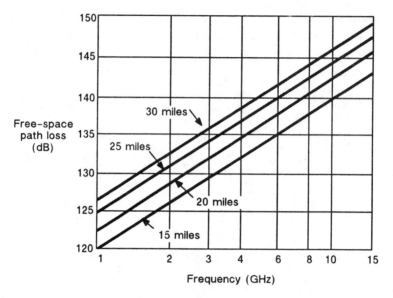

Figure 2-11. Free-space path loss versus frequency and path length.

on the wavelength, the difference in length between the two paths, and whether the grazing angle at the projection is small enough to cause a phase reversal at the reflection. The strength of the reflected wave determines the limits of reduction or reinforcement of the direct wave. The phase relative to the direct wave determines where, within those limits, the effect will lie.

Figure 2-12 illustrates a direct path, d, from A to B and an indirect path, d_1, from A to C to B. Clearance above intervening terrain is usually described in terms of Fresnel zones, which are ellipses of revolution around the line-of-sight path, as shown in vertical cross section in Figure 2-12. The first Fresnel zone is the surface from which a reflection reaching the receiving antenna will have traveled one-half wavelength farther than the direct wave. The nth Fresnel zone defines paths $n/2$ wavelengths longer than that of the direct wave. The locations of the zones depend on the wavelength and the length of the direct path. Experience indicates that clearance should be at least 0.6 times the distance to the first Fresnel zone all along the direct path to achieve transmission loss that approximates the free-space loss. Somewhat

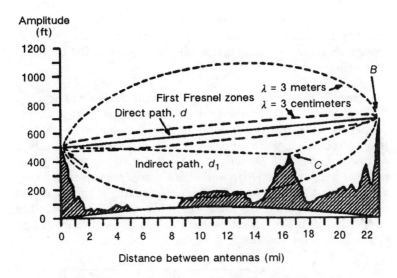

Figure 2-12. Typical profile plot showing first Fresnel zones for 100 MHz (3 meters) and 10 GHz (3 centimeters).

greater clearance than that is usually provided, however, to reduce deep fading under adverse atmospheric conditions. Effective path clearance is not constant but varies with atmospheric conditions, which can bend the direct wave away from a straight line as a result of variations in dielectric constant.

For determining suitable antenna heights, the obstacle having the least Fresnel clearance for prevalent atmospheric conditions is located and then used as a fulcrum to allocate height to the antennas to provide suitable clearance. Path tests with portable antennas are sometimes made to verify the height of the principal obstructions, path reflectivity conditions, and optimum antenna heights.

Fading. Heavy ground fog or very cold air over warm earth can cause enough atmospheric refraction to obstruct the line-of-sight path and increase its loss substantially throughout a wide frequency band. This type of fading sets in slowly and clears up slowly; its only remedy is the use of higher antennas.

Another, faster type of fading is caused by interference between two or more rays in the atmosphere. These separate rays between transmitter and receiver are the result of irregularities in the way dielectric constant varies with height. Fading of both types influences the margins that must be built into the transmission system.

Figure 2–13 shows the median duration of fast fading on a 4–GHz system. It indicates an inverse relationship, that is, the deeper the fade, the less its duration. For example, a 16–dB fade has a median duration of 50 seconds; a 43–dB fade, only 2 seconds. About one percent of the fades may last ten times or more as long as the median and about one percent may last only one–tenth as long or less. On line–of–sight paths, much of the multipath fading occurs at night when there is little or no wind or convection to break up atmospheric layers that cause irregularities in refraction and result in multipath transmission.

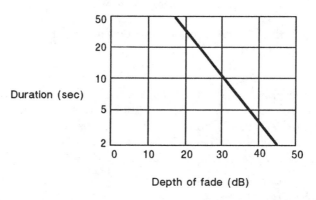

Figure 2–13. Median duration of fast fading at 4 GHz.

In addition to normal fading effects, atmospheric conditions can cause a beam–focusing effect that can raise the received signal by (typically) 6 dB and occasionally as much as 17 dB. The receiver must be able to tolerate such upfades without overloading.

The number and the severity of fades increase with repeater spacing and frequency. Although multiple paths are usually overhead, ground reflections are sometimes involved. Effects of multipath fading can be reduced by the use of alternate frequencies, adaptive equalizers, or antennas at different heights. The

antennas may have different horizontal locations, angular align-
ments, or beam patterns.

Absorption. Rain and water vapor increase path losses mark-
edly at the higher microwave frequencies. Figure 2–14 shows the
estimated atmospheric absorption versus frequency for several
concentrations of rain in the atmosphere. The increase of loss
with frequency is caused by the greater absorption and scattering
of energy as the wavelength approaches the size of the raindrops.
Systems operating at 11 GHz and above are vulnerable to rain

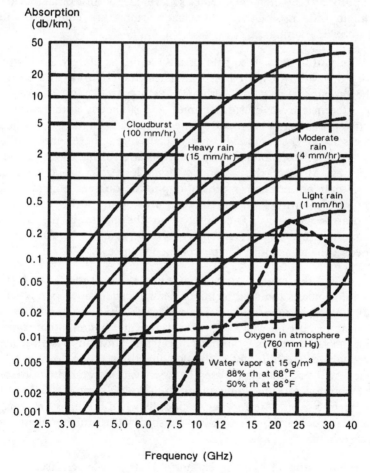

Figure 2–14. Estimated atmospheric absorption.

attenuation and cannot rely on inband frequency diversity for protection of service.

Antennas

A number of different types of antenna have been used for microwave radio systems. Today, most newer installations use a circular horn–reflector design that has proved to be economical, versatile in its broadband capability, and rugged in the face of exposure to the elements. Older square–faced horn reflectors are still in wide use. Other short–haul systems are equipped with parabolic antennas.

Characteristics. The gain of an antenna is closely associated with the width of the beam it radiates; the narrower the beam, the greater the gain. Although a narrow beam minimizes interference from outside sources and adjacent antennas, too narrow a beam may be deflected from its target by unusual stresses on the antenna tower. Therefore, there must be a balance between antenna gain and resistance of the tower to such stresses. Most of the antennas in modern microwave systems have half–power beam widths of one to two degrees. Figure 2–15 shows relationships among antenna area, gain, and beam width for any frequency. The abscissa in the figure is the actual antenna area; "actual antenna gain" is taken as 3 dB below theoretical to account for miscellaneous losses.

Not all the energy from an antenna is radiated in the main beam. Some is radiated in minor beams, called sidelobes, which are sources of interference. The energy radiated in the backward direction must be well controlled in repeater systems that transmit the same frequency in both directions. (In many systems, the frequencies are different in the two directions.) Side–to–side and back–to–back coupling losses between various combinations of transmitting and receiving antennas, all at the same station, must be high to avoid interference, especially when fading is being experienced. Transmitter outputs are some 60 dB higher than receiver inputs.

Polarization. Adjacent channels in the received frequency spectrum usually have polarizations opposite to those of the

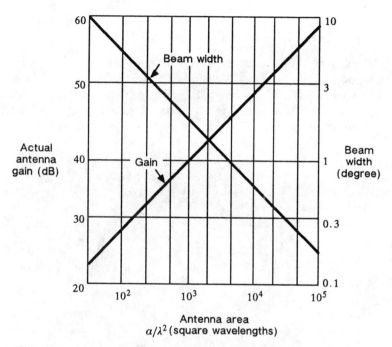

Figure 2-15. Approximate antenna area, gain, and beam width.

transmitted signals. This improves discrimination between adjacent channels and facilitates the design of networks for combining and dropping channels. Cross–polarization discrimination, the ratio of the power received in the desired polarization to that in the undesired, is usually in the range of 25 to 30 dB for an entire repeater section.

Typical Designs. Beaming microwave energy is quite similar to beaming light energy with reflectors and lenses. In both cases, the function of the equipment is to transform a spreading spherical wavefront into a plane wavefront that travels toward its objective in a narrow beam. Antenna gains of 30 to 50 dB are usual in microwave transmission.

The parabolic (or dish) antenna is fed from waveguides having outlets at the paraboloid focus. As many as four waveguides may be used to feed the antenna at the same time. Such antennas of

5– to 10–foot diameter are used mostly on short–haul systems but sometimes on lightly loaded long–haul routes.

The horn–reflector antenna, shown in Figure 2–16, combines a vertical horn and a small section of a large paraboloid surface. The energy is fed from a waveguide orifice placed at the focus of the paraboloid and flows upward, spreading out in the horn. The paraboloidal surface changes the direction of the energy to

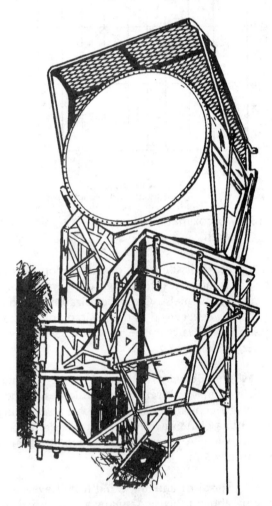

Figure 2–16. Horn–reflector antenna.

horizontal and also changes the wave front from spherical to plane, thus confining the energy to a beam spread of about two degrees. This type of antenna is capable of about 40–dB gain at 4 GHz and of successively higher gains in the 6– and 11–GHz regions. Good impedance match of the waveguide feed to the antenna results in high return loss. The horn–reflector is a broadband antenna that can be used with both vertical and horizontal polarization in the 4–, 6–, and 11–GHz bands. It has only small sidelobes and a front–to–back ratio (the ratio of the power measured at the front of a directional antenna to the power measured at the back of the antenna) of about 90 dB.

Since path losses between two microwave antennas are the same no matter which transmits and which receives, separate consideration of receiving antennas is unnecessary except when considering space diversity arrangements. The reversibility of the two roles, however, makes it clear that each antenna must be precisely aimed at the other to achieve maximum gain.

Waveguides

Waveguides prevent radio waves from spreading as they emanate from a source, usually a precisely placed loop or coaxial probe, and force them to propagate within a restricted path. The major use of waveguides is to conduct energy in microwave radio systems from transmitter to transmitting antennas, and from receiving antennas to receivers.

Losses in waveguides are minimized by using the dominant mode but attenuation is still considerable because of power losses in the walls of the guide where the traveling waves induce currents. At 4 GHz, the loss in a 1.25 x 2.50 inch brass guide is about 1.5 dB per 100 feet. This is high compared to losses in wire lines at much lower frequencies, but substantially lower than the losses that would be experienced in wire lines or coaxial cable at microwave frequencies. The velocity of propagation in a waveguide is close to, but always less than, that in free space.

Uniformity of structure is as important in waveguides as in other linear transmission media. Changes in size or shape of cross section, holes or projections in the walls, and misaligned joints distort the electromagnetic field and generate unwanted modes that result in transmission losses and delay distortion. Reflections can be caused by bends or twists that are not gradual enough or by improper terminations at the sending or receiving end. Where irregularities are unavoidable, they are minimized by means of impedance–matching techniques.

Waveguide isolators can be made that effectively limit transmission to only one direction by means of accurately placed magnetic ferrites and magnets. The magnets are placed outside a section of waveguide to produce magnetic fields in the ferrites that are located inside. These devices prevent energy reflected from transmitting antennas or discontinuities in the waveguides from interfering with the operation of components such as traveling–wave tube amplifiers.

Chapters 17 through 22 of this volume give additional information on microwave systems.

2-5 MOBILE RADIO TRANSMISSION

Both conventional–mobile and cellular–radio transmission requirements are different from those of microwave transmission; the medium is used in a different way and lower frequencies are better suited to the service [4,5]. Chapter 22 provides a detailed description of mobile and cellular–radio communication.

2-6 FIBER OPTICS

Fiber optics has matured from the first trial in 1977 where 672 circuits were carried a distance of 1.5 miles to systems that can carry 193,536 voice circuits over virtually unlimited distances.

The advent of fiber optics required the addition of several new components to the traditional digital carrier systems that multiplex several low–bit–rate digital signals into a higher–bit–rate system. The main components of a fiber optic system are: a transmitter, a receiver, and a fiber optic link to connect the two [6]. A block diagram of these components is shown in Figure 2–17. The transmission/multiplex equipment transmits electrical signals that the fiber optic transmitter converts to optical signals for transmission through the optical fiber. The optical signal is converted back to electrical signals by the far–end receiver. Typical systems today are unidirectional (i.e., one fiber is used to transmit and one to receive).

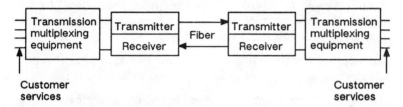

Figure 2–17. Fiber optic system components.

When first introduced, fiber optic systems were implemented for long distance and interoffice applications. As the costs of the fiber and the multiplexers decrease, exchange carriers are finding more uses for fiber optic systems in the loop or distribution environment. This trend has required the manufacturers to develop systems that will function properly in both central offices and remote terminals.

Some of the advantages of using fiber optic transmission systems rather than copper systems are:

(1) Fiber systems have larger information–carrying capacity.

(2) Fiber systems can be economically upgraded to greater transmission capacity as growth occurs.

(3) Fiber cable is lighter, smaller, and more flexible than copper cable; it has negligible interfiber crosstalk.

(4) Glass fiber is nonconductive; thus, 60–Hz induction, lightning, and other problems inherent in copper cable are minimized or eliminated.

Optical Fibers

Optical fibers used for communication are made predominantly from silica (SiO_2) which, in pure form, has a very low loss in the infrared region [0.80 to 1.60 micrometers (μm)] of the optical spectrum. The optical fiber is constructed with a cylindrical core of a higher index of refraction than the cladding material. This difference in index of refraction gives the optical fiber its guiding properties. The index of refraction of either the core or the cladding (or both) are changed from the values of pure silica by the incorporation of small amounts of dopant materials, such as phosphorus and germanium [7].

An optical fiber is manufactured by first making what is called a preform and then performing a process called drawing.

A fiber preform (typically 1 meter in length) is fabricated using one of three processes. Corning uses a process called outside chemical vapor deposition (OCVD), AT&T Technologies uses modified chemical vapor deposition (MCVD) (also called inside chemical vapor deposition) and Nippon Telegraph & Telephone (NTT) suppliers use a vapor axial deposition (VAD) process.

After the silica preform has been fabricated, an optical fiber can be drawn. The preform rod is lowered into an oven at a controlled rate, where it reaches a high enough temperature to soften. The fiber is then drawn to a diameter dependent on the rate of rotation of the take-up drum and the rate of feed of the preform into the oven. The drawn fiber will have the same characteristics as the preform.

The fiber is protected with a layer of coating material, which is usually an epoxy acrylate. Individual fibers are then placed into slots, tubes, bundles, or ribbons to form units that are stranded together to form the fiber cable structure. Several layers of protection may be used depending on the application.

Four major fiber cable structures exist: the ribbon cable, the slotted core or channel cable, the loose tube cable, and the tightly bound cable. In the ribbon design, several individual fibers are combined into a flat ribbon. In the channel or the loose tube design, one or more fibers are placed in an insulating slot (or channel) or buffer tube. Typical values for the number of fibers in a ribbon, channel, or tube range from 1 to 12 and cable sizes range from 1 to 144 fibers.

Two major types of silica-based optical fiber exist: multimode and single-mode. The two types are shown in Figure 2-18 with their typical dimensions and index of refraction profiles. Both optical fibers have an outer diameter of 125 μm. The distinction between the two types of optical fiber arises from the differing core diameters and refraction–index profiles.

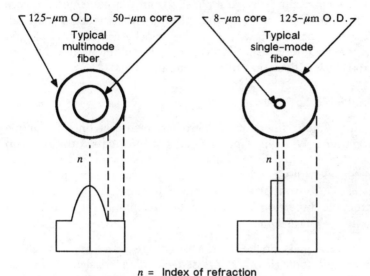

n = Index of refraction

Figure 2-18. Multimode and single–mode optical fibers.

If the core dimension is only a few times larger than the wavelength of the light to be transmitted, only one of the originating modes will be transmitted at low loss. The others will be attenuated. For wavelengths of 1.3 to 1.55 μm, the core is usually less than 10 μm in diameter for single–mode. Typical multimode fibers have a ratio of core to cladding diameter of 50/125, 62.5/125, and 85/125 μm. The trend, however, is to use single–mode fibers for all applications.

Multimode Fibers

Typical multimode fibers, designated either step–index or graded–index, support hundreds of propagating modes, each of which travels at a slightly different velocity. The core diameter of the multimode fiber normally used is 50 μm, but other special designs of multimode fibers exist with core diameters of 62.5 and 85 μm. The graded–index multimode fiber is designed to reduce pulse distortion by nearly equalizing the velocities of these propagating modes. With this type of fiber, the index of refraction decreases approximately parabolically from the center of the core to the boundary between the core and the cladding material. However, the equalization of mode velocities is not perfect, and the information transmission capacity of multimode fibers is substantially less than that of single–mode fibers.

Single–Mode Fibers

Single–mode fibers are constructed such that only one mode propagates. With this type of fiber, the information transmission capacity is limited by chromatic dispersion, which is a result of the wavelength–dependent velocities of propagation in the fiber material. Conventional single–mode fibers have their minimum chromatic dispersion, and hence their maximum transmission capacity, near 1.31 μm.

Conventional single–mode fibers are classified as either matched–cladding or depressed–cladding designs. In the matched–cladding design, the cladding has the same index of refraction from the core–cladding interface to the outer surface of the fiber. In the depressed–cladding type, there are two layers of cladding material. The index of refraction of the inner cladding, which is adjacent to the fiber core, is lower than that of the outer cladding, which is typically undoped silica.

Single–mode fibers can also be designated as either dispersion–shifted or dispersion–flattened. The dispersion–shifted fiber is designed so that the wavelength of minimum dispersion is "shifted" to 1.55 μm. At this wavelength, the attenuation can be significantly lower than at 1.31 μm. This fiber design may give significantly longer unrepeatered distances at higher information transmission rates than the unshifted design when conventional lasers or light–emitting diodes (LEDs) are used.

Although not commercially available at the time of publication, dispersion–flattened single–mode fibers appear to be an attractive design. The dispersion is low in both the 1.31–μm window and in the 1.55–μm window.

Fiber Parameters

Both multimode and single–mode fibers are subject to geometrical imperfections due to the manufacturing process. The parameters of concern for both multimode and single–mode fibers are: core diameter, cladding diameter (125 μm), coating diameter (250 μm), core and cladding noncircularity, and concentricity error (the offset between the center of the core and the center of the cladding).

The numerical aperture (NA) of a multimode fiber is another parameter. NA is defined as the sine of the maximum angle of acceptance for coupling optical power into the fiber:

$$NA \ = \ \sin \ a, \ 2a = \text{full acceptance angle.}$$

For an optical fiber in which the index of refraction decreases uniformly and monotonically from n_1 (core refractive index) to n_2 (cladding refractive index), the theoretical numerical aperture is given by:

$$NA \ = \ \sin \ a \ = \ \sqrt{n_1{}^2 - n_2{}^2}$$

Nominal NAs are in the range of 0.20 to 0.29.

Single–mode fibers are characterized by the mode–field diameter (MFD) and the cutoff wavelength. The MFD (spot size) is a measure of the width of the guided optical power's intensity distribution in the core and cladding. Typical values for the MFD are in the 9.0–to–10.0–μm range. The cutoff wavelength is the wavelength below which a single–mode fiber is capable of propagating more than one mode and above which only a single (fundamental) mode can operate.

Generic and geometric requirements for optical fiber are included at the end of the chapter.

Splicing

A splice is a permanent or semipermanent connection of two fibers. Permanent splices are made either by electric–arc fusion or by chemical bonding. Semipermanent splices are made with the aid of a mechanical device holding the fiber ends together [8].

Electric–arc fusion splicing is currently the most widely used splicing method. The essential idea behind this method is basic to glass: heat the fibers and fuse them together.

Bonding fibers together is a method of chemically "gluing" two fiber ends together. The adhesive material is usually a synthetic polyester. Since the fiber end faces do not come in direct contact, the adhesive must serve as an index–matching material to provide a consistent refractive index at the joint. Alignment can be achieved by bonding each fiber within a ferrule and then using another mechanism to align the two ferrules.

Bonding or fusing under controlled conditions produces low–loss splices. The splicing loss is governed by the concentricity of the fibers to be joined, the mechanical accuracy of the angular and longitudinal alignment, and the physical matches between core sizes, indexes of refraction, and mode–field spot sizes [6]. Splicing loss becomes important when maximum repeater spacing is desired. Production results have been reported [9] indicating that for an 8–μm core fiber (single–mode) the average eccentricity was 0.25 μm. Mean losses of 0.05 dB were achieved for a bonded or fusion splice.

Mechanical splices are semipermanent; they can be re-entered, if necessary, without cutting or breaking the fiber. They can also be made without the use of costly splicing tools. In mechanical splices, the fibers are held together with a connector that aligns them. The alignment is usually accomplished by adjusting the outer surface of the fiber. There are two classes of mechanical splice: single–fiber and multifiber. Multifiber mechanical connections, such as the array splice, are generally used with ribbon–type cable designs. Mechanical splices are normally used to reduce splicing times. They involve some exposure to small temperature–induced misalignments that induce variations in loss. Connector losses for a 12–fiber array splice have been reported in Reference 9 to have a mean of 0.4 dB.

A study of one manufacturer on the reliability of optical cables and splices on installed systems has been presented in

Reference 10. Three key fiber characteristics are discussed: strength, attenuation due to effects of hydrogen, and resistance to losses caused by microbending. Fiber coating plays a dominant role in protecting the fiber surface, preserving the intrinsic fiber strength and minimizing microbending. The objective of the coating is to package the fibers without degrading their initial transmission characteristics and to keep them stable over the design life. For this reason the fibers are generally mechanically isolated from tensile, torsional, and bending stresses.

In reporting on installed reliability, the reference indicates that data over a period of about one year on fibers of total length of 5300 sheath–km showed the usual cable cuts by construction activity, gunshot, hurricane, etc. and no failure of the intrinsic fibers themselves. The study covered two major splicing techniques: the mechanical mass–etched silicon linear array, and the electric–arc fusion splice. After early field trials, there was no report of permanent loss of a fiber path due to installation breaks or high loss for linear array splicing, and only two failures out of 2889 field fusion splices. These limited data suggest that installed fibers have excellent reliability.

Limitations

Existing fiber optic systems contain fundamental limitations on both the distance and the bit rate at which information can be transmitted. These limitations are determined by the attenuation of the signal and by the spreading of the digital pulses caused by modal and chromatic dispersion within the fiber.

In general, for single–mode systems operating under approximately 0.5 Gb/s, regenerator section length is limited by loss and not by dispersion. At higher bit rates, however, the length is limited by dispersion. Thus, it is necessary to check whether a regenerator section's length is limited by dispersion.

Fiber Attenuation. Fiber attenuation, or loss of the light energy, of silica–based fiber at long wavelengths has three major causes: Rayleigh scattering, absorption, and bending loss.

Rayleigh scattering is caused by the microscopic nonuniformity of glass and its refractive index. A ray of light is partially scattered into many directions, thus some of the light energy is lost. Since the structure of glass is much finer than the wavelength, the attenuation due to scattering decreases with wavelength. It is proportional to $1/\lambda^4$.

Absorption is caused by interactions with impurities in the silica glass or the glass itself causing unwanted reradiated light. Loss peaks at about 1.39 μm are caused by a water OH–radical impurity. This must be controlled to prevent loss spreading into the usable wavelength bands. (The attenuation curve in Figure 2–19 clearly shows why communication link designers prefer the 1.31 and 1.55 μm wavelengths.) Losses measured for high–quality, late–vintage, doped–silica fiber production have been reported [11] to be less than 0.40 dB/km and 0.22 dB/km at 1.31 μm and 1.55 μm, respectively. Also, excellent concentricity of the core versus cladding has been maintained, which allows splicing to be accomplished easily with little additional loss. Research is continuing on nonsilica glass, which theoretically offers much less loss. Plastic fibers are also available for intrabuilding use in such applications as a local area network (LAN) for data.

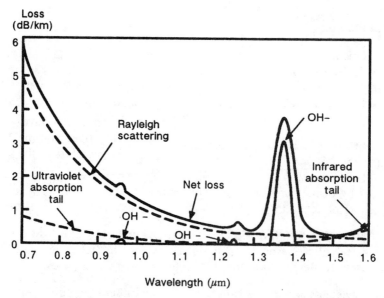

Figure 2–19. Optical fiber attenuation.

Attenuation due to bending exists in the following forms: mac-robending and microbending. Macrobending is loss that is attrib-utable to macroscopic deviations of the axis from a straight line (curvature loss). Microbending loss occurs from sharp curvatures involving local axis displacements of a few micrometers and spatial wavelengths of a few millimeters. Such bends result from optical fiber coating, cabling, packaging, installation, and aging.

Dispersion in Fiber Bandwidth. Fiber bandwidth is defined as the information–carrying capacity of the fiber link. It is limited by the amount of pulse spreading and the response of source and detector. The dispersion of a fiber is measured in picoseconds of pulse–spreading per kilometer of fiber per nanometer of source spectral width [ps/(km–nm)].

Fiber bandwidth and the related total dispersion (pulse broad-ening) are characterized by two main effects: *chromatic disper-sion* (also called intramode or spectral dispersion) for single-mode fiber, and *modal dispersion* (also called intermode or mul-timode dispersion) for multimode facilities. The former can be subdivided into material dispersion and waveguide dispersion.

Material dispersion refers to the wavelength dependence of the fiber's refractive index n and the associated differences in speed of light. Most practical light sources have a spectral width of at least one nanometer. Different components within this spectrum travel at slightly different speeds.

Waveguide dispersion is pulse broadening in a fiber due to spectral components traveling at slightly different speeds, a wave-length dependence related to the geometry of the fiber and the shape of the index profile. The reason is that the geometry of the fiber causes the propagation constant of each mode to change if the wavelength changes.

The slope of material dispersion is positive. The slope can be negative for waveguide dispersion. This can be used to shift the point of zero dispersion or to "flatten" the dispersion.

Most conventional lightly doped single–mode silica fibers [7] have one of two refractive–index profiles. That shown by Figure 2–20(a) as matched–cladding fiber applies where the index of

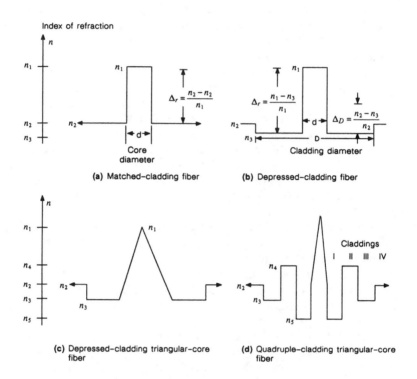

Figure 2-20. Single-mode fiber refractive index profiles.

the fiber matches that of silica. That shown in Figure 2-20(b) describes depressed-cladding fiber, where the index of the cladding next to the core is less than that of pure silica to better confine the optical power distribution to the core. Zero dispersion for these fibers occurs at about 1.3 μm. The wavelength of zero dispersion can be shifted by changing the index profile to a triangular shape, as shown in Figure 2-20(c), so that zero occurs near 1.55 μm where the lowest loss can be obtained. Further, by balancing waveguide dispersion against material dispersion over a wider range of wavelengths, a dispersion-flattened fiber can be made. Flattening the dispersion would enhance the bandwidth properties of the fiber over a greater range of wavelengths, thus allowing many optical channels with low-loss transmission and providing enormous bandwidth. A comprehensive discussion on tailoring the optical characteristics of dispersion–shifted fibers for application near 1.55 μm is contained in Reference 12. The index profile for this design is shown in Figure 2-20(d). Examples of the dispersion values for these fibers are shown in Figure 2-21(a) for material and waveguide dispersion, and in Figure 2-21(b) for the total dispersion.

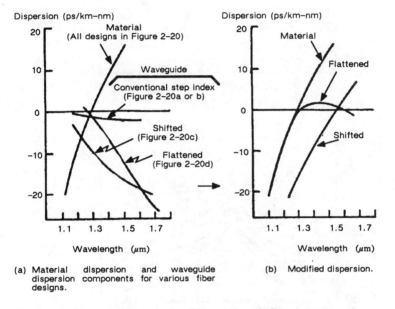

(a) Material dispersion and waveguide dispersion components for various fiber designs.

(b) Modified dispersion.

Figure 2-21. Single–mode fiber dispersion versus wavelength.

Figure 2-22(a) shows that conventional fiber loss is minimal at about 1.55 μm and has zero dispersion near 1.3 μm. Figure 2-22(b) shows the bandwidth–length product to be greater at zero dispersion but with dependence on spectral width of the source. For example, with a source spectrum of 40 nm (such as for an LED transmitter) the bandwidth–length product for the fiber at zero dispersion would be about 10 GHz–km and, for a source spectrum, δλ, of 2 nm (for a laser), over 100 GHz–km. For an equivalent 3–dB power penalty at an error rate of 10^{-9}, the bandwidth–length product in terms of gigahertz times kilometers is determined [13] by:

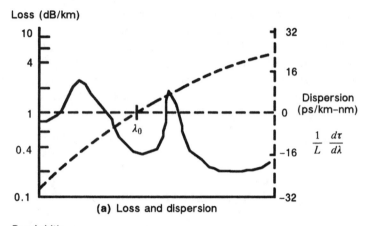

(a) Loss and dispersion

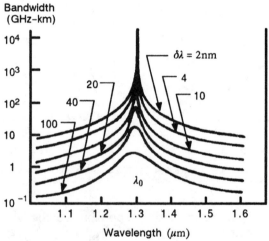

(b) Bandwidth ($\delta\lambda^2$ at peaks and $\delta\lambda$ elsewhere)

λ_0 = Zero-dispersion crossover wavelength

$\delta\lambda$ = Line width of source spectrum

Figure 2-22. Single–mode fiber transmission characteristics.

$$(B)(L) \leq \frac{340.5}{(\sigma)\left|\dfrac{d\tau}{d\lambda}\right|} \qquad (2\text{-}5)$$

off the wavelength of minimum dispersion

68

$$(B)(L) \leq \frac{11207}{(\sigma)^2 \left| \frac{d^2\tau}{d\lambda^2} \right|}$$ (2-6)

at the wavelength of minimum dispersion

where: B = Bit rate in Gb/s

L = Length in km

σ = The rms half-width of the source spectrum in nm.

$\frac{d\tau}{d\lambda}$ = First derivative of the refractive index, τ, with respect to wavelength, λ

$\frac{d^2\tau}{d\lambda^2}$ = Second derivative.

Chromatic Dispersion. Chromatic dispersion limits the bandwidth of single-mode fibers. It results from the wavelength dependence of the velocity at which light travels. Light rays with different wavelengths travel along fiber at different velocities in the same medium; the same wavelengths travel at different velocities in different media. Since the optical sources (laser diodes) presently used produce light over a significant range of wavelengths (e.g., from laser-diode "chirping"), and since each wavelength component of the pulse travels at a slightly different velocity, the pulse spreads in time as it travels down the fiber.

The dispersion disappears at a wavelength called the "zero-dispersion wavelength." Ideally, the laser would operate at this wavelength, and the ultimate bandwidth would be very high. However, due to manufacturing variations and aging, possible laser operating wavelengths cover a fairly broad range. Therefore, to ensure optimum performance of any fiber with any source, it is necessary to have a low dispersion over the range of operating wavelengths of the source rather than specifying a lower dispersion merely at one wavelength.

A principal characteristic of single-mode fiber optic systems is that, for a given span length, they exhibit less pulse broadening

69

than multimode systems, provided that the central wavelength is sufficiently close to the fiber's zero–dispersion wavelength.

Modal Dispersion. In contrast to single–mode fibers, multi-mode fibers exhibit an additional source of pulse broadening that is due to the different propagation speeds of the different modes. Since this is usually a larger effect than chromatic dispersion, multimode systems exhibit more pulse broadening.

The different propagating modes of light carrying the message literally zigzag down the fiber core, angling from side to side because of total internal reflection between the core and its surrounding transparent cladding. The zigzag path taken by the light in the higher transverse modes means that those rays follow longer paths than the rays of the fundamental transverse mode, which travel directly down the center of the core. Because of these different path lengths, pulses following the transverse modes are gradually spread: those along the higher modes arrive at the receiver somewhat later than the rays of the fundamental mode. This phenomenon is known as modal dispersion. Thus, even though in each digital pulse all the rays have left the source at the same time, modal dispersion broadens the pulse as it travels down the fiber to the detector. The amount of broadening is a function of length and worsens as distance increases.

Noncoherent Transmission. Several noncoherent (direct detection, on–off keying) optical channels can be operated over the low–loss/low–dispersion ranges of an optical fiber. This requires filters to separate the optical channels. Such devices (filters) are called wavelength–division multiplexers [14]. Currently, such multiplexers using multimode operation are designed to support two channels in the 1.30–μm wavelength band and three channels in the 1.50–μm region. Laboratory tests have demonstrated the possibility of using 10 to 18 channels of 1– to 2–Gb/s "narrow spectrum" lasers and direct detection. This, however, does not use the available fiber bandwidth efficiently because of several limitations such as source spectra, multiplexer filter technique, modulation–induced effects such as frequency chirp and mode–partition noise, and fiber dispersion characteristics. The available fiber bandwidth can be estimated from considering only wavelength regions having low loss (less than 0.5 dB/km or so), such as from 1.27 to 1.35 μm and from 1.48 to 1.60 μm. This provides a total wavelength band of 200 nm and corresponds to a huge frequency bandwidth of about 29 terahertz to support the few noncoherent channels. Coherent transmission can provide many more channels.

Coherent Transmission. The available fiber bandwidth could be used more efficiently if coherent transmission [15,16,17] could be obtained so that the optical frequencies could be down-converted to radio frequencies and processed electronically with existing technology for improved sensitivity, filtering, and equalization. This requires several stringent design considerations: a laser with a very narrow line width or single-frequency spectrum and single longitudinal mode, very high frequency and phase stability, automatic polarization correction, automatic frequency control of the source and of the local receiver laser, etc.

A comprehensive mathematical treatment of several coherent-receiver designs in the 1.3-to-1.6 μm lightwave band is provided in Reference 15. It was found that the theoretical quantum limit on receiver sensitivity can be approached with phase shift keying (PSK) and homodyne detection. However, laser phase noise, causing a broad spectrum [typically 5 to 50 MHz in early distributed-feedback (DFB) lasers], limits this approach unless the phase noise is reduced. Theoretically, it was found that for moderate data rates (500 Mb/s), frequency shift keying (FSK) with direct-laser, wide-deviation modulation appeared to be possible.

Reference 16 focuses on using coherent lightwave technology in the network for exchange trunks of 6- to 30-mile length and loop-feeder lines of 1.6- to 6-mile length. In this study it was postulated that many trunk groups of 2.4 Gb/s and many subscriber lines of 600 Mb/s would be needed and could be provided more easily with coherent transmission techniques than with conventional methods. The reference notes that the combined spectral widths of the source laser and the local laser introduce impairments that depend on the modulation chosen. This width must be small compared with the modulation spectral width. With narrow spectra and single-mode lasers, single-mode fiber dispersion may not be significant for span lengths up to 30 miles or so at rates of several gigabits per second. It may be a controlling factor at greater bit rates or span length. However, maintaining the source polarization in the fiber is important because the state of received polarization must match that of the local laser. As the fiber polarization changes with temperature, frequency, stress, etc., means must be provided to correct for these changes automatically. Reference 16 notes that present capabilities for noncoherent modulation are only two to ten channels each of about 1.0 Gb/s, whereas for coherent modulation, 20 to 50 channels each of about 2.4 Gb/s each may be possible for interoffice or loop–feeder applications.

Reference 17 presents a recent overview of the state of the art in coherent optical detection. To show the advantages of this technology, the reference indicates that receiver sensitivity for coherent detection approaches the ideal limit and is about 100 times that realized for direct detection used in noncoherent detection. It also indicates that the selectivity to pick out (electronically) the desired channel from many could be improved by about 1000 times over optical selectivity. The reference lists the results of laboratory coherent–detection experiments in several countries as reported in the literature for several modulation schemes with bit rates up to 2 Gb/s. A measure of performance of these experiments was included in terms of rate × distance (Gb/s × km), which varied over a range from 21 to 300, currently a high value.

From the foregoing, however, it is apparent that coherent transmission is still in its infancy and requires advances in technology to realize its advantages.

Generic Optical Fiber Requirements

The generic specifications for optical fiber and fiber cables given in Reference 7 for outside plant application cover the specific requirements for optical, geometric, mechanical, cable–jacket, environmental, and electrical–protection features. Also, performance verification procedures, a program analysis for quality and reliability control, and a standard optical cable code are included. In addition, the reference lists many documents, a few from the American Society for Testing Materials and 38 from the Electronic Industries Association, relating to optical fibers and cables. After discussing the coding system some of the generic requirements are presented in the following.

The standard code has three code fields:

$$M_1M_2 \quad S_1S_2S_3S_4S_5S_6 \quad NNN$$

where the first is a manufacturer code and the third is a code indicating the number of working fibers in the cable. The first character, S_1, of the middle field defines the mode of the fiber and wavelength at which the attenuation is specified, as shown in Table 2–4. The second character, S_2, in conjunction with S_1 indicates the maximum attenuation or the minimum bandwidth (in MHz × km) of several different fibers as indicated in Tables 2–5 to 2–8. For example, for single–mode, Table 2–5 covers an attenuation range from 0.40 to 0.70 dB/km. It often happens, of course, that lower–cost fibers have relatively high loss.

Table 2–4.   Character S_1—Wavelength at Which Attenuation is to be Specified

Fiber Type	Usable Wavelengths (μm)				
	0.85	1.30	1.55	0.85 and 1.30	1.30 and 1.55
Single–mode	–	1	–	–	2 or 3
Dispersion–shifted	–	–	6	–	7
50/125 multimode	K	L	–	M	–
62.5/125 multimode	P	Q	–	R	–
85/125 multimode	T	W	–	Y	–

Attenuation Coefficient (dB/km). The objective for the average attenuation coefficient of all fibers in a cable is to be no greater than 80 percent of the maximum coefficient given in Tables 2–5 to 2–8.

Table 2–5.   Character S_2 for Conventional Single–Mode Fiber

Character	1.30 μm Attenuation (dB/km)
4	0.40
5	0.50
6	0.60
7	0.70

Character S_2 defines the transmission performance of the cable. This character is keyed to the S_1 character. The meaning of S_2 is different for every S_1. First, consider conventional single–mode fibers, $S_1 = 1$, 2, or 3. The S_2 character defines the specified maximum individual–fiber attenuation in the cable. The maximum individual–fiber attenuation at 1.55 μm depends on the first character, S_1. If $S_1 = 1$, then the 1.55–μm attenuation is not specified. If $S_1 = 2$, then the maximum individual–fiber attenuation at 1.55 μm is the same as at 1.30 μm shown in Table 2–5. If $S_1 = 3$, then the maximum individual–fiber attenuation at 1.55 μm is 0.10 dB/km less than at 1.30 μm.

For dispersion–shifted single–mode fibers, which are optimized for use at 1.55 μm, $S_1 = 6$ or 7. If $S_1 = 6$, then only the attenuation at 1.30 μm is specified. If $S_1 = 7$, then the maximum individual–fiber attenuations at 1.30 μm and 1.55 μm are defined. These are given in Table 2–6.

Table 2–6. Character S_2 for Dispersion–Shifted Fiber

Character	Attenuation (dB/km)	
	at 1.30 μm	at 1.55 μm
2	0.40	0.25
3	0.50	0.30

For 50/125 multimode fibers, with $S_1 = K$, L, or M, the character denotes both the minimum allowable bandwidth (in MHz × km) and the maximum attenuation (in dB/km). Because of the large number of possible combinations of attenuations and bandwidths at the two wavelengths, only a few of the more common combinations are coded, as shown in Table 2–7. Other combinations not shown are coded as $S_2 = X$. For $S_1 = K$, only the 0.85–μm attenuation and bandwidth values apply (the upper of the two attenuation headings and the left bandwidth column). For $S_1 = L$, only the 1.30–μm values apply (the lower of the two attenuation headings and the right bandwidth column). For $S_1 = M$, both 0.85–μm and 1.30–μm values apply.

Table 2-7.   Character S_2 for Multimode Fiber

| Minimum Bandwidth (MHz × km) | | Maximum Attenuation (dB/km) | | |
| 0.85 μm | 1.30 μm | 0.85 μm: 2.6   3.0   3.5 | | |
		1.30 μm: 0.8 1.0 1.6		
300	400	G	N	U
500	800	F	M	T
600	1000	E	L	S
NA	1200	D	K	R
NA	1500	C	J	Q

The code also covers 62.5/125 and 85/125 multimode fibers. As with 50/125 fibers, only a few of the most common attenuation and bandwidth combinations are coded, as shown in Table 2-8. Combinations not shown are coded $S_2 = X$. For $S_1 = P$ or T, only the 0.85-μm values apply. For $S_1 = Q$ or W, the 1.30-μm values apply. For $S_1 = R$ or Y, both values apply.

Table 2-8.   Character S_2 for   62.5/125   and   85/125 Multimode Fiber

| Minimum Bandwidth (MHz × km) | | Maximum Attenuation (dB/km) | | |
| 0.85 μm | 1.30 μm | 0.85 μm: 2.6   3.0   3.5 | | |
		1.30 μm: 0.8 1.0 1.6		
150	300	F	M	T
200	600	E	L	S
250	800	D	K	R
NA	1000	C	J	Q

Attenuation Coefficient vs. Wavelength. For single-mode fibers, the coefficient between 1.285 and 1.330 μm shall not exceed that at 1.31 μm (or 1.30 if so specified) by more than 0.1 dB/km. (For multimode fiber, such variations are to be agreed upon by the buyer and the supplier). This is to provide a low-loss transmission window.

Water Peak Attenuation. The coefficient at 1.38 μm should not exceed an objective of 3 dB/km to control this contamination.

Attenuation Uniformity. The attenuation of a continuous fiber is to be distributed uniformly throughout its length such that there is no discontinuity in excess of 0.1 dB. Splices made in manufacturing must be at least 1 km apart and must meet the attenuation requirements as part of the fiber. In practice, this means that bonded or fused splicing with accurate concentricity is necessary to produce splice losses of the order of 0.05 dB or less.

Attenuation with Bending. For multimode fibers, the attenuation introduced when 100 turns are wound on a 75−mm diameter mandrel, including the intrinsic attenuation of 23.6 meters of fiber, is not to exceed 0.5 dB at any usable wavelength. For single−mode fibers, the attenuation of these 100 turns shall not exceed 1 dB at 1.55 μm.

A discussion on macrobending (loops that are much larger than the core, such as one inch in diameter) and microbending (deflections of the fiber axis that are small compared to the core, such as 2 nm rms) is included in Reference 9. The reference shows the calculated added fiber losses in terms of dB/km versus MFD for depressed−cladding and for matched−cladding fibers operating at 1.31 μm. It is shown that the depressed−cladding fiber is more resistant to these losses due to a smaller MFD (better optical−power containment). Since these losses increase as wavelength increases, the depressed−cladding design is better suited for operation at longer wavelengths such as 1.55 μm.

Chromatic Dispersion (Single−Mode Fiber). For conventional single−mode fibers, the zero−dispersion wavelength, λ_o, is to be between 1.295 and 1.322 μm, with a nominal value of 1.31. In addition, the maximum value of the dispersion slope at λ_o, S_{omax}, is to be no greater than 0.095 ps/(km × nm^2).

For dispersion−shifted single−mode fibers, the zero−dispersion wavelength should be between 1.54 and 1.56 μm, nominally at 1.55 μm. In addition, S_{omax} should be no greater than 0.07 ps/(km × nm^2). However, standards for the measurement and specification of the chromatic dispersion for dispersion−shifted single−mode fibers are still being developed, and the above objectives may be revised. This specification format permits the user to calculate the maximum dispersion over any wavelength window proposed for use.

For conventional single–mode fibers, D_{max}, the maximum value of dispersion over a window λ_{min} to λ_{max}, can be found as the larger of:

$$\frac{S_{omax}\,\lambda_{min}}{4}\left[1-\frac{\lambda_{omax}^4}{\lambda_{min}^4}\right]$$

or

$$\frac{S_{omax}\,\lambda_{max}}{4}\left[1-\frac{\lambda_{omin}^4}{\lambda_{max}^4}\right].$$

Multimode Bandwidth. The minimum bandwidth is to be specified at the wavelength of intended use either by the end–to–end bandwidth requirement of the cable span or by an individual–reel bandwidth requirement. Recommended minimum bandwidth categories for the three multimode fiber designs are given in Tables 2–7 and 2–8.

Cutoff Wavelength (Single–Mode Fiber). The cutoff wavelength of a cabled fiber, λ_{cc}, is to be between 1.25 and 1.03 μm. As an alternative, a supplier may specify the cutoff wavelength of an uncabled fiber, λ_{cf}, which is to lie between 1.29 and 1.13 μm. This is to prevent multimode operation causing modal noise and pulse broadening.

Mode–Field Diameter (Single–Mode Fiber). The nominal MFD for conventional single–mode fibers is to be no less than 8.7 μm and no greater than 10 μm. For dispersion–shifted single–mode fibers, the nominal should be between 7 and 8.7 μm. However, these values depend on the measurement technique used, and as industry standards for MFD measurement for dispersion–shifted single–mode fibers are now being written, revisions may be required. A range about the specified nominal is to be less than ±10 percent (requirement) and should be less than ±6 percent (objective) for both conventional and dispersion–shifted single–mode fibers.

Geometric Requirements for Optical Fiber

Multimode Optical Fibers.

Core Diameter. The fiber is to have a core diameter of 50, 62.5, or 85 μm as appropriate. The greatest permissible deviation from the nominal value for all designs is ±3 μm.

Core Noncircularity. Core noncircularity is to be less than 6 percent.

Numerical Aperture. The nominal value of NA shall be as follows:

50/125 fiber	0.20 to 0.23
62.5/125 fiber	0.27 to 0.29
85/125 fiber	0.26

For a given design, the maximum permissible deviation from the nominal value is ± 0.02.

Single–Mode Optical Fibers.

Concentricity Error. The maximum offset between the center of the core and the center of the cladding is to be less than 1.0 μm.

Optical Fiber Cable. The primary function of the optical fiber cable is to protect the fibers from damage and mechanical stress during installation and use. Optical fiber cable structure can be categorized into four constructions:

Construction 1 – All–dielectric cable in which the transmission members are optical–only and the strength members and sheathing are dielectric.

Construction 2 – Cable in which the transmission members are optical, but in which metallic materials are used for strength members, sheathing, or both.

Construction 3 – Cable in which optical and electrical transmission members are used, and strength members or sheathing are dielectric.

Construction 4 – Cable in which the transmission members are
both optical and electrical, and in which metallic materials are used for strength members
and sheathing.

Current cable designs that serve to protect the optical fibers
from environmental, placing, and handling dangers include:
loose tube (an example is shown in Figure 2–23), slotted core,
ribbon (an example is shown in Figure 2–24), tightly bound or
tight buffer, and fiber bundle.

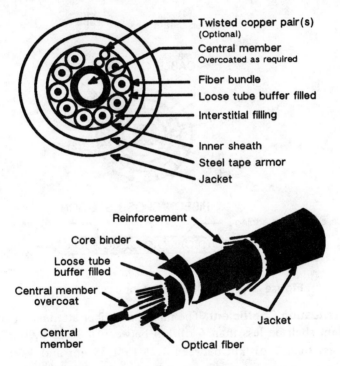

Figure 2-23. Examples of loose tube cable design.

Intrabuilding Optical Fiber Cable

Generic requirements for intrabuilding optical fiber cable are
covered in Reference 18. These are similar to those indicated
above for outside plant cable except the allowable attenuation

coefficient is much greater as noted below. Some of the optical requirements follow.

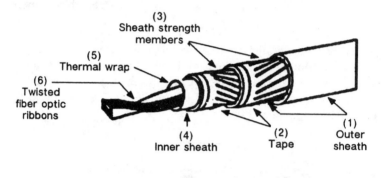

CABLE CROSS SECTION

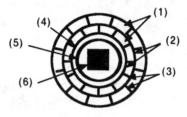

RIBBON CROSS SECTION

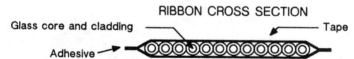

Figure 2-24. Ribbon-type optical cable.

Attenuation Coefficient. The multimode fiber attenuation coefficient shall be less than 6 dB/km between 0.80 to 0.90 μm, and less than 2 dB/km between 1.25 to 1.35 μm and 1.50 to 1.60 μm.

The single-mode fiber attenuation coefficient shall be less than 2 dB/km between 1.25 to 1.35 μm and 1.50 to 1.60 μm. Also, as an objective, the single-mode fiber attenuation should be less than 5 dB/km from 0.8 to 0.9 μm.

Multimode Fiber Bandwidth. The minimum bandwidth of a cable containing 50/125 multimode fiber is to be 300 MHz-km at 0.85 μm and 400 MHz–km at 1.3 μm. The minimum bandwidth of a cable containing 62.5/125 or 85/125 multimode fiber shall be 150 MHz–km at 0.85 μm and 300 MHz–km at 1.30 μm. The reason for this requirement is that some control of multimode bandwidth is required on short spans of optical cable to assure a minimum performance for future use.

Cutoff Wavelength (Single–Mode Fiber). Cutoff wavelength must be controlled to prevent a single–mode fiber optic system from operating in the fiber's multimode region. Multimode operation would lead to increased noise and reduced bandwidth.

For all intrabuilding cables, the cutoff wavelength, λ_{cc}, of cabled fiber, is to be less than 1.25 μm as measured on the minimum length of cable installed (3 meters for riser and distribution cables). For single–mode interconnect cables (pigtails, jumpers, and patch cords), a minimum cable length of 2 meters is recommended.

Chapter 14 contains additional information on fiber optics.

References

1. Eager, G. S. et al. "Transmission Properties of Polyethylene Insulated Telephone Cables at Voice and Carrier Frequencies," *Communications and Electronics*, AIEE Paper 59–778 (Nov. 1959).

2. Jachimowicz, L. et al. "Transmission Properties of Filled Thermoplastic Insulated and Jacketed Telephone Cables at Voice and Carrier Frequencies," *Conference Record*, IEEE International Conference on Communications (Philadelphia, PA: June 1972).

3. Bullington, K. "Radio Propagation Fundamentals," *Bell System Tech. J.*, Vol. 36 (May 1957), pp. 593–626.

4. Young, W. R., Jr. "Comparison of Mobile Radio Transmission at 150, 450, 900, and 3700 MC," *Bell System Tech. J.*, Vol. 31 (Aug. 1952), pp. 1068–1085.

5. Hamsher, D. H. *Communication System Engineering Handbook* (New York: McGraw–Hill Book Company, Inc., 1967), Chapter 17.

6. Personick, S. D. *Fiber Optics—Technology and Applications* (New York: Plenum Press, 1985), Chapter 2.

7. *Generic Requirements for Fiber and Optical Fiber Cable,* Technical Reference TR–TSY–000020, Bellcore (Iss. 2, Dec. 1986).

8. *Splicing Machines for Single–Mode Fiber Cable,* Technical Reference TR–TSY–000041, Bellcore (Iss. 1, Dec. 1985).

9. Cohen, L. G. and D. Kalish. "Single–Mode Fiber: From Research and Development to Manufacturing," *AT&T Technical Journal,* Vol. 66, No. 1 (Jan./Feb. 1987), p. 19.

10. Szentesi, O. I. "Reliability of Optical Fibers, Cables and Splices," *IEEE Journal on Selected Areas in Communications,* Vol. SAC–4, No. 9 (Dec. 1986).

11. Flegal, W. M., E. A. Hanleg, et al. "Making Single–Mode Preforms by the MCVD Process," *AT&T Technical Journal,* Vol. 65, No. 1 (Jan./Feb. 1986).

12. Cohen, L. G., W. A. Read, and H. T. Shang. "Tailoring Optical Characteristics of Dispersion–Shifted Lightguides for Applications Near 1.55 μm," *AT&T Technical Journal,* Vol. 65, No. 5 (Sept./Oct. 1986).

13. Ogawa, K. "Considerations for Single–Mode Fiber Systems," *Bell System Tech. J.,* Vol. 61, No. 8 (Oct. 1982).

14. Cohen, L. G. "Trends in U.S. Broadband Fiber Optic Transmission Systems," *IEEE Journal on Selected Areas in Communications,* Vol. SAC–4, No. 4 (July 1986).

15. Salz, J. "Coherent Lightwave Communications," *AT&T Technical Journal,* Vol. 64, No. 10 (Dec. 1985), pp. 2153–2210.

16. Cheng, N. K., P. Kaiser, and R. E. Wagner. "Coherent Lightwave Systems for Interoffice and Loop–Feeder Applications," *IEEE Journal of Lightwave Technology,* Vol. LI–5, No. 4 (Apr. 1987).

17. Henry, P. S. and R. A. Linke. "Coherent Optical Detection: A Thousand Calls on One Circuit," *IEEE Spectrum* (Feb. 1987).

18. *Generic Requirements for Intrabuilding Fiber Optic Cable*, Technical Reference TR-TSY-000409, Bellcore (Iss. 1, June 1987).

Telecommunications Transmission Engineering

Section 2

Local Plant Facilities

The quality of transmission is influenced in many ways by local plant facilities, among which are loops or access lines. These are significant in determining transmission quality because two of each are used on every connection. Many trunks are included in local plant facilities; they too have an effect on transmission quality.

The variety of transmission equipment located in central–office buildings and the switching equipment itself, which provides a multitude of transmission paths, must all be carefully controlled to assure satisfactory service. These connect with switching facilities, located on customer premises, that also affect the quality of service as seen by the end user.

Chapter 3 is devoted to discussions of loop facilities, including feeder and distribution plant. The loop facility portion briefly discusses the resistance and long–route design plans and describes a number of supplementary electronic equipment types that are used to improve transmission and to extend loop ranges. The discussion of feeder and distribution plant includes the carrier serving area concept, which guides the evolution to a network able to provide digital services using distribution facilities. The chapter includes the digital subscriber line for integrated services digital network (ISDN) basic–rate access.

Chapter 4 discusses voice–frequency trunk transmission facilities, with emphasis on the present generation of repeaters and terminating equipment. The performance and application of various types of equipment are compared. Finally, the chapter discusses the application of echo control to network trunks.

Chapter 5 discusses voiceband data transmission in the loop plant and the adaptation of loop facilities to the needs of data transmission. The types of equipment found at typical data stations are described and the features of data sets are discussed.

Chapter 6 covers facilities found in the local plant for services with bandwidths appreciably above voice frequency. Included are descriptions of facilities for high–capacity digital services, ISDN, local area data, Public Switched Digital Service, the Digital Data System and Basic Dedicated Digital Service, special fiber–based services, program and video channels, and wideband analog services.

Switching machines are unquestionably the largest items of central–office equipment, but there are also many items of transmission equipment mounted in central offices. Chapter 7 describes the transmission paths through the switching machines together with transmission circuit–terminating and auxiliary equipment and the switching–system functions that affect transmission performance. The sources and control of central–office transmission impairments are also discussed. The chapter also describes the digital switching interface equipment, including that for ISDN, found in central offices.

Chapter 8, the final chapter in this section, is a parallel to the previous chapter, but covers switching equipment used at customer premises. Included are private branch exchanges and key systems. Emphasis is placed on transmission characteristics of this equipment that differ significantly from those of central–office equipment.

Telecommunications networks in the United States provide a wide variety of services that affect the lives of everyone. Telecommunications services that enable people to talk to each other involve computers that communicate and a variety of voice, data, and signalling functions. A communications system must supply the means to accomplish this in an ever–evolving environment. Such a system is made up of a complex aggregate of electronic equipment and transmission media that provide a multiplicity of channels over which speech and digital messages, along with associated signalling information, can be transmitted. Vast and complex telecommunications systems have grown and are still growing rapidly. This expansion has been driven by customer growth, technological discoveries that promote innovations in equipment design and facility usage, and the political and economic climate in the United States. These changes have resulted in the orderly growth of telecommunications networking and the rendering of communications services throughout the United States, North America, and indeed the world.

Chapter 3

Local Plant Facilities

3-1 LOOP PLANT

Loops and their associated station equipment affect the quality of transmission perceived by the customer. Industry specifications for telephone sets are given in *EIA Standard EIA–470* [1]. Since the customer chooses the type and quality of station equipment, this chapter will focus on the loop plant from the serving end office to the customer's network interface (NI).

Loops play a large role in transmission because two of them are used in every network connection. Loop facilities often share supporting structures with power lines and are thus susceptible to power–line influence. They are exposed to the weather and construction activities and are thus subject to damage that can result in loss of service or harm performance via noise or crosstalk. Special–services circuits also use these facilities and must be protected against the same impairments.

Transmission performance in the loop plant is controlled by loop cable layouts that are engineered to take advantage of the statistical distributions of resistance and loss. If the design rules are not applied, the number of limiting (high–loss) loops may significantly increase and grade of service for built–up connections may deteriorate substantially because the number of connections between high–loss loops would increase. The application of digital loop carrier (DLC) systems reduces the need for long, high–loss metallic loops. Survey results covering the performance of loops for voice and integrated services digital network (ISDN) applications are covered in Chapter 4 of Volume 3; loop planning considerations are discussed in Chapter 5 of that volume.

Where loop lengths are limited by signalling considerations, it is possible to extend the ranges by application of signalling range extenders. However, if this is done without regard to transmission considerations, performance may suffer noticeably unless voice compensation (gain and equalization) is applied as well.

3-2 FEEDER AND DISTRIBUTION PLANT

The modern distribution network is made up of two major parts: feeder plant and distribution plant [2,3]. Figure 3–1 is a schematic representation of a feeder route, its branch or subsidiary feeder routes, and distribution routes.

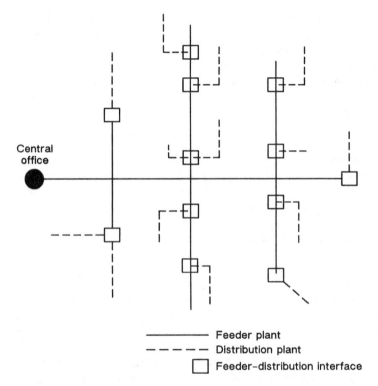

Feeder plant
Distribution plant
Feeder-distribution interface

Figure 3-1. Feeder and distribution plant.

The feeder portion of the network comprises wire cables of various gauges, digital span lines using those cables, optical fibers, and even radio. It can transport voice–frequency (VF), digital, or multiplexed signals. Pair gain is accomplished using

90

digital or analog carrier systems. Feeder cables provide large numbers of cable pairs, physical or electronically derived, from the office to strategic remote locations called serving area interfaces or simply, interfaces. These are cross–connection points in the network that connect the feeder plant coming from the office to the distribution plant that terminates at the customer's NI. Sections of the feeder plant are augmented on a periodic basis to accommodate growth.

The relief period for wire feeder plant varies between companies, but typically ranges from 4 to 15 years. Local geography and the locations of customers and rights of way determine the placement of feeder routes. Major highways are often paralleled by feeder routes. Many subfeeders or branch feeder routes emanate from the four or five major feeder routes leaving the typical office.

Distribution plant usually consists of smaller cables that connect the feeder plant to the customer's NI. Distribution plant is designed to meet the ultimate requirements for an area (meaning the greatest customer demand expected for the life of the plant being designed). Copper cables of 26 or 24 gauge are the predominant element of the distribution facilities. Rural distribution wire is sometimes used for long distances from cables to individual rural customers. Distribution network design requires more distribution pairs than feeder pairs, so distribution cables are more numerous, but smaller in cross section, than feeder cables.

Multipled, Dedicated, and Interfaced Plant

Design of the loop plant treats loops on an aggregate, instead of an individual, basis, so large cross sections of facilities are designed with similar transmission characteristics. This simplifies distribution network design, especially when multiple gauges of cable are used.

The major distribution network designs currently used by exchange carriers are multipled, dedicated, interfaced (serving area), and carrier serving area (CSA) plant. The CSA concept is designed to accommodate DLC and digital techniques such as ISDN; it is discussed later in the chapter.

Multipled plant design involves splicing two or more distribution pairs to a single feeder pair, as illustrated in Figure 3–2. That is, feeder and distribution plant are combined with no interface between them. This procedure provides flexibility to accommodate future assignments by providing multiple appearances of the same loop pair at several distribution points. In times when multiparty service was common, it accommodated field–bridging of party–line stations, saving feeder pairs at the cost of added field work for rearrangements. However, adding new feeder pairs forced line and station transfers to relieve the distribution cables. Because changing existing plant or adding new facilities is labor intensive and because party–line service continues to shrink, multipled plant design has been largely replaced by other designs.

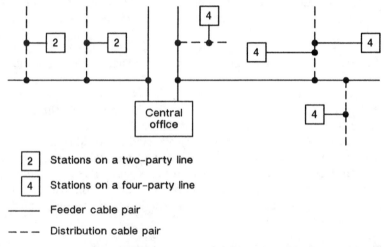

2 — Stations on a two–party line

4 — Stations on a four–party line

——— Feeder cable pair

— — — Distribution cable pair

Figure 3–2. Multipled plant design.

Dedicated plant provides a permanently assigned cable pair from the office main distributing frame (MDF) to each customer's NI (excluding multiline business customers). Party–line loops are bridged together at the central office. Dedicated plant largely eliminates expensive transfers of lines and stations, but at the cost of low pair use and relatively little flexibility. For new construction dedicated plant has been superseded by interfaced plant.

Interfaced plant uses a manual cross–connection and demarcation point between feeder and distribution plant. The cross–connection, or interface, allows any feeder pair to be connected to any distribution pair. This increases flexibility and reduces outside–plant investment and labor costs. Compared to multipled and dedicated plant, interfaced plant provides greater flexibility in the network. The serving area concept, discussed below, uses the interfaced plant design.

Serving Area Concept. Portions of the geographical area of a wire center are divided into discrete serving areas to be administered under the serving area concept [4]. The outside plant within the serving area is the distribution network. It is connected to the feeder network at a single interconnection point, the serving area interface. Figure 3–3, a typical configuration for the serving area concept, illustrates the use of the interface. All pairs at the input and output of the interface are terminated on connecting blocks that provide interconnection between feeder and distribution pairs.

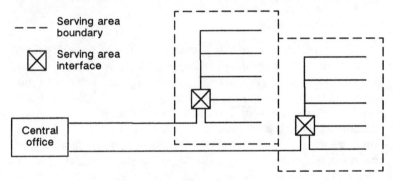

Figure 3–3. The serving area concept.

The concept provides for the expansion of permanent and reassignable services, yet minimizes future rearrangements; it simplifies and reduces engineering and plant records necessary to design, construct, administer, and maintain outside plant; and it reduces and improves maintenance activities in terminals and enclosures. It aids transmission by minimizing bridged taps, a distinct advantage in providing services of bandwidth greater than voice. The serving area concept also accommodates the use of analog or (especially) digital carrier in the feeder plant.

Investment economies are realized by separating the distribution and feeder facilities. For example, distribution facilities may be sized to serve the ultimate needs of the area, whereas the installation of feeder facilities can be deferred until needed. Distribution cables are sized to provide a minimum of two cable pairs to each anticipated residential unit; these pairs are permanently wired to the serving area interface. The optimum size of each serving area, in the range of 200 to 600 residential units, is determined by geographical constraints and predicted population density. In areas where growth is uncertain, reassignable plant can be built and converted to the serving area concept as growth characteristics become apparent.

Operating expense for the serving area concept is less than for the dedicated outside plant plan because of better-designed equipment and simplicity of record maintenance. The provision of at least two distribution pairs per residential unit increases the cost of the cable network, but this cost is offset by higher average feeder use and reduced station connection and repair costs.

Carrier Serving Area

The evolution to a network that can readily provide digital services through its distribution facilities is guided by the carrier serving area concept. A CSA is a geographical area that is or may be served by DLC from a single remote terminal (RT) site analogous to the serving area interface. Within the CSA, all loops, without conditioning or design, are capable of providing conventional message service, 64-kb/s and lower digital data service, and most two-wire, locally switched voiceband special services. (See Figure 3-4.) These loops are positioned toward ISDN basic-rate access with two B and one D channels; in particular, the CSA concept can evolve into an ISDN serving area plan.

The maximum loop length in a CSA is 12 kft for 19-, 22-, and 24-gauge cables and 9 kft for 26-gauge cables. These lengths include any bridged tap that may be present. The maximum allowable bridged tap is 2.5 kft, with no single bridged tap longer than 2.0 kft. All CSA loops must be nonloaded and should not consist of more than two gauges of cable. (Extended CSAs with long loaded distribution cables may be used in rural areas where the main demand is for basic voice service.)

The area around the serving end office, within a distance of 9 kft for 26-gauge cable and 12 kft for coarser-gauge cables,

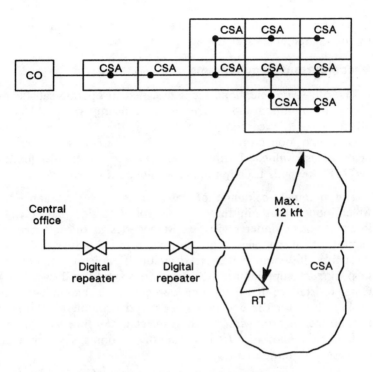

Figure 3–4. Carrier serving areas.

although not a CSA, is compatible with the CSA concept in terms of achievable transmission performance and services.

In some cases, an RT site that terminates high–capacity fiber facilities serves as a fiber hub. It distributes DS1 channels on fiber or T1 spans to subtending RT sites that are usually farther away from the central office, and provides DS1 services and ISDN primary–rate access directly to customer locations.

Loop Resistance Limits

The basic function of a loop is to furnish a two–way transmission path between a central office and an end user. It must provide a dc connection to operate the end user's equipment and a transmission path for supervisory, address, and ringing signals. The loop length over which these signals may be transmitted is limited by the conductor resistance of the loop and is influenced by the characteristics of the equipment at both ends.

Direct-Current Requirements

The 500-type telephone set is designed to operate satisfactorily with a minimum loop current of 20 milliamperes (mA). The efficiency of the carbon microphone in the 500-type set decreases with loop current and deteriorates rapidly with currents below this value. Furthermore, dual-tone multifrequency (DTMF) keypads usually require a minimum of 20 mA.

The nominal maximum of 1500 ohms is the resistance to which loops are administered for control of outside plant facility insertion losses under revised-resistance-design rules. A typical central office supplies loop current from a 48-volt battery through a 400-ohm battery feed circuit. (Semiconstant-current loop-current supplies are also used in some digital switches.) Other resistances that determine loop current include allowances of 430 ohms for the end user's registered equipment, 25 ohms for 500 feet of drop wire, 10 ohms for central-office wiring, and a 10-percent allowance (a maximum of 150 ohms) for resistance increase with temperature.

Supervisory and Dial Signalling Limits

The maximum loop resistance that can be tolerated for supervision and dial signalling in electromechanical offices is usually determined by the operating parameters of the line relay, the dial-pulsing relay, and the trunk supervisory relay. However, the requirements for ring tripping sometimes establish the maximum loop resistance rather than requirements for the operation of these relays. Later offices—analog electronic and digital—rely on ferrod sensors or voltage comparators for supervision and pulsing, so their resistance limits are higher, 1600 ohms or more. In these cases, the need to deliver 20 mA or more to the station becomes limiting. Equipment reference data for a given type of central-office equipment list the controlling parameter.

Distribution Network Design

To ensure acceptable transmission in the distribution network, design rules are used to control loop transmission performance.

Loops are designed on a global basis to guarantee that loop transmission loss is appropriately distributed statistically and that no loop in the distribution network exceeds the signalling range of the office.

Prior to 1980, loops were designed using the resistance design (RD) and long–route design (LRD) plans. The presently recommended design plans applicable on a forward–going basis (redesign not required) are: revised resistance design (RRD), modified long–route design (MLRD), and concentrated range extension with gain (CREG).

RRD rules specify that loops 18 kft in length or less (including bridged tap) be nonloaded and have loop resistances of 1300 ohms or less; loops 18 kft to 24 kft in length (including bridged tap) be loaded and have loop resistances less than or equal to 1500 ohms, office range permitting; and loops longer than 24 kft be implemented using DLC as first choice or MLRD as second choice. The outside plant engineer specifies the cable gauge by using a combination of the two finest gauges that will meet the resistance limit. RRD limits bridged tap to less than 6 kft for non-loaded cable, while for loaded cable the end section plus bridged tap must be between 3 kft and 12 kft. (A bridged tap is considered to be any branch or extension of a cable pair in which no direct current flows when a station set is connected to the pair in use.)

MLRD applies to the design of loops having resistances between 1500 and 2800 ohms. This equates to a maximum of 82 kft (15.5 mi) of 22–gauge cable. All cables are to be loaded. A combination of two cable gauges is used along with the required range extension and gain. Gain is applied, either 3 or 6 dB according to cable length, holding the 1000–Hz loss of the loop to between 4 and 8 dB. The bridged–tap and end–section requirements are compatible with RRD for loaded cable.

The CREG plan allows for use of finer–gauge cable facilities by providing a repeater behind a stage of switching concentration in the office. In this way, the range extension circuitry is shared rather than dedicated to each loop. CREG design applies to loops having loop resistances up to 2800 ohms. Its loading, bridged tap, and end–section requirements are compatible with RRD and

97

MLRD. However, it is not available in digital offices, and has not been widely applied in those electronic analog offices that can accommodate it.

The new design plans offer improved transmission performance over the old plans, and all provide approximately the same minimum loop transmission loudness ratings.

3-3   LINE TREATMENT

Signal Repeating Equipment

A variety of loop signalling units without VF gain features are available. These are known as range extenders, signalling repeaters, or dial long–line units. The functions of these units include the repeating of ringing signals, the repeating and regenerating of dial pulses, and the boosting of dc line current for improved performance of supervisory circuits, station–set microphones, and DTMF oscillators. Some designs disable repeaters in the idle state or apply idle–circuit terminations. Designs are made more complex when party–line or coin–line service is involved and when automatic number identification is needed on two–party lines.

Signalling Range Extender

Central–office resistance limits for exchange–carrier coin lines may be extended up to 2400 ohms by using a typical signalling range extender (SRE). The SRE equipment provides range extension on up to ten coin lines in a shelf assembly. In addition to the range extender plug–in units, the shelf accommodates an inverter unit that converts 48 volts dc to a 10–kHz square–wave output voltage. An alarm and transfer unit distributes the inverter output to the range extenders, provides alarm indications in the event of failure, and optionally provides transfer to an alternate inverter.

Each range extender rectifies the square–wave signal received from the inverter. The 24–volt rectified signal is filtered and applied to the line as illustrated in Figure 3–5. When the station set

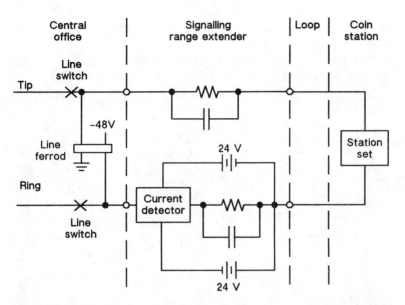

Figure 3-5. Application of signalling range extender to coin station line.

is on-hook, no current flows and the range extender is idle. When the station is off-hook, current flow is sensed and a 24-volt battery of appropriate polarity is connected in series with the line. This battery augments the current flow, assists the operation of the ring-tripping circuits in the central office, and boosts the "collect" and "return" battery currents sent to the station. It thus improves supervision, dialing, and transmission performance. The SRE provides no gain; however, it may be used with a repeater when gain is required.

Message Signal Gain

The application of dedicated VF gain equipment to individual loops tends to be costly. However, where service must be furnished over long noncarrier routes, LRD with range extension and gain is feasible. The equipment for these applications is almost always mounted at the central office end of a loop. Figure 3-6 shows a typical device of this type, which extends the range of supervision, dial pulsing, and ring tripping while providing a 78-volt battery feed to the station. By sensing the amount of loop current, it sets a negative–impedance repeater circuit to give either 3 or 6 dB of gain. It also affords a dc through–path for testing and party identification for automatic message accounting on two–party lines.

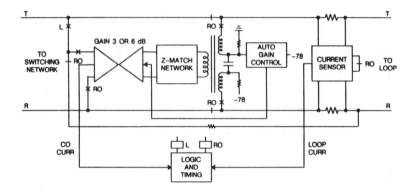

Figure 3–6. Range extender with gain.

Bridge Lifters

The transmission loss caused by a parallel or bridged connection may be made negligible by the use of a bridge lifter. This device produces low series impedance in the current–carrying pair and produces simultaneously high impedance in the unused bridged pair(s); thus, the impedances of the unused pairs are isolated from the through connection.

Relays or semiconductors may be used but saturable inductors are most commonly used as bridge lifters because they are relatively inexpensive and require no maintenance. A typical application is shown in Figure 3–7(a). When no current flows in loop 1 or loop 2, the inductance of the toroidal windings is high and the bridging loss of either loop is low. When current flows, as in the off–hook condition, the toroid is magnetically saturated so that the insertion loss of the affected windings is low. Thus, transmission in the circuit that carries current is not materially affected by the coil insertion loss or by the bridging loss of the parallel connection. The losses are shown qualitatively in Figure 3–7(b).

100

Actual losses are functions of frequency and of the impedances of the connected circuits.

Although bridge lifters can be installed at remote locations (field bridging), they are usually used in the central office (CO bridging). They are used to preserve transmission performance on party lines and, similarly, on secretarial–service lines and off–premises extensions.

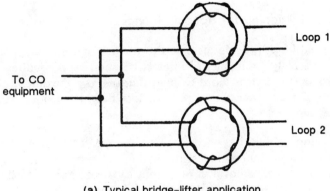

(a) Typical bridge–lifter application

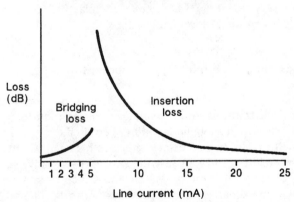

(b) Typical loss characteristics

Figure 3-7. Saturable inductors used as bridge lifters.

Maintenance Terminating Units

On long loops to hard–to–reach customer locations, it is often economical to provide a maintenance terminating unit (MTU) at

101

the interface with the customer's equipment. This makes it possible to lift off the station equipment by remote command, thus determining whether a trouble is in the network or the customer equipment. The MTU typically responds to a coin–control potential ($\pm$130 volts), disconnects the premises equipment for a timed interval, and presents a distinctive signature to the central–office test system.

Loop Conditioning for Special Services

Normal loops provide losses up to 8 dB. For centrex applications, the high community of interest between users requires repeaters on the longer loops to hold the loss to a maximum of 5 dB. Similar considerations apply to loops used for other voice special services.

To support digital services at bit rates greater than 64 kb/s, loops require additional design. Additional restrictions on loss and bridged tap, removal of build–out capacitors, and coordination with other services in the same cable may be required. For 1.5–Mb/s services and DLC systems, regular T1 spans may be built by conversion of loop cable.

Network Channel Terminating Equipment

Voice–frequency terminating equipment is used to meet the wide range of transmission, signalling, and test requirements for special services over metallic facilities. Terminal equipment at the end office provides the necessary interface between two–wire and four–wire facilities and can provide transmission only, signalling only, or both in single units. When end–office treatment is not sufficient, the exchange carrier provides network channel terminating equipment (NCTE) at the customer location to terminate analog special–service lines or trunks.

Since there are a variety of serving arrangements, there are many equipment units—generally a different plug–in unit for each. However, some units are multifunctional and can be used for more than one serving arrangement. Serving arrangements include two–wire and four–wire operation; signalling by loop, ground–start, duplex, or single–frequency techniques; impedance compensation; and four–wire loop–back. Such features as automatic self–equalization and gain setting are available.

3–4 LOOP CARRIER FACILITIES

Analog Loop Carrier

Analog carrier systems, both single–channel and multichannel, have been available for loop application for about 25 years. The single–channel systems provide an additional channel (called an add–on channel) by using a frequency spectrum above the VF band. The frequencies used are usually 28 kHz toward the station and 76 kHz toward the office. Some systems use compandors in the 76–kHz direction, or in both, to control the perceived level of noise. These systems are usually used in congested areas to defer new cable installations.

The multichannel systems are used in low–growth areas, typically on long loops. They furnish four to eight channels on a single cable pair. Unlike the single–channel systems, they do not attempt to use the physical cable pair as a VF path. They provide either a lumped (concentrated) remote terminal where customer connections are made, or a distributed remote terminal arrangement where customer connections are made in several locations along the same system. They generally operate with double-sideband AM signals, using transmitted carriers at 8–kHz intervals in the band from 12 to 156 kHz. Equivalent–four–wire operation requires only a single nonloaded cable pair. Individual channels use compandors in both directions for noise control. The carrier terminals, any intermediate repeaters that are needed, and the telephones themselves are all powered by dc current sent over the carrier pair. The multichannel systems are used in low–growth areas, typically on long loops.

With the dominance of digital technology, analog loop carrier placements have largely stopped, although existing systems continue to provide satisfactory service.

Derived Local–Channel Systems

Special carrier systems are in limited use for two purposes: for local–area data transmission at 4.8 to 64 kb/s, and for alarm services. A typical application of the former type involves a data subscriber loop carrier system similar to single–channel analog carrier. In this case, the 28– and 76–kHz carriers are phase–shift keyed with a 4.8–kb/s data stream. Other techniques like time-compression multiplexing ("ping-pong" operation) may be used. Such systems are common in a central–office–based local area network (CO–LAN).

In the case of alarm services, an on–off alarm signal at very low speeds (10 b/s or less) originates at the station. It is added digitally on an exclusive–or basis (modulo–2 addition) with a much faster pseudorandom digital stream. This action moves the spectrum of the alarm signal up into the voiceband and spreads it uniformly across the band. This signal is then superimposed onto a regular loop pair, nonloaded or loaded, that is simultaneously used for voice service. The telephone user hears only a small increase in the background noise level. At the serving central office, a receiving terminal combines the incoming spread–spectrum signal with a replica of the pseudorandom digital stream to extract the original alarm signal.

Digital Loop Carrier

DLC became feasible in the 1970s as an economical alternative to metallic facilities for long feeder routes (Figure 3–8). While there was some use of a system supplying 40 lines on a DS1 span by use of delta modulation, all present–vintage systems use pulse code modulation (PCM). The most basic system consists of a central–office terminal (COT), a digital carrier facility, and an RT. On the subscriber side of the RT is distribution plant constructed with traditional metallic cable pairs. The COT time-division multiplexes 64 kb/s onto the connecting digital carrier facility for transmission of each channel to the RT. DLC systems are based on interoffice PCM technology as discussed in Chapter 13, but also may provide either concentration or low–bit–rate-voice (LBRV) coding to derive two or more station lines from a single DS0 slot.

DLC systems have extensive maintenance features allowing single–ended maintenance from the end office. Among the features are automatic switching when span facilities fail, remote

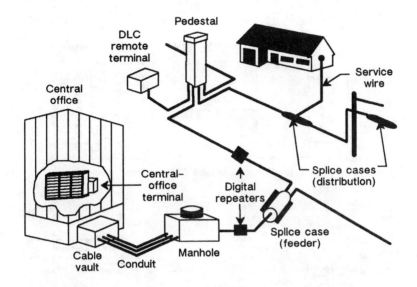

Figure 3-8. Distribution network—digital loop carrier.

alarm capabilities, and remote testing of digital facilities and the distribution plant. To support maintenance and testing, metallic pairs are usually required for fault sectionalization on the digital line, and as order wires and test pairs. Fiber–based DLC systems are also common.

A basic DLC configuration is shown in Figure 3–9(a). RTs terminate the digital facility, multiplex individual circuits, and accept interchangeable channel units to provide cable pair terminations for customer services. For universal DLC systems, the COT is a digital channel bank that provides physical appearances of the circuits corresponding to the derived cable pairs at the remote terminal. The circuits are cross–connected and routed in the same manner as metallic facilities.

Integrated digital loop carrier (IDLC) systems terminate directly in the switching network of a digital office, avoiding the cost of a COT and a conversion from digital to analog. The earlier versions lack the reassignment flexibility of universal digital loop carrier (UDLC) systems, do not gracefully accommodate special services, and need to be traffic–engineered to avoid misloading the switch. They also do not accommodate bridged

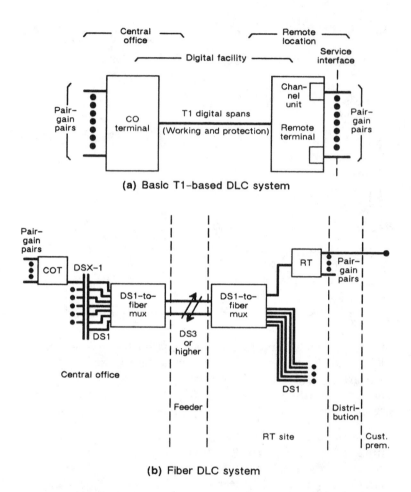

(a) Basic T1-based DLC system

(b) Fiber DLC system

Figure 3-9. Digital loop carrier systems.

stations or extensions. However, later designs incorporate the features of a digital cross-connect system (DCS) to provide flexibility, allowing segregation of nonlocally switched special services from circuits that terminate in the switch. The newer systems are able to handle party lines. The availability of a "side-door port" on the switch to allow special services to share the IDLC system makes this concept more attractive.

An IDLC system has the COT integrated into the end-office digital switch. The office configuration consists of a T1 office repeater bay with a DSX–1 digital signal cross–connection to a switch interface unit, to work directly with T1 span lines. Where fiber spans are involved, the office contains fiber termination equipment and multiplexers to convert from the fiber transmission rate to DS1. Digital radio and its associated multiplexers are also used occasionally. Network office terminal equipment (NOTE) is also available to interface DLC or IDLC systems with interoffice transmission systems, DCSs, or high–capacity multiplexer derived facilities (e.g., digital radio and fiber systems). NOTEs are T1 office repeaters with added features to meet maintenance and data–link protocol requirements of the DLC remote terminal.

Figure 3–9(b) shows a layout based on currently available fiber optic systems with DS3, or higher transmission rates. The provision of service over metallic or fiber optic systems depends on media costs and capacity requirements. Table 3–1 shows the equipment–related elements associated with using DLC systems.

Table 3–1. DLC System Elements

Feeder Plant
   Remote terminal
   Digital line (T1 spans, radio, or optical fibers)
   Structure (poles or conduit)
   Repeaters (if used) (manholes, apparatus cases)
   Lightguide interconnection terminal (if used)
   Multiplexers (if used)
   RT housing (controlled environment vault, hut, or
      cabinet)
   Land for RT housing

End Office
   Main distributing frame (if used for DLC)
   Office cabling
   Digital signal cross–connect
   Central–office terminal (if used)
   Lightguide interconnection equipment (if used)
   Multiplexers (if used)
   Office repeater bays (if used)
   Line interface modules (if used)

Current Deployment. DLC in the exchange carriers currently consists largely of AT&T SLC®–5 and SLC–96 systems, the Northern Telecom DMS®–1 Urban and the Ericsson TIMESPAN 128™ systems; however, numerous other systems have entered the market.

At the end of 1984 about 3 percent of all available subscriber circuits, 2 percent of all in–use circuits, and 0.5 percent of all in–place pairs in the subscriber network were derived by DLC facilities. However, the growth rate of DLC is rapid, leading to high penetration of the loop environment.

Most DLC installations have been made in suburban and rural areas. Installations of several hundred lines are now appearing in industrial parks and commercial centers to support special services. In these cases, distribution cable sections are relatively short. In special cases, the DLC terminal is placed at the customer's premises. For cases where a high concentration of nonlocally switched special services are involved, a DLC RT may be matched with a DCS in the serving central office, yielding a configuration called integrated network access.

Present System Capabilities. Present DLC systems were designed primarily for economical VF services but also serve digital transmission needs. They are based on 64–kb/s slots. Most are based on in–slot signalling, with newer systems designed to accommodate ISDN–type separate channel signalling and 64–kb/s clear channel capability for basic–rate (2B+D) access lines.

The channel (pair) capacity for each system depends on its design. Table 3–2 lists the modularity of three current DLC systems. Dual–channel basic telephone service plug–ins are available that provide two pair–gain pairs per physical slot. Special-service plug–ins generally allow only one circuit per physical slot to allow for four–wire operation and because concentration is not used. Newer channel–unit designs and system architectures are providing more flexible use of the carrier facility capacity, for example, the option to use LBRV coding to cut the need for DS1

SLC is a registered trademark of AT&T.

DMS is a registered trademark of Northern Telecom.

TIMESPAN 128 is a trademark of Anaconda-Ericsson.

Table 3-2. Modularity of Three Currently Available DLC Systems

System	DS1 Lines	MTS Channels	Available Time Slots	MTS Channels Per Plug-In or Line Card
DMS-1 Urban	2	112*	47	
	2	104*	47	2 for
	4	272*	95	MTS
	4	264*	95	
	4	256*	95	
	6	384*	143	
	6	376*	143	
	6	368*	143	
	8	544*	191	
	8	536*	191	
	8	528*	191	
SLC-96	3	48	48	
T1	3	48-2n**	48	2 for
	2	48	24	MTS
	2	0	24	&
	5	96	96	1 for
	5	96-2n**	96	coin
	3	96	48	
	3	64	48	
	3	0	48	
SLC-96	2	96	96	
Fiber DS2	2	192	96	
	2	0	96	
TIMESPAN 128	1	32	23	
	1	64	23	4 for
	1	128	23	MTS
	2	32	46	
	2	64	46	
	2	128	46	

MTS = message telephone service.

*Special services replace MTS on one-for-two basis.

**n = number of coin lines.

facilities in half. Among the features is a reduction in the number of different channel units.

DLC systems support a wide range of different services. Table 3-3 presents a list of service applications available on present-day systems and indicates the relative frequency of each kind.

Table 3–3. Digital Loop Carrier Systems—Spectrum of Services

Type of Service	Percent Usage
Message telephone service (POTS)	80
Centrex	5
PBX–CO trunks and WATS	3.5
Foreign exchange	2.5
Voice–grade private line	6.5
Digital and other private line	2.5

Basic telephone service circuits, both single and multiparty, are the major uses of DLC. But DLC also supplies a wide variety of coin services, VF special services, wideband program channels, security alarms, digital data port services, and others. Special channel units providing zero–loss or gain–transfer functions expedite the provision of switched special services on a non-designed or despecialized basis.

New Developments. DLC systems were developed to use the in–place feeder plant economically. Events in the past few years show that DLC will assume a major role in the digital revolution that has reached the loop plant. Channelized services delivered over fiber optic systems operating at the 135–to–565 Mb/s data rates are common. Even higher data rate transmission systems are expected as optical transmission is improved and becomes more economical.

3–5   DIGITAL SUBSCRIBER LINE FOR ISDN

A new digital subscriber line (DSL) provides customers with digital access to a digital end office over the present nonloaded, two–wire loop plant, as shown in Figure 3–10. This is based on the need to provide customers with basic access digital service as part of the evolving ISDN described in Volume 3.

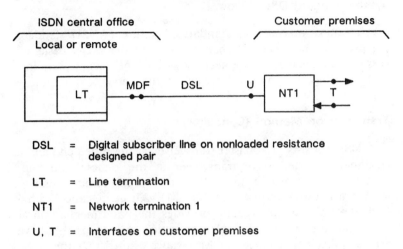

Figure 3–10. ISDN digital subscriber line.

The standard DSL provides up to 144 kb/s of throughput in each direction for two B channels of 64 kb/s each and one D channel of 16 kb/s. The B channels contain the message information (voice or data). They traverse the digital network, switched or nonswitched, with digital integrity, and, for voice, are decoded at the terminating ISDN customer. The D channel operates in a packet mode, providing signalling and control of the B channels and packet data transport. In addition to the 144–kb/s bidirectional customer data (2B+D) rate, the line rate includes overhead bits that are added to support performance monitoring, framing, and timing functions for a total of 160 kb/s. The line rate, however, is 80 kilobaud as a quaternary code is employed. [Prestandard lines use alternate mark inversion (AMI) or 4B3T codes.]

The standardization of this access facility proved to be a formidable technical task because of the variable high–frequency properties of the existing loop plant (such as impedances, frequency response, crosstalk coupling, and noise) and the data processing required to overcome these impairments. Several transmission methods were investigated. The generic technical objectives and requirements of the recommended method, using echo–cancelling techniques, are presented in Reference 5. Some, for the standard DSL, follow.

An American National Standards Institute (ANSI) standard [6] presents the electrical characteristics of the ISDN basic access signal appearing at the network side of the network terminal and describes the physical interface at the network side.

Transmission Method (Canceller)

A DSL consists of a master transceiver at the office end and a customer–provided slave transceiver at the remote end connected by a two–wire loop. The customer–premises unit is termed a network termination 1 (NT1). An echo–canceller hybrid, the heart of the system, provides the basic mechanism at each end to achieve full–duplex operation over loops that have bridged taps and changes in wire gauge. Restricting the pulse shape with bounds on its spectral density, scrambling the input binary stream, and forming a quaternary line code all help to minimize crosstalk interference and provide for adequate transmission range.

Electrical Characteristics

Line Code. The line code is designated 2B1Q; i.e., successive pairs of binary bits are coded into quaternary form as shown:

First Bit	Second Bit	Quaternary Symbol
1	0	+3
1	1	+1
0	1	−1
0	0	−3

Transmitted Pulse Shape. The allowed transmitted pulse template is shown in Figure 3–11 in normalized terms. The peak of the highest pulse is 2.5 volts. The total power of the transmitted (scrambled) signal is 13.75 dBm ±0.5 dB in the frequency band from 0 to 80 kHz.

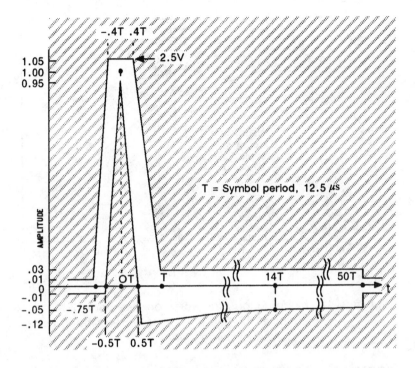

Figure 3–11. Transmitted pulse template, amplitude versus time.

Baud Rate. The line rate of the quaternary code is 80 kilobaud ±5 ppm.

Error Ratio. When transmitted over any of a set of 15 loops with simulated same–system crosstalk noise and power–line induction noise as defined in Reference 5, the bit error ratio is to be less than 10^{-7}. The crosstalk noise is simulated by shaped and attenuated white noise representing 49 DSL disturbers in the same binder group. The worst–one–percent values of near–end crosstalk (NEXT) loss (controlling) that have been used in modeling the effects of crosstalk interferences are shown in Figure 3–12 for a range of disturbers in a 50–pair binder unit. The induction noise represents the levels of 60 Hz and its odd harmonics, third through the eleventh, found on loops.

The range of tolerable sinusoidal input jitter at the master transceiver end that will meet error requirements is shown in

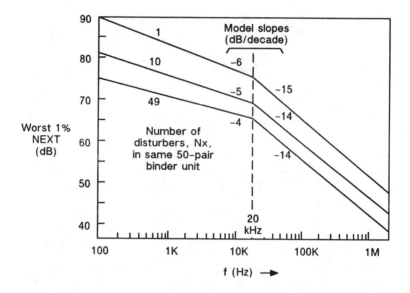

Figure 3–12. Model slopes for worst–one–percent NEXT for 18 kft of 22–gauge PIC cable, terminated in its characteristic impedance.

Figure 3–13. The generated jitter is not to exceed 0.1 UI peak–to–peak (UI stands for unit interval, the reciprocal of the baud rate, or 12.5 μs in this case).

Message Propagation Delay. The one–way delay for this facility (without the loop) should not exceed 1 ms in either direction of transmission. Delay times of nonloaded wire pairs are negligible in comparison.

Line Format

The DSL line format has basic frames and superframes. The basic frame organization is 120 quaternary elements in 1.5 ms (80 kilobaud), shown in Figure 3–14. The frame contains bit allocations for a sync word (SW) of 18 bits; information transport of 12 $\times$ (2B+D) = 216 bits where each B = 8 bits and D = 2 bits; and overhead, M, of 6 bits. The superframe organization is eight basic frames of 12 ms per superframe. It is shown in Figure 3–15 for the office–to–customer direction. It contains the framing,

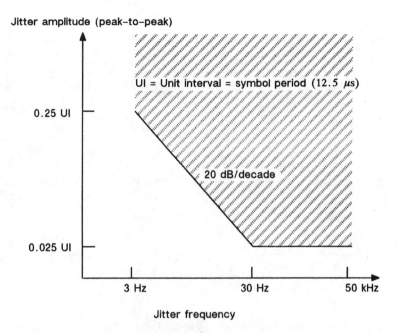

Figure 3-13. Range of permissible sinusoidal input jitter, at office end.

transport, and M bits. The superframe for customer-to-office is similar except for a few bits assigned to maintenance functions. As noted, the superframe is delayed from the other direction by 60 ±2 quaternary symbols. The M-bit assignments include those for an embedded operations channel, cyclic redundancy error check, and a far-end block-error bit. The serial time relationships of the frames and superframes are shown in Figure 3-16.

Idle Code and Scrambling. Unused customer channels are filled with binary ones. The data stream in each direction (except for the SW) is scrambled with a 23rd-order polynomial.

Timing. The master transceiver at the office is synched to the network. The customer end is slaved to the signal received from the office. When free-running, the customer end is to have an accuracy of ±32 ppm (stratum 4 clock).

115

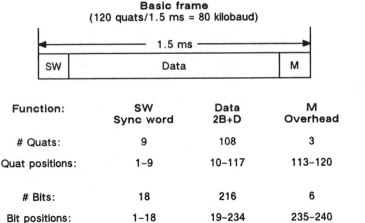

Basic frame
(120 quats/1.5 ms = 80 kilobaud)

Function:	SW Sync word	Data 2B+D	M Overhead
# Quats:	9	108	3
Quat positions:	1–9	10–117	113–120
# Bits:	18	216	6
Bit positions:	1–18	19–234	235–240

Quat = Quaternary symbol for 2 binary bits
2B+D = Customer data channels B1, B2, and D

Figure 3–14. Basic DSL frame.

Line Interface

The nominal input impedance of the equipment as seen from the line is 135 ohms. The return loss to 135 ohms is to be greater than 26 dB from 5 kHz to 200 kHz. Sealing current is provided.

Application Rules

The ISDN–DSL will use pairs in the loop cable plant. In the same cable sheath will be pairs carrying baseband voice, data, and other transmission services. As with other cable–carrier systems, engineering rules are being formulated for the application. The rules will cover the allowable loop loss, loop makeup, crosstalk compatibility constraints, etc. A goal of the application is to allow easy selection and assignment of pairs suitable for DSL operation without special conditioning or field tests to determine qualification for such use. In brief, the rules will indicate that a "clean" pair is needed to avoid excess loss (i.e., no load coils or bridge lifters, limited bridged taps, etc). The rules will permit

		Framing	2B+D	Overhead bits (M1–M6)					
	Quat positions	1–9	10–117	118s	118m	119s	119m	120s	120m
	Bit positions	1–18	19–234	235	236	237	238	239	240
Super-frame #	Basic frame #	SW (Synch word)	2B+D	M1	M2	M3	M4	M5	M6
A	1	Inverted SW	2B+D	EOC	EOC	EOC	act	1	1
	2	SW	2B+D	EOC	EOC	EOC	1	1	FEBE
	3	SW	2B+D	EOC	EOC	EOC	1	CRC_1	CRC_2
	4	SW	2B+D	EOC	EOC	EOC	1	CRC_3	CRC_4
	5	SW	2B+D	EOC	EOC	EOC	1	CRC_5	CRC_6
	6	SW	2B+D	EOC	EOC	EOC	1	CRC_7	CRC_8
	7	SW	2B+D	EOC	EOC	EOC	1	CRC_9	CRC_{10}
	8	SW	2B+D	EOC	EOC	EOC	1	CRC_{11}	CRC_{12}
B, C, …									

All bits other than the synch word are scrambled.

1 = Reserved bit
act = Activation bit
CRC = Cyclic redundancy check:
    covers 2B+D & M4

EOC = Embedded operations channel
FEBE = Far-end block–error bit
m = Mark
s = Space

Figure 3–15. DSL superframe and bit assignments.

operating ranges up to 18 kft with restrictions (for example, 16.5 kft of 26 AWG plus 1.5 kft of 24 AWG with no bridged tap) and less with bridged taps, depending on their location and length).

The rules will allow normal DSL performance with worst–one–percent crosstalk coupling loss and 49 disturbing DSLs. There will be crosstalk constraints, however, on the use of other systems in the same cable sheath depending on their spectra, coupling loss, and receiver susceptibility. Usually the constraints are in terms of allowable operation in the same, adjacent, or nonadjacent binder groups of the cable. In general it is expected that the standard DSL *cannot* operate in any binder group with early or present–vintage single–channel analog

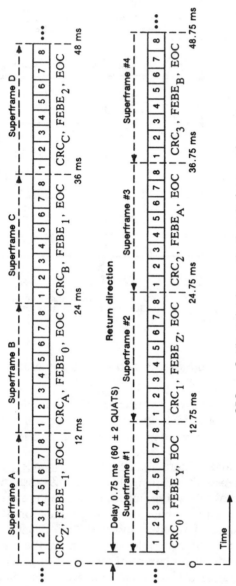

Figure 3-16. DSL line format.

CRC_τ = Cyclic–redundancy–check code for superframe τ.

EOC = Embedded operations channel

$FEBE_\delta$ = Far-end block-error bit for superframe δ.

$\boxed{i}$ = ith 1.5-ms basic frame in given superframe.

subscriber carrier systems, in the same or adjacent binder groups with multichannel analog subscriber carrier, or in the same binder group with data–over–voice or long 15–kHz program services. The DSL, however, is expected to operate in any binder group with plain old telephone service, T1 span lines, Digital Data System or Basic Dedicated Digital Service data, Public Switched Digital Service, and any combination of these systems. ISDN networks are covered in Volume 3. Interface coordination is discussed further in Chapter 26 of this volume.

3-6   PHYSICAL STRUCTURES IN THE DISTRIBUTION NETWORK

Physical structures support telephone transmission media. These physical structures include poles, towers, conduit, manholes, huts, and controlled–environment vaults.

The most common cable structure is the pole line. Buried cable is now used wherever feasible, but pole lines remain an important structure. Pole lines are designed for the environment they serve with a high strength–to–load ratio. Factors such as weather (the frequency, severity, and damaging effects of ice and wind storms) determine their design.

According to the load carried and terrain features, poles from 25 to 125 feet are used. Guys or braces are used to support poles where there are unbalanced tensions or changes in the direction of pull. Several kinds of wood (such as southern pine) and preservative treatment (such as copper salts) are used in the manufacture of telephone poles.

Suspension strand is used to support cables. It has varying breaking strengths from 6000 to 25,000 pounds. Self–supporting cable requires no separate strand; it uses a built–in strand. This simplifies the placing operation.

In rural or suburban areas, cables are often buried directly in the ground. New buried cables generally are of filled construction to prevent the intrusion of water. Splices may be made in the ground, or in pedestals above ground. The depth of buried cables is usually from two to three feet depending on location, governmental regulations, and likely future excavations such as road widenings or new fences.

In more congested areas, cables are placed in conduits. Manholes are used for splicing. Conduit has a hierarchy: there are main, subsidiary, and branch conduits. Main conduit provides protection and links feeder sections of plant. Subsidiary conduit links the feeder route to a customer location or to distribution plant. Branch conduit links the underground feeder route to plant (feeder or distribution), which is aerial, attached to a building, or directly buried.

The length of a conduit section is based on several factors, including the locations of intersecting conduits and manholes for ancillary equipment such as repeaters or loading coils, the lengths of cable reels, acceptable pulling tension, and physical obstructions. Pulling tension is determined by the weight of the cable, the coefficient of friction, and the geometry of the duct run. Plastic conduit has a lower coefficient of friction than does concrete or fiberglass conduit, and thus allows longer cable pulls. The ability to make long pulls is an important consideration in placing fiber cables because it allows the avoidance of splices. Fiber pulls of several thousand feet are routine. Conduit sections themselves typically range from 350 to 700 feet.

A major advantage of conduit is the ability to reuse cable spaces without excavation by removing smaller cables and replacing them with larger cables or fiber facilities. With the increasing use of optical fiber cables, small inner ducts for fiber cables are pulled into existing ducts, thus increasing the capacity of the conduit. Three or four 1–inch inner ducts can be placed in one 4–inch duct.

As loop electronics permeates the distribution network, equipment enclosures are becoming more widespread. These enclosures are designed to house multiplexers, RTs, and other loop-electronics equipment. They may have a controlled environment to regulate temperature and humidity. Prefabricated or custom-built huts and housings or cabinets are used in remote areas. In congested areas or where right of way is difficult to obtain, the underground controlled–environment vault provides a dry, temperate underground location for electronic equipment.

References

1. *EIA Standard EIA-470,* "Telephone Instruments with Loop Signalling for Voiceband Applications" (Washington, DC: Electronic Industries Association, Iss. 1, Jan. 1981).

2. Long, N. G. "Loop Plant Modeling—Overview," *Bell System Tech. J.,* Vol. 57, No. 4 (Apr. 1978), pp. 797-804.

3. "Distribution Network," *Notes on the BOC IntraLATA Networks—1986,* Technical Reference TR-NPL-000275, Bellcore (Iss. 1, Apr. 1986), Section 12.

4. Bergholm, J. O. and P. P. Koliss. "Serving Area Concept—A Plan for Now with a Look to the Future," *Bell Laboratories Record,* Vol. 50 (Aug. 1972).

5. *ISDN Basic Access Digital Subscriber Lines,* Technical Reference TR-TSY-000393, Bellcore (Iss. 1, May 1988).

6. *ANSI T1.601-1988,* "Integrated Services Digital Network—Basic Access Interface for Use on Metallic Loops for Applications on the Network Side of the NT-Layer 1 Specification" (New York: American National Standards Institute, Sept. 1988).

Chapter 4

Voice–Frequency Trunk Facilities and Circuit Equipment

Network trunks, the uses they fulfill, and the transmission requirements they must meet to operate properly in telecommunications networks may be considered separately from the physical facilities that support them. These facilities include transmission media (cable pairs or carrier channels) and transmission equipment in central offices and at customers' premises. Voice–frequency (VF) trunks use various types of loaded and nonloaded cable pairs.

Voice–frequency transmission equipment provides amplification, impedance matching, equalization, and interfacing between VF facilities and carrier channels. It also joins two–wire and four–wire facilities. A number of types of hybrid–based repeater are used on two–wire trunks and special services, and have largely replaced earlier negative–impedance types. Two general types of equipment, differentiated mainly by physical design, are currently in wide use: the metallic facility terminal (MFT) and the "400"–type families. Plug–in units for each family, or both, are offered by a number of manufacturers, as well as adapters to use units of one family in the mountings of another. Each is available with mountings intended for central–office or premises installation, the latter including single– and multiple–circuit packages with local powering. Plug–ins for the two families provide essentially the same functions [1]. This text uses the MFT family as a convenient example.

4-1 TRANSMISSION CONSIDERATIONS

A switched network must satisfy simultaneously a number of transmission objectives in order to assure generally satisfactory communication. The objectives include those relating to noise,

123

crosstalk, loss, and echo. Keeping noise at acceptable values requires longitudinal balance of inside and outside plant, good cable shielding, and signal amplitudes that ensure adequate signal-to–noise ratios. Controlling crosstalk requires control of level differences within groups of cable pairs, preservation of longitudinal balance, and spectral compatibility. Meeting echo objectives requires a good impedance match between lines and repeaters and loss low enough for good received volume but not so low that echo or near–singing becomes annoying.

Although nearly all connections that involve only VF transmission are short enough that reflection is no problem, most long connections include VF end links. Echoes produced in these end links cannot be eliminated, but must be controlled by maximizing the structural return loss in loaded cable pairs and using impedance compensators. It is also important that other VF facilities and equipment be kept relatively free of echo–producing reflections. An echo from a distant terminal may be attenuated by an increase in net loss. However, this is not practicable in individual connections since net loss cannot be adjusted for each built–up connection as a function of echo; each link must have an assigned loss, dependent upon delay, that limits echoes in that link to allocated values. Loss and echo are controlled by the via net loss (VNL) design of the analog network and by later digital–oriented, fixed–loss plans.

Initially, loading was the only economical means for reducing attenuation in cable pairs. By modern standards, load–coil spacing was variable (3000, 6000, or 9000 feet) and inductance quite high (e.g., 135– or 175–mH coils). A number of loading systems evolved but the H88 system ultimately became the only one significantly used. It combines a reasonably long spacing with acceptably low attenuation. Its passband in local cable is only slightly narrower than that achieved in carrier channels.

Loading makes attenuation of a cable pair relatively uniform throughout the passband, but there is enough residual attenuation/frequency distortion to require equalization in trunks or lines long enough to need gain. The equalization serves three purposes: (1) it provides naturalness in the transmitted speech, (2) it prevents instability of the facility at low frequencies where reflections would otherwise cause singing or near–singing, and

(3) it assists the performance of voiceband data terminals. Equalization is incorporated in VF repeaters. A repeater is commonly understood to mean a two–way amplifier and the equipment to support its operation.

The development of economical repeaters gave significant improvement in transmission on trunks and special services and saved materially on cable costs by permitting the use of finer-gauge wire. These efforts led to the design of the negative–impedance E6 repeater for two–wire circuits, the V4 repeater for four–wire circuits, and the current integrated–circuit designs in the various types of MFT and "400" equipment.

Today's repeaters are the result of continued efforts to reduce cost, size, and power requirements and to group in one assembly all of the transmission, signalling, and test–access equipment needed at a given location.

4-2 VOICE-FREQUENCY EQUIPMENT

All transmission and signalling functions required at the terminals of message trunks and most special–services circuits can be provided in one MFT or "400" equipment assembly. The required functions are provided by selected plug–in units that may be automatically interconnected, depending on the version chosen, when inserted into the equipment shelf. The connectors on the shelf are permanently wired to produce the desired interconnection. By this design approach, facility terminals eliminate much of the wiring congestion associated with earlier designs. This concept was used in the V4–type repeaters but has been extended considerably in the facility terminal designs [2].

The equipment itself is compatible with older E–type or V–type repeater equipment that may be in use in other parts of a trunk or circuit and with carrier facilities. The terminals provide interface circuits for central–office switching machines and private branch exchanges (PBXs). MFTs may be used on circuits employing loaded or nonloaded cable pairs of 19– to 26–gauge and for special cases involving bridged taps, mixed gauges, and a variety of end–section lengths.

Equipment Features

Plug–in units may be selected to provide a repeater for any of three transmission modes. The first, called the 22–type, uses hybrid transformers and two amplifiers in two–wire circuits rather than the negative–impedance principles of the E–type repeaters. A second type, the 44–type repeater, is used when four–wire circuits are connected at both terminals; it replaced the earlier 44V4 repeater. Two versions of this repeater are available, one for use at an intermediate point and one for use at a terminal of a four–wire circuit. The third type provides an interface between a two–wire circuit and a four–wire circuit. It is similar to the older 24V4 repeater in its functions and is also available in two versions, the 24–type and the 42–type. The two versions provide the necessary flexibility for circuit interfaces of two–wire to four–wire or four–wire to two–wire in progressing from a designated repeater input port to a designated output. The three basic configurations are illustrated in Figure 4–1.

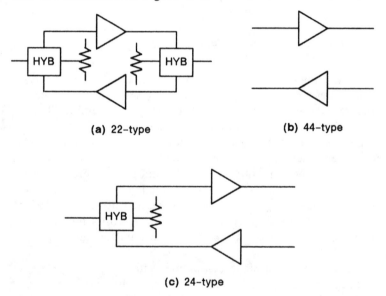

(a) 22–type   (b) 44–type

(c) 24–type

Figure 4–1. Metallic facility terminal transmission configurations.

Two shelf arrangements are provided, each with spaces for 12 plug–in units. Where treatment is required only for transmission

126

or signalling, plug–in equipment for 12 circuits may be used. If both signalling and transmission treatment is needed, two approaches are available. One is to use combined–function units in a single mounting. In the other, adjoining pairs of plug–in transmission and signalling units are used. Each shelf is then arranged to provide treatment for six circuits. The signalling interface is provided by standard leads normally designated as A and B, E/SG and M/SB, and SX and SX1. Access points for switched–access maintenance systems may be provided as part of the mounting bay.

Transmission Features

A number of transmission features are available and may be selected for use. For example, four terminating impedances may be provided to satisfy specific circuit needs: 1200 ohms, to match H88–loaded cable; 900 ohms, to operate into two–wire switches; 600 ohms, to work into office equipment, nonloaded cable, or customer interfaces; or 150 ohms, to obtain partial equalization of program circuits on nonloaded cable by a deliberate impedance mismatch. Gain adjustment of the amplifiers is typically continuous over the range from −20 to +24 dB. Transmission plug–in units containing impedance compensators, balancing networks, and equalizers are available to satisfy network trunk or special–services needs.

Equalizers compatible with those of the V4 family or of equalized carrier channel units are used in the receiving portions of the repeaters. These equalizers are active circuits. In many cases, equalizer and amplifier gain settings are made by "prescription design" with tabulated data that pertain to the various facilities in which these repeaters can be used. Adjustment is also possible on the basis of measurements made after installation. Figure 4–2 shows a few of the hundreds of low–frequency and high–frequency equalization shapes that can be selected.

Equalized gain units satisfy various transmission needs. One unit provides only flat gain in the transmitting path of the four–wire portion of 24–, 42–, and 44–type repeaters. A second unit provides flat gain and equalization in the receiving path of the four–wire portion of 24–, 42–, and 44–type terminal repeaters

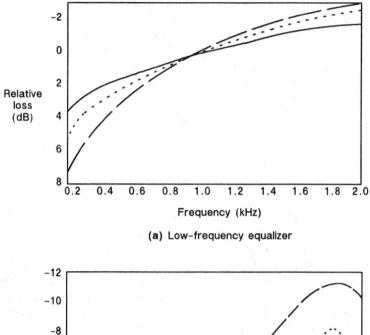

(a) Low-frequency equalizer

(b) High-frequency equalizer

Figure 4-2.   High- and low-frequency equalizers.

and in both directions in 44–type intermediate repeaters. Designs are available for loaded and nonloaded cable pairs. In the four-wire portions of some units, e.g., a 24–type repeater application, preequalization is provided in the transmitting path.

A third type provides flat gain for loaded–cable applications of 22–type repeaters. A fourth device provides gain and equalization in 22–type repeaters used with nonloaded cable pairs and in repeaters used with mixed loaded and nonloaded cable pairs.

Balancing networks are available in two forms: the original type, using active networks to simulate the impedance–versus–frequency of loaded or nonloaded cable pairs, and a later type in which echo canceller technology is used. In this version, the voice signal is digitized, signal–processed to remove the signal reflected from the two–wire side, and then decoded to analog.

4–3 VOICE–FREQUENCY EQUIPMENT COMPARISONS

Each of the various vintages of VF equipment has had advantages in its application and fulfilled major needs at the time it was available.

Bandwidth and Stability

In the two–wire facility terminal design shown in Figure 4–1(a), the impedance matching and equalization functions are separate and independent. Impedance match to the cable pairs is provided by the balancing networks of the two hybrid transformers, and the hybrids themselves, while equalization is provided by a portion of the amplifier circuitry. Therefore, both functions can be fulfilled with greater accuracy and flexibility than in earlier repeaters.

Circuits consisting of several four–wire sections equipped with these repeaters and their adjustable equalizers can meet bandwidth and stability requirements. Where return losses of cable pairs are inherently too low for two–wire operation with negative–impedance repeaters, four–wire operation is practicable. As previously mentioned, reflections in the four–wire section are confined to the repeater sections in which they originate by the blocking effect of the one–way amplifiers. Four–wire VF trunks are technically possible far beyond the distances at which they are economical. Four–wire extensions from carrier terminals, as in PBX tie trunks that terminate on a customer's premises are convenient to design and install.

Return Loss and Echo

The substantial blocking of reflections that originate within the cable and at cable–repeater junctions makes the echo performance of four–wire facilities practically independent of such reflections. In four–wire repeatered facilities, the reflections are attenuated by approximately 70 dB of loss at each amplifier. In contrast, a negative–impedance or a 22–type repeater amplifies reflections as well as the speech signal. As a consequence, it is difficult to attain acceptable return loss and control of echoes on a switched facility employing more than two of these repeaters.

Losses and Transmission Level Points

The repeaters can transmit into loaded or nonloaded cables at a maximum transmission level point (TLP) of +6 dB with only a small chance of creating crosstalk or of being overloaded by the loudest talkers. Crosstalk–coupling losses between loaded pairs in the same cable dictate that level differences between repeater outputs and inputs be limited to about 15 dB, or about 19 miles of 22H88 cable. That figure, therefore, is the limiting repeater section length for repeatered loaded trunks and a −9 dB TLP is the lower limit for inputs from cable pairs to repeaters. Because crosstalk coupling between nonloaded pairs is less than that between loaded pairs, TLP differences for nonloaded cable pairs could be allowed to reach 21 dB (about 12 miles of 22–gauge), but equalization capabilities are not generally sufficient for repeater sections with that much loss.

Loss objectives for direct and access trunks can be met by two– or four–wire VF facilities. Where the loss and annual temperature range of the metallic facilities are very large, it may be impractical to avoid instability at the lowest temperatures or unacceptable loss at the highest temperatures. However, the wide use of digital carrier has largely removed this consideration.

Signalling

Voice–frequency repeaters must be capable of passing address and supervisory signals. In some cases, it is necessary that these signals also be amplified. The various types of repeater that have been discussed differ in the manner in which such signals are processed.

All types of ac signal in the voiceband, such as 2600–Hz single–frequency, multifrequency, DTMF, and inband coin–control, are amplified and transmitted by repeaters. Supervisory dc, dial pulse, and 20–Hz ringing signals are bypassed around amplifiers and other units on separate paths included in the shelf wiring and the plug–in units. Modest resistance penalties (e.g., 50 ohms) must be added in computing signalling ranges.

4-4 OTHER TERMINATING AND SIGNALLING FUNCTIONS

The wide availability of MFT and "400" mountings made them attractive to package nonrepeater circuit equipment in compatible plug–ins. Table 4–1 summarizes both the repeater equipment and the auxiliary units that are available in one family or the other. These units flexibly provide functions that originally required dedicated hard–wired equipment.

For many customer–premises uses [3], a terminal repeater must provide functions not needed in a central office. A good example is a tone–controlled loop–back feature for remote testing [4]. Such a loop–back typically connects the send and receive sides of a four–wire circuit together, on an equal–TLP basis, so that continuity of the circuit can be verified. A 2713–Hz tone activates a detector that operates a looping relay. Release of the loop–back requires either a second application of tone or a preset time interval. The choice of 2713 Hz was based on its falling in the 2450–to–2750–Hz single–frequency signalling band; when the customer applies power in this band he or she is expected to apply at least equal power below this band, making it possible to use guard circuits to prevent false loop–backs.

4-5 VOICE-FREQUENCY FUNCTIONS OF DIGITAL CARRIER CHANNEL UNITS

Where digital carrier facilities are used for interoffice circuits, which is the usual case today, the use of external equipment for

Table 4-1. Typical Functions—Plug-in Circuit Equipment

Repeaters

22 ⎤   ⎡ Terminal & intermediate
42 ⎢   ⎢ For loaded & nonloaded cable
44 ⎦   ⎢ Conventional & adaptive
                      ⎢ Single 22 or dual 22
                      ⎣ Alone or with signalling included

Signalling Range Extenders
Loop-start   Battery-boost (72-volt)
Ground-start
Toll-diversion   Signal-repeating

Signalling Converters
DX-to-E&M
SF-to-E&M - regular and for radio base stations
SF-to-loop
LS/GS-to-E&M
Simplex-to-E&M for AIOD data links
Private-line automatic ringdown
Private-line manual ringdown
Code select ringdown
DTMF to dial pulse
Impedance Compensators for PBX-CO Trunks
Bridges
Two-wire   Active
Four-wire   Passive
Split-band, for telemetry and alarm bridging service
Delay and Amplitude Equalizers
Program Amplifier-Equalizers
Four-Wire Terminating Sets
Private-Line Transfer Relays
Multi-Impedance Repeat Coils & Adjustable Pads
Sealing-Current Generators
Voice Private-Line NCTE - PBX tie trunk
                      - Battery-feed
                      - with test-tone generator
Data Private-Line NCTE - with loop-back
                      - with automatic equalization
Time-Compression Multiplex Adapters for PSDS

terminating and signalling functions would be costly in terms of investment (mountings, plug-ins, switched maintenance access points) and expense (craft labor to install multiple frame jumpers and adjust equipment in multiple locations). As a result, carrier channel units offer most of the functions afforded by the MFT/"400" families: two-wire-to-four-wire conversion, single-frequency or duplex signalling, gain transfer, equalization, etc. Certain carrier bays include maintenance access points. Thus, cable pairs from a private–line customer's location, for example, can be jumpered directly into a channel bank for transmission to a distant office. These same features are convenient in extending special services into a digital loop carrier remote terminal.

These VF functions have gone past the technology of VF repeaters; "intelligent" channel banks allow for hands–off setting of gain, equalization, balance, and signalling options, either by local keyboard control or from an unlimited distance. They also allow self–adjustment on many special–services circuits by using a test transponder at the station. The transponder provides test signals that let the channel bank set the options in the affected channel unit.

4-6 ECHO SUPPRESSORS/CANCELLERS

Under the VNL plan, every connection that would likely incur a round–trip (echo path) delay of 45 ms or more would be designed with an echo suppressor. Echo cancellers have replaced the echo suppressor and may be used on VNL and fixed–loss designed networks.

Echo cancellers function as a digital circuit that may be used in either an analog or a digital trunk. A typical canceller will improve echo path loss by about 40 dB, provided that the initial echo path loss is at least 6 dB and that the round–trip delay in the echo path ("tail section") does not exceed the buffer limit of the echo canceller. Most cancellers in production today operate at DS1 level. Many provide for automatic disabling for use with half–duplex voiceband data transmission methods.

References

1. Bell System Technical Reference PUB 43002, *Functional Criteria—Voice Frequency Terminating Equipment—Metallic Facilities—Central Office*, American Telephone and Telegraph Company (Iss. 1, Nov. 1982).

2. Clark, M. and G. R. Porter. "The Metallic Facility Terminal: Special Help for Special Services," *Bell Laboratories Record*, Vol. 54 (Sept. 1976), pp. 215–219.

3. *Functional Criteria—Voice Frequency Network Channel Terminating Equipment—Metallic Facilities*, Technical Reference TR–TSY–000007, Bellcore (Iss. 1, Feb. 1985).

4. Bell System Technical Reference PUB 43004, *Functional Criteria—Voice Frequency Transmission Equipment—Maintenance Terminating Unit—4–Wire Special Services*, American Telephone and Telegraph Company (Iss. 1, July 1983). (Replaced by Bellcore Technical Reference TR–TSY–000007.)

Chapter 5

Voiceband Data Facilities

The transmission of various types of data signal is an increasingly important part of telecommunications service. A past history of strong growth is likely to continue as digital facsimile machines and "information gateway" services become more popular. Many signal formats are used. The required bandwidths vary from the extremely narrow bands used for telegraph signals, which are frequency–division multiplexed into the voiceband, to the full voice–bandwidth transmission of one data signal at 19.2 kb/s.

Voiceband data service may be provided by point–to–point private lines, private–line switched networks, or the public switched network. Although the facilities used for these modes of service are similar, the nature of the service is such that the manner of treating the facilities may be quite different. In private or public switched–network operation, the variety of transmission paths and the variable number of trunks that may be encountered in successive connections make precise equalization difficult. For point–to–point line operation, the transmission facilities are dedicated to a particular service and may be engineered to optimize performance.

Performance parameters that affect the quality of data transmission include random and impulse noise, channel bandwidth, intermodulation distortion, phase jitter, and gain or phase hits. These impairments must be related to appropriate transmission objectives and evaluated with respect to the available types of facility.

The facilities used for data transmission include wire pairs, carrier channels, voice–frequency (VF) equipment, and data sets. While some of these facilities can be described in general terms, specific examples are used for illustrative purposes.

5-1 TRANSMISSION CHANNELS

Data signals are usually transmitted between two customer-owned terminals: multiplexers, remote job entry stations, personal computers, facsimile machines, or "dumb" terminals. Data station equipment provides the interface between the business machine and the transmission channel. These channels have a number of components that can be classified according to the facilities that provide them and the way in which those facilities are related to the message network.

For point–to–point private–line services, interoffice channels are dedicated to data signal transmission and special engineering is often used. The customer may order "C" conditioning, which controls the degree of attenuation–frequency distortion and envelope delay distortion (EDD), or "D" conditioning, which requires the use of only modern–vintage carrier facilities to limit intermodulation distortion, or both.

Hybrid applications between networks are possible, as in the case where a customer dials through the network to reach a port on a packet assembler/disassembler (PAD) in an exchange–carrier office. The customer's data then flow through a packet network to their destination.

Access Facilities

In addition to loops, access facilities include foreign exchange (FX) and wide area telecommunications service (WATS) lines. Access facilities may use simple cable pairs, with or without digital loop carrier (DLC). FX circuits normally include interoffice carrier channels.

Where data transmission requirements for attenuation distortion (slope) or EDD cannot be met, special designs may be required. Some exchange carriers today offer premium–conditioned access lines that have limited delay distortion and flattened frequency response to meet the needs of customers who wish to send high–speed data on a dial–up basis.

Improved equalization of loops can be achieved by adding a repeater at the serving central office. Figure 5–1 shows the improvement in loss and slope on a long nonloaded loop resulting from adding a suitable repeater. Slope can also be controlled by limiting the lengths of bridged taps and loaded–cable end sections. EDD can be reduced sizably by using DLC channels in place of long loaded loops.

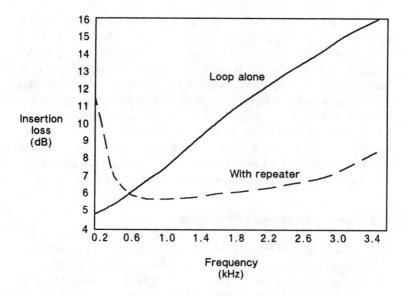

Figure 5–1. Effects of modern repeater on loss.

Although most electronic private branch exchanges (PBXs) provide performance equal to that of direct access facilities, data transmission performance on connections through an electromechanical PBX is sometimes poorer than on direct facilities due to impulse noise. Therefore, the customer may prefer to order a direct facility, especially for signal transmission at rates above 300 b/s.

Interoffice Facilities

Between end offices, the usual variety of transmission facilities may provide channels for data signals. These include analog carrier on cable or radio, digital carrier on copper, radio, or optical fiber, and VF cable. Over the message telecommunications network, the trunks used are adequate for most data transmission, especially with digital facilities and tandem switches. The number of trunks in tandem is a function of network routing under a varying traffic load, and may affect speech and data transmission quality if the trunks or switches are analog.

Where data transmission is performed on a point–to–point private–line service, the channels used for interoffice connections are furnished over the same types of facility as those used for message trunks. However, the channels are dedicated to data transmission and can be economically treated for data. Gain units and equalizers may be installed as required to obtain the desired performance. If the signals to be transmitted are particularly susceptible to EDD and the normal routing includes an analog carrier system with excessive delay distortion in the multiplex equipment, special equalization may be provided or the circuit may be assigned to facilities with less delay distortion.

5-2 TRANSMISSION PERFORMANCE

As in any type of signal transmission, satisfactory performance in providing data service involves the generation of a suitable signal format, the control of channel transmission characteristics, and the control of impairments. The relationships among these important parameters differ somewhat in switched network and point–to–point services [1,2].

The differences are due mainly to: (1) the variable length and makeup of connections in switched services versus the fixed channel composition in point–to–point services and (2) the fact that a wider range of routings is available in point–to–point services. Many impairments are uniquely identifiable with specific types of facility.

Objectives

Transmission objectives for data services are specified to satisfy an acceptable level of performance for low band (<600 b/s), medium band (1200–3600 b/s), and high band (4.8–19.2 kb/s) [3,4].

The basic criterion for judging the quality of data transmission is error ratio. In many cases, the objectives and performance values are expressed in terms of bit error ratio, i.e., the number of errors in a given number of transmitted bits. However, bulk data is usually sent in large blocks. Where errors are detected, the entire block is retransmitted. For these types of service, error performance is more appropriately expressed as block error ratio. The error–performance objective is then stated in terms of blocks containing 1000 bits of data, a representative number for business machine operation.

Most data channel transmission impairments can be expressed in terms of an equivalent *noise impairment*. An impairment, such as EDD, can be rated by determining the improvement in signal–to–noise ratio needed to maintain the error rate obtained in the channel when impaired only by Gaussian noise. This method of rating quantifies the extent to which transmission is degraded by the added impairment and can be used to estimate the error rate due to other interferences. The equivalent noise impairment also provides a method of evaluating the accumulation of impairments from several tandem links of a connection.

To avoid crosstalk or intermodulation and to prevent overloading of analog carrier systems, the amplitudes of switched–network voiceband data signals are limited to a maximum power at the main distributing frame of −12 dBm (−13 dBm0) averaged over any three–second interval. Four–wire private–line circuits are designed to have a nominal 1–kHz loss of 16 dB from transmitter to receiver (10 dB for two–wire). The tolerance on this value is ±4 dB to provide ample margin for loss variations, particularly where analog facilities are involved. Switched–network losses are controlled by the via net loss or fixed–loss plan.

Impairments

Many of the impairments to which data signals are sensitive are more commonly encountered in certain types of facility. One notable example is random noise, which is relatively large in analog carrier systems and increases with mileage. By contrast, the noise level in digital transmission is both low and constant.

Impulse noise is commonly related to particular systems or environments and was at one time a dominant cause of data transmission impairment. The occurrence of impulse noise has fallen greatly as electromechanical switches have been replaced. Some types of switching machine, notably large step–by–step entities with rotary out–trunk switches, produced excessive impulse noise and it was often necessary to remote–home data circuits on offices that did not use such switching machines.

Envelope delay distortion is another impairment that can be related to certain facilities. A common source of delay distortion is the sharp cutoff characteristics of analog multiplex equipment, especially the channel banks. The distortion is noticeably less in digital facilities because of relaxed filter requirements. For private–line service over dedicated facilities, this characteristic can be equalized; in switched–network applications, the number of multiplex terminals encountered varies from connection to connection and only an estimated average amount of distortion can be equalized. Departures from the average values must be tolerated (by providing adequate margin in data–set design and operation) or must be equalized by adaptive equalizers, which are included in the higher–speed units. The highest–speed data sets use advanced transmission techniques like trellis coding and maximum–likelihood detection to gain margin against this and other impairments.

Similarly, intermodulation distortion, phase jitter, and phase or gain hits may be identified with specific systems. Digital padding, used in some modern switches, carrier terminals, and digital bridges, produces a small degree of nonlinear distortion. Multiple digital codings and decodings using low–bit–rate voice (LBRV) techniques tend to impair transmission above 4800 b/s, especially if the codings do not use a common clock. Phase and gain jitter are most often found in broadband analog carrier systems. When these impairments are excessive in point–to–point data circuits, the selection of alternative facilities is often the most economical solution to the problem. When troubles of certain types occur consistently in message network service, the trouble is likely to be in the data station or loop facilities (which are not switched) or in the first–choice trunk to the selected distant office. The possibility also exists of digital timing slips occurring on a trunk group, an impairment of little concern for voice traffic but important for high–speed data. The trouble then must be cleared or alternative facilities used.

140

The evaluation of data transmission performance and the identification and correction of specific trouble conditions often require network technical support (NTS) in installation and maintenance procedures for craft personnel.

The NTS program provides for assistance where normal methods are insufficient. The assistance may be in the form of consultative or on–site participation by operations, engineering, or vendor personnel as required. The program is applied to intercompany as well as intracompany problems, that is, to cooperation between the exchange carrier and the equipment vendor or interexchange carrier. Test procedures to determine the most likely source of impairment have been devised. They are used to identify a trouble, to help in isolating the trouble to a specific part of a circuit, and to provide insight as to how adjustments can be made to obtain a solution.

For switched–network services, tests are made and results compared with objectives to determine compliance with the *minimum acceptable performance* (MAP). In these procedures, tests and measurements are made of attenuation/frequency distortion (slope between 1000 and 2800 Hz), EDD, C–notched noise (C–message noise measured while a holding tone is transmitted), phase jitter, second– and third–order intermodulation distortion, and impulse noise. The procedures involve taking a statistical sample of data from several independently established connections. This concept is consistent with the reality that an exchange carrier cannot guarantee the digital performance of customer–provided data sets.

5-3   VOICEBAND DATA STATIONS

Voiceband data service involves a variety of customer–provided data sets (modems) that provide the interface between the business machine and the line. A data set designed for private–line use is connected to the line through an exchange–carrier–supplied network channel terminating equipment (NCTE) package which provides gain, equalization, and loop–back testing. A Federal Communications Commission (FCC)–registered set designed to work over the switched message network is connected to the access line, either directly or via a "fixed loss" loop pad, through a modular jack.

A digital interface exists between the data set and the customer-operated terminal equipment, such as a computer, that provides the data signal. Unless the data set is integral to the terminal, this interface must satisfy a standard interface specification such as *EIA Standard EIA-232-D* [5].

Data Sets

Each type of data set uses the voiceband spectrum to transmit a signal format appropriate to a given application. The wide variety of signal spectra and formats and the transmission characteristics of the switched message network lead to variations in transmission performance from data set to data set and from connection to connection. Service offerings for private-line and switched-network use are provided by a variety of data sets.

One type of set provides low-speed (up to 300 b/s) transmission of data signals in a serial format to provide low-speed services. Signals are typically asynchronous and operate in a start-stop manner to transmit each character similar to a teletypewriter signal. Each transmitted character is represented by a 5- to 8-bit code.* The start of each character is recognized by a start bit; the receiver recognizes the end of the character by counting the information bits, a parity bit, and a stop bit. Intercharacter timing is not controlled, thus making the overall bit stream asynchronous.

Other data sets operate at medium and high speeds (600 to 3600 b/s) to provide medium-speed synchronous or asynchronous serial transmission over private-line or network facilities. Full-duplex operation on two-wire connections is available at speeds of 1200 b/s or even higher. Other sets of this type provide higher-speed data transmission at rates up to 19.2 kb/s.

Analog Interface

The tip and ring appearance of a cable pair at the customer premises is the interface point for voiceband data stations with

---

* The American Standard Code for Information Interchange (ASCII) seven-bit code is most commonly used.

the facilities network. Certain electrical and transmission characteristics are described at this analog interface and specified in the FCC registration rules for data sets [6]. Special interfaces also apply, for example, FCC–registered adapters provided by the customer that screw onto the transmitter cup of a telephone handset and deliver a "modular" tip–and–ring jack for the data set, or telephone sets that have auxiliary data jacks. Certain secure telephones for encrypted–voice use produce a data stream at 4800 b/s into the network.

Since the impedances of access facilities vary widely, the input impedance of data stations must be a compromise value. A value of 600 ohms resistive is common for compatibility with the impedances of most repeaters and carrier equipment.

Surge and hazardous voltage protection are typically provided at the analog interface by a line coupling transformer in data sets. These transformers are normally designed for at least 1500 volts rms isolation between primary and secondary windings to protect data set circuitry against any large longitudinal voltage that might result from contact of the cable pair with power lines or from lightning surges. They are also designed to provide good longitudinal balance to minimize induced power–line interference and avoid crosstalk between the cable pair used for data transmission and other pairs in the same cable. The station equipment is protected from high transient voltage by the normal carbon protector blocks or gas discharge devices that automatically ground the line conductors when voltages exceed 350 to 600 volts, depending on the type of protector.

The output level from the data set may be a "permissive" value of –9 dBm, designed to permit application anywhere and to deliver a –12 dBm level to the serving wire center through an average loop loss of 3 dB. This is the most common design. The level may also be a higher value, up to –4 dBm, with the exchange carrier providing a "fixed–loss loop" pad to build out the loop attenuation to a standard value. As a third option, the exchange carrier may supply a data jack with an internal resistor that programs the modem to deliver an output of 0 to –12 dBm, in 1–dB steps, to deliver –12 dBm to the office. Acoustically coupled data sets are designed to provide comparable levels through a normal telephone set. Thus, the station equipment can compensate for the loss of any practical loop.

References

1. Bell System Technical Reference PUB 41004, *Transmission Specifications for Voice Grade Private Line Data Channels*, American Telephone and Telegraph Company (Oct. 1973).

2. Bell System Technical Reference PUB 41005, *Data Communications Using the Switched Telecommunications Network*, American Telephone and Telegraph Company (May 1971).

3. *Voice Grade Switched Access Service—Transmission Parameter Limits and Interface Combinations*, Technical Reference TR–NPL–000334, Bellcore (Iss. 2, Dec. 1987).

4. *Voice Grade Special Access Service—Transmission Parameter Limits and Interface Combinations*, Technical Reference TR–NPL–000335, Bellcore (Iss. 2, Dec. 1987).

5. *EIA Standard EIA–232–D*, "Interface Between Data Terminal Equipment and Data Circuit Terminating Equipment Employing Serial Binary Data Interchange" (Washington, DC: Electronic Industries Association, 1986).

6. Federal Communications Commission. *Rules and Regulations, Title 47, Code of Federal Regulations, Part 68* (Washington, DC: U.S. Government Printing Office, Oct. 1987), Section 68.308(b)(4).

Chapter 6

Wideband Facilities

Signals that occupy a bandwidth wider than voiceband usually require special transmission facilities. Among these signals are high–capacity digital services, integrated services digital network (ISDN) access lines, digital data, local area data channel (LADC) service, Public Switched Digital Service (PSDS) data, special fiber–based services, program channels, and television signals. The facilities involved are the transmission media and central–office–mounted equipment. Both central–office equipment and complementary equipment at the customer's location may provide regeneration, gain, equalization, impedance matching, and maintenance features necessary to integrate wideband services with the telecommunications plant. For digital services, the exchange–carrier facilities normally terminate in a simple registered–jack interface, with customer–premises equipment providing the above functions. For analog services, the exchange carrier provides the network channel terminating equipment (NCTE) to deliver a complete, technically specified channel.

6–1 FACILITIES FOR HIGH–CAPACITY DIGITAL SERVICES

Digital private–line services at speeds of 1.5 Mb/s and, to a growing extent, 45 Mb/s are a highly active service offering. Demand for special speeds also occurs occasionally.

Service at 1.5 Mb/s is provided by any of the full array of DS1 facilities in the loop and interoffice plant: T1 spans or DS1 channels on any facility of higher capacity. Loop T1 spans are designed in the same fashion as, and are mixed in the cable with, spans for digital loop carrier (DLC) systems or ISDN primary–rate access lines. However, because they are not usually coterminous with DLC systems, they frequently involve route junctions at which signal levels must be coordinated to assure compatibility.

They also involve customer–premises end sections requiring an allowance for the attenuation in the customer's building cable. The preferred interface to the customer is via a "smart jack," able to loop back the receiving direction toward the central office upon receipt of a digital test code, thus allowing remote trouble sectionalization. These services occasionally involve customer-ordered protection switching and/or route diversity. Where fiber loop facilities are used, they frequently extend from the serving central office to a "fiber hub" with multiplexers, from which other fiber facilities or T1 spans extend to the customer site. Direct–to–premises digital radio may be used occasionally.

For 45 Mb/s, fiber facilities are the most common choice, with digital radio (interoffice or direct–to–premises) available as an option. Because the DS3 signal is a common facility building block, 45–Mb services can be mixed with DS3s for other purposes on a fiber or radio route operating at 135, 405, 560 Mb/s, etc.

6-2 ISDN FACILITIES

ISDN basic–rate access lines use a 160–kb/s loop format with two B channels at 64 kb/s each, a D channel at 16 kb/s, and 16 kb/s of capacity reserved for performance monitoring and maintenance functions. The standard ISDN line format is a 2B1Q (two–binary–to–one–quaternary) four–level code discussed in Chapter 3; however, there are prestandard designs using bipolar alternate mark inversion (AMI) coding or time–compression multiplexing. The 2B1Q code is inherent in the digital subscriber line (DSL), which is intended to have a range compatible with the size of a carrier serving area [1]. For ISDN DLC systems, channel units are currently available that preempt three derived pairs (three DS0 slots) to derive one AMI–based DSL; however, systems of higher technical efficiency are likely to become available. Where ISDN access lines are served on a remote–exchange basis, the interoffice (and loop) DS1 facilities that they use must be conditioned for 64–kb/s clear–channel capability (64CCC).

Primary–rate access for ISDN involves 23 B channels plus one D channel, each at 64 kb/s. With framing and performance-monitor pulses added, the result is a DS1 data stream. Where

146

more than 23 B channels are involved to a particular customer terminal, the second and later DS1s may be used for 24 B channels each. Primary–rate access lines are constructed the same as DS1 high–capacity services, using the same choices of T1 spans or channels on higher–capacity fiber or digital–radio systems. This applies whether the primary–rate access line is solely in local loop plant or extends on interoffice facilities to a remote–exchange serving office. Unlike DS1 services or ordinary DLC facilities, they require 64CCC via bipolar–with–eight–zero–substitution (B8ZS) coding. In practice, this means that certain early-vintage multiplexers (e.g., DS3–to–DS1) must be refitted for B8ZS, adapted by addition of zero–byte time–slot–interchange (ZBTSI) coders and decoders, or avoided.

6-3 FACILITIES FOR LOCAL AREA DATA CHANNELS

Most exchange carriers offer limited–distance data channels that are intended for short–range transmission of data at 300 b/s through 19.2 kb/s. The customer supplies a simple and inexpensive data set that gains its simplicity by use of uncomplicated data modulation techniques like two–level phase shift keying or Digital Data System (DDS) style AMI coding. As a result, most of the spectrum applied to the line at high data speeds is well above the voiceband.

These channels are usually tariffed for use only within a wire-center area [2]. They must use nonloaded cable pairs; DLC facilities are not suitable for the necessary bandwidth. A typical tariff offers the service for distances of up to six route–miles between stations at 2.4 or 4.8 kb/s, four miles at 7.2 kb/s, three miles at 9.6 kb/s, or two miles at 19.2 kb/s. The individual channels are two–wire; the customer rents two channels for full–duplex use.

Normal resistance design loops connected back–to–back at the serving wire center are satisfactory for this service, except that those at "loaded" distance (18 kft or longer) must be deloaded. The loss limits include margin for bridged taps of normal length. Coordination rules are necessary to avoid interference to single-channel analog loop carrier systems or 15–kHz program channels.

6-4 PSDS LOOPS

Public Switched Digital Service gives customers the ability to make dialed connections and send duplex data at 56 kb/s, either locally or as access to an interexchange carrier (IC). Interoffice trunking for PSDS involves ordinary DS1 facilities between digital switches; there is no requirement for 64CCC.

Local loops for PSDS vary somewhat with the manufacturer of the serving switch. If using wire, they use a single nonloaded cable pair for full–duplex operation. Coordination rules typically require the avoidance of the same binder group as is used by single– or multichannel analog loop carrier. The loop loss is limited to 45 dB at 72 kHz (40 dB if the serving wire center contains an electromechanical switch, because of the higher expected impulse noise). As a result, loops on pure 26–ga cable without bridged taps in a nonelectromechanical office area are satisfactory out to 14 kft; inclusion of 24–ga cable extends the range under the same conditions to 22 kft. Where a bridged tap is present, it causes a 72–kHz loss penalty of up to 12 dB, depending on gauge and length; a typical 1–kft 26–ga tap involves a loss of about 3 dB. Long loops may also need voiceband equalization and signalling treatment.

Because not all offices are PSDS servers, it is often necessary to serve users on a remote–exchange basis. In this case, the loss of any nonloaded trunk cable that is used comes out of the total loss budget. In practice, the use of Dataport–equipped carrier systems for either loop or interoffice transport avoids most of the loss and deloading problems associated with wire facilities. The carrier system(s) must be timed from the area synchronization network for compatibility.

6-5 LOCAL FACILITIES FOR DDS AND BDDS

Digital data services are provided in two ways. The original offering involved DDS [3]. The newer Basic Dedicated Digital Service (BDDS), as marketed under a variety of service names, uses ordinary digital carrier facilities with special Dataport channel units. Switched message network service and digital services are independently provided but the systems that provide these services share the facility network. Synchronous digital data transmission is available at a number of *service speeds*. Duplex service is provided on point–to–point and multipoint private lines. The signals are routed exclusively over digital facilities. DDS and BDDS signals are often combined with other signals for transmission over shared facilities [4].

The four common service speeds provided in the DDS and BDDS offerings are 2.4, 4.8, 9.6, and 56 kb/s. Some regions also offer a 1.2– and a 19.2–kb/s speed, and "secondary channel" services in which the normal DDS/BDDS customer–interface rates are raised to 3.2, 6.4, 12.8, or 72 kb/s, respectively. Synchronous signals are accepted at any one of these signalling rates from customer terminal equipment. They are transmitted over loop facilities to the central office and combined with other DDS/BDDS signals by time–division multiplexing.

Customer–Premises Equipment

A data service unit (DSU) is used at customer premises to link the transmission facility with the data source (computer or business machine). It provides conversion from the business–machine interface to the interface jack connecting to the exchange–carrier loop.

The interface of the DSU with the customer terminal typically meets the EIA–232–D specifications [5] at the 2.4–, 4.8–, 9.6– and 19.2–kb/s service speeds. The interface for 56 kb/s is usually based on CCITT Specification V.35. Where the secondary–channel feature is in use, the DSU serves as a two–channel multiplexer to combine/separate the two data streams at 2.4 + 0.133 kb/s, 4.8 + 0.266 kb/s, 9.6 + 0.533 kb/s, or 56 + 2.667 kb/s.

The customer–provided DSU provides equalization of the receiving cable pair, loop–back testing capability, and network protection [6]. Signals from the customer terminal to the DSU must be synchronized at the specified service speed. In the transmitting direction (toward the central office) the DSU accepts synchronous binary data signals from the customer terminal and converts them to a properly shaped, bipolar return–to–zero format for transmission on the loop. In the receiving direction, it

149

amplifies, equalizes, and slices the incoming signals before further processing. In addition, the DSU provides signal coding and decoding, timing recovery, synchronous sampling, and the generation of and response to control signals. All timing is derived from the bipolar bit stream received from the loop.

Signal Formats. The bipolar signal used for data transmission between the customer premises and the central office is illustrated in Figure 6-1. The signal is transmitted at the rate corresponding to the service speed selected by the customer (or higher, in the case of secondary-channel operation). The 2.4-, 4.8-, and 9.6-kb/s rates are called subrate speeds because they can be multiplexed into a 64-kb/s DS0 bit stream. By contrast, the 19.2- and 56-kb/s services occupy a full DS0 facility.

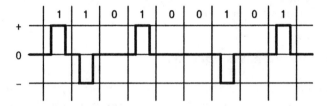

Figure 6-1. Bipolar return-to-zero 50-percent duty-cycle data signal.

Data is normally transmitted in bipolar form, which requires that successive *1*s in the signal be transmitted with alternate plus and minus polarities. However, bipolar violations are used in the signal to convey special information. Specially coded sequences are used when: (1) the distant DSU is transmitting an idle code to indicate that no data message is being transmitted, (2) a trouble condition exists in the receiving path, (3) the DSU is being tested from the digital service node, or (4) in the absence of the secondary-channel feature, a series of six or more *0*s (seven for 56 kb/s) appears in the customer data signal. Such a series of *0*s, not normally allowed in the transmitted signal, is replaced by coded bipolar violations that are detected at the receiving DSU. The bipolar violations are then removed and the proper number of *0*s restored to the signal before it is passed on to the receiving terminal equipment. Thus, there is no restriction on customer data sequence.

Loop Facilities

The DSU at the customer premises is connected to the serving wire center by a four-wire nonloaded loop, possibly including a Dataport-equipped DLC channel. Where the local serving office is not equipped for DDS service, the loop can be extended through that office over interoffice cable facilities to a DDS office. The interoffice connection is then regarded as a part of the loop. More typically, Dataport-equipped carrier systems are used in lieu of interoffice cable. For 56-kb/s service, a repeater may be used in a long loop if DLC facilities are unobtainable.

Loop Facility Application. The maximum nominal insertion loss for a DDS/BDDS loop is 31 dB at a frequency numerically equal to one-half the bit rate. A 3-dB allowance is included to accommodate the actual measured loss. (Some vendors offer terminal equipment having a slightly greater range.) Thus, the selection of loop facilities depends on the gauges of cable pairs available and on the specified service speed. The relationships among service speeds, wire gauges, insertion losses, and maximum loop lengths are given in Table 6-1. For mixed-gauge applications, the maximum loop length is specified approximately by the 31-dB overall loss limitation and the insertion losses, given in the table. (In practice, service over the longer lengths shown would involve digital carrier instead of nonloaded wire because of its greater availability in today's network.) Sections of 25-ga low-capacitance cable, used in interoffice trunk cables, may be included in interoffice loops. At DDS frequencies, this cable gives losses slightly less than 24-ga normal-capacitance cable.

In addition to these limits, for the higher data speeds the use of cable pairs in separate cable units is recommended to minimize the risk of interference with 15-kHz program services and some analog transmission systems. Load coils are not permitted and the length of allowable bridged taps is limited. Mixed cable pair gauges are normal; insertion loss for each gauge can be determined for any combination from the loss values given in Table 6-1.

Central-Office Terminations. DDS/BDDS access facilities on wire are terminated in the central office by an office channel unit (OCU) to match the customer service speed. On the loop side,

Table 6-1. Loop Losses and Lengths for DDS/BDDS

Wire Gauge	Bit Rate (kb/s)					
	2.4		4.8		9.6	
	Loss†	Loop*	Loss†	Loop*	Loss†	Loop*
19	0.27	114.8	0.36	86.1	0.46	67.4
22	0.42	73.8	0.55	56.4	0.72	43.1
24	0.55	56.4	0.73	42.5	0.96	32.3
26	0.74	41.9	0.96	32.3	1.25	24.8
	19.2		56		56 w/SC	
	Loss†	Loop*	Loss†	Loop*	Loss†	Loop*
19	0.59	52.5	0.76	40.8	0.86	36.0
22	0.96	32.3	1.28	24.2	1.45	21.3
24	1.31	23.7	1.80	17.2	2.04	15.2
26	1.73	17.9	2.40	12.9	2.72	11.4

† Losses are insertion losses, in dB/kft, between 135-ohm terminations at the frequency corresponding numerically to one-half the bit rate.

* Lengths are maximum acceptable for 31-dB design loss, in kilofeet.

the OCU functions in a manner similar to that described for the DSU regarding gain and equalization. In addition, it sends a low value of dc, called sealing current, to the loop and customer-premises equipment. This current maintains a low resistance at splices and other connection points by breaking down small accumulations of dirt and oxides. A reversal of the sealing current polarity, initiated in the OCU, is used at the DSU to establish a loop-back condition. The dc current reversal is made in response to a control code from the digital service node.

Where Dataport-equipped DLC or interoffice carrier is used, the carrier channel unit provides the OCU function. On the central-office side of the OCU, other functions performed to satisfy system requirements include flexible cross-connection, optional submultiplexing, and digital hierarchy multiplexing.

6-6 FACILITIES FOR SPECIAL FIBER SERVICES

Depending on customer needs and local policy, customized fiber facilities are often made available on a special-tariff basis.

These may consist of simple nonequipped fiber pairs that extend between customer sites. They are termed "dark fiber" because the customer provides the light sources (and receivers) that make them operational. They may also comprise fiber span lines at defined operating speeds (139, 405, 565 Mb/s, etc.) with terminating equipment supplied by the exchange carrier. In a few cases involving long distances, the customer provides the span terminating equipment and the exchange carrier supplies an intermediate regenerator.

These specialized facilities are popular with ICs for "last mile" purposes: extending from an IC fiber terminal on a railroad right–of–way to the IC's terminal building in the same town. They also find application with major customers and government agencies.

Future broadband ISDN access lines at speeds of 150 to 600 Mb/s are expected to rely almost exclusively on fiber facilities direct to the user's premises, with SONET (synchronous optical network) multiplexing at central offices and at fiber hubs in the loop area [7]. Such lines will take advantage of "fiber to the home" or "fiber to the curb" facilities.

6-7 PROGRAM FACILITIES

Program channels require wideband facilities. The normal services offered today under the access–service tariffs require top frequencies of 3.5, 5, 8, or 15 kHz. Except for very short lengths of cable for 3.5–kHz service (with only two or three load points), ordinary H88–loaded cable is unsuitable for any of these services. Nonloaded cable is applicable, with lengths between equalizing repeaters of up to 12 dB attenuation ("bare pair") at 1 kHz or 30 dB at the top frequency. Bridged taps of normal lengths can be accommodated readily.

For 3.5–kHz service, a single voice channel on a present–vintage loop or interoffice carrier system provides a suitable facility. Where it is necessary to connect two carrier systems back–to–back, it is strongly preferable to use a digital cross–connect system (DCS) instead of using an added stage of decoding and recoding with its attendant loss of high frequencies.

At one time, specially loaded cable pairs were used for program service. These involved low–inductance loading coils of 44, 22, 11, or 7.5 millihenries (mH) at spacings coded H (6 kft), B (3 kft), B/2 (1.5 kft), or B/3 (1 kft). Thus, H44, H22, B44, B22, B/2–11, etc. loaded pairs were occasionally found. These loading plans provided cutoff frequencies as high as about 20 kHz. However, the use of such facilities has nearly disappeared. Likewise, analog carrier with special 5–, 8–, or 15–kHz terminals was once used to some extent.

Digital carrier facilities have the advantages of ready reuse of the channels upon discontinuance of the program service, of not requiring deloading or reloading of cable pairs, and of using any base facility, including fiber. They are fundamentally incapable of causing frequency shift, which would be troublesome in transmission of music if not controlled. Compared to long equalized aerial cable pairs, they do not exhibit temperature–induced changes in frequency response, winter midnight to summer noon. They also promote digital interconnection with ICs. Table 6–2 compares some coding methods presently available for digital systems. National standards [8] are available for 15–kHz program facilities having excellent levels of total harmonic distortion of the order of 0.2 percent and signal–to–quantizing–distortion ratios of 50 dB or better.

Table 6–2. Audio Coding Methods

Service (kHz)	Voice Slots	Line (kb/s)	Sampling Rate (kHz)	Signal–to– Distortion (dB)
3.5	1	64	8	>35
5	2	128	16	>35
5–STL*	3	192	16	>50
8	3	192	16	>35
15	6	384	32	>50

* Studio–to–transmitter link.

6-8 TELEVISION FACILITIES

There is continuing demand for short–distance television facilities to interconnect broadcast studios and transmitters and to connect these points through an exchange–carrier television operating center (TOC) to other facilities. The intracity facilities may also be used to provide closed–circuit service for news or sports pickups. The signal to be transported may be simple video, or may be video with one or two 15–kHz audio channels diplexed onto the television signal by means of frequency modulated carriers in the vicinity of 5.2 and 5.8 MHz.

DS3 High–Capacity Channels

Where end–to–end television transmission is via digital means, local facilities are also digital, usually at the DS3 (44.736 Mb/s) rate, based on the use of coders–decoders (codecs) that compress a full–color, full–motion signal that would otherwise require about 90 Mb/s. The resulting transmission requirement involves a DS3 high–capacity channel on any suitable facility; the feasible distance is unlimited.

Analog Fiber

Many of the needs for intracity transmission are met by fiber facilities equipped with pulse frequency modulation (PFM) terminals. The typical range between repeaters varies between 2 and 22 miles, depending on the wavelength, use of light–emitting diode (LED) or laser transmitters, and the choice of single–mode or multimode cable. These facilities are covered in more detail in Volume 3. The fiber facilities themselves are described in Chapter 2 of this volume.

Wire Media

Some baseband video signals are transmitted on 16–gauge shielded cable pairs, often combined in cables with ordinary trunk pairs. The 124–ohm characteristic impedance of the pairs is controlled in manufacture so that, when properly terminated at a repeater or terminal, reflections are held to a minimum. The attenuation characteristic of these cable pairs is illustrated in Figure 6–2. The low–frequency attenuation is very low, so amplifier gains and equalizer designs are determined primarily by the high–frequency loss of the cable pair. While the main use of these pairs is in television transmission, they are also used in wire–line entrance links for microwave radio systems for message use.

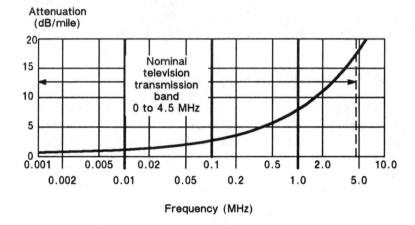

Attenuation (dB/mile)

Frequency (MHz)

Figure 6–2. Typical attenuation/frequency characteristic for 16–gauge video pairs.

Television signals are highly susceptible to interference from crosstalk of other signals into the television channel. In addition, the concentration of energy at discrete frequencies in television signals has the potential of crosstalk interference from the television channel into other channels. These problems are avoided by the use of shielded cable pairs. For intraoffice wiring, 75–ohm coaxial cable may be used.

A2–Type Video Transmission System. The A2–type system provides a well–equalized, 4.5–MHz video channel. A basic system consists of a transmitting terminal, a receiving terminal, and the interconnecting shielded cable pair. Such a minimal system can be used to compensate for 82.5 dB of cable loss at 4.5 MHz, the loss of about 4.5 miles of cable. Repeaters may be used to extend the length of the system. Each added repeater increases the permissible cable loss by 82.5 dB. Thus, one repeater added at the midpoint of the cable span extends the length of a system to about 9 miles. Multirepeater systems up to 30 miles long have been used. Each system provides a one–direction transmission facility. Even where two directions of transmission are provided, the system for each direction is independent of the other.

Figure 6–3 shows a typical two–section layout of an A2–type system. All amplifiers used in the receiving and transmitting terminals use negative feedback and have a flat gain/frequency characteristic. The compensation for the loss/frequency characteristic of the cable is provided entirely in the equalizers. Therefore, the amplifier gains must compensate for the losses of these equalizers as well as for cable loss. The system is lined up in accordance with the voltage levels shown in Figure 6–3. These levels are designed to prevent noise penalty or amplifier overload.

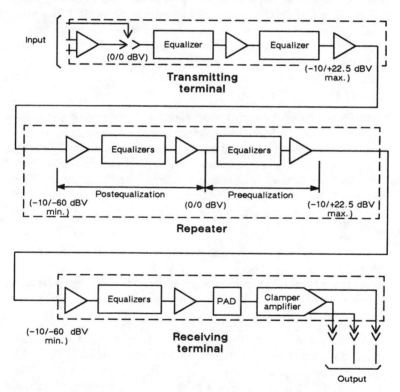

Figure 6–3. Typical A2–type system transmission layout.

Fixed equalizers are used in terminals and repeaters to provide most of the equalization of the cable characteristic. With these equalizers, the square–root–of–frequency component of line loss can be equalized to within a residual deviation of ±1.25 dB at 4.5 MHz. For short repeater sections, a flat–loss pad is normally used so that the loss of pad plus equalizer is properly compensated by the following flat–gain amplifier. Equalization of the residual deviation is provided by adjustable equalizers located in the receiving terminal. With the combinations of equalizers and amplifiers that can be used in the system, the video channel can be made flat to within ±0.1 dB over the band from 30 Hz to 4.5 MHz, a span of over 17 octaves in frequency. This wide band requires complex equalizers and accurate impedance matching between the cables and the electronic equipment. Pre– and postequalization is used in order to limit the required range of adjustable equalizers, to maximize the signal–to–noise ratio, and to minimize overload penalties that could occur if all equalization were placed at one end of a link. Envelope delay distortion at the high–frequency end of the band may be corrected by delay equalizers installed in the receiving terminal according to the overall length of the circuit.

A4–Type Video Transmission System. This system provides a video channel 10 MHz wide over shielded video pairs up to 0.5 mile long. In addition, a span of about 0.3 mile is achievable with unshielded balanced cable pairs; with unbalanced coaxial cable, a span of about 500 feet is the recommended maximum. The system can be used as a temporary or permanent video link, as in portable use to connect a mobile pickup unit to exchange carrier facilities.

The A4–type system consists of a very small and simple transmitter, a cable pair, and a receiver that provides amplification, equalization, clamping, and power supply functions. No repeater is required because the system is designed only for very short single–link circuits.

The only function of the transmitter is to convert an unbalanced 75–ohm input to a balanced 124–ohm output with 0–dB gain. It receives power over the cable from the receiver. If the interface is 124–ohm balanced at the input, a transmitter is not used.

Equalization is provided in the receiver over the video band up to 10 MHz. Receiver gain can compensate for a loss of up to

9 dB at 4.5 MHz. Since there are differences in low–frequency characteristics among the cables that may be used, a variable low–frequency equalizer is also provided. Amplification is provided by fixed–gain amplifiers and a clamper that maintains the signal at a fixed 0–dBV reference value. Levels are adjusted by means of adjustable attenuators to give a 0–dB insertion loss for the system.

6-9 WIDEBAND ANALOG FACILITIES

Wideband analog service is offered to customers using frequency–division multiplex technology. This service is included in special–access tariffs as described in Volume 3, and is offered to both ICs and end users [9].

These services are packaged as WA1 for 12 equivalent voiceband channels, WA2 for 60 channels, and WA2A for 600 channels. All three are offered with channelizing equipment at a hub central office designated by the exchange carrier with the intention of extending voice channels to an exchange–carrier switch or end users' premises, or of continuing group or supergroup channels to a second hub location. WA1 service can be provided over short distances by using ordinary cable pairs, suitably equalized, while the wider bandwidths need facilities similar to those employed for video channels. Although wideband analog service is still offered, high–capacity digital service has become far more popular.

Other special–access services provide for the transmission of synchronous serial data, generally including a voiceband coordinating channel, between the end–user network interface and the IC point of termination [10]. Two data–oriented analog channels, WA3 and WA4, offer bandwidths between 300 Hz and 44 kHz. There are also wideband analog offerings. Access service WD1 provides for 19.2 kb/s, access service WD2 provides for 50 kb/s, and access service WD3 provides for 230.4 kb/s. (Note that all are considered technically obsolete.) The channel includes a 303–type data set as the NCTE. Access service WD4 provides for 56–kb/s operation without the coordinating channel. This service may be used for access to a DDS. These services may all be provided over short distances with the use of nonloaded cable pairs equipped with wideband loop repeaters. Over larger distances, digital carrier may be used. As with wideband analog services, however, these offerings have been eclipsed by 19.2–kb/s data on voiceband channels, 56–kb/s DDS and BDDS offerings, and 1.5–Mb/s high–capacity channels.

References

1. *ISDN Basic Access Digital Subscriber Lines*, Technical Reference TR–TSY–000393, Bellcore (Iss. 1, May 1988).

2. Bell System Technical Reference PUB 41028, *Data Communications Using Local Area Data Channels*, American Telephone and Telegraph Company (Iss. 1, June 1979).

3. Knapp, N., Jr., N. E. Snow, et al. "The Digital Data System," *Bell System Tech. J.*, Vol. 54, No. 3 (May/June 1975), pp. 811–964.

4. Aprille, T. J. et al. "Dataport—Digital Access Through D4," *Bell System Tech. J.*, Vol. 61, No. 9 (Nov. 1982), pp. 2703–2720.

5. *EIA Standard EIA–232–D*, "Interface Between Data Terminal Equipment and Data Circuit Terminating Equipment Employing Serial Binary Data Interchange" (Washington, DC: Electronic Industries Association, 1986).

6. Federal Communications Commission. *Rules and Regulations, Title 47, Code of Federal Regulations, Part 68* (Washington, DC: U.S. Government Printing Office, Oct. 1987), Section 68.308(h).

7. *Metropolitan Area Network Generic Framework System Requirements in Support of Switched Multi–Megabit Data Service*, Technical Advisory TA–TSY–000772, Bellcore (Iss. 2, Apr. 1989).

8. *ANSI T1.305–1989*, "American National Standard for Telecommunications—Compatibility Characteristics of 14/11 Bit Coders/Decoders—15 kHz Program (New York: American National Standards Institute, 1989).

9. *Wideband Analog Special Access Service—Transmission Parameter Limits and Interface Combinations*, Technical Reference TR–NPL–000339, Bellcore (Iss. 1, Oct. 1987).

10. *Wideband Data Special Access Service—Transmission Parameter Limits and Interface Combinations*, Technical Reference TR–NPL–000340, Bellcore (Iss. 1, Oct. 1987).

Chapter 7

Central–Office Equipment

The transmission characteristics of central–office equipment result from a variety of technologies, circuits, transmission paths, and interrelated switching and transmission functions. The transmission paths through the central–office include the wiring and cabling between the cable vault where central–office cable is connected to outside plant, intraoffice tie cables, terminating trunk circuits, and (where switching is involved) transmission paths through the switching system. In addition to being parts of the office transmission paths, trunk circuits provide auxiliary functions (e.g., a signalling interface, impedance matching, and sometimes four–wire–to–two–wire conversion) that are related to transmission. These functions, as well as switching–system functions, are discussed in terms of their effects on transmission. For example, the sequencing of calls involves many processes such as battery–feed transfer, battery–feed reversal, the switching of idle–circuit terminations, and pulse code modulation (PCM) coding and decoding.

Transmission through a central office is further complicated by two– and four–wire operation used for both switching and transmission. Line and trunk impedance values vary widely and strongly influence the design of the central–office auxiliary and interface circuitry.

A growing number of central offices provide interface functions for transmitting and switching digital signals. Some of the interfaces are points of transition from analog to digital signal form while others may accept a digital signal directly from a loop or transmission system for introduction into a digital switch system.

All of these features must be designed and maintained to control transmission impairments. All of the impairments that normally affect transmission (noise, echo, loss, slope, digital timing slips, crosstalk, harmonic distortion, etc.) may be caused by central–office equipment.

7-1   CENTRAL-OFFICE TRANSMISSION PATHS

Outside plant cables usually terminate in a vault in the basement of or immediately outside a central–office building. These cables are spliced to tip cables that route through the building to main distributing frames (MDFs). Jumpers are used at the MDFs to connect switching systems with other central–office equipment and with loops and trunks. The MDF also provides protection from unwanted voltages such as those due to lightning and crosses with power lines. The interconnections involve interfaces among signalling, switching, and transmission equipment. While the cables between the distributing frame and the vault are within the central–office building, they are usually considered part of the outside plant. Central–office transmission performance is typically evaluated between MDF appearances.

In addition, other distributing frames are often used in a central office. These cross–connection facilities are changed continuously by moving jumpers in the frames so that cable pairs may be connected to different equipment items or to other cable pairs as required.

Intraoffice Wiring

Direct and multiple wiring is used to provide transmission paths within a central office. In addition, there is a large amount of cabling that is not directly related to transmission such as the fibers or cabling that carry the control signals to operate the switching system.

These wiring paths must meet stringent requirements for dc resistance, transmission loss, slope, return loss, and interference. Path lengths may be quite varied, so to control cross–office losses and loss variations, the maximum lengths of these paths are often specified as design requirements. Similarly, wire gauge, pair twisting, separation between wires that carry different amplitudes or types of signal, and, in most cases, the relative locations of various equipment items are also specified so that transmission objectives can be met.

Switching Networks

The matrix of switching devices through which connections are established is called a switching network. The switching devices and how they are arranged in a network in different switching systems vary widely. The variations may result in a different set of transmission problems in each type. The types most commonly used are crossbar, analog electronic, and digital switching systems.

Crossbar Systems. The following description is typical of the network that is formed by switching systems that use common control of crossbar switches.

Two switch sizes are used to provide switching crosspoints. A 100-point switch has ten horizontal paths and ten vertical paths; a 200-point switch has ten horizontals and twenty verticals. At each crosspoint, the contacts are arranged in groups of three or six depending on the type of transmission path (two-wire or four-wire) and the number of supervisory and control leads to be switched. To achieve high reliability and low noise, each precious-metal contact is arranged as a parallel pair on a bifurcated contact spring.

Five selecting bars are associated with the horizontal paths, two paths to each of the bars. Under control of the switching logic circuits, each bar may be rotated slightly, by electromagnets, in either direction to operate selecting fingers that enable a connection from the selected horizontal row to any vertical path through the switch. The vertical paths are also controlled by electromagnets. The ability of these magnets to operate the crosspoint contacts and to hold them operated depends on the position of the horizontal selecting finger. Thus, when a crosspoint is to be operated, the appropriate horizontal bar rotates in a direction to move the upper or lower selecting finger. When the appropriate vertical magnet operates, only the selecting finger at the desired crosspoint can operate contacts. When the contacts are closed, the operated magnet is released, leaving the crosspoint contacts clamped in the operated position by a hold magnet. The hold magnet is released upon call completion. To avoid double connections, the switch and its controls are arranged so that only one crosspoint can be closed at one time in any horizontal or vertical path. However, each switch can establish up to ten simultaneous connections.

Arrays of crossbar switches are interconnected to provide switching networks for use in local or tandem offices. The common–control logic circuits for these networks are called markers.

Electronic Switching Systems. Electronic switching systems use stored program control (SPC). With SPC, the steps involved in making connections reside in a stored program (software). New services can be added by making changes to this stored program rather than redesigning or rewiring circuits.

Some networks use metallic contacts; others use electronically controlled time–division switching of digital signals. In the metallic networks, the basic element used to switch a transmission path is a miniature sealed reed contact. This contact assembly is used in pairs or quads to switch a two–wire or four–wire transmission path. Switching is accomplished by changing the polarity of magnetic forces in square–loop magnetic material. The desired polarity to operate or release the reed contacts is induced by the application of high–current, short–duration control pulses to coils surrounding the contact assembly. A pulse applied only to a horizontal row or vertical column of switches places all the contacts in the row or column in the open condition. When a pulse is applied simultaneously to a row and column, the crosspoint at the intersection of the row and column is closed. The square–loop (remanent) magnetic material is called remendur: the reeds are a ferrous material and the switch assemblies are called ferreeds [1]. In later designs, the reed contacts are actually composed of the square–loop material; external magnetic material is not required. These switch assemblies are called remreeds.

Most ferreed and remreed switches are combined in matrices of 64 crosspoints arranged in a square array of 8 horizontal rows and 8 vertical columns. Within these 8 × 8 arrays, switching controls and transmission paths are combined to provide network

166

configurations as required. Control circuits allow only one crosspoint to operate at a time in any row or column.

As in all switching networks that use metallic crosspoints, satisfactory transmission is related to the lengths of paths through the switches and the lengths of multiple wiring. However, the reduced size of the switching network compared to earlier designs considerably relaxes the problems of cable length. The exposure of the transmission paths to the wiring that carries the high–current pulses to operate crosspoints is controlled to avoid excessive impulse noise. As a result, the impulse–noise level is sizably less than in an electromechanical switch.

Digital Switching Systems. In digital switching systems, the message signal is PCM–coded into digital form, that is, a sequence of discrete electrical pulses. Transmission and switching are integrated functions; logic circuits, time–slot interchanging, and gate circuits are combined to achieve the desired interconnections electronically. The transmission problems found in electromechanical networks, such as those due to multiple wiring, are essentially nonexistent. However, there are other concerns. For example, different delays due to different path lengths through a central office might produce pulse transpositions and timing slips, which could cause noise, crosstalk, and data failures. However, by keeping path lengths under control, the digital switching system produces less crosstalk and impulse noise than its electromechanical counterparts and the advantages of an all–digital network dictate deployment of digital switching systems.

Remote Switching Devices. Modern switches allow for the use of subtending remote switching devices known as remote switch units, remote switching modules, etc. These are semiautonomous switch matrices that normally depend on their host switch for call control but can usually stand alone for local calling in case of failure of the control links. They are widely used to replace small electromechanical community dial offices with two or three remotes homed onto a given host. They also find use for close–to–the–premises centrex switching and are occasionally used for loop pair–gain (concentration) purposes. Analog remotes connect to the host via zero–loss two–wire trunks. Digital remotes use either DS1 facilities or dedicated fiber channels for their trunking.

Switching for Integrated Services Digital Network. Integrated services digital network (ISDN) access lines may be the basic–rate type with two 64–kb/s B plus a 16–kb/s D channel totaling, with overhead, 160 kb/s. They may also be the primary–rate type with 23 B channels and a 64–kb/s D channel totaling, again with overhead, 1.544 Mb/s. In either case, the ISDN office must either switch a B channel (for circuit–switched voice or data) or redirect it to a permanent 64–kb/s path to a distant station (for "channel–switched" private–line services). The switch must also pick out the data on the D channel and either use it for call control or direct its data packets into a packet network. ISDN loops enter the office in 2B+D digital subscriber line (DSL) format with 2B1Q coding, in 2B+D form on special digital loop carrier (DLC) channels, or in 23B+D combinations on DS1 facilities.

The switch (exchange termination) may be an adjunct collocated with an analog electronic switch and controlled by its processor. More often, it is a digital switch with basic–access line cards or a primary–rate interface. As shown in Figure 7–1, the switch provides circuit switching of B channels, including connecting them to crossover trunks into the existing message network. The D–channel handler directs signalling packets from the D channel into a Signalling System No. 7 (common–channel signalling) packet network, and sends data packets from the D channel into a separate public packet network. The use of a distinct signalling network allows circuit–switched connections to be used for full 64–kb/s data without regard to bit format or zeros limits.

Switching for PSDS. Two methods, depending on the switch, are used for handling 56–kb/s Public Switched Digital Service (PSDS) data. In analog electronic systems, the data enters the office from the station loop in a time–compression multiplex (TCM) format, in which the loop signal is at 144 kb/s, half–duplex, in order to obtain 56–kb/s duplex transmission. The signal is converted to 56 kb/s for transmission through the switch network. Duplex operation on a two–wire network takes place by the use of hybrids to separate the two directions. If the call is to leave the office on a trunk, a carrier channel unit on the trunk side of the switch accepts the 56–kb/s two–wire data and interfaces with the four–wire duplex DS0 path of the outgoing

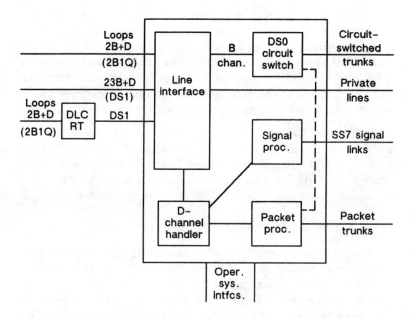

Figure 7-1. ISDN switch.

carrier system. In digital switches, the 56-kb/s data operation is simpler: the customer's data stream is transferred directly via special line cards into the digital switch fabric.

Switching for Packet Service. Packet data transmission involves the conversion of a customer's data stream into sections called packets, typically 128 to 1024 bits long. Each packet is given a header identifying the source and destination addresses for the data and giving other control information [2]. It also receives a checksum for error-detection purposes. Packets from one customer are then interleaved with those from many others for transmission over a high-speed trunk, usually at 56 or 64 kb/s, to a distant switch. An incorrect checksum at the receiving end indicates that a transmission error has occurred; the receiving switch then requests retransmission of the defective packet. Correct packets are reassembled into a continuous stream to the distant customer terminal. Features like asynchronous-to-synchronous adaptation or code conversion may be included.

The switch for packet applications, the packet assembler–disassembler, is basically a special–purpose computer. It provides many low–speed ports and a few high–speed trunk terminations. For dial–in applications, especially from small offices not needing a full packet switch, it is common to add an access concentrator with many ports connected to a conventional message–network switch, and a medium–speed link to the packet switch.

Broadband Switches. Future switching systems will need to accommodate multimegabit switched data services for such applications as high–definition television. Switching at speeds of the order of 150 Mb/s will be needed, either via a new switch [3] or an outboard module controlled by an existing switch design [4].

7-2 TERMINATING AND ANCILLARY CIRCUITS

Many individual circuits in a central office have a bearing on transmission performance. For example, trunk circuits provide battery feed and are directly in the transmission path of message network connections. These battery–feed circuits often perform multiple functions. Circuits indirectly related to transmission interface with other circuits such as those for controlling billing information, identifying numbers, and signalling. There are also circuits directly in the transmission path to perform special functions. Among these are conference circuits, switchable pads and amplifiers, and idle–circuit terminations. Connections made to operators involve transmission problems that have a direct impact on network performance.

The way the signalling and transmission interface is provided involves a compromise between signalling range and transmission performance. Resolution of the compromise often has a direct effect on the selection of facilities (wire–gauge, range extenders, repeaters, carrier, etc.) in a particular serving area. Trunk circuits also provide impedance matching; this function and the use of drop build–out capacitors are closely related to the necessity for meeting through– and terminal–balance requirements for echo control where two–wire tandem switching is used.

Line Circuits

A line circuit is used at a switching system to terminate a loop that is serving an exchange access line. The primary function of a line circuit is to signal a request for service to the switching system, which prepares for call direction information that follows.

A typical line circuit in an analog electronic switch consists of a ferrod sensor through which battery and ground are fed to the line. The ferrod sensor can be considered a transformer whose coupling is controlled by line current in the control windings. The coupling induces a signal from the primary winding to the secondary winding. The primary and secondary winding to the transformer are associated with the interrogate and readout circuits and are referred to as the interrogate and readout windings, respectively. Ferrods are used in other status–sensor functions throughout the switching sequence.

If the end user is on–hook (no line current in control windings), the interrogate signal induces a signal in the readout winding. If the end user is off–hook (line current in control windings), the coupling is destroyed by magnetic saturation of the core and the interrogate signal cannot induce a signal into the readout winding. A typical ferrod connected for loop–start operation is shown in Figure 7–2. An off–hook condition causes the switch to connect a receiver circuit to accept dialed digits and return dial tone.

Figure 7–3 shows a typical line circuit used in a digital switch. The loop connects, through an isolation transformer, to a hybrid circuit that separates the two directions of transmission. In the transmit direction (toward the switch), a codec–and–filter chip provides low–pass filtering and analog–to–digital (PCM) coding. An "access" chip then passes the 64–kb/s coded speech, with on–hook/off–hook supervision bits included, via a bidirectional digital bus into the switch fabric. In the receive direction, 64–kb/s data passes from the bidirectional bus through the access chip into the receive side of the codec–and–filter chip. Here it is decoded and filtered into an analog voice–frequency (VF) signal. Entering the hybrid, it then feeds through the isolation transformer toward the loop. The PCM coding and decoding functions are identical to those described in full detail in Chapter 13. The decoding level is adjustable under software control (translators) to give an overall loss of 0 to 6 dB.

The subscriber line receives its dc current feed from a −48V source through resistors and the isolation transformer. A

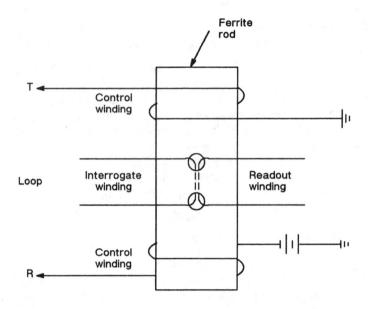

Figure 7-2. Typical ferrod arrangement.

supervision circuit examines the voltage drop across the resistors to determine on— or off—hook status. A cutoff relay is present to lift the battery feed. It serves two purposes. Where a new digital switch is being prepared to replace a working analog switch in the same building, the cutoff relay in the line circuit is held operated, via the cutover hold bus, during the transition period of several weeks when both switching machines are wired to the same subscriber line, thus preventing interference. In ongoing use, the cutoff relay allows direct access from loop—testing equipment (on the test—access bus, via the TA relay) without the normal battery supply. A third relay, RG (ringing generator), transfers the line to the ringing bus, a source of 20—Hz ringing current combined with −48V dc, to ring the line. A final control feature sets the impedance of the balancing network in the hybrid, under control of software translations, to match loaded or nonloaded loops.

The line circuit illustrated is for normal loop—start operation. A more complex version, with two additional relays, is used for ground—start lines, as with private branch exchange—central office (PBX—CO) trunks. Where integrated DLC facilities are used,

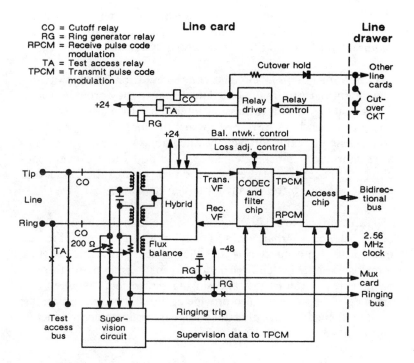

Figure 7-3. Typical digital-switch line circuit.

the line circuit is similar to that of Figure 7-2, but is located in the remote terminal. The digital signal enters the switch in DS1 groups.

The loop-resistance limits of digital and electronic analog switches tend to be higher than for electromechanical units. Limits of 1600 to 1900 ohms are typical.

Trunk Circuits

Trunks are the transmission paths that interconnect switching systems and portions of switching machines. In the absence of digital switching, most trunks terminate in a trunk circuit at each end. Each trunk circuit connects the transmission medium to a specific terminal on the switching network at which the trunk terminates. Many trunk circuit types are found in the telecommunications network because of the variety of functions performed, the variety of trunks used in the network, and the requirements of the different switching systems.

Functions. Trunk circuits connecting nondigital switching equipment perform many functions because they provide switching, signalling, and transmission interfaces. In many cases, battery and ground are furnished toward the loop from a trunk circuit at its end of the connection. Such a circuit typically contains a transformer or blocking capacitors (or both) that provide coupling for speech signals between the two parts of the circuit and confine the dc to the circuit for which it is intended.

Trunk circuits are designed to provide a high degree of longitudinal balance so that longitudinally induced currents are not transformed into interfering metallic voltages. In trunk design, a transformer may match impedances so that terminal and through balance (echo return loss and singing return loss) requirements are met. Trunk circuits also provide additional protection against unwanted high voltage that may appear on metallic conductors due to lightning or power-line faults.

Most trunk circuits provide the interfaces that permit signalling over the trunk. Included are supervisory components that recognize the on-hook or off-hook state of the connection. These differences in state may provide both supervisory and address signalling information on the tip and ring (T and R) leads or on other signalling leads for use locally and at a distant office. In addition, signalling information may be extended from the trunk circuit to automatic message accounting equipment.

In analog electronic switching systems, trunk circuits are constructed as small plug-in units rather than the permanent wired relay plates in earlier systems. Trunk circuits may also be in "digital carrier trunk" format in which D4-type channel banks provide a DS1 interface to the switch. Mounted in switching frames rather than the usual transmission bays, these channel banks are effectively merged into the switch. For signalling, the A- and B-bit path of the carrier terminal directly enters a data bus into the switch logic; there is no need for per-channel signalling equipment or leads.

Effects of Trunk Types. Trunks are classified in a number of ways to satisfy the needs of transmission and traffic organizations.

One method of classifying trunks is by the directions of call origination. A two-way trunk provides for call origination in either direction; a one-way trunk, in one direction only. The trunk circuits for one-way and two-way trunks have different signalling interface requirements, which are further complicated by the signalling requirements of the switching system at each end of the trunk.

Both trunks and switching systems can be either two-wire or four-wire. Any combination of these may be found, for which provision must be made in the transmission design of the trunk circuit, which provides the interface at the point of interconnection. Each application requires the use of a different design of trunk circuit. Many intrasystem trunks (junctors) are required to provide connections to service circuits such as dial, busy, audible ringing, and reorder tones, and to announcement devices associated with certain number services (special information tones, vacant number, disconnected service, etc.).

Intersystem trunks include all of the various trunks required in the message network hierarchy. Each of these may be one-way or two-way, two-wire or four-wire, analog or digital, direct, tandem-connecting, intertandem, high-usage, or final-route. Operation of one of these trunks may involve echo cancellers, switchable pads, idle-circuit terminations, and analog-to-digital and digital-to-analog conversions.

Some trunks that interconnect switching systems provide operator services and others remain in a network connection after the operator has disconnected. Where the connection from the operator to the network trunk is made by bridging, the trunk circuit must have low loss in the through-trunk connection and high-impedance bridging of the operator trunk. The bridged operator trunk is connected to the through trunk by a path through the switching network. After the operator has completed the necessary action, the bridged connection is released.

Some trunks provide connections from a network trunk to local or centralized automatic message accounting equipment. The requirements on these trunks depend on whether the message trunk is in a flat–rate or message–rate portion of the network.

Typical Trunk Circuits. The more significant features and functions of these circuits can be demonstrated by a few schematic drawings chosen to illustrate specific points.

The principal connections to trunk circuits are dedicated to transmission and signalling. Certain designations are consistently used for trunk circuit leads having specific functions. In many cases, these designations are applied to leads other than those used in trunk circuits (e.g., many signalling unit and VF repeater leads).

Lead Designations. Common designations for the tip and ring transmission leads are T, R, T1, and R1. The T and R designations are used generally to designate the tip and ring leads of two–wire circuits where no distinction between two circuit ports is needed. Where a distinction must be made, T and R are usually used for the leads at the port facing the switching equipment and T1 and R1 for the leads at the port facing the transmission facility. At two– to four–wire conversion points, the two–wire leads are designated T and R. The four–wire leads that transmit away from the conversion point are also labeled T and R; the leads that receive from the distant point are designated T1 and R1.

Where an equipment item interconnects two four–wire circuits, the T, R, T1, and R1 leads are assigned depending on the application and functional designation of the interconnecting circuit. Signalling leads are also given standard designations. These include E, M, SX, SX1, A, B, SG, and SB. Illustrations of some applications are given in Figure 7–4.

The designations E and M identify leads that interconnect trunk circuits and signalling circuits. These leads are always related in such a way that the E lead signals from the trunk circuit toward the local switch, and the M lead signals from the switch toward the distant end. The relationship of E and M signalling leads to transmission circuits and the directions of signalling are illustrated in Figure 7–4(c). An open–circuited E lead represents an on–hook condition at the distant end. Similarly, the M lead is used to signal toward the distant end of a trunk; an on–hook

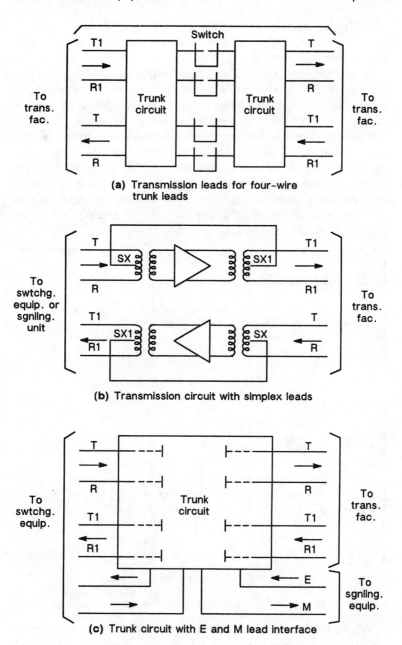

(a) Transmission leads for four-wire trunk leads

(b) Transmission circuit with simplex leads

(c) Trunk circuit with E and M lead interface

Figure 7-4. Transmission and signalling lead designations.

condition at the near end is represented by a ground on the M lead and an off–hook condition by −48 volts. In the original E and M method of signalling, as shown in Figure 7–5(a), the signals are changed by opening and closing single–wire circuits. With each change of state, this arrangement can produce high–amplitude transients that may induce errors in control or impulse noise in transmission. The newer circuit arrangement of Figure 7–5(b) preserves the orderly grounding plan of electronic switching systems. It is used to avoid noise by providing paired–wire signalling. The SG (signalling ground) and SB (signalling battery) leads are coupled back between trunk and signalling circuits so that inductive transients are suppressed by cancellation. In this arrangement, the local on–hook condition is represented by an open rather than a grounded M lead.

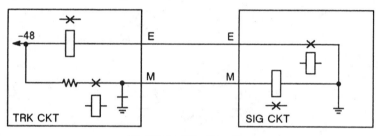

(a) Single-wire signalling

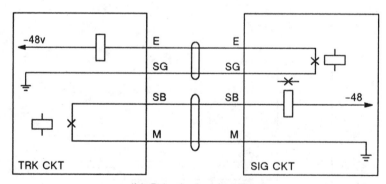

(b) Paired-wire signalling

Figure 7–5. Simplified schematic of E and M lead signalling.

Where dc signals are transmitted over cable pairs, dc continuity can be provided around a transmission circuit by use of simplex leads (SX and SX1) as illustrated in Figure 7–4(b). DC signals may also be applied across the tip and ring conductors of a pair. In this case, access to the pair may be over A and B leads connected by way of the terminals of the midpoint series capacitors in line transformers. Lead associations provide logical interfaces between transmission and signalling circuits. The A lead is associated with the tip side of a transmission circuit and the B lead with the ring side. Where A and B leads of DX signalling circuits connect to SX and SX1 leads, an association is maintained between A, SX1, T1, and R1 leads and between B, SX, T, and R leads.

Battery–Feed Circuits. When a connection is established through an analog switch, current is generally supplied to a loop and a trunk from a trunk circuit or a junctor. (Junctors interconnect portions of the switching networks of electronic analog and crossbar systems.) Most battery–supply or battery–feed circuits can be classified into two general categories, repeating coil circuits and bridged impedance circuits.

Figure 7–6(a) illustrates a typical repeating–coil battery–feed circuit. Battery and ground are fed independently to the loop and trunk. The capacitors, designated C, complete the voice signal current coupling through the repeating coil windings. The capacitance values are chosen to be as small as practicable (e.g., 2 μF) without causing excessive transmission loss or attenuation distortion. The relays are used for supervisory signal information. The relay and repeating coil windings have sufficient resistance (typically 400 ohms total) to limit the battery current on short loops to acceptable values. At the same time, these windings carry the maximum values of dc that may arise from a trouble ground or short–circuit condition on a loop.

A design criterion used for these circuits is that a trouble ground condition may destroy a component but may not create a fire hazard. Shunt losses to speech currents are limited by the inductance of these coils. The windings are well balanced to suppress the conversion of induced longitudinal currents into interfering metallic voltages.

Figure 7–6(b) illustrates a typical bridged impedance battery–feed circuit. It is used for intraoffice connections in crossbar and other electromechanical systems. Although it does not provide

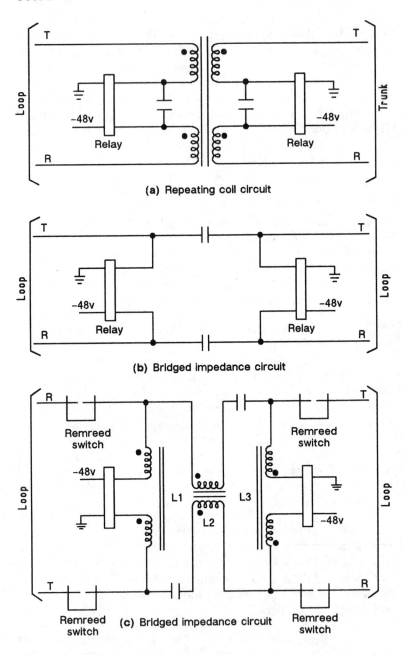

(a) Repeating coil circuit

(b) Bridged impedance circuit

(c) Bridged impedance circuit

Figure 7-6. Typical battery–feed circuits.

longitudinal–current isolation, it is much simpler and less expensive than the circuit of Figure 7–5(a) and performs satisfactorily in many applications. Intraoffice (loop–to–loop) connections in some electronic systems receive battery current from a junctor circuit located at the midpoint of the switching network. The circuit, shown in Figure 7–6(c), is an example of a bridged–impedance battery–feed arrangement with some unique features. The windings of the inductors designated L1 and L3 suppress longitudinal currents whose path is through the grounded battery supply. The inductor designated L2 limits large currents that might be caused by power crosses or lightning in order to prevent damage to fragile circuit elements, especially sealed–reed switch contacts. The polarities of the windings of L2 are such that the inductance is minimized for voice signals that circulate through the circuit but is high for unwanted longitudinal currents. This battery–feed circuit has an insertion loss of about 0.25 dB over the voiceband.

Two–Wire Switching of Four–Wire Trunks. In some analog electronic switching systems, provision is made for the two–wire switching of four–wire trunks by a technique called HILO. Equivalent four–wire switching is achieved by providing two switched metallic conductors and an unswitched metallic common return path instead of four physical wires in the switching network. This configuration is unbalanced to ground; sending and receiving amplifiers are used to reduce the possibility of crosstalk and other noise sources. The impedance to ground at the sending amplifier is very high and at the receiving amplifier very low; thus, the name HILO. This is shown in Figure 7–7.

The remreed switch is instrumental in making the HILO four–wire system work since there is a reduced trunk link network size and shorter cabling lengths, and, therefore, reduced interference. In addition, the remreed switch provides better magnetic shielding than ferreed switches and thereby provides better transmission on the unbalanced line [5].

Exchange Termination for ISDN. The exchange termination (ET) architecture to provide for basic and primary ISDN terminations in digital switching equipment includes DSL, DLC, umbilical to a remote switch unit (RSU), and a foreign exchange (FX) arrangement from a foreign central office to the ISDN switch.

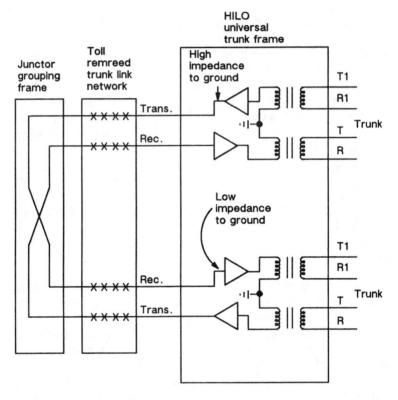

Figure 7-7. Two-wire switching of four-wire trunks.

Basic terminations provide up to 144 kb/s of information for use by centrex, PBX, business, and residence customers. Primary interfaces provide up to 1.536 Mb/s of information, which uses the T1 format over metallic wire carrier or optical fiber for application with digital PBXs, local area network (LAN) users, and high-capacity digital service (HCDS) customers.

As illustrated in Figure 7-8, ETs for ISDN provide access to five interoffice networks: circuit switched, channel switched, packet switched, signalling, and wideband.

In an electronic analog switching environment, a number of options for providing ISDN capabilities are possible. One option is the capping of the switching equipment with a new ISDN switch to serve ISDN lines. Another option is to use an ISDN RSU. A

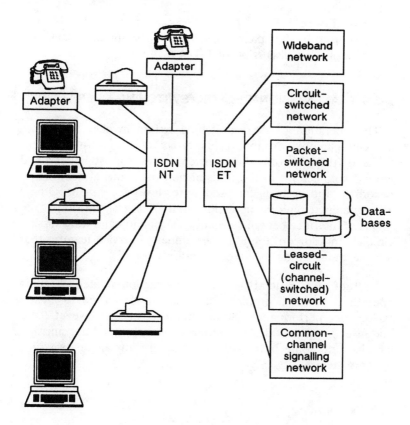

Figure 7–8. ISDN architecture.

third option would be to use a stand–alone ISDN ET with the analog electronic switching equipment. Another option is to provide a digital adjunct (DA) to the electronic switching equipment to provide digital switching capabilities. The DA connects digital switching equipment modules to the analog electronic switching equipment to perform this task.

Packet Switches. Packet switching equipment provides convenient, organized, and cost–effective local switching of data in much the same way PBXs have historically done for voice. A powerful feature of packet switches is their ability to statistically multiplex local end–user data channels on high–bandwidth facilities for efficient wide–area interpremises transmission. As shown in Figure 7-8, ISDN interfaces are compatible with and are supported by data packet switches. See Volume 3, Chapter 3 for an expanded discussion of ISDN features.

7-3 TRANSMISSION-RELATED SWITCHING OPERATIONS

The operation of every switching system involves sequences and call manipulations that have a direct impact on transmission. Some of these involve the transfer or reversal of battery and ground connections in the transmission path, digital coding and decoding, and even digital padding for level adjustment. Others are signalling circuit manipulations that affect transmission at the points of interface between switching, signalling, and transmission circuits. In addition, there are a number of service features that involve transmission in direct or indirect ways.

Each of these general classes of transmission-related switching operations involved problems that had to be solved to ensure satisfactory performance. Some of the solutions have affected end-user equipment designs, others have influenced transmission circuits, and some have had their primary impact on switching systems themselves.

Call Sequencing

Battery Reversals. In the course of establishing connections, the sequence of operations in an analog switching system involves the transfer of battery and ground connections from one circuit to another. Each time such a transfer is effected, electrical transients are transmitted to one or both ends of a connection. These transients are minimized by the sequence of operations designed into the switching system but they cannot be eliminated completely. Circuits may be provided with diodes bridged across receivers to suppress such transients and to make them less annoying to a listener. These diodes shunt down over a design threshold to absorb the sharp instantaneous voltage peaks of the transient.

An aggravated transient results when the battery and ground connections to a metallic loop or trunk are reversed. This reversal is used often to signal that the called party has answered. When reversal occurs, the capacitance of the metallic conductors must be discharged and charged in the reverse polarity, thereby resulting in a transient that is more severe than with the example described in the paragraph above.

Loop-Start. An example of call sequencing of a typical digital end office may be described as follows [6]. A user's equipment appears as a very high resistance to the switching system while on hook; hence, an open-circuit condition exists. To initiate a call, the user provides an off-hook signal by closing the tip-to-ring through a resistance of about 200 ohms, causing a dc current to flow from the line circuit of the switching system. The line unit detects the current as a seizure signal. This process of monitoring the loop status is called dc loop supervision. The request for service initiated at the calling end is called a seizure. This service is known as loop-start because a loop closure, rather than a connection to ground, is used as a seizure. The response of the switching system to a seizure is the application of a dial-tone signal superimposed on the dc loop current flowing in the circuit.

After receiving dial tone, the user originating the call will send the address of the called party.

Most switching systems monitor from the beginning of dial tone until the detection of the first address code information character. If no address character is received in 5 to 40 seconds, the loop may be connected first to an announcement, then to a receiver-off-hook (ROH) tone, and then to an open-circuit condition for up to 1.2 seconds. If an on-hook signal is received and the loop remains on hook, it will eventually be restored to an idle state.

After sending the called address information, the calling party may hear various call progress tones as the call moves toward the called party. Audible ringing would indicate a successful connection, while several tones or announcements would indicate other conditions.

The called party is alerted by a ringing signal. The ringing signal is nominally an 88-volt 20-Hz signal, superimposed on 48-volt nominal dc voltage. There are other forms of ringing used in the telephone industry. In these other forms, the ringing frequency can vary from approximately 15 to 70 Hz, with the ac ringing voltage and the dc supervisory voltage varying widely. However, the vast majority of situations are covered by the nominal values given above. The ringing signal is not continuous, but rather consists of a ringing interval followed by a silent period. The typical silent interval is four seconds. As a result, a line could be seized for as long as four seconds before seizure would be recognized by the end user. The end user may attempt to originate a call during this interval. This is not considered a problem since the person originating the call is usually the person to whom the call is being directed.

The called party answers the ringing signal by going off hook. This trips (removes) the ringing signal and cuts through the talking path. The tripping interval is typically 200 ms, although ringing can continue for longer periods before being tripped.

A call is ended by both calling and called loops going on hook. In most cases, the call can also be ended by either the called or calling party going on hook. This action is called disconnect; it brings the end–user equipment to its idle state when little or no dc loop current flows in the circuit. There is no signal sent to either the called or calling loop at disconnect.

Ground Start. Ground–start signalling for two–way dial facilities (PBX–CO trunks) was introduced in the early 1920s. Its purpose is to reduce the likelihood of seizure of the facility by both ends of the circuit during the interval between rings, otherwise known as glare. Ground–start signalling gives a dc signal at the time the line is seized. This is an important difference between loop–start and ground–start.

Ground–start signalling is typically used on two–way PBX–CO facilities with direct outward dialing (DOD) and dialed or attendant–handled incoming calls. In addition, ground–start signalling is typically used on automatic call distributor (ACD) services and automatically originated data lines. The ground–start line conductors transmit common–battery–loop supervision, loop–dial pulses or dual–tone multifrequency (DTMF) address signalling, alerting signals, and electrical voiceband energy. Ground–start lines are often used rather than loop–start lines to provide:

(1) a signal that can act as a start–dial signal—it is not necessary to detect dial tone

(2) a positive indication of a new call

(3) an indication to calling or called party of distant–end disconnect under normal operation.

In the idle state, the switching system applies a negative dc voltage to the ring conductor and keeps the tip conductor floating. Referring to Figure 7–9, an office with conventional (ground–referenced) battery would use option C to ground permanently the positive side of the battery supply.

Note that to describe the call states in ground–start, it is necessary to assume the actions that the end–user equipment can take.

In the idle state, an open–circuit is presented tip to ring and ring to ground. The end user has a detector connected tip to battery to detect a seizure (off–hook) from the switching system. The resistance of a typical detector is 10,000 to 20,000 ohms.

To initiate a call, the loop is grounded on the ring side of the line by operating contact S in Figure 7–9. The resultant current flow in the ring conductor is detected by the line circuit. In turn, the positive side of the battery is applied to the tip side of the line and, in switching systems with floating battery, contact A is opened to remove ground from the battery supply. The result is that in switching systems with conventional battery, the tip is grounded. In switching systems with floating battery, there is a voltage between tip and ring, with ring the more negative of the two leads. The switching systems using floating battery will remain in the floating–battery mode until the line becomes idle again. The end–user equipment will detect the ground on the tip or voltage between tip and ring with the ground detector and will respond by closing the loop–closure contacts and opening contact S. This places the line in the loop mode.

The line will remain in the loop mode for addressing, call processing, and communication states. The line reverts to the ground–start mode only when either end goes idle. All actions already covered for a loop–start line apply when a ground–start line is in the loop mode.

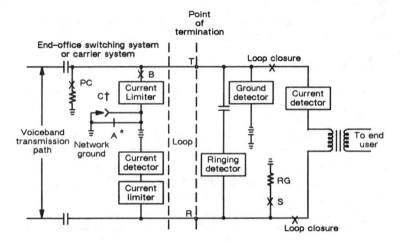

* Contact A applies to floating batteries only and is closed in
  the idle and service request states.
† Option C applies to conventional battery only and is permanently closed.

Figure 7-9. Operation principle of ground-start signalling.

At disconnect, four different combinations can occur. The switch or end user can disconnect first, and the line can have conventional battery supply or floating battery supply. The possible disconnect sequences are as follows.

(1) When the switch disconnects first on a line with conventional battery, the switch removes ground from the tip, which in turn removes current from the line. It then idles the line in preparation for a new call. Some switching systems guard the line during the disconnect interval; some do not before returning to idle.

(2) When the switch disconnects first on a line with floating battery, the switch removes battery from tip and ring, which in turn removes current from the line. The switch measures a guard time before returning to idle. The end user may or may not have a guard time between detecting a disconnect and making the line idle (ready for a new call).

(3) When the end user disconnects first on a line, the loop is opened.

To initiate a call to a loop, the switch connects a ringing circuit to the line. This applies ground to tip, negative battery to ring, and 20–Hz ringing to ring. Since ringing may or may not be present when the call is initiated, the ground will make the line busy at the end user. Ringing alerts the end user, who answers the call by closing the loop contact (Figure 7–9). The switch responds by tripping the ringing signal and connecting the talking path. With conventional battery, ground is on tip and negative battery is on ring. With floating battery, ground is removed from tip (open contact A). The ungrounded supply is connected positive side to tip and negative side to ring. These battery conditions continue until disconnect. Disconnect is identical to that described for calls originated by the end user.

Switched Transmission Operations

There are a number of transmission features and functions that are provided by switching systems. For example, the stability of two–wire circuits frequently depends on the existence of a suitable termination at the input and output terminals. A circuit condition that can often produce instability is the open–circuit termination that exists when a line is idle. To prevent instability under these circumstances, the switching system is arranged in many cases to apply an idle–circuit termination. The enabling and disabling of repeaters is also often controlled by switching systems. The disabling of repeaters accomplishes the same purpose as the application of idle–circuit terminations.

The loop range extender (LRE) is an optional feature available with a typical electronic switching system. A repeater (range extension unit) is placed in the B links between the line–switch frames and junctor–switch frames of the line–link network. An intraoffice call with LRE is shown in Figure 7–10. The LRE improves transmission performance and extends the office signalling and supervisory range on long metallic loops. Location of the LRE feature in the B links is economical because it enables several loops to share the same repeater.

7–4   DIGITAL SWITCHING INTERFACES

In addition to the facilities and equipment required for VF communications, central–office buildings house other types of

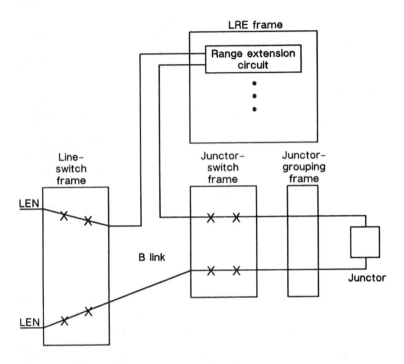

Figure 7–10. Line-to-line call with loop range extension.

transmission equipment. Among these are equipment units that provide interfaces between digital and analog portions of a facility network. Some of the interface equipment units are more conveniently described as parts of major systems; among these are the D–type channel banks used with T–type carrier systems.

Analog VF switching evolved as a way to interconnect loops and trunks via switching networks primarily using the previously mentioned electromechanical step–by–step, crossbar, and sealed–reed switches. These are referred to as *space–division switching* networks. Switching may also be accomplished by electronically directing the pulses of digitally encoded signals according to the desired interconnection pattern. This method is known as *time–division switching.*

In general, digital signals are switched through a digital switching system by filling a buffer at the input to the system and then making appropriate changes in "time–slot" assignments for each channel to fill an outgoing buffer for transfer to the appropriate time slot of an outgoing channel. These time slot changes are accomplished in the switching system by circuits that are collectively called the time–slot interchange.

Signals to be switched by a digital switching system must be coded in accordance with a specific format base, usually in the DS1 signal format employed in the T1 carrier system [7].

The line circuits in a digital end office contain, or connect to, analog–to–digital coders/decoders. When the transmission facilities between switching systems are digital, no analog–to–digital or digital–to–analog conversion is necessary. The trunks then terminate directly on the switch in 24–circuit groups via equipment typically termed a digital trunk unit. Switching is implemented by making appropriate changes in time–slot assignments of the pulses that represent each channel via the time–slot interchange. Figure 7–11 shows an intraoffice connection through a digital switch.

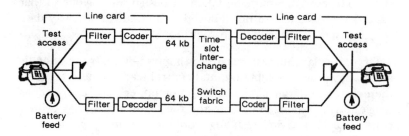

Figure 7–11. Basic intraswitch connection.

Interfaces to Analog Trunks

In a certain, shrinking number of cases, it is necessary to connect analog trunks to a digital tandem switch. Where the trunks are on metallic cable, a normal D–type channel bank provides the needed conversion. Where they are on analog broadband carrier, a transmultiplexer or L–T connector converts two 12–channel analog channel groups to one 24–channel digroup to connect to the switch. Where they are on N–type analog carrier, they must be converted to voice frequency through an N–type terminal, then multiplexed into digital form through a D–type channel bank.

7-5 SOURCES AND CONTROL OF IMPAIRMENTS

The environment in central offices makes the control of transmission impairments essential if high–quality performance is to be maintained. Central–office circuits and equipment arrangements may be the source of transmission deterioration, partly because of the high concentration of equipment and wiring, and partly because of the interfaces between different kinds of circuit.

Noise

A transmission impairment generated in electromechanical central offices is impulse noise. Switching functions, such as the operation and release of relays and switches, produce high transient voltages. Care must be taken in design and layout so that excessive transients are not induced into circuits that carry data or other signals susceptible to such noise.

Of particular interest regarding impulse–noise generation is alarm, bay power distribution, and control leads. Where feasible, these leads and the circuits they interconnect are operated as longitudinally balanced circuits and the leads installed as twisted pairs. The cost saving resulting from single–wire ground–return operation is often tempting but where circuits are so operated, induced transients are difficult to control.

Other noise sources in electromechanical offices produce interferences, such as contact noise and battery noise, that are more nearly like random circuit noise. Contact noise is due primarily to the buildup of dirt and other high–resistance materials on the surfaces of electrical contacts. Contacts on relays and other switching elements are made of precious metal and the contacts are designed to have a wiping action as they make and break to help prevent the accumulation of dirt and other pollutants. Most relay contacts now are of the bifurcated design, which, in effect, puts two contacts in parallel to enhance reliability, or are sealed against contamination.

Common–battery supply circuits are also a source of interference similar to random noise. All of the transmission and switching circuits in an office that operate from the common battery share battery–feed circuits as a common impedance, which is kept as low as possible (a small fraction of an ohm). Even though the coupling impedance is extremely low, the total power of the many coupled–in signals can be significant and usually has the quality of random noise. The coupling of this impairment into transmission circuits is controlled in design so that it is not a significant source of message–circuit noise. Additional filters are installed in battery supply leads on each equipment frame (talk battery) to further reduce the battery impedance at this localized distribution point.

Digital offices produce a highly consistent level of noise (about 18 dBrn). The noise is inherent in the coding/decoding process; thus, the same level occurs on intraoffice and interoffice connections.

Crosstalk

In analog central–office equipment, there are many exposures to crosstalk between transmission circuits and from announcement and tone sources into transmission circuits. These sources of impairment are controlled in design and by maintenance effort. Signal amplitudes and transmission level points must be maintained at design values.

In some cases, where wide discrepancies exist between signal amplitudes in adjoining circuits, crosstalk is minimized by routing the circuits through cable or wiring paths that are separated physically. The separation is specified by installation instructions and must be maintained if performance is to be satisfactory.

Coupling Circuits

The combined need for isolating battery–feed circuits from one another while providing signal coupling between circuits is generally solved by the use of capacitors, inductors, and transformers. These circuits can degrade performance by introducing

193

transmission deviations or by restricting bandwidth. However, their characteristics are determined primarily by design, and unsatisfactory performance is usually due to a trouble condition or to errors in wiring.

Loss and Echo Control

Impairments can result from excessive transmission loss or insufficient return loss in central–office circuits and equipment. Transmission losses are controlled primarily by design and, where excessive, are usually caused by a trouble condition. Return losses are controlled by the application of through– and terminal–balance procedures. Digital offices are, by their nature, four–wire, which eliminates the need to consider office cabling.

Battery Voltage

The common–battery supply used in central offices consists of large batteries in which voltage is maintained at nominal values with permissible fluctuations of several volts. The charge is maintained by applying a primary power source of commercial 60–Hz power through appropriate rectification and control equipment.

If the primary commercial supply fails, the load is taken up by emergency generating equipment driven by a diesel or turbine engine. In the event of multiple failure, the battery carries the operating load without primary supply but only for a limited time. Most batteries are selected to provide a minimum of four hours reserve capacity at peak traffic load. Under such conditions of power failure, battery voltage will gradually decrease. Many systems use regulated power converters, which compensate for wide variations in battery voltage until the end of useful battery charge.

References

1. Feiner, A. "The Ferreed," *Bell System Tech. J.*, Vol. 43 (Jan. 1964), pp. 1–14.

2. Tobagi, F. A. "Computer Communications Networks," *Reference Data for Engineers: Radio, Electronics, Computer,*

and Communications, Seventh Edition (Indianapolis, IN: Howard W. Sams and Company, Inc., 1985), pp. 26–2 to 26–8.

3. Holcomb, J. E. "Frontiers in Switching Technology—Part One: The Next–Generation Switch," Bellcore EXCHANGE, Vol. 3, Iss. 5 (Sept./Oct. 1987), pp. 23–27.

4. Warr, M. "CO Technology in the 1990s," *Telephony* (Aug. 22, 1988), pp. 26–28.

5. Laane, R. R. "HILO—An Improved Transmission Scheme for Semiconductor Switching Networks," *Bell System Tech. J.*, Vol. 50 (Mar. 1971), pp. 1089–1093.

6. *Notes on the BOC IntraLATA Networks—1986*, Technical Reference TR–NPL–000275, Bellcore (Iss. 1, Apr. 1986), pp. 6–18, Sec. 2.43–2.45.

7. *LSSGR, LATA Switching Systems Generic Requirements*, Technical Reference TR–TSY–000064, Bellcore (Iss. 2, July 1987).

Additional Reading

Kosmider, J. J. and L. R. Moffitt. "Taking the Measure of Switching Systems," Bellcore EXCHANGE, Vol. 3, Iss. 2 (Mar./Apr. 1987), pp. 8–13.

Pasternak, E. J. and S. A. Schulman. "Centrex Customer Rearrangement System: Taking the Pain Out of Change," Bellcore EXCHANGE, Vol. 2, Iss. 3 (May/June 1986), pp. 28–32.

Personick, S. D. and P. W. Smith. "Frontiers in Switching Technology—Part Three: Photonic Switching," Bellcore EXCHANGE, Vol. 4, Iss. 1 (Jan./Feb. 1988), pp. 2–7.

Chapter 8

Business Communications Systems

Business customers have many communications needs beyond the basic services provided by the telecommunications network, where an exchange access line furnishes the ability to communicate with all other customers having access to the same network. One of these needs is rapid, convenient, and economical intercommunications among employees. In some cases, these needs must be filled at only a single location; in other cases, between two or more locations that are distant from one another. This type of service is furnished by a class of equipment that can be referred to as business communications systems.

The strategy of furnishing business communications service depends on the size of the business, how it is dispersed over different locations, and the number of people at each location. Also, how its needs are fulfilled depends on the services to be provided in addition to the basic feature of intercommunication, particularly any need for combined voice and data service.

Typically, where customer needs are concentrated at one location, service may be provided by a key telephone system (KTS), a private branch exchange (PBX), or a centrex system. These provide local intercommunication services and a number of other desirable features. PBX and KTS equipment are usually located at the customer premises; centrex systems normally use switching equipment located in the central office. Centrex is described in fuller detail in Volume 3.

Where corporate activities are dispersed, business communications systems may be expanded into a network of interconnected PBXs, KTSs, and centrexes. The scattered locations may each be served locally by a PBX and the PBXs may be interconnected by tie trunks; the overall network in this case is called a tandem tie–trunk network. For very large service needs, a network of switching systems may be located in central–office buildings and may be interconnected by network trunks. A PBX at each customer location is connected by access lines to the network, called a switched services network (SSN). On intranetwork connections, these private switched networks perform functions similar to the local, tandem–connecting, and intertandem switching functions of the switched message network. Some aspects of transmission are unique to this type of arrangement.

An emerging replacement for such specialized private arrangements is the private virtual network (PVN), which uses message–network facilities, common–channel signalling, and data–base control to simulate a private network while sharing the actual facilities with other users.

Other types of business communications service include those provided by automatic call distributors (ACDs) and telephone answering services (TASs). ACDs are arranged to distribute a large number of incoming trunks or lines to a smaller number of positions at which incoming calls are usually served directly by attendants. The service at a TAS is one in which incoming calls are answered for the customers of the answering service. Messages are recorded and forwarded at a later time.

In some respects, KTS and PBX equipment has significant common operating features; ACD and TAS equipment features are also somewhat similar. The main similarity between KTSs and PBXs is that both provide multiple access to a switched network (public and private) as well as intrasystem communications without requiring access to the network. Thus, there are circuits in these layouts that are similar in function to exchange–service loops, i.e., circuits that connect stations to switching equipment. Circuits, similar to PBX–central office (PBX–CO) trunks, connect the ACD or TAS equipment to a switched public or private network. Incoming calls terminate at attendant positions. The service is predominantly incoming and there is little provision for the initiation of outgoing calls. In TAS equipment, there is usually no way of extending a connection to another switchboard or station; however, provision may be made to transfer connections from an ACD to an associated PBX attendant or station.

The majority of PBXs, centrexes, ACDs, and TASs are administered by attendants at key–type consoles or display terminals. In some cases, KTS arrangements also have a central station that may be regarded as an attendant position. Thus, all four equipment categories can use some form of attendant administration.

The market for business communications systems comprises a wide variety of customer preferences, environments, and communication styles. As a result, there is available a variety of products and services that add to the complexity of this field of application. While most of the variations primarily affect the switching and signalling designs, transmission designs are also somewhat affected.

8-1 KEY TELEPHONE SYSTEMS

A KTS allows a station to be used to pick up and hold one of several lines or trunks [1]. Customer requirements for key telephone service may be satisfied by a wide variety of available systems [2]. Some have only one station or line and others have up to 40 stations or lines. Typical key station arrangements are provided with pushbutton access to 2, 3, 5, 8, 16, or 32 lines.

These systems also provide for intercommunication (intercom) between stations of the system. The circuits that terminate at a key system may be local exchange lines, wide area telecommunications service (WATS) or 800–service lines, foreign exchange (FX) lines, PBX station lines, tie lines to a distant KTS, and the like. Transmission on connections to each of these types of line should be nearly equivalent to satisfy customer perceptions. In addition to the primary requirements of pickup, hold, and intercommunication, KTSs also may provide a number of other features, some of which affect transmission. Some of these features are:

- controlled privacy or exclusion
- interstation signalling
- incoming call transfer
- conference and drop–off transfer
- multistation intercom and outside conferencing.

KTSs may be used in a number of different ways to achieve conference or add–on service. In the simplest key stations, more than one button may be depressed simultaneously, giving a station access to more than one line at a time and to the intercom circuit. Transmission quality may be degraded with this arrangement because, with each line added to the connection, transmission loss increases and return loss deteriorates due to changes in the terminating impedance. In other systems, true add–on and conference circuitry are provided and may be designed to compensate for these deteriorations.

Remotely located, independently operated KTSs may be interconnected by tie lines similar to intercom lines. These tie lines are not ordinarily interconnected with other circuits to establish connections beyond the KTSs. They are basically two–point, two–wire private lines.

KTSs are designed so that features can be provided as selected by the customer. One commonly used feature is a lamp display that indicates the state of each line that is terminated at the station. The following chart shows the indications normally provided by this busy–station lamp.

Line State	Lamp Indication
Idle	Dark
Busy	Steady illumination
Ringing	Flashing (60 flashes per minute)
On hold	Winking (120 flashes per minute)

In addition to the line–state indicators, lamps may be provided to indicate, for example, that the attendant has a message waiting for the user or that the add–on feature (for conferencing) is in use. In addition to these commonly used features, others may be provided optionally. These include hands–free operation, voice signalling over the intercom to a loudspeaker system, privacy and exclusion arrangements, manual or dial intercom signalling, speed calling, zoned paging, data jacks for external modems or facsimile machines, and memory recall dialing. In some systems, provision is also made for music to be transmitted to calling parties when their connections are placed on hold and for tones to be transmitted to calling parties are placed in a camp–on condition (waiting for a busy called party to become available). This feature involves the application of stringent design requirements so that two callers whose connections are in the hold condition cannot communicate with one another. The loss between two such connections, called talk–through loss, should be in excess of 60 dB.

Key telephone service was initially provided by custom–engineered assemblies of lamps and keys that were subsequently standardized and called wiring plans. The service expanded and evolved to a degree of standardization, so that the range of features commonly used may be provided by circuit cards called key telephone units (KTUs), mounted in key service units and connected to the stations with 25–pair cables. The later key systems use three–pair or even one–pair cabling, giving a large saving in installation cost, and use microprocessor control. In particular, because they include switching to concentrate a large number of stations onto a smaller number of trunks, these "hybrid" systems are nearly indistinguishable from small PBXs. Their feature set includes such "PBX" options as station message detail recording (SMDR), which records details on long–distance calling for use in allocating costs among departments.

8-2   PRIVATE BRANCH EXCHANGE SERVICES

Where a customer has a large number of employees who need telephone communication among themselves as well as with others outside the organization, the required services are often provided by the use of one or more PBXs. In this type of business communication system, connections may be established between stations served by the PBX, between these stations and trunks terminated at the PBX, and between trunks.

PBX arrangements cover a wide range of sizes, features, uses, and applied technology [3]. Sizes range from small systems that can accommodate up to 20 station lines to machine switching systems that can serve 10,000–plus station lines. The largest installations are, in effect, customer–owned central offices. Features may include intraPBX dialing by any station, attendant services, direct inward dialing (DID), direct or attendant–assisted dialing to remote locations over PBX–CO or PBX tie trunks, toll diversion, and SMDR or automatically identified outward dialing (AIOD) number and calling station [4]. Multiport conference circuits are available for use with PBXs. These circuits can simultaneously bridge PBX–CO trunks or PBX station lines in various combinations. Key telephone station lines can be among those connected through such a conference bridge. Simple, single–station add–on capability may also be provided in some PBXs by dialing an appropriate code. Digital PBXs that switch both voice and data are becoming increasingly common and will figure heavily in the evolution to ISDN.

A PBX may serve just one group of users at a single location or at a number of locations and it may be used as a switching center in a large and complex private telecommunications network. There are many thousands of PBXs in service using a range of technology that includes step–by–step, crossbar, electronic, and digital switching systems. Both space–division and solid–state time–division switching systems are used. Time–division PBXs use either pulse amplitude modulation (PAM) or pulse code modulation (PCM) techniques. PCM has become the dominant method, especially for combined voice–data use and DS1–level access to remote locations.

PBXs have evolved into the ability to provide both voice and data service. Some of them have added data features like the ability to bridge dissimilar local area networks (LANs) together [5]. They often include data links for remote dial–up mainte- nance and connection to a centralized network–management sys- tem [6].

Station Lines and Tie Trunks

Stations are connected to an associated, attended or unat- tended PBX via station lines. These are analogous to loops that connect stations to the serving central office in the switched mes- sage network. The stations may be collocated with the PBX or remotely located (off–premises). In either case, they may be in- dividual or multipled stations, or they may comprise a KTS oper- ating from the PBX. The loss and resistance limits for on– and off–premises station lines were originally established by complex relationships with the loss and resistance limits for PBX–CO trunks, but "barrier" PBXs that provide their own battery feed remove this complication. Federal Communications Commission (FCC) registration rules [7] divide the allowable loop resistance for PBX station ports into three classes: 0–199 ohms, 200–899, or 900 ohms and above. Some popular digital PBXs offer the option of digital telephone sets that operate on a 64–kb/s four-wire basis over limited distances, typically up to 5000 feet.

The interconnection of PBXs is accomplished by circuits called tie trunks. These may form parts of extensive electronic tandem networks. These are sometimes considered a class of networks within a larger class called switched–services networks in which separate locations are interconnected by network trunks and access lines. The FCC rules define the transmission gains and losses permitted between tie–trunk ports of PBXs so as to avoid excessive levels in the exchange carrier network.

PBX Types and Services

While there may be some small manual PBX systems in operation, most PBXs are automatic switching types with some form of attendant console. Centrex service provided by an exchange carrier is an alternative to ownership of a PBX. This service may be provided by all or a portion of the serving central office switching system. It has an advantage to the customer because of the absence of floor space needed for on–site switching equipment, the reduced need to tie up capital that would be needed to finance a PBX, and the promise of smooth adaptation to ISDN technology.

PBX switching and attendant equipment is located on the customer premises while centrex services are provided by central–office switches. As with central–office systems, there are two general categories of PBXs, electromechanical and electronic. PBX systems have evolved from progressive/direct–control, step–by–step through common–control crossbar, to electronic control of electromechanical ferreed networks, and finally to time–division switching.

Direct Dialing Services. The introduction of direct distance dialing in the switched message network led to enhancements in PBX services. Two significant features that resulted are DID to a PBX station without attendant assistance and direct outward dialing (DOD) over the switched message network with SMDR or AIOD for billing information. With SMDR, the PBX records billing details; with AIOD, it passes them to the serving central office for recording.

A typical modern PBX offers least–cost routing whereby an outgoing long–distance call is directed to the lowest–cost facility that is available at the moment. Based on the dialed digits, the PBX selects a CO, FX, WATS, or tie trunk, or a direct inte-rexchange carrier (IC) access line. If necessary, it adds the routing digits to reach a specific IC. If the selected path is busy, it route–advances to the next more expensive path. This feature minimizes costs, but may result in variable transmission losses between two given points.

These features, and many more, are provided by some PBXs and by central–office switching systems that provide centrex service. For centrex service, the operator console is located at the customer premises. The switching equipment may be dedicated to centrex service or may be a portion of the serving central–office switching system. It may also be a remote switching module located near the customer and slaved to a central–office switch. In centrex service arrangements, each station line terminates directly at the central–office switching system.

Attendant Facilities

With most PBXs, there are attendant consoles operated by a customer employee or employees. These attendant facilities are usually located at the customer premises, even when the switching equipment, as with centrex, is located at the central office. The attendant answers and completes incoming calls routed to the customer directory number and provides operator assistance to the PBX station users as required. In a network that contains main and satellite PBXs, the main PBX attendants serve the satellites by way of tie trunks and data links. There are no attendant facilities at satellite PBXs.

Many types of operator console, with or without CRT (cathode ray tube) displays, are used for these attendant services. The selection is based on the number of lines and trunks involved and on the desired operating features. In console operation, the attendant connection can be held, if necessary, for monitoring but is broken in most cases after the attendant has established the desired through connection.

Transmission Considerations

Many aspects of transmission in large PBX installations are similar or identical to those found in central offices. The same care in design, manufacture, installation, and operation is exercised regarding direct and multiple wiring layouts, trunk and line cards, switching network organization, and office grounding as in similar central–office situations. However, there are a number of ways in which PBX transmission issues differ significantly from those found in central offices.

Central–office and PBX transmission problems differ primarily because PBXs must often be regarded as an extension of, or supplement to, the telecommunications network but with unique service features.

In some installations, PBXs provide service to a specific group of stations that are essentially collocated, while in others, the PBXs are interconnected as parts of electronic tandem networks or SSNs. These may be very large and the trunks between PBXs must be designed to meet transmission requirements according to the same general criteria as those applied to the telecommunications network. The customer, of course, has the freedom to design a transmission loss plan to meet particular needs. Establishing suitable objectives is further complicated by universal service connections that permit the interconnection of the private SSN and the telecommunications network but with certain restrictions designed to maintain an acceptable grade of service.

Designing transmission circuits associated with attendant facilities requires meeting established limits. These circuits should not introduce excessive loss or degrade echo performance by reducing return losses. In addition, they should not introduce excessive transmission contrast for attendants or other network users and they must provide satisfactory sidetone performance for the attendant console or switchboard. Sidetone objectives are similar to those established for auxiliary services in the telecommunications network. The trend toward fully digital (PCM) PBXs makes it feasible to connect PBX–CO and PBX–PBX trunks on a 24–channel DS1 basis. This avoids most of the transmission problems associated with individual circuits.

In addition to the network and trunk aspects of PBX services discussed above, transmission performance is significantly affected by station lines and the interactions between station lines and network connections (such as private–network access lines, PBX–CO trunks, FX trunks, long–distance trunks, tie trunks, and off–premises extensions). Where sizable groups of off–premises station lines are needed from a digital PBX, the customer has the option of using DS1 channels from the PBX to channel banks at the distant site. This allows the use of very low losses on the station lines.

8-3   CALL DISTRIBUTORS AND TELEPHONE ANSWERING SYSTEMS

Incoming calls from the telecommunications network constitute most of the traffic for call distributors and telephone answering systems. These calls terminate at an attendant console and only a small percentage are extended beyond the attendant position. Transmission problems at the terminating positions for these systems are similar to those encountered in incoming service to a PBX operator position. Central–office connections are by way of trunks similar to PBX–CO or FX. Attendant circuits are like those used at PBX switchboards or console positions.

The switching functions performed by an ACD provide service approximately according to the sequence of arrival of calls and distribute the calls among available attendants equally to maximize efficiency of the attendant group. Some crossbar ACDs are still in use; however, most of them are digital.

ACDs are widely used by exchange carriers to provide auxiliary operator services such as directory assistance and call–intercept services. Similar services are also supplied commercially for such business customer applications as airline or railroad reservation bureaus and department store catalog departments. Installations range in size from about 10 operator positions to 500 or more. Most are in the 10–to–100–position range.

The public safety answering point (PSAP) for 911 emergency service may use a key system for terminating small numbers of incoming trunks at dispatchers' positions. However, larger systems typically use ACDs to distribute the traffic. With enhanced 911 service, the dispatcher display includes the name, address, and number of the calling party, as obtained from a separate data base and forwarded to the ACD.

Automated–attendant controllers are in growing use. With these, callers receive a synthesized voice announcement inviting them to key a one–digit code to select answering attendants in particular subject areas. The effect of these systems is to provide a stage of switching ahead of a group of ACD positions.

While incoming calls seldom go beyond the attendant position, provision is usually made for attendants to originate outgoing calls and receive other than ACD calls. These features, provided through an associated PBX, are usually needed for an attendant to obtain the information necessary to service the incoming calls properly. Provision is also made to extend calls in overflow or night–transfer situations and for call transfer.

ACD facilities are sometimes used to provide centralized attendant service for several PBXs. Calls that require attendant service at any of these PBXs are routed over released–link trunks to the ACD. When the attendant determines the disposition of the call, this information is fed into the switching system and then, after the proper connection is established, the link to the attendant is released.

Large multilocation ACD users may use advanced 800 services to direct calls to the ACD site serving a particular geographic area, with out–of–house redirection of traffic to a distant ACD.

ACD services may be furnished to relatively simple attendant positions by appropriately programming an electronic switch in the central office. This is a specialized version of centrex service used primarily for incoming call distribution.

Telephone answering service (TAS) is provided by organizations whose principal functions are to receive incoming calls for their customers, record messages, optionally alert customers via radio paging, and relay the messages to the customers at a later time. Little provision exists for switching or interconnection among the circuits that terminate at a telephone answering system position. The communications channel for each client is usually concentrated (switched) before appearing at the attendant console. The typical present–day TAS is a CRT–based ACD console with no identifiable appearance of a specific line.

A typical TAS connects to patrons' lines in three ways, as shown in Figure 8–1. The simplest is via a secretarial extension bridged onto the patron's line at the serving central office. As with off–premises extension lines, bridge lifters are used to isolate the leg not in use, avoiding transmission impairment. The called line is identified to the TAS by its physical connection. In a second method, the patron uses call–forwarding service, which redirects incoming calls to a DID trunk to the TAS. The TAS recognizes the called line by the digits sent to it on the DID trunk.

For interoffice or interexchange applications where the costs of groups of secretarial extensions would be excessive, in cases where call–forwarding is not desired, the TAS firm provides a concentrator. Normally located at a second premises of the TAS in the distant wire–center area, the concentrator connects to secretarial extensions of the patrons' telephones. It switches them onto a small number of trunks going to the TAS. Because the traffic load is small, high concentrations are feasible, typically up to 768 lines onto 16 trunks. The TAS identifies the called patron line by information sent to it over a data link from the concentrator, and controls the concentrator via the same link. While most installations are much smaller, a typical system can be fully developed to serve 1000 patrons via up to 29 incoming trunks and six attendant positions. The information presented to the attendant can be as simple as the identification of the called patron and an abbreviated account code, or can be a fully detailed CRT display with extensive case–by–case call–handling instructions. Thus it is an ACD with added information features.

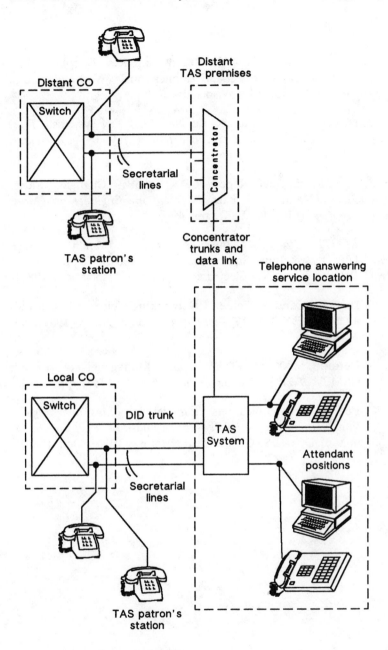

Figure 8-1. Typical TAS serving arrangement.

References

1. *EIA Standard EIA-478*, "Multi-Line Key Telephone Systems (KTS) for Voiceband Applications" (Washington, DC: Electronic Industries Association, 1981).

2. Madrid, J. "The Old and the New PBX/Key Systems," *Telephone Engineer and Management* (May 15, 1987), pp. 53–64.

3. "TE&M Special Report—CPE Trends: Changing Sides, Places, Names, and Faces," *Telephone Engineer and Management* (May 1, 1988), pp. 49–55.

4. *EIA/TIA Standard EIA-464A*, "Private Branch Exchange (PBX) Switching Equipment for Voiceband Applications" (Washington, DC: Electronic Industries Association, 1989).

5. Day, J. F. and A. Feiner. "Networking Voice and Data with a Digital PBX," *AT&T Technology*, Vol. 2, No. 3 (1987), pp. 22–29.

6. Detrano, M. K. and D. W. Rajala. "Managing Networks with CSM," *AT&T Technology*, Vol. 2, No. 1 (1987), pp. 30–33.

7. Federal Communications Commission. *Rules and Regulations, Title 47, Code of Federal Regulations, Part 68* (Washington, DC: U.S. Government Printing Office, Oct. 1987).

Telecommunications Transmission Engineering

Section 3

Analog Carrier Systems on Wire Lines

The evolution of modern equalizers, amplifiers, and regulators made possible increasingly wider bandwidths for wire–pair and coaxial cable transmission. During the period before digital techniques became feasible, increased demands for service brought about increasingly efficient usage of cables via the application of electronic techniques and reduced the cost per channel–mile steadily.

This section covers analog interoffice carrier systems. Subscriber loop applications are described in Chapter 3.

The long–haul, high–capacity wire pair and coaxial transmission systems created the initial pressure for the development of suitable frequency–division multiplex equipment, in which each channel is assigned a separate portion of the broadband channel. The organization of this equipment evolved into a hierarchy of multiplex capability ranging from a 12–channel group to a spectrum of 13,200 channels for a fully equipped coaxial system. Most of the same multiplex arrangements are used with analog microwave radio systems. Chapter 9 describes the various types of multiplex equipment and their channel capacities.

Analog transmission systems are designed to satisfy signal–to–noise requirements over specified bandwidths. The spacing between repeaters is an important parameter that depends on bandwidth and signal–to–noise objectives as well as on achievable circuit designs. The relationships among these parameters are discussed in Chapter 10 in terms that apply to any analog cable transmission system.

Chapter 11 describes analog systems for wire–pair lines. These are principally the N–type systems for use on cable pairs. Each type of system uses multiplex equipment designed especially for this application.

Chapter 12 discusses coaxial cable transmission systems. It describes the general characteristics of North American systems and presents a detailed description of the L5E design as the highest development of this technology.

Chapter 9

Frequency-Division Multiplex for Broadband Systems

Analog transmission systems, whether using cable or micro-wave radio, require multiplex equipment to derive multiple channels from the line facility. In some cases (e.g., N carrier), the multiplex equipment is unique to the complete transmission system; such terminals are discussed in Chapter 11 with the systems that they support. With broadband transmission involving coaxial cable and microwave radio systems, the multiplex forms a distinct hierarchy and can be regarded as a system in its own right. This chapter covers multiplex terminals for broadband systems.

Frequency-division multiplex (FDM) equipment uses modulators/demodulators, filters, carrier supplies, amplifiers, pads, and hybrid coil circuits for combining and splitting transmission paths. The circuits and equipment evolved with new technology and with ever-broader bandwidths. The basic group of 12 4-kHz channels in the frequency band of 60 to 108 kHz was established for J- and K-type carrier systems in the 1930s. The multiplex hierarchy has since expanded to circuit loads as high as the 6000 channels carried on single-sideband microwave radio and the 13,200 channels on the L5E coaxial system.

The modulating and multiplexing processes that assemble a broadband, multichannel signal are reversed at receiving terminal points where individual signals are recovered for routing to their destinations.

9-1   THE FDM HIERARCHY

Figure 9-1 shows schematically how the basic FDM hierarchy is derived by means of five modular frequency translations, each of which places signals in larger groupings at higher frequencies.

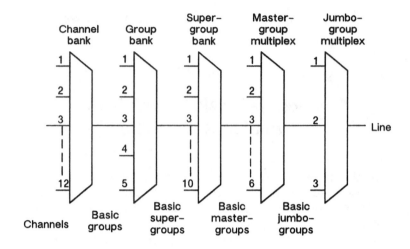

Figure 9-1. Basic FDM hierarchy plan.

In this arrangement, the input and output frequency band of each unit of equipment [except the voice–frequency (VF) input and final output] is designated as a basic assembly of channels. For example, the outputs of channel banks and the inputs to group banks are known as basic groups. Each is a block of 12 channels occupying the band from 60 to 108 kHz. Similarly, groupings at other points in the hierarchy are the basic super-group (60 channels placed between 312 and 552 kHz), the basic mastergroup (600 channels, 564 to 3084 kHz), and the basic jumbogroup (3600 channels, 564 to 17,548 kHz). The output at any level in the hierarchy may be used as a line signal feeding a broadband analog transmission system. It may also be used in part as a complete line signal (e.g., a partially equipped mastergroup for 240 channels) or as part of a complete line signal (e.g., a supergroup added to three mastergroups for 1860 channels.)

Four–wire transmission is used throughout FDM equipment. Office wiring uses balanced shielded pairs at group level and co-axial cable at higher levels. Where the 4–kHz channels connected to the multiplex originate as two–wire, the necessary interface equipment (four–wire terminating and single–frequency signalling) is built as plug–in units that integrate the needed functions into a single assembly.

214

Channel Banks

Two general designs of channel bank are in wide use. Although the A5–type is still found, the newer A6B is more common. The two vintages are compatible; i.e., circuits operate satisfactorily with an A5–type bank at one end and an A6B at the other.

A third design, not called a channel bank although it performs similar functions, is the direct–formed supergroup bay. It combines 60 VF signals into a supergroup spectrum without intermediate group multiplexing stages. Other special versions termed "direct–to–line" are used in light–route applications, as are "frequency–agile" (programmable) units for special uses.

A5 Channel Bank. The A5 bank and its predecessors were conceptually quite simple. In the transmitting direction, each voice channel received low–pass filtering with a cutoff frequency of about 3.5 kHz, then fed a double–balanced modulator. The modulator also received one of 12 carrier signals spaced 4 kHz apart, at 108, 104, 100 . . . through 64 kHz, for channels numbered one through 12, respectively. The output of the balanced modulator contained little carrier or VF signal, comprising mainly the upper and lower sidebands of the specific channel carrier frequency. After high–pass filtering to remove any remaining VF signal, the signal was applied to a lattice filter made up of multiple quartz crystals. This bandpass filter selected the lower sideband, rejecting the upper one. It also blocked any residual carrier that might have leaked through the modulator. With the outputs of the 12 filters combined, the result was a package of 12 lower sidebands between 60 and 108 kHz with suppressed carriers.

In the receiving direction, the process was reversed. The incoming 60–to–108–kHz spectrum fed 12 more bandpass filters. The output of each filter was a single channel, i.e., the lower sideband of one of the 12 channel carriers. Each output went to a balanced demodulator that was also fed the relevant carrier frequency. This resulted in 12 individual VF outputs, each of which was fed through a one–stage VF amplifier before reaching the receiving output of the bank.

Filters designed to separate the 4–kHz channels had to have very sharp cutoff characteristics to provide the necessary discrimination between adjacent VF channels and adjacent group frequency bands. The cutoff characteristics of practical filters reduced effective channel bandwidth, nominally 0 to 4 kHz, to about 0.2 to 3.4 kHz.

A6B Channel Bank. The A6B–type bank typifies the highest development in the series of A–type channel banks. It is much more complex than earlier designs, but offers improvements in size and performance made possible by advances in technology [1].

A block diagram of the A6B bank is shown in Figure 9–2. The group band is formed by two steps of modulation. The first step places each channel in a preassigned frequency position near 8 MHz. The translated channels are combined. Then, in the

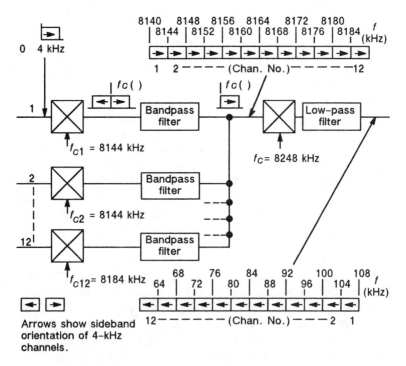

Figure 9–2. A6B channel bank—transmit side.

second step of modulation, the entire group is translated down to the basic group frequency band.

Each of the 12 input circuits is coupled to a modulator that also receives a carrier in the range of 8140 to 8184 kHz. The double-sideband output of each modulator passes through a bandpass filter that selects the upper sideband. The 12 signals combine to form a band from 8140 to 8188 kHz. This signal band is next passed through a second modulator driven by a carrier at 8248 kHz. The double-sideband modulator output signal is then filtered to select its lower sideband, which is a signal spectrum between 60 and 108 kHz, identical to that at the output at an A5 channel bank. The receiving side of the A6B bank basically reverses the process, returning 12 VF signals.

The two-step modulation process permitted the application of a new design of channel filter with multiple resonators formed in a single monolithic quartz crystal. (Another manufacturer offered a similar product with multiple-crystal 8-MHz filters.) These filters are more readily optimized at frequencies near 8 MHz than at the basic group frequencies used in the A5 modulation plan. They are also much smaller physically. Other new technology used in the A6B included hybrid integrated circuits for amplifiers, pads, and other circuit elements.

Direct-Formed Supergroup. Sixty VF signals may be combined directly to form a supergroup signal in the frequency band between 312 and 552 kHz. The direct-formed supergroup (DFSG) was intended for large-office applications requiring circuit growth in multiples of 60, to avoid the costs of group banks. The signal spectrum and orientation of individual channel sidebands are identical to those in the basic supergroup. Thus, it is not necessary to have DFSG equipment at both ends of a carrier system; one end may use a DFSG while the other uses conventional group bank/channel bank equipment.

The modulation and multiplexing plan for the DFSG is similar to that in the A6 channel bank. Twelve channels are modulated to the 8-MHz region and combined into a group band spectrum. The five group bands are then modulated down directly into the 312-to-552-kHz supergroup band. Thus, the DFSG combines the functions of five channel banks and a group bank.

Program Terminals. Program audio signals are transmitted with 5-, 8-, and 15-kHz bandwidth. Terminal equipment separate from channel banks can be used to translate such signals into the 60-to-108-kHz basic group band. A 5-kHz program channel displaces VF channels 6 and 7 (80 to 88 kHz); an 8-kHz channel displaces channels 6, 7, and 8 (76 to 88 kHz). The program signal is combined with the remaining signals from the A-type bank between the channel bank output and the group bank input. The two sets of signals are separated at the receiving terminal between the output of the group bank and the input of the channel bank. For 15-kHz stereo service, a special terminal is used that occupies the full 60-to-108-kHz group band. It places both 15-kHz channels on a single-sideband basis into the group spectrum and provides per-channel gain regulation.

Wideband Modems. Special modems are occasionally used for transmission of data signals up to 50 kb/s in the group band and up to 250 kb/s in the supergroup band. This terminal equipment, like the program terminals, is not part of the multiplex equipment as such. The data terminals are separately mounted and cabled to the group or supergroup distributing frames for cross-connection to the multiplex equipment.

Group and Supergroup Banks

Blocks of channels are combined in the next steps of the multiplex hierarchy to form 60-channel supergroups in a group bank and 600-channel mastergroups in a supergroup bank. Equipment representing the later developments in this area is exemplified by the LMX-3 family [2].

LMX-3 Equipment. Figure 9-3 shows how the group banks in the LMX-3 equipment are arranged to produce the 60-channel basic supergroup. The channel orientation is inverted in the modulation process so that VF channels appearing as lower sidebands in the basic group appear as upper sidebands in the basic supergroup. No guard space is used in the spectrum between 4-kHz channels or between group bands. Hybrids in each of the five group band inputs insert a 104.08-kHz regulating pilot into the group spectrum before frequency conversion.

After translation to supergroup frequency, the groups are bridged together in a combining multiple. With amplification and

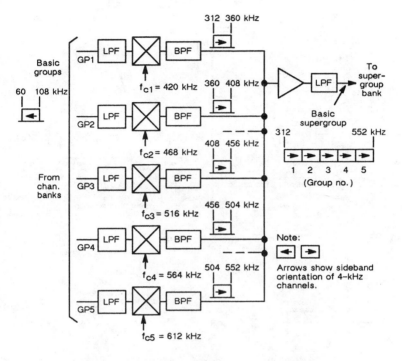

Figure 9–3. Group bank—transmit side.

low–pass filtering, they emerge in the 312–to–552–kHz super-group band along with the pilot tones. The receiving direction basically reverses these operations and regulates levels based on the received pilots.

The transmitting supergroup bank is shown in Figure 9–4. After modulation, supergroups are combined at the outputs of the bandpass filters. Passing through amplification and a common bandpass filter, the composite signal forms the basic mastergroup designated U600 (U for "universal"). This is the standard format used on almost all analog radio and coaxial carrier systems.

The supergroup numbering, which covers the ranges 13 to 18 and 25 to 28, is a result of the way in which the multiplex evolved. In each of the numbered sequences, the first digit derives from old "submastergroup" designations that are now of only historical interest. The second digit corresponds to a super-group number taken from the original L600 multiplex hierarchy

219

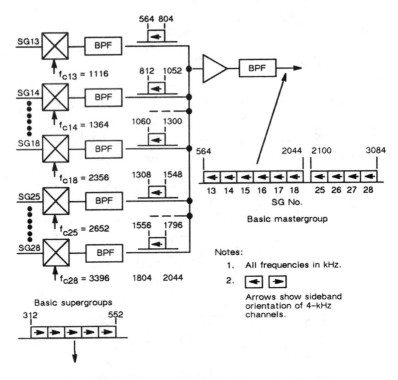

Figure 9-4. Supergroup bank—transmit side.

discussed later. There are guard bands of 8 kHz between most pairs of supergroups. The guard band between supergroups 18 and 25 is 56 kHz wide. This band was initially provided to facilitate separating the two submastergroups.

The LMX–3 equipment is compatible with earlier models that use the U600 frequency allocation, e.g., systems operate with LMX–2 or equivalent at one end and LMX–3 at the other. Compared to its predecessors, LMX–3 equipment features significant reductions in space and power consumption via use of integrated circuits and modern components. It provides better access arrangements for test and maintenance, extensive use of plug–in units, and improved distributing frame designs. Several optional bays are included, each providing both directions of transmission. One design (group–bank bay) comprises entirely group assemblies with basic–group inputs and basic–supergroup outputs;

another (supergroup–bank bay) contains only supergroup assemblies with basic–supergroup inputs and basic–mastergroup (U600) outputs. A combined bay, providing both group and supergroup assemblies to form one mastergroup, is another member of the family. Most of the electronics consists of plug–in modems providing modulators and demodulators, common carrier supply drive amplifiers, bandpass filters, and pilot regulating amplifiers.

Distributing Frames. The distributing frames expedite the work carried out in the network in respect to carrier installations and rearrangements. In the peak years for broadband transmission, it was estimated that the assignments of at least half of all long–haul channel groups changed each year. Large numbers of supergroup and mastergroup assignments also changed each year. Thus, the multiplex hierarchy, as illustrated in Figure 9–5, must provide for easy reconfiguration of carrier systems. Rearrangements required considerable time and effort when carried out by cabling changes in the absence of cross–connection facilities. This led to the provision of improved group and supergroup distributing frames (GDFs and SGDFs) and a mastergroup distributing frame (MGDF) as shown in Figure 9–5. These frames are

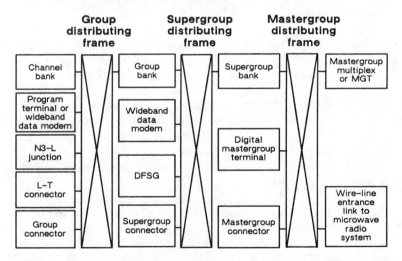

Figure 9–5. Distributing frames for rearrangements within the FDM hierarchy.

each designed with access points having equal TLPs to permit simple rearrangements without adjustments. Typical GDF and SGDF arrangements allow for up to 500 two–way group cross–connections or 250 supergroup cross–connections. Color coding and alphanumeric designations identify terminals and cross–connections. The GDF cross–connections use shielded pairs terminated in small connectors that plug into sockets in the frame. In the SGDF, miniature coaxial cable is used with snap–on connectors. Connector sockets are multipled in pairs to permit in–service rearrangements.

Central cross–connection for basic mastergroup facilities (supergroup banks, mastergroup multiplex, mastergroup translators, mastergroup connectors, and single–mastergroup wire–line entrance links) is provided by the MGDF. This equipment also provides access for other functions such as basic mastergroup restoration and automated maintenance testing. As with the SGDF, cross–connections use miniature plug–ended coaxial cables, multipled for in–service reassignment. Cable loss and slope equalizers are included for all line–side connections. A separate panel may be used with the cross–connect frame to terminate mastergroup trunks and other restoration equipment. A typical MGDF can handle a maximum of 42 two–way mastergroups. The MGDF allows direct application of automated transmission measuring systems.

Thus complete end–to–end transmission packages (groups, supergroups, mastergroups) are built up, using cross–connections at intermediate sites, from cable, radio, and satellite facilities.

The U600 and L600 Mastergroups. Figure 9–4 shows the spectrum of the U600 [3] mastergroup as a ten–supergroup package occupying 564 to 3084 kHz. This spectrum is the standard for transmission systems with 600–channel or greater capacity [4,5] and for 600–channel interconnections between exchange and interexchange carriers.

An earlier arrangement was the L600 mastergroup, a ten–supergroup spectrum lying between 60 and 2788 kHz. It was designed for use with the L1 carrier system but was also sometimes applied to TD–2 radio and light–route radio systems. Supergroups 1 through 4 of this arrangement can be used to channelize

2–GHz radio systems that have limited bandwidth. For compatibility, LMX–3 equipment offered the L600 spectrum as an option. However, L600 is not compatible with U600 systems or with radio routes that use data–under–voice arrangements and thus enjoys only limited use.

Mastergroup Multiplex and Translators

A number of multiplex arrangements translate and combine U600 mastergroup signals for transmission. Typical earlier designs were the MMX–2C (cable) and MMX–2R (radio). A jumbogroup multiplex (JMX) was introduced with the L5 carrier system.

A family of mastergroup translators superseded the MMX family and the JMX. These designs use individual self–contained mastergroup shelf mountings, which permit flexible application. Examples of such system applications include the provision of two mastergroups for 6–GHz short–haul, three for 4–GHz long–haul, four for 6–GHz long–haul, and ten for single–sideband AM radio systems. For coaxial systems, six mastergroups are combined for L4 and blocks of seven and eight mastergroups are assembled for the 22–mastergroup L5E. Reliability of this equipment is such that protection switching is not normally required. A spare translator may be patched into service for maintenance or restoration.

The mastergroup translator equipment has built–in carrier and pilot generation, alarm, and dc power supply circuits. Frequency translation is via plug–in modulators and demodulators. These units also provide regulation and squelch functions. That is, automatic level control is available, with the provision that, if a given mastergroup's level is grossly excessive, that mastergroup is cut off so as not to overload the transmission facility. Combining and separating of mastergroups occur in a separate panel nearby. The segregation of modulation/demodulation from signal combining/ separating functions and the use of plug–in circuits resulted in an equipment arrangement much more flexible than that of mastergroup multiplex arrangements.

There are several variations of this equipment. The first, called mastergroup translator, series A (MGT–A), provides a spectrum identical to that of the MMX–2. In particular, the guard bands between mastergroups vary from 168 kHz (between mastergroups 1 and 2) to 616 kHz (between mastergroups 5 and 6). The inputs to the MGT–A are normally U600 mastergroups. However, it is possible to transmit an L600 spectrum in the first (lowest frequency) mastergroup position since it is not modulated to another frequency band. This feature permitted reuse of existing L600 equipment where the transmission system bandwidth allowed it, e.g., on radio routes. The MGT–A offers one–for–one protection as an option, with automatic switching, for installations combining up to three mastergroups.

A second design, called MGT–B, translates the mastergroups to frequency positions such that the guard bands between mastergroups are a constant 168 kHz. This spacing, shown in Figure 9–6, made more efficient use of the overall spectrum and allowed the transmission of an expanded number of 4–kHz channels over the L5E carrier system and over wider–band microwave

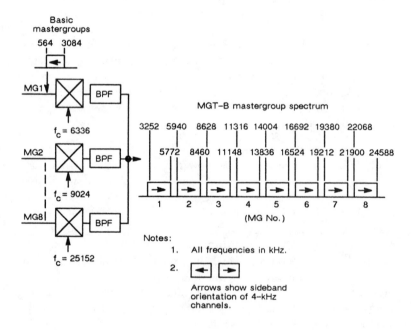

Figure 9–6. Formation of multimastergroup spectrum by MGT–B.

radio systems. The MGT-B is somewhat less flexible than the MGT-A. The fixed spacing precludes mastergroup branching (splitting two contiguous mastergroups apart via filters), requiring demodulation to basic mastergroup frequencies instead.

A third design, for light-route terminating applications, uses the same frequency allocations as the A-series and is designated MGT-AT. It does not provide several of the features, such as squelch and regulation, found in other designs. As an option, redundant path transmission was provided to increase reliability when terminating mastergroups at unattended locations.

Multimastergroup Translators

The multimastergroup spectrum shown in Figure 9-6 may be used in various combinations to provide signals for transmission over specific systems. Figure 9-7 shows how the spectrum is formed for the 22-mastergroup L5E carrier system. A single step of modulation moves each multimastergroup to its assigned place in the spectrum. Note the relatively close spacings between

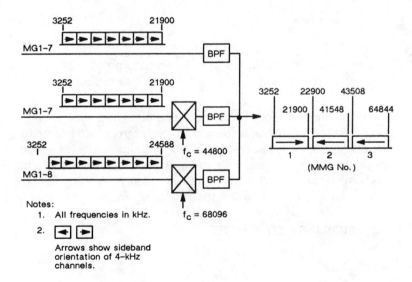

Figure 9-7. Formation of L5E line signal using three MGT-B spectra.

225

multimastergroup spectra. This efficient spacing, and the close spacing between mastergroups in the MGT–B arrangement, permit the fitting of 22 mastergroups onto an L5E line. Figure 9–8 shows the formation of a ten–mastergroup array for transmission over a single–sideband microwave radio system.

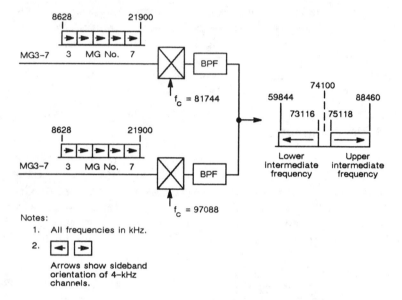

Notes:
1. All frequencies in kHz.

2. Arrows show sideband orientation of 4–kHz channels.

Figure 9-8. Formation of the ten–mastergroup spectrum for single–sideband microwave radio.

The multimastergroup equipment contains automatic protection switching so that one spare multimastergroup modulator or demodulator can protect up to 20 working units in cable applications and up to 15 in radio systems. Transmitting and receiving circuits are protected independently. A 13,920–kHz pilot signal is used to activate the switching circuits.

9-2 AUXILIARY EQUIPMENT

Connectors

Blocks of 12, 60, and 600 channels are convenient in providing trunks and special services between communities of differing sizes. Such administrative flexibility is provided by the use of connectors that permit efficient system interconnections. The principal function of a connector is to provide an undistorted passband for the desired signal and to attenuate all signals outside the passband, e.g., remnants of the next supergroup above or below after demodulation.

Group Connectors. A typical group connector gives an inband transmission characteristic (60 to 108 kHz) flat within ±0.2 dB, with out–of–band signals attenuated relative to the passband by at least 85 dB. A separate connector is used for each direction of transmission. The connectors are cabled to the GDF for jumpering to group banks.

Group connectors are used judiciously. Wideband data transmission requires connectors that include delay equalization to control inband delay distortion. With gain and delay equalization, accumulated distortion typically limits the number of connectors in tandem to five.

Supergroup Connectors. The 60–channel supergroup is often a convenient unit of channel capacity between two points. Thus, many system interconnections involve supergroup connectors. With a typical connector, the passband is flat to ±0.2 dB between 312 and 552 kHz and out–of–band signals are attenuated by at least 90 dB. The connector contains an adjustable equalizer to compensate the dominant attenuation/frequency distortion of the previous supergroup section; as many as four connectors may operate in tandem.

Mastergroup Connectors. The mastergroup connector passes the 564–to–3084–kHz band. Equalizers correct deviations in the attenuation/frequency characteristic caused by the bandpass filter and by office cables between the connector and the mastergroup multiplex. Other features and functions vary from one connector type to another: one–way versus two–way operation, pilot–blocking filters, adjustable gain to maintain transmission level points (TLPs), patching jacks, level padding, etc.

The N3–L Junction

Inherent incompatibilities between N3/N4 and broadband systems must be resolved if these systems are to be interconnected without demodulation to voice frequency. These incompatibilities are resolved by use of the N3–L junction, an adaptor that removes the differences in group–band frequencies, transmitted carriers versus low–amplitude pilots, and compandored versus noncompandored channel operation. Thus, group–band interconnection is made possible.

System Incompatibilities. The basic broadband group consists of 12 single–sideband channels between 60 and 108 kHz plus the regulating and alarm pilot at 104.08 kHz.

The N3 or N4 line signal, detailed in Chapter 11, consists of two 12–channel single–sideband groups, one occupying 36–132 kHz and the other located between 172–268 kHz and thus requiring frequency translation. It includes 12 high–amplitude carrier signals for regulation, frequency correction, and demodulation. If transmitted over broadband facilities, these carriers would cause overload and interference. Thus, they must be attenuated by 15 dB for transmission over the broadband facility and then enhanced to their original amplitudes for further transmission over N–type facilities.

Compandors are used in all N–type systems. The N3–L junction adjusts TLPs so that the compressed signals from an N–type system do not overload the broadband system.

Junction Types. The N3–L junctions are designated as types A, B, and C. The A–type junction translates directly between N–type line signals and broadband group signals. The B–type junction terminates two 12–channel N3/N4 groups that have been formed into two broadband groups. The line side of this junction contains channel groups; the drop side consists of 24 VF channels. The C–type junction terminates one 12–channel group of a composite system and extends the second group over broadband facilities. Typical applications of these three junction types are shown in Figure 9–9.

The junctions provide the necessary functions for each application: correction of any frequency shift that may have occurred in the N–carrier line, alarm/squelch/restoral controls, attenuation of the N3 carriers, and 8.5–dB attenuation of the whole N3 signal to account for its high average power because of companding, frequency translations, and the complements of these operations.

228

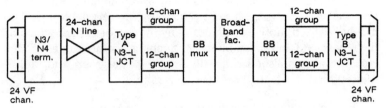

(a) Application of A– and B–type junctions

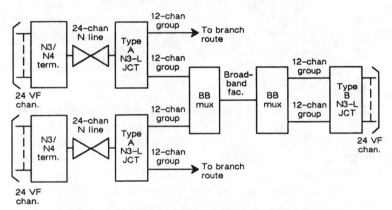

(b) Alternative application of A– and B–type junctions

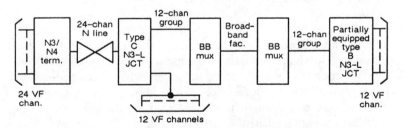

(c) Application of B– and C–type junctions

Figure 9–9. Typical arrangements of N3–L junctions.

Branching

Long–haul broadband transmission systems must permit drop-ping, blocking, and adding circuits flexibly along the route. These branching functions can be fulfilled by using multiplex equipment and the various types of connector but, for very large systems, can be realized more economically by the use of combinations of high–pass and low–pass filters. Branching arrangements of this type are accomplished primarily at the mastergroup and multi-mastergroup levels in the FDM hierarchy.

The most comprehensive mastergroup branching arrangements are those for the six–mastergroup L4 coaxial system. In L4, any combination of contiguous mastergroups may be blocked or passed by the application of high–pass and low–pass branching filters. These are used at main stations where multiplex equipment is located to complete the addition and deletion of mastergroups from the high–frequency line. These arrangements also block, insert, or pass line pilot signals as required.

Similar arrangements provide jumbogroup signal administration in an L5 coaxial system [3]. These facilities may be combined with L4 mastergroup branching filters to provide flexible mastergroup arrangements for L5 systems. The L4 filters are also used for branching in some microwave systems. However, the availability of mastergroup translators with their greater flexibility has cut into the use of these filter arrangements.

Undersea Cable Interconnections

A unique feature of most undersea cables is that they use 3–kHz channelization instead of the 4–kHz channels that are otherwise standard. Facilities carrying a mixture of 3–kHz and 4–kHz channels would produce undesirable intermodulation products and other interferences. Therefore, undersea cable VF channels are transformed to 4–kHz channels at the first office location encountered in the United States.

9-3   SYSTEM CONSIDERATIONS

The structure of the analog multiplex hierarchy evolved from specific transmission system needs. Each step featured the application of new technology, the consideration of interrelated objectives (e.g., for bandwidth usage, transmission quality, and reliability), and the preservation of compatibility with existing arrangements. The overall process had to allow for flexible expansion and future innovations.

Efficiency Factors

In addition to increased use of bandwidth in transmission media, design economies were found as the multiplex hierarchy evolved. These advantages included the use of common equipment whose cost is shared by many circuits. Such common equipment includes pilot and carrier supplies and maintenance equipment. Advantages also derive from multiplex arrangements that permit terminal equipment to be used at different levels of the hierarchy for systems involving different bandwidths and base facilities.

Bandwidth Use. At each step in the evolution of a given type of transmission system, the use of the medium was extended in bandwidth by such techniques as using shorter repeater spacing on cable or increasing the transmitted power on radio. These bandwidth increases led to complexities in multiplex design that differ from those that influence transmission system design. Ultimately, equipment must balance performance and cost.

To make most efficient use of assigned bandwidth, there is always pressure to place channels in the spectrum as close together as possible. However, close spacing imposes stringent requirements on the bandwidth allowed for filter discrimination, i.e., for the filter attenuation to increase from its minimum (inband) value to its maximum (out–of–band) value. This problem grows as the top transmitted frequency is increased because the bandwidth required for transition is a percentage of the frequency at which the transition must occur. Thus, more complex structures were required for the higher–frequency filters than for lower–frequency filters with the same guard bandwidth. The requirements for sharp cutoff and high out–of–band attenuation produce inband amplitude–frequency and phase–frequency distortions (e.g., ripples) that are hard to control and that tend to accumulate systematically when terminals are connected in tandem. Attempts to control these distortions or to equalize them out would raise equipment costs.

231

One compromise in multiplex equipment in response to application needs is illustrated by the shift in frequency allocations of the MMX–2 mastergroup multiplex as compared to the earlier MMX–1. In the original design, there was a constant guard bandwidth of 80 kHz between mastergroups. In the MMX–2, the guard bands were made approximately four percent of the center frequency of each band. This approach gave improved transmission/frequency performance in the filters and related equipment that provide flexibility in system layouts. Without the proportional bandwidth, the functions of dropping, blocking, re-inserting, and through–connecting cannot be accomplished except by demodulation to basic mastergroup frequencies. However, in the design of the MGT–B and the MMGT, there was a return to the original approach of minimizing the guard bandwidths at the expense of reduced flexibility. Thus, increased numbers of channels were made available. This approach was deemed appropriate because the growth of service made it desirable to administer channels in larger blocks, and because improved filter design techniques were available.

Another change in the multiplex hierarchy in the interests of using bandwidth better is the location of group and supergroup pilots. Originally, these pilots were assigned frequencies near the middle of their respective bands (i.e., 92 kHz for groups). However, they were later moved to frequencies near the band edges (104.08 kHz for groups) to allow better use of these bands for wideband data signals. In anticipation of later needs for wideband signals in the mastergroup, the pilot was placed fairly near the band edge. By contrast, the multimastergroup pilot is placed near the center of the multimastergroup translator spectrum at a frequency selected to optimize analog transmission. These pilot frequencies are shown in Table 9–1.

Common Equipment. A discussion of the application of common circuits and equipment is appropriate. Three categories of equipment are of interest: carrier and pilot supplies, modems, and maintenance equipment.

Carriers, which are multiples of 4 kHz, must be provided at every stage of the multiplex. Pilots are used for regulation, alarms, and protection switching at all steps. These signals must be precise and reliable. Great frequency accuracy is required in

Table 9-1. Pilot and Control Frequencies in North American FDM Equipment

Spectrum	Frequency (kHz)
Basic group	104.08
Carrier failure alarm	100.08
Basic supergroup	315.92
Basic mastergroup	2840.00
Basic jumbogroup	5888.00
Multimastergroup (for	13,920.00
alarms and switch control)	

demodulating a signal from, for example, 65 MHz to voice with less than 1 Hz of frequency shift. Amplitude and phase jitter must be extremely small even in the presence of noise or variations in supply voltage. Such factors encourage the use of common equipment because the cost of large numbers of individual signal sources meeting stringent requirements would have been excessive. (In limited cases, such as the mastergroup and multimastergroup translators, emphasis has shifted from common equipment to flexibility of application.)

A typical office that uses FDM equipment contains one or more reliable primary frequency supplies (PFSs), an office master frequency supply (OMFS), and/or a jumbogroup frequency supply (JFS) with duplicated oscillators and drivers that switch to spare automatically in the event of failure. The operating frequencies of these units are synchronized to a reference signal originating in a master frequency standard. These signals are transmitted nationwide through regional frequency supplies. In the event of failure of the standard, synchronization is maintained by the regional supplies.

The output signals of the primary frequency supplies are at 4, 64, 128, and 512 kHz. These signals drive multiport distribution networks feeding a number of bays of multiplex equipment. Signals at 1.024, 2.56, and 20.48 MHz are generated in jumbogroup frequency supplies to synchronize JMX and multimastergroup equipment. Within the multiplex bays, pilot and carrier frequencies are generated and distributed as required.

Many modulators and demodulators use identical circuits and equipment and are combined in single–unit modems. Maintenance features that have been incorporated in the multiplex equipment are also furnished on a common basis so that test sets and circuits, built–in and external, can serve multiple bays of equipment.

Transmission

A carrier system must simultaneously meet such service and transmission objectives as bandwidth, distortion limits, signal–to–noise performance, and reliability. For economic reasons, allowable transmission impairments are allocated primarily to the line with only small amounts allotted to terminal equipment. Overall transmission performance of systems depends on operating features that must be provided. These include flexible interconnection between systems and circuits, transmission stability, and the provision of TLPs compatible with other parts of the transmission plant.

Standard TLPs. The inputs to channel banks consist of four–wire VF circuits. The TLP at the four–wire VF input on the transmitting side is −16 dB. At the VF output on the receiving side, the TLP is +7 dB. These standard TLPs are also used in the N–type analog system and can be provided readily in the T–type digital systems. Thus, with only rare exceptions, an analog–carrier channel has 23 dB of gain from the input to the output. These TLPs and gains facilitate orderly interconnection of systems throughout the plant. Even though analog transmission systems require a wide range of TLPs internally, the input and output TLPs are fixed. TLPs are also standardized at higher levels of the hierarchy: for basic groups, −37.4 in, −5 out at the GDF; for basic supergroups, −21.1 in, −28.6 out at the SGDF; and for basic mastergroups, −30 in, −17.8 out at the MGDF.

Within some transmission systems, TLPs must vary with frequency. Where these specifications are step functions of frequency (for example, applying each mastergroup to a transmission system at a different TLP), gain or loss may be applied in the FDM equipment. Where the TLPs are continuous functions of frequency, as in radio systems, a preemphasis network between the multiplex and the line equipment provides the necessary characteristic.

Level Stability. Broadband amplifiers used in FDM equipment maintain stable gain despite aging of components, temperature changes, or variations in supply voltage. This stability results from the use of negative feedback and of pilot–controlled regulators in the receiving circuits of the multiplex. Group, supergroup, and mastergroup transmission is regulated. Pilots are inserted in the transmitting equipment and picked off in the receiving equipment, after demodulation to basic supergroup and basic group frequencies, to control regulation loops. Regulators generally maintain transmission at the pilot frequency to within ±0.1 dB of the required value.

Transmission Response. At each level in the multiplex above channel level, the attenuation–frequency characteristic is designed to be flat within approximately ±0.05 dB over any 4–kHz portion of the transmission band. This accuracy in transmission is easily met over the center frequencies but band edges tend to roll off in spite of the use of high–performance crystal filters. The cumulative departure from flat transmission through ten pairs of transmitting and receiving terminals is typically 0.25 dB or less.

Envelope delay distortion is not normally corrected in the multiplex equipment since few applications need it. For voiceband or wideband data channels having unusually tight requirements, any required delay equalization is accomplished externally to the multiplex.

Combining and Separating Circuits. Many combining and separating points are used to combine signals of different frequencies into a composite spectrum and to separate them at receiving terminals for direction to their destinations. Hybrids and resistance–pad circuits are commonly used in conjunction with filters for these purposes.

The choice between hybrids and resistance pads depends on allowable loss at the point of application, any need for impedance transformation, sensitivity to circuit–to–circuit interaction, and cost. Hybrid circuits tend to have less through–circuit loss and higher coupling loss (transhybrid loss). They easily provide impedance transformation, but cost more. The control of impedances involves the designs of the filters and combining and separating circuits. The relationships among return loss, attenuation-frequency distortion, power transfer, and cost must all be considered.

Signal–to–Noise Considerations. In a long–haul broadband transmission system, the terminals are allocated only a small portion (31.2 dBrnc0) of the overall 4000–mile noise objective (40 dBrnc0). This low value of noise is suballocated to the individual terminals (via estimates of the number of tandem terminals in a long system), and to levels of the FDM hierarchy within each terminal. The noise allocation is further broken down as to type and source of noise.

Gains and losses (and therefore TLPs) in the multiplex equipment are selected for best signal–to–noise performance. The basic requirements are generally satisfied by minimizing the combined effects of thermal and intermodulation noise; however, compromises must sometimes be made to avoid other problems such as single–frequency interference or crosstalk.

Due to the large number of modulation steps and carriers that must be used, the generation of unwanted single–frequency tones is a danger in FDM equipment. Carrier leakage through a modulator, ground loops, intermodulation among pilots and carriers in amplifiers, and inadequate suppression by filters are all sources of single–frequency interference and crosstalk. Circuit elements in FDM equipment are designed to minimize these problems and are carefully placed physically relative to one another to control them. FDM frequency plans were designed to minimize the occurrence of interfering tones or signals from unwanted sidebands or intermodulation products.

Reliability

The design of the FDM hierarchy was influenced in many ways by reliability considerations. This became increasingly true as bandwidths and channel loads in the multiplex equipment increased. The goals of avoiding significant deterioration or complete failure required the use of basically reliable components, the selective application of redundancy, the use of well–defined maintenance equipment and procedures, and the provision of alarms to indicate incipient failure or outage. Pilot signals are monitored continuously to determine whether circuits are drifting from normal gain settings. The loss of a pilot signal triggers an alarm and, where protection switching is available, brings backup facilities into use.

Redundancy. Alternate transmission paths are provided in multiplex equipment for use in case of failure of the working path. Inputs and outputs to these standby paths are available for restoring service in the event of failure of the high–frequency line. In such circumstances, broadband restoration plans often use the standby equipment to bypass a failed section of line. In some cases, this equipment is switched into service; in others it must be patched manually. Redundancy is also used in the ancillary circuits associated with the multiplex equipment. Supplies for carriers, pilots, and synchronizing signals all contain redundant circuits.

Carrier Failure Alarm. An optional maintenance feature called carrier failure alarm (CFA) minimizes the effect of a system failure on calls that are involved in the failure. This feature is analogous to the carrier group alarm (CGA) feature used in N– and T–carrier. Switch blocking and delay in completing new calls are minimized by making failed trunks appear busy, thus reducing the unproductive use of common equipment in switching machines. Connections involved in the failure immediately receive on–hook supervision, stopping toll charges. A single–frequency alarm pilot can be transmitted in the basic group band at 100.08 kHz for CFA control. The functions of pilot transmission and detection and alarming are associated with the channel bank output at basic group frequency. Where the multiplex equipment does not include such alarm features, switching machines usually provide similar protection against the effects of failure by making a voice–path assurance check while setting up a connection.

Maintenance Features. Maintenance arrangements include the provision of test points to permit manual measurements of voltages or pilot levels and of automatic measuring systems. Scanners sequentially check all pilot levels and regulator gains.

References

1. Bleisch, G. W. "The A6 Channel Bank," *IEEE Transactions on Communications Technology*, Vol. COM–20 (Apr. 1972), pp. 196–201.

2. Couture, R. W., C. V. Fanuele, and T. R. Helmes. "The New LMX–3 Multiplex Terminals," *Conference Record*, IEEE International Conference on Communications (June 1975), Vol. 1, pp. 8–1 to 8–5.

3. Members of Technical Staff. *Transmission Systems for Communications*, Fifth Edition (Murray Hill, NJ: AT&T Bell Laboratories, Inc., 1982), pp. 114–116 and 317–328.

4. Freeman, R. L. *Telecommunications Transmission Handbook*, Second Edition (New York: John Wiley and Sons, Inc., 1981), pp. 79–91, 97–99, 102–107, and 114–120.

5. "Wire Transmission," *Reference Data for Engineers: Radio, Electronics, Computer, and Communications*, Seventh Edition (Indianapolis, IN: Howard W. Sams and Company, Inc., 1985), pp. 35–26 to 35–30.

Chapter 10

System Design Features

High–quality analog amplifiers have made it possible to overcome the losses of transmission lines over increasingly wide bandwidths and to modulate and combine a multiplicity of signals. These factors, added to the use of single–sideband modulation, give efficient use of the wire line. Other advances have raised the signal–to–noise ratio, enhanced transmission stability, added reliability, and improved maintainability.

An effective system design requires that numerous system parameters meet transmission objectives. This requires the solution of simultaneous equations that relate these objectives to bandwidth, signal–to–noise performance, load capacity, line loss, repeater spacing, and repeater gain. The process is iterative: results are re–analyzed to match improvements in performance, objectives, and computing techniques. The process requires consideration of subtleties in the performance of the line and its repeaters, many of which are unimportant or absent in the case of digital systems.

Initial computations to determine technical feasibility and economic attractiveness are usually straightforward. However, the process becomes complex as refinements are introduced [1]. System equalization and regulation, intermodulation effects, overload performance, and the inclusion of margins to handle in–service variations all complicate system calculations. Other considerations may be introduced by frequency allocations, special modes of transmission (e.g., equivalent four–wire), limits on repeater spacing or placement, and second–order transmission irregularities in the wire line (e.g., small echoes at splices).

Analog cable carrier systems employ either four–wire transmission, in which the two directions of transmission are on separate one–way facilities, or equivalent four–wire transmission, in which

239

the two directions use separate frequency bands over one pair of conductors. The four–wire design is used in land coaxial carrier systems to supply the full potential bandwidth of the line in both directions and to allow simple repeaters. The equivalent four–wire mode is normal in submarine cable systems and in analog loop carrier, as a means of economizing on wire facilities at the cost of more complex electronics. The N–type paired–cable systems originally used four–wire transmission exclusively but later received the option of equivalent four–wire.

The discussion of system design is presented to clarify terminology and to demonstrate the relationships among specific parameters [2,3].

10-1 THE DESIGN PROCESS

The transmission design of an analog cable system is determined analytically by adjusting repeater spacing, bandwidth, and signal levels to meet signal–to–noise objectives over the life of the system. Many parameters affect the achievable performance. The process involves determining the lowest allowable signal level that can meet objectives for signal–to–thermal–noise and, in paired–cable systems, crosstalk, and the maximum allowable signal level that satisfies intermodulation and overload objectives. If there is no spread between these two values, a design is not possible. If there is a spread, the design may be optimized at signal amplitudes that provide the largest total signal–to–noise ratio without reaching overload and give the greatest margins for departures from this ideal. Finally, if these margins are too small or too large, a skilled analyst may adjust the repeater spacing, bandwidth, or cost.

While this chapter focuses on wire–line carrier telephone systems, most of the theory involved also pertains to such applications as analog cable television systems.

Design Relationships

The design parameters for an analog transmission system are related to one another mathematically by the rule that system performance must equal system objectives. Most of the parameters vary with either time or frequency. For refined design computations, they must be expressed as functions of frequency and in statistical terms. For initial calculations and for present purposes, fixed average values are generally assumed and the highest transmitted frequency is used to determine feasibility. Where margins are appropriate, they may be included as mathematical terms in the expressions for performance.

In considering the relationships among parameters, a common reference point is necessary for analysis. The zero transmission level point (0 TLP) is commonly used. A convenient reference point in many intermediate computations is the output of a repeater. The TLP at this point is related to 0 TLP by a factor defined as C dB, the nominal gain from the output of a repeater to 0 TLP. This factor may be a function of frequency, or may be constant, depending on the specific design. For initial calculations, the value of C is usually assumed constant with frequency and equal to the value at the top frequency.

Repeater Gain. A basic design requirement is that the transmission loss of the medium must be compensated by the gains of repeaters along the line. This requirement is expressed by

$$L_x = nG_R \mathrm{dB}$$

and

$$G_R = \frac{L_x}{n} \mathrm{dB} \qquad (10\text{--}1)$$

where L_x is the loss of the line for the distance X over which the design is to apply, G_R is the gain of each repeater, and n is the number of repeaters. Thus the nominal repeater spacing for the system is X/n. Equation 10–1 assumes that the losses of a series of identical lengths of cable are exactly compensated by the gains of an equal number of repeaters. The equation must apply at all frequencies in the transmitted band even though it is used in initial studies as if it applied only at the top frequency.

Thermal Noise and Load Capacity. These two parameters may combine to limit the design of a system; thermal noise may

241

set the "noise floor" and load capacity the "overload ceiling." With paired cables, impulse noise originating in switching machines may also be a significant parameter. Thus, it is necessary to compute the performance for each of these parameters and relate them.

In a system of n repeaters, it can be shown that the total thermal noise existing in a 3–kHz band, expressed as an annoyance factor, is

$$W_{n0} = N_R + G_R + 10 \log n + C + 88 \text{ dBrnc0}. \quad (10\text{–}2)$$

The term N_R defines the noise in dBm at the input to a repeater (where the signal amplitude is lowest) in a 3–kHz band. The terms N_R, G_R, C, and W_{n0} in Equation 10–2 may all be functions of frequency. If the accumulated noise is to be equal to or less than the system objective for this impairment, W_{NS}, and if a margin for system misalignment, A_N, is to be included, then

$$W_{n0} + A_N \leq W_{NS}.$$

Thus,

$$N_R + G_R + 10 \log n + C + 88 + A_N \leq W_{NS}. \quad (10\text{–}3)$$

The load capacity of a system is conveniently expressed in terms of a single–frequency signal whose power equals that of the total multichannel load. The repeaters must be capable of carrying this amount of power, usually expressed in dBm0, with a margin so that departures from normal system performance or from the predicted load do not cause overload.

The single–frequency power for the repeater capacity and the system requirement are designated P_R and P_S, respectively. These power values are related by

$$P_R + C - A_P \geq P_S \text{ dBm0} \quad (10\text{–}4)$$

where A_P is the overload margin to be provided in the design.

Equation 10–4 is deceptively simple in appearance. The factors that make up the load requirement are variable and must be treated statistically for the derivation of P_S. These factors include the variation of talker volume and the loading effect of combined signal power and its variation. In addition, the load capacity of a repeater may depend on frequency. For present purposes, it may be assumed that the value of P_R in dBm applies at the output of the repeater, at the top frequency.

Intermodulation. System design may be limited by an "intermodulation ceiling." Equations may be written for noise due to intermodulation among the multiplexed signals transmitted through the repeaters. In these equations, W_2 and W_3 represent the annoyance factor of the noise due to second– and third–order nonlinearities in the repeaters. In broadband systems that provide several hundred channels or more, the effects of these impairments are subjectively very similar to the interfering effect of thermal noise. The power of intermodulation noise is thus added to the power of thermal noise to evaluate the total impairment. However, the mechanisms by which W_2 and W_3 are generated and the manner in which they are related to signal amplitudes and system transmission response are quite different. Thus, the impairments are computed separately and combined only in the final evaluation. The two equations are

$$W_2 = M_2 - C + 10 \log n + K_2 \quad \text{dBrnc0} \qquad (10\text{-}5)$$

and

$$W_3 = M_3 - 2C + 20 \log n + K_3 \quad \text{dBrnc0.} \qquad (10\text{-}6)$$

In these equations, M_2 and M_3 represent the second– and third–order modulation coefficients for line repeaters in terms of the ratio of 0–dBm0 single–frequency signals to the second– and third–order products at the repeater output. The factors K_2 and K_3 relate single–frequency impairments to the statistics of impairments due to intermodulation among signals. These properties include the number of channels in the system, the activity factor associated with a speech message load, the variation of signal energy in each channel with time and frequency, the number of intermodulation products generated, etc.

There are two essential differences between Equations 10–5 and 10–6. First, the term C, which appears unmodified in

243

Equation 10–5, is multiplied by 2 in Equation 10–6. This difference results from the mathematical relationships of signal–to–interference ratio resulting from second– and third–order intermodulation. Second, the terms $10 \log n$ in Equation 10–5 and $20 \log n$ in Equation 10–6 represent the difference in the laws of addition of intermodulation products generated in successive repeaters. The difference results from the fact that the phase–frequency characteristics of the cable and repeaters are essentially linear.

The computed intermodulation noise must be equal to or less than the objectives. Thus, Equations 10–5 and 10–6 may be used to write system design equations:

$$W_2 + A_2 \leq W_{2S}$$

or

$$M_2 - C + 10 \log n + K_2 + A_2 \leq W_{2S} \qquad (10\text{–}7)$$

and

$$W_3 + A_3 \leq W_{3S}$$

or

$$M_3 - 2C + 20 \log n + K_3 + A_3 \leq W_{3S}. \qquad (10\text{–}8)$$

The factors A_2 and A_3 are margins to handle uncertainties and variations.

Use of the Basic Equations. Five of the previous equations are used to establish system parameters. Equation 10–1 equates repeater gain to cable section loss. Equation 10–3 relates factors that effectively define the noise floor, that is, the value below which signal levels may not drop without violating the objective for signal–to–thermal–noise. Equation 10–4 establishes the overload ceiling, 10–7 the intermodulation ceiling where second–order products predominate, and 10–8 the intermodulation ceiling where third–order products are controlling.

Equations 10–1 and 10–3 may be combined with each of the other three to eliminate C and G_R. When this is done, three system equations may be written. The first is the equation for a system limited by thermal noise and overload:

$$\frac{L_X}{n} + 10 \log n \leq (W_{NS} - N_R) - (A_N + A_P) - (P_S - P_R)$$

$$- 88 \text{ dB}. \qquad (10\text{--}9)$$

The second is the equation for a system limited by thermal noise and second–order intermodulation:

$$\frac{L_X}{n} + 20 \log n \leq (W_{NS} + W_{2S}) - (N_R + M_2) -$$

$$(A_N + A_2) - (88 + K_2) \text{ dB}. \qquad (10\text{--}10)$$

The third equation represents a system limited by thermal noise and third–order intermodulation:

$$\frac{L_X}{n} + 20 \log n \leq (W_{NS} + W_{3S}/2) - (N_R + M_3/2) -$$

$$(A_N + A_3/2) - (88 + \frac{K_3}{2}) \text{ dB}. \qquad (10\text{--}11)$$

In the development of a new system, the loss characteristic of the line and the objectives $(P_S, W_{NS}, W_{2S}, \text{ and } W_{3S})$ are usually known. Estimates of other parameters are made on the basis of previous designs, desired goals as to bandwidth or channel capacity, state of the art, and the designer's judgment. The estimates and the known objectives and media characteristics then indicate feasibility. The results determine approximate repeater spacing and suggest whether overload or intermodulation is likely to be controlling in the system. The computations are refined so that the final design represents economical compromises among margins, repeater spacing, and bandwidth as well as manufacturing, installation, operation and maintenance costs.

Implementing The Design

Some of the basic relationships discussed above are straightforward. However, most of the parameters and their interrelationships are more complex than may be evident. These complexities naturally enter the analysis process.

Transmission Level Points. As previously mentioned, TLPs at the outputs of line repeaters are specified by the term C used in developing the system equations. Figure 10–1 illustrates a simplified system layout in which the factor C is assumed to be constant over the transmitted band. The layout assumes an ideal case in which there are n identical repeater sections in which the repeater gain, G_R dB, exactly compensates the cable loss, $-G_R$ dB. Only one direction of transmission is illustrated. Even though C is shown as constant over the band, C usually varies with frequency and the TLP generally depends on frequency at points within the system other than the repeater output as shown at point R.

Thermal Noise. Thermal noise is classically computed by

$$P_a = kTB \quad \text{watts}$$

where k is Boltzmann's constant $(1.3805 \times 10^{-23}$ joule per degree Kelvin), T is the absolute temperature in degrees Kelvin, and B is the bandwidth in hertz. The available noise power at 290 degrees Kelvin (near room temperature) may also be expressed as

$$P_a = -174 + 10 \log B \quad \text{dBm.}$$

These expressions apply at any point in the system. However, the effect of noise is greatest at points where signal amplitudes are weakest, e.g., at the inputs to line repeaters. Where other thermal noise sources are significant, the noise amplitudes are usually measured or computed, translated to equivalent values at the repeater input, and added to the input noise. Such sources are sometimes internal to the repeaters. In addition, amplifiers at equalization points or at terminals also contribute thermal noise that must be added to that originating in line repeaters to compute total system noise.

As illustrated at point R of Figure 10–1, thermal noise is constant over the frequency band at which cable transmission is practical.

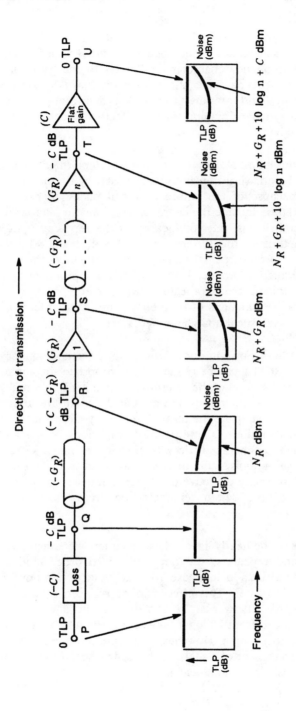

Figure 10–1. Simplified line layout with diagrams of level and thermal noise.

Note: ( ) = gain in dB

247

However, the noise originating at point R is amplified in the repeater and appears at the repeater output (point S) with an amplitude–frequency characteristic similar to the gain curve of the repeater. This characteristic is maintained as additional noise is accumulated and translated to 0 TLP as shown at points T and U. The analyst must manipulate these factors to achieve the desired objectives.

Intermodulation Noise. The analysis of impairment caused by intermodulation, very similar to that caused by thermal noise, is complex because of the nature and multiplicity of parameters involved. These include the characteristics and amplitudes of the fundamental signals, the nonlinearity of the repeater input–output characteristic, the system attenuation–frequency response, the number of fundamental signals (which influences the number of intermodulation products), the orders of the products, and the laws of addition from repeater to repeater. Most of these parameters are functions of frequency, time, system length, etc. As a result, statistical analysis is necessary.

The variation of intermodulation noise with frequency as measured at 0 TLP can be reduced by appropriate shaping of the TLPs across the band of the system. The shaping is accomplished by preemphasis–deemphasis networks at the input and output of the system. These make the term C frequency–dependent. While this design technique is often useful, variations of the attenuation–frequency characteristic with time have similar effects on intermodulation noise and must be taken into account. Their control is a primary objective of a system equalization plan. The departure of the system characteristic from ideal is called misalignment.

Because of the nearly linear phase–frequency characteristics of the line and repeaters, the dominant third–order modulation products tend to add in phase (termed voltage addition) from repeater to repeater. This effect can be reduced by the use of nonlinear–phase networks. By this means, the law of addition may be reduced from $20 \log n$ (where n is the number of repeaters) nearer to $10 \log n$. However, consideration must be given to possible impairment of signals, such as high–speed digital pulses, that are sensitive to nonlinear phase.

248

Overload Effects. The effects of overload, the criteria for de-
fining it, and many of the statistical properties of signals that may
cause it are discussed in Volume 1. Two types of system impairment are of concern. The first, sometimes called "hard overload," results in a complete breakdown of transmission. This type
of failure is rare; even so, some systems have specific design features to avoid it.

More commonly, signal levels exceed design values by
amounts small enough that the primary manifestation of an
overload is an increase in intermodulation noise. The margin, A_p
of Equation 10–4, is provided for such signal–amplitude excur-
sions. In choosing the amount of margin, the statistics of the
multichannel signal to be transmitted must be analyzed to determine its mean value and standard deviation. This analysis is
influenced by the amplitude–frequency characteristic of the
signal at the output of the line repeater. In addition to the
nominal TLP characteristic, the effects of sources of misalignment in the system must be considered.

Intermodulation noise depends directly on signal levels. The
term C controls these amplitudes and thus, indirectly, the intermodulation noise. Below the repeater overload point, the change
in noise is predictable from the power–series representation of
the input–output characteristic of the system. When measured at
0 TLP, modulation noise varies inversely with the change in the
value of C. Second–order noise varies decibel per decibel; third–
order noise varies 2 dB per each decibel change in C. When C is
reduced to the overload point, the noise increases faster than
predicted. Furthermore, just one overloaded repeater can cause
a marked deterioration in system intermodulation performance.
In operation, the most serious sources of overload are (1) the
application of excessively strong signals and (2) any failure to
maintain system equalization that causes signals of otherwise satisfactory levels to reach overload.

Certain system design options must be used with care because
of overload relationships that are involved. One is the application
of compandors, which increase the mean values and reduce the
standard deviations of the signals transmitted. Thus, it may be
necessary to reduce signal amplitudes (by increasing the value of
C) depending on the overload margin in the system. The net

249

result may be a significant reduction of the signal–to–noise advantage expected from the use of the compandors. A second feature that affects overload performance is the use of a time–assignment speech interpolation (TASI) system. This type of system, applied at the terminals of, for example, ocean–cable systems, increases the capacity of the system by assigning channels to talkers only when speech energy is present at the input. Fast channel switching is initiated by speech detectors on each input channel and by high–speed logic circuits that connect appropriate incoming and outgoing lines through an idle channel. This arrangement increases the effective talker activity on the system and can raise the power load by a factor of two or three. It must be considered in the provision of overload and intermodulation margin.

Optimization. For a given set of design parameters, transmitted signal levels are chosen for best signal–to–noise performance. While the mathematical treatment is a valuable part of the analysis, noise–loading tests of working systems are often made to verify the design value of C and evaluate system performance.

10–2 EQUALIZATION

The term equalization is used to cover a number of techniques for correcting the transmission characteristic of a system or a circuit. The equalizer precision needed in analog cable carrier systems is illustrated by the following. The loss of 4000 miles of coaxial cable at 65 MHz, a high transmitted frequency in the L5E system, is approximately 125,000 dB. In terms of the allowable variation of net loss of a network trunk (approximately ±1 dB), the tolerance on the transmission variation after equalization is 1/125,000 × 100 or 0.0008 percent.

Fixed and variable equalizers are used to correct attenuation–frequency characteristics, delay–frequency variations, or both. Variable equalizers may be adjusted automatically or manually, locally or remotely, continuously or in steps. In this treatment, the emphasis is placed on attenuation–frequency equalization.

Functions and Objectives

The need to correct the attenuation–frequency characteristic of a transmission system derives from a number of different but related transmission objectives. For each objective, margin must be provided to accommodate system misalignment. The system equalization is based in part on the need to maintain signal–to–noise and overload performance within the available margins.

In the idealized system of Figure 10–1, repeater gain exactly compensates for the loss in the preceding cable section. In a system designed for maximum signal–to–noise ratio, any misalignment impairs signal–to–noise performance. Thus, one design objective is to provide equalizers of sufficient adjustability, accuracy, and bandwidth, located at positions in the system such that the signal–to–noise margin is not exceeded when the system is operated properly.

A second design objective for equalization is to control positive misalignment (i.e., that which raises signal amplitudes) so that overload margin is not exceeded. Misalignment, even over a relatively narrow band, can cause overload that adversely affects performance over the whole bandwidth of the system due to the response of feedback amplifiers to an overload signal.

A third equalization objective concerns channel loss objectives. In the types of system under consideration, designed primarily to provide 4–kHz channels, misalignment typically covers a band much wider than the channel bandwidth. Thus, system misalignment has a minimal effect on the transmission characteristic of an individual voice channel; the principal effect is on the overall net loss of the channel. The multiplex terminals contain pilot–controlled regulators to maintain the net loss within close limits, but the range over which these regulators operate is limited. The range covers mainly the control of variations within the multiplex equipment itself, not the line facility. Thus, the equalization system must be precise enough to avoid affecting the net loss of the individual channels.

An equalization objective in coaxial systems is to make a protection line closely similar to the working lines it protects. If the attenuation–frequency responses of such lines differed appreciably, a transmission gain hit would be experienced each time lines were switched.

The final objective for the design of equalizers is the stable flat response that may be required for the transmission of wideband signals. This objective is most difficult to meet for television or high–speed digital transmission. For example, it may be desirable to replace mastergroup speech loads with digital terminals that each transmit several DS1–level digital signals. The possibility of such applications must be recognized in system design.

Equalizer Types

Equalizers may be categorized several ways. For present purposes, consider fixed and variable equalizers as the two most important categories; within each of these, there are several subcategories.

Fixed Equalizers. The most common fixed equalizer in a cable system is the fixed–gain line repeater, which is an equalizer plus an amplifier. The principal function of a line repeater is to provide gain in compensation for cable loss. Since cable loss is essentially proportional to the square root of frequency above a few tens of kilohertz, the repeater gain must match this characteristic closely. This match is difficult to obtain economically, so two additional types of fixed equalizer are usually required. Both are closely related to line repeater design.

In laying out a system geographically, line repeaters can seldom be located at precisely the nominal spacing. To minimize cost, it is common practice to use a single design of line repeater. Tolerances in repeater spacing are then provided by a set of spacing rules that basically have two features: (1) spacings that are longer than nominal are offset immediately by short spacings and (2) a series of long spacings is not usable. Short spacings are generally not offset by compensating long sections. Instead they are built out to the loss of the nominal spacing by networks with loss characteristics that closely simulate the losses of short sections of line. These line build–out networks are, in effect, a series of fixed equalizers.

The loss characteristic of cable conductors tends to be a smooth function of frequency. The compensating gain of line repeaters can match this loss characteristic very closely but the match can never be perfect. Furthermore, the closer the match, the higher the cost of the repeater. An economic balance is commonly achieved by allowing deviations from ideal design to accumulate over a specified number of repeater sections and then to compensate with a fixed "deviation" equalizer. The amount of accumulation allowed balances the performance penalties of misalignment (margins must be provided for these effects) and the costs of feasible equalizers. For perspective, consider the L5E coaxial system with its nominal repeater spacing of one mile. Suppose each repeater had an excess gain at some frequency of just 0.01 dB. If uncorrected, this deviation, small as it is, would accumulate through the 4000 repeaters of a maximum−length system to $0.01 \times 4000 = 40$ dB. Gain deviations as small as 0.01 dB are difficult to measure in practice and are essentially impossible to control in design, manufacture, or operation. The deviations are allowed to accumulate to a reasonable magnitude set by available margins and feasible equalizers. They are then corrected by deviation equalizers distributed along the route.

Variable Equalizers. Several types of variable equalizer are used. The attenuation−frequency response provided and the range and manner of adjustment depend on the system characteristics to be compensated. A brief discussion of these equalizers will relate equalizer designs to system operating characteristics.

The largest changes in system attenuation−frequency response come from the variation of temperature. In most modern systems, there are two major effects. The first, and usually by far the larger, is the change in the loss of the cable. This shift occurs smoothly with temperature variations and is almost completely a square−root−of−frequency effect. That is, for a given change in temperature, the change of loss in decibels at one frequency relative to the change of loss at another frequency is proportional to the square root of the ratio of the frequencies. The second major effect is the change of the gains of the line repeaters with temperature.

For specific temperature ranges, the changes in attenuation−frequency response and gain are predictable. They are relatively smooth functions that can be accurately reproduced in discrete−component networks. The variations occur mainly from season to season in buried−cable systems, and mainly from hour to hour in aerial paired−cable systems. They are large, and so are usually corrected continuously. The equalizers are adjusted automatically in response to changes in pilot tones transmitted at controlled amplitudes. These signals are picked off the line, rectified, and compared with a dc reference voltage. The voltage difference, or error signal, is then used to adjust the equalizer in such a direction as to return the pilot signal to its proper value. This process is called regulation. Repeaters that incorporate this feature are called regulators or regulating repeaters.

There are many causes of misalignment within a system. In addition to the fixed and variable systematic deviations previously discussed, others occur randomly. These deviations are usually small in each repeater or equalizer but may accumulate to excessive values. As with other deviations, they are controlled via adjustable equalizers along the route.

The equalizers that cancel accumulated random deviations are usually a group of adjustable units whose characteristics correct almost any transmission deviation in the band. These equalizers may be adjustable in small steps or may be continuously adjustable by varying an element such as a resistor or capacitor. The adjustments are usually manual but may be remotely controlled from a central location by digital circuits.

Another type of equalizer, the adaptive equalizer, is designed as a delay line with taps. The delayed signals from the taps are individually weighted and summed to yield an equalized signal. The adaptive equalizer is used to reduce attenuation–frequency distortion and delay distortion in digital circuits automatically in response to an algorithm based on the characteristics of the transmitted signal. The adjustment minimizes the error rate over the channel being equalized. This equalizer design is used on some digital transmission channels derived from analog facilities. However, it is not normally used to equalize an analog facility that will be used only as part of an analog system.

Equalization Plan

The provision of equalization for an analog cable system usually requires satisfying a number of different criteria simultaneously. The equalizers must be producible at reasonable cost and must provide specified characteristics and adjustment range. Adjustment procedures must be practical in the operating environment.

Theoretically, equalizers may be placed anywhere along the transmission line and may equalize any characteristic of any magnitude. However, the location of equalizers and the magnitude of the distortion to be corrected have profound effects on system overload and signal–to–noise performance. Figure 10–2 shows the signal–to–thermal–noise penalties for three equalization plans for a range of positive and negative values of channel misalignment.

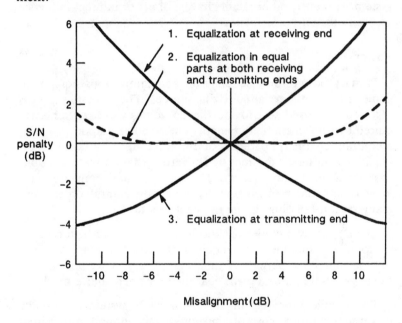

Figure 10–2. Signal–to–noise penalties due to misalignment.

The penalties shown by curves 1 and 3 are mirror images in respect to nominal signal level for a range of amplitudes and for positive and negative misalignments. If the equalizers are divided so that half the misalignment is corrected at each end of the line, the penalties are significantly reduced. For misalignments of about ±5 dB, penalties are insignificant. With this method of equalization, it can be shown that signal–to–noise penalties from intermodulation noise are also small over this range of misalignments.

This widely used strategy, called pre– and postequalization, increases the complexity of equalizer adjustments somewhat. Thus, where misalignments are small, it is more common to place equalizers only at the receiving end of a line section.

10-3 ANCILLARY SUBSYSTEMS

The transmission medium and the electronic equipment required to overcome line loss are of primary importance in the system. However, other factors have a direct or indirect influence on transmission performance.

Power

Primary power for essentially all communications equipment comes from commercial 60–Hz ac sources. The primary supply is rectified and used to provide the dc voltages and currents required by transmission equipment. The rectifier output maintains a constant charge on batteries of 24, 48, 130, or 140 volts. Individual system needs are met by converters that derive other voltages from the battery supply. The batteries and converters are located with the transmission equipment in central offices and main–station buildings along the cable route.

The dc supply includes backup features to assure high reliability for the communications equipment. The batteries carry the full load for short periods of time when the primary power fails. Local generators pick up the load if the power failure persists.

The remote repeaters of an analog cable system are usually powered by direct current, current–regulated and transmitted over the line. The direct current is furnished from the central office or main station and combined with the signal currents via filters at the connection to the line. At each remote repeater, similar filters separate and recombine power and signal currents.

Maintenance and Reliability

Analog cable systems incorporate many features to give reliability and to provide access and facilities for maintenance. In addition, building design, cable route selection, and cable placement (aerial, buried, use of ducts, degree of lightning protection, etc.) all affect the reliability and maintainability of systems.

Transmission equipment is distributed over long distances. Of necessity, it is often located in places that are difficult to reach. For these reasons, it is necessary to equip each system to recognize trouble conditions, to isolate the trouble to a particular section of line, and then to identify the location of the fault so that repair personnel may be dispatched to the correct location. Separate telephone facilities (order wires) and data links are also provided to assist maintenance personnel.

Cable systems normally operate with a fully equipped and powered spare line on each route. The spare does not normally carry service. Service is transferred to this line to allow maintenance work or to restore service when a working line fails. In coaxial systems, the transfer may be accomplished manually or automatically by line protection switching equipment. In paired–cable systems with their smaller channel capacity, switching lines on a manual "patch" basis suffices.

Terminal Arrangements

The main–station and terminal buildings used with cable systems contain equipment in addition to that described in relation to power, maintenance, and reliability, particularly that for multiplexing signals in preparation for transmission over the line. Related equipment is required to drop, block, and insert circuits; these facilities provide the flexibility for efficient interconnection of various types of system. Carrier and pilot signal generators and highly precise frequency control equipment are also located at system terminals.

References

1. Members of Technical Staff. *Transmission Systems for Communications*, Fifth Edition (Murray Hill, NJ: AT&T Bell Laboratories, Inc., 1982), pp. 287–293, 329–362, and 383–454.

2. MacDonald, R. A. et al. "Common Carrier Transmission," *Reference Data for Engineers: Radio, Electronics, Computer, and Communications,* Seventh Edition (Indianapolis, IN: Howard W. Sams and Company, Inc., 1985), pp. 38-3 to 38-12.

3. Freeman, R. L. *Telecommunications Transmission Handbook,* Second Edition (New York: John Wiley and Sons, Inc., 1981), pp. 418-445.

Chapter 11

Short–Haul Analog Carrier Systems

A number of analog carrier systems are used on wire lines. These systems can meet allocated transmission requirements (noise, crosstalk, level stability, etc.) for distances up to about 200 miles. They are thus termed "short–haul" analog systems. Because of their channel capacity of 24 circuits or less, they are also commonly called "narrowband" to distinguish them from "broadband" coaxial cable and radio systems of much greater capacity. Their physical structure emphasizes simplicity, flexibility, and low getting–started cost. While these systems have been largely replaced by digital facilities, they are still important in some rural areas where growth is slow and circuit cross–sections are long and thin. The general families into which these systems fall are types N, O, and ON carrier.

The short–haul systems have several common features. They all use syllabic compandors to improve the user–perceived noise level by about 25 dB and their crosstalk performance by about 20 dB. This allows use of existing wire facilities with only relatively minor preparation. The compandor (compressor–expandor) compresses the dynamic range of speech levels at the transmitting end by two–to–one, then expands the range at the receiving end in a complementary way. The compandor gain varies at a syllable–by–syllable rate.

These systems employ grouped frequency allocations, interchanged at repeater points, to give transmission equalization and to allow single–cable operation without special treatment for crosstalk. Line repeaters for these systems use pilot tones related to the channel carriers to regulate levels. This offsets line–loss variations resulting from changes in temperature. The earliest systems included a signalling feature for each channel built into the terminal, using a 3700–Hz "out–of–band" tone. Later versions omitted this feature in favor of external 2600–Hz signalling units because of their increased flexibility.

11-1 O-TYPE SYSTEMS

While O–type open–wire carrier systems have nearly disappeared, their basic layout is of interest because it originated at the same time as the "N" family and because it later contributed to the evolution of cable carrier. O–type systems provided four-channel stackable groups [1], giving 4, 8, 12, or 16 single-sideband voice channels on an open–wire pair over a range of about 15 to 150 miles. They operated on an equivalent–four-wire basis (both directions of transmission on one wire pair) by use of frequency division. The systems were used in various combinations to coordinate with the operating frequencies of other types of carrier on the same open–wire line. They were as follows.

OA systems used two carrier frequencies in each direction (6 and 14 kHz one way, 24 and 32 kHz the other way). The result was four two–way circuits, each using the upper or lower sideband of each carrier on a "twin–channel" basis. The resulting total spectrum on the line extended between about 2 and 36 kHz. Because of the relatively low line losses at these frequencies, OA systems up to roughly 50 miles did not need repeaters. On longer routes, a simple line repeater was needed, supplying equalization switch–selectable in steps. Regulation of gain at the receiving side of the terminal (or of a repeater) used the two incoming carrier frequencies. The OA repeater or terminal could reduce a variation of 40 dB in the level of the incoming signal to about 1.5 dB at the output. Like all other "O" equipment, it was locally powered.

OB systems had a structure similar to that of OA, with carriers of 44 and 52 kHz in one direction and 64 and 72 kHz the other way. Total line spectrum was thus about 40 to 76 kHz. The line loss at OB frequencies, compared to those for OA, was both higher and more variable due to the effects of temperature, rain, and especially icing. (On open wire at carrier frequencies, a layer of ice causes considerable increases in loss. The "skin effect" forces some of the line current to travel in the high–resistance ice coating.) Thus, more complex repeaters were needed at closer intervals. The OB repeater used "frequency frogging" to equalize the line loss versus frequency: the incoming low band (40–56 kHz) was modulated against a 116–kHz carrier in the repeater, delivering a high–band spectrum of 60 to 76 kHz for transmission into the next line section. In the opposite direction of transmission, the incoming high band was inverted ("frogged") into the low band. This process equalized the loss versus frequency of the line. It gave an approximate cancellation of the line slope (the difference in loss between the lowest and highest frequencies transmitted). The repeater also provided the usual gain regulation.

OC systems used the next allocation above OB, with transmitted carriers of 84 and 92 kHz in one direction and 104 and 112 kHz the other way. This system used a frequency–frogging repeater like that for OB.

OD systems employed the highest frequency allocation, with carriers of 124 and 132 kHz in one direction and 144 and 156 kHz in the other. The OD repeater was also a frequency–frogging type.

A progressive rise in line frequency causes increases in line loss, in transmission irregularities from imperfections in the line, in variability of line loss, and in intersystem crosstalk. These impairments called for shortened repeater spacing and for elaborate pair–transposition schemes. So the lower–frequency systems were the most common and OD the least. It was normal practice to use, for instance, one open–wire pair to serve two outlying towns from a city. The closer of the towns would be served by the high–frequency OC and OD systems, while the farther location would be handled by the low–frequency OA and OB systems. With each wire pair carrying up to 16 carrier channels, a 20–pair open–wire route had a nominal capacity of 320 circuits.

In addition to the usual OA–OD design, at least two manufacturers developed an OJ frequency allocation to coordinate with the channel frequencies used by the then–existing type J 12–channel system on the same pole line. Another maker provided electric power utilities with a 20–channel version of the "O" family for use as power–line carrier. By using the OB–OC–OD frequency allocations, plus added OE and OF assignments, it was possible to place the channels between 40 and 248 kHz on a high–tension transmission line.

The use of a single carrier to provide two channels, occupying the upper and lower sideband respectively, conserved active devices (oscillators) at the cost of stringent requirements on the sideband filters. Because the highest energy in a voice signal is at frequencies in the 300–to–600–Hz range, the resulting sidebands for the two channels were close together. Any crosstalk from filter leakage was intelligible, not frequency–inverted. Later single–sideband terminals used an all–lower–sideband spectrum to ease the filter requirements.

11-2 N-TYPE REPEATERED LINES

The N–type carrier systems transmit 12 or 24 voice channels over cable pairs. Twelve–channel operation found use in short–haul applications up to roughly 35 miles; 24–channel systems were appropriate for longer systems in the 35–to–200–mile range where the cost of the line facility had to be shared more efficiently and a more expensive terminal was thus affordable. The same carrier line design is used regardless of the terminals. In most applications, two pairs are used in the same cable, one for each direction of transmission. As with the OB–OC–OD open–wire systems, frequency frogging is used at each repeater to minimize crosstalk and provide equalization.

Three vintages of N–carrier repeater are in use. The first was an electron–tube design (N1), many of which were converted to solid–state operation by using networks of field–effect transistors and other components in plug–in packages. There is also an early solid–state unit (N1A). The final design (N2) provided considerable improvements in noise and other transmission factors. Some N–carrier repeaters have been adapted for "equivalent four–wire" transmission over a single cable pair.

Transmission Plan

All N–carrier terminals and line equipment use the same basic transmission plan. The signals are transmitted in a high–frequency group (172 to 268 kHz) or in a low–frequency group (36 to 132 kHz). A terminal receives the group opposite to that which it transmits. At each repeater, the two groups are interchanged by a modulation process in which a 304–kHz carrier is used. Thus a repeater may receive signals in the low group from both directions and transmit in the high group in both directions (a low–high repeater) or vice versa (a high–low repeater). The high–low version is illustrated in Figure 11–1. Multiple frequency translations along the carrier line are shown in Figure 11–2. The frequency–frogging process at each repeater

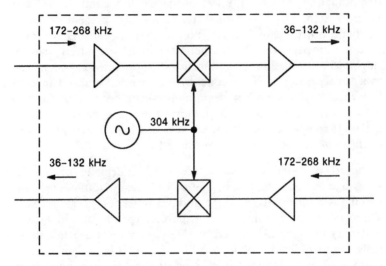

Figure 11-1. Frequency frogging at a high–low repeater.

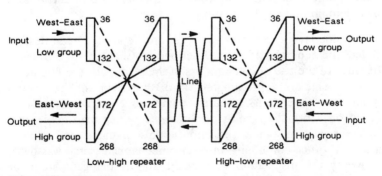

Figure 11-2. Frequency translations along an N–carrier repeatered line.

serves three purposes. It blocks circulating crosstalk paths around the repeater, it provides basic equalization, and it gives equal average repeater spacings for the two directions of transmission.

The design of N–type systems is based on the use of a spectrum of carrier signals spaced eight kHz apart [2]. The carriers provide signal power for regulation, frequency correction, and demodulation. The total power of the carriers controls the regulation system. If 12–channel terminals are present, double-sideband transmission is used and the channel carriers are transmitted directly. If 24–channel terminals are used, single-sideband transmission is employed with suppressed carriers; however, every other carrier frequency is reinserted and transmitted. The regulation system is necessarily powerful because of the wide daily temperature changes experienced by aerial cable: a change of 100°F, night to midday, is entirely possible. Thus, substantial changes in line loss must be regulated out.

Paired or quadded cables are used, normally of 19– or 22–gauge but occasionally of 16– or 24–gauge. Nominal repeater spacing is 5 miles for 19–gauge and 3.5 miles for 22–gauge pairs. There is no specific limit on the percentage of pairs in a cable that may be assigned to carrier. N–type systems are not nominally compatible in the same cable with T1 digital facilities, for reasons of noise induced into some of the "N" channels. However, in some cases special engineering has yielded successful joint operation as either a transition expedient for modernization or a semipermanent installation.

The line layout, repeater spacings, and repeater circuit designs reflect the general principles described in Chapter 10. However, because of the use of compandors in the terminals, the line noise requirements are approximately 25 dB less stringent than would otherwise be needed. Repeater spacing in N–carrier systems is based on satisfactory noise performance rather than achievable repeater gain. In some cases, impulse noise in cable sections near a central office containing an electromechanical switch was overcome by the installation of a fixed 20–dB flat–gain amplifier ahead of the offending section to increase signal levels or by adding a separate carrier–only entrance cable.

It is only realistic to cite a disadvantage of short–haul analog systems compared to digital facilities: the heavy emphasis on line equalization (discussed in detail later) means much greater difficulty in rearranging or rerouting carrier systems. Thus, digital transmission has an inherent flexibility that is important where rates of rearrangement are high.

N2 Repeaters

The block diagram of an N2 repeater is shown in Figure 11–3. ("N2" here refers specifically to a *repeater* design, usable with any terminal in the "N" family. The N2 *terminal* is a wholly separate device.) Repeaters are placed in pole– or pedestal–mounted cabinets, in equipment bays in central–office buildings, and in bays in repeater huts at power–feed points.

Repeater Design. The N2 repeater, like earlier designs, is a plug–in unit; it is an assembly of five plug–in subunits. The subunits are two identical modulator units, two identical amplifier assemblies, and an oscillator unit. These plug–in arrangements make repairs significantly simpler than for the earlier types.

The N2 repeater can be discussed conveniently in terms of: (1) amplification, modulation, and filtering; (2) equalization and regulation; and (3) remote powering. Earlier repeaters used the same repeater spacing, transmission level points (TLPs), and general gain regulation arrangements.

Amplification, Modulation, and Filtering. The amplifiers shown in Figure 11–3 are of negative–feedback design. Signals are amplified at the input by a preamplifier for good noise performance. They then feed a modulator, also driven by a 304–kHz crystal oscillator, for the frequency–frogging process. A three–stage amplifier provides additional gain after modulation. The amplifiers provide proper terminations for the modulators and cable pairs.

The placement of the filters at the input and output of the modulator in Figure 11–3 determines the mode of repeater operation, high–low or low–high. At the inputs to the modulators, filters accept the desired group and suppress any noise or other signal outside the group band. The filters at the outputs of the modulators suppress the unwanted components of the modulated

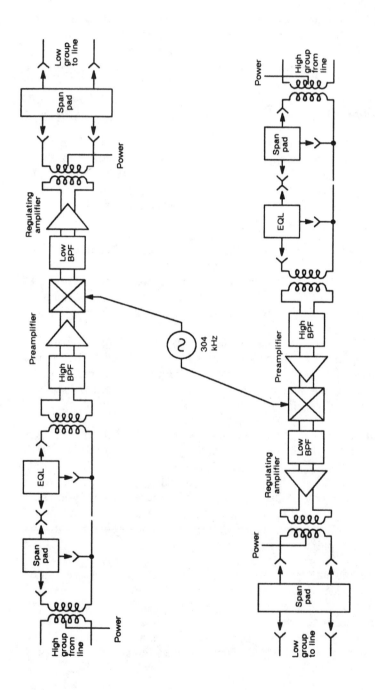

Figure 11-3. N2 repeater-block diagram.

signal and any 304–kHz signal that may leak through the modulator.

Equalization and Regulation. As mentioned before, the primary equalization of cable slope is accomplished by means of frequency frogging. For some short systems, no further equalization is needed. In addition, the repeater accommodates fixed plug–in equalizers whose frequency response complements that of the line. The final correction of line deviations, on systems typically ten or more repeaters long and/or using cable other than 19–gauge, involves plug–in deviation equalizers. A combination of four equalizer types compensates for miscellaneous deviations. These network characteristics, designated slope, bulge, cubic, and quartic, are illustrated in Figure 11–4. These fixed equalizers have several values: for slope, ±3, ±6, or ±9 dB; for bulge distortion, +2 or +4 dB; for cubic or quartic distortion, ± 1 dB each. (Positive slope implies that the higher–numbered

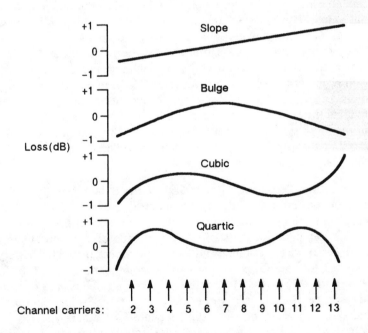

Figure 11–4. Loss–frequency characteristics of N–carrier deviation equalizers.

channel carriers contain more power than the low–numbered ones.) Such supplemental equalizers may be required where repeater sections are odd in number or unequal in length and thus do not balance out adequately. Methods are specified for determining the best equalization at each repeater. For example, it is normal practice to have the line slope near zero in a cable section that is exposed to impulse noise to spread the exposure evenly among all the voice channels.

Deviation equalizers are used in long systems where the fixed networks used at repeaters cannot perform adequately. These equalizers are continuously adjustable over a range of ± 10 dB of slope and ± 5 dB each of bulge, cubic, and quartic corrections.

Flat–gain adjustments are made by the selection of plug–in span pads at the input and output of a repeater, as shown in Figure 11–3. The span pads have flat losses in steps of 2 dB from 0 to 44 dB. Thus, by proper span–pad selection, the flat gain of a repeater may be adjusted to within a decibel of the desired nominal value. The flat–gain regulator provides the final adjustment by compensating for loss changes due to temperature variations. The regulator operates on the basis of the total power, which is concentrated primarily in the channel carriers. The operating gain of the repeater can be determined by an in–service measurement of the resistance of the regulating thermistor used in the feedback network of the main amplifier. The preselected value of the input span pad is confirmed from this measurement, assuring that the regulator operates in the middle of its range under nominal conditions.

Repeater Powering. Repeaters mounted in a central office can be powered directly by the central–office battery of −48 volts. Remote repeaters are powered by simplex connections over the carrier pairs. A constant–current regulator compensates for changes in wire resistance induced by temperature. The battery supplies for remote powering can be combinations of +130, 0, −48, and −130 volts. In remotely powered repeaters, the operating voltage of each unit is internally regulated. Typical operating current, in a span not including repeaters of other types, is 85 mA. Up to four remote repeaters are powered in each direction from a central office, even where repeater sections are of maximum length. Thus, up to nine cable sections can exist between power–feed points. Where central–office buildings are not available, repeater huts containing battery plants provide the necessary power feed.

Cross–Connect Facilities. A cross–connect point provides flexible interconnection of cable pairs and terminals. For the N2 repeatered line, power–feed connections are made in an equipment frame called a line build–out (LBO) bay. LBO networks and equalizers plug into this bay. The N2 cross–connect bay is separate from the LBO bay; thus, cross–connections are free of powering voltages. In addition, TLPs are controlled to facilitate interconnection among incoming cable pairs, outgoing cable pairs, office mounted repeaters, and terminals.

Equivalent Four–Wire Lines. Some N–carrier lines use only a single cable pair in equivalent four–wire operation. Directional filters that meet stringent requirements permit this mode of operation while meeting crosstalk and deviation limits. The filters are used in conjunction with an ordinary repeater unit. Phase equalizers may be included to correct the delay distortion introduced by the filters and thus prevent "washout" of double–sideband signals. The block diagram of a repeater point is given in Figure 11–5. The advantage of this arrangement is the two–to–one saving of cable pairs, which typically allows deferring a cable reinforcement until a new all–digital cable can be justified.

11–3 N–TYPE TERMINALS

The development of multiplex terminals for N–carrier systems began with the N1 electron–tube design and evolved in step with the line repeaters. As the use of open–wire line facilities diminished, the O–type terminal equipment was gradually adapted for use on N–carrier lines. This produced the ON1 and ON2 terminals. Like N1 repeaters, these early designs were often converted to solid–state operation by use of plug–in transistor networks. Later terminals include the N2 solid–state unit, which provides 12 double–sideband channels in the same general format as in N1, and the N3 and N4 terminals, which each provide 24 single–sideband channels. Unlike the case with digital terminals, the channel units for "N" are deliberately limited in options; any

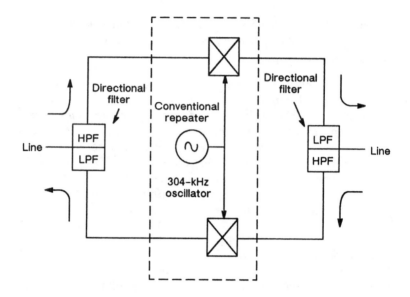

Figure 11-5. Equivalent four-wire repeater.

choice of signalling or special–services transmission features is made by selecting the proper external single–frequency signalling unit instead.

The N2 Terminal

The N2 terminal develops its channels in a double–sideband, transmitted–carrier format in the high–group band as illustrated in Figure 11–6(a) [3]. This group signal spectrum is applied directly to the carrier line where high–group transmission is required or, as shown in Figure 11–6(b), is modulated into the low–group band. The selection of high– or low–group transmission depends on the number of repeaters (frequency–frogging points) on the carrier system end–to–end and on the need to coordinate with other "N" systems in the same cable. In the figure, 12 channel carriers are shown, numbered 2 to 13. Normal operation involves the use of this allocation; there is also a channel 1, used only in rare cases where outside interference (e.g., from a very–low–frequency radio station) makes one of the other assignments unusable. Regardless of the frequencies used, the

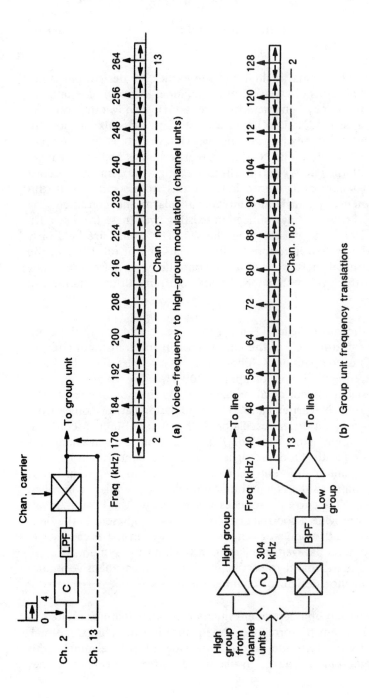

Figure 11-6. Frequency translations in transmitting side of N2 terminal.

channels are numbered 1 through 12 for inventory and assignment purposes.

The N2 terminal is similar to the earlier N1 design, but is improved in terms of variation of net channel loss with time, attenuation–frequency characteristic, channel bandwidth, random noise, intermodulation, impulse noise, and crosstalk. Minor differences nominally prevent the two vintages from being compatible end–to–end. The N2 (and later) terminals include a carrier group alarm (CGA) and trunk processing arrangement to detect system failure and remove failed trunks from service. With this equipment, system failure initiates an alarm and conditions the affected trunks. Any connection existing over these trunks is disconnected so as to stop time charges. The trunks are held busy until the system is restored. Upon clearance of the trouble, the two terminals perform a series of continuity and noise tests, using two of their voice channels, before returning all the channels to service.

As shown in Figure 11–6(a), the voice signal enters the compressor portion (C) of the compandor in the transmitting terminal. The compandor is followed by a low–pass filter having a high–frequency cutoff of about 3200 Hz. The voice–frequency (VF) signal (voice, data, or signalling) is then modulated to the high–group N–carrier band. The modulating carrier comes from a free–running crystal oscillator in the channel unit; a common carrier supply is not needed. The signal from a given channel is combined with 11 other signals that have been similarly processed to fall at different frequency positions in the group band. At the input to the channel unit modulator, there is a controlled dc bias. This current produces the necessary modulator unbalance to provide a controlled carrier signal component in the double–sideband modulator output. The power in these carrier signals controls flat–gain regulators throughout the system. The use of double–sideband transmission permits an inexpensive inductor–capacitor design for channel filters.

The group units provide a number of other features related to overall system performance. Preequalization of cable slope may be introduced in the transmitting side of the terminal, with postequalization also available in the receiving side.

Preequalization is via plug–in networks giving +9 to –9 dB of slope in 3–dB steps.

At terminals that receive high–group input from the line, the group signal is flat–gain regulated and then connected to filters that select individual channel signals. Additional regulation of each channel is provided at that point, based on the level of the specific channel carrier. The channels are then demodulated. Where the terminal is arranged for low–group receiving from the line, the signal is first modulated into the high group; then the above processes are followed. The use of the transmitted carrier for demodulation means that minor frequency errors from the distant terminal's oscillator, and from the 304–kHz oscillators in the repeaters, are unimportant.

The N2 terminal, like all others in the "N" family, uses the standard VF TLPs of –16 dB sending into the terminal and +7 dB receiving. The maximum total power of the 12 channels sent into the line in high–group operation is +12 dBm; in low–group operation it is +3 dBm.

N2 terminals exist in terminal–only bays holding up to eight terminals in an 11–1/2 foot bay, and in packaged arrangements incorporating terminals, single–frequency signalling units, test access, and patching in a single rack.

The N4 Terminal

The final development in the "N" family of terminals is the N4. This is a 24–channel single–sideband design that is operable end–to–end with the N3 [4] and compatible earlier units but uses later components and design techniques. As a result, it gives high packaging density (12 terminals in an 11–1/2 foot bay), low power consumption (reduced about six to one compared to its predecessor), and improved maintenance features.

The N4 terminal assembles two 12–channel groups, using techniques comparable to those used in the A5–type channel bank described in Chapter 9, then combines them into the "N" line spectrum. The terminal is diagrammed in Figures 11–7, 11–8, and 11–9.

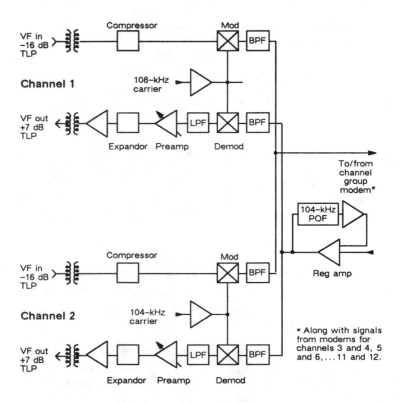

Figure 11–7. N4 double–channel modem.

Figure 11–7 shows the double–channel modem unit used in the terminal. In it, each voice circuit enters on the usual four-wire basis, with a TLP toward the carrier system of –16 dB. The circuits are paired physically: channels 1 and 2, 3 and 4, etc. of a group share circuit packs. The voice signal first receives compression, then is modulated with one carrier out of 12 in a spectrum of 64, 68, . . . through 108 kHz. The modulator is balanced to suppress the carrier. A crystal bandpass filter selects the lower sideband of the modulation process and suppresses any carrier that escapes the modulator. The result, combining the outputs of all the twin–channel modems, is thus two 12–channel groups, each in the spectrum of 60 to 108 kHz.

In the receiving direction, the two channel groups each feed the receive sides of six double–channel circuit packs. Each pair

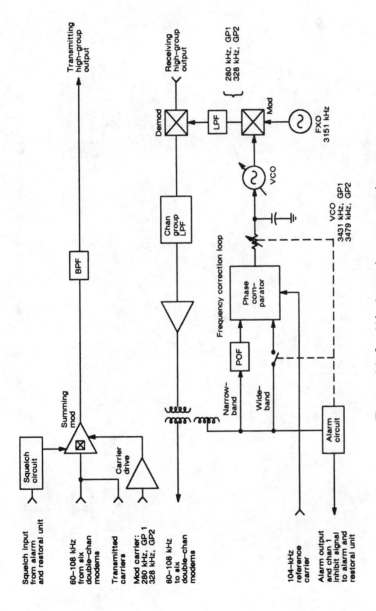

Figure 11–8. N4 channel–group modem.

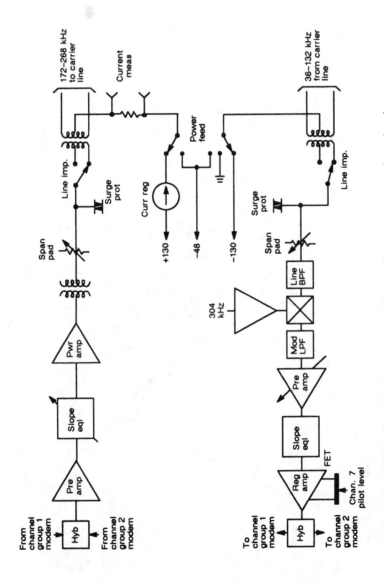

Figure 11–9. N4 high–group–transmit/low–group–receive circuits.

of signals (1 and 2, . . . , up through 11 and 12) receives individual level regulation based on its accompanying pilot signal. The signals then pass through crystal filters and are demodulated using the appropriate carrier in the 64-to-108-kHz region. After low-pass filtering and level expansion (decompression), the signals are amplified to the standard receive level of +7 dB TLP.

The next equipment item provides translation to and from "N" high-group frequencies. This uses a pair of channel-group modems, one of which is depicted in Figure 11-8. Each outgoing channel group has six regulating carriers reintroduced into it, at frequencies of 64, 72, . . . through 104 kHz. Then the channel group is individually modulated against a carrier of 280 kHz (group 1) or 328 kHz (for group 2), yielding 24 channels between 172 and 268 kHz. The total of 12 regulating carriers satisfies the requirements of the "N" repeatered line as well as allowing double-channel regulating functions in the distant terminal. The resulting signal, after bandpass filtering, is the high-group spectrum.

In the receive direction of the channel-group modem, the 24-channel signal is modulated against a carrier of 280 or 328 kHz. Each of the two channel-group modems thus yields one of the two original 60-to-108-kHz groups, each containing six regulating carriers. The incoming signals and carriers have all received minor frequency errors because of repeated frogging operations in the repeaters based on up to 40 or so independent 304-kHz oscillators. So a frequency correction unit is included in each group's receiving equipment. Using a phase-locked loop, it compares the incoming 104-kHz line pilot with a precise 104 kHz supplied in the terminal. The loop controls the frequency of an oscillator operating at 3431 kHz (for group 1) or 3479 kHz (for group 2). The loop has two bandwidths: 400 Hz to acquire lock, 60 Hz to maintain it. The narrow operating bandwidth guards against phase jitter that might result from interfering speech sidebands near 104 kHz. The adjusted signal at 3431 or 3479 kHz is then mixed with a fixed oscillator of 3151 kHz, yielding the 280- or 328-kHz carrier for translating to group frequency.

In the third equipment block, the high-group signals from the channel-group modems may be applied to the line directly, in high–group–transmit terminals, or may be modulated against the usual 304–kHz carrier for low–group–transmit applications. Figure 11–9 shows the circuits for high–group–transmit/low–group–receive use. After outputs of the two channel–group modems are combined in a hybrid, the outgoing signal may be presloped by +11 to −11 dB in 1–dB steps. The same total power levels apply as in N2: +12 dBm maximum in the high group, +3 dBm in the low group. The exact level is adjustable via pads of 0, 10, 20, or 30 dB, plus a variable control having an 11–dB range. As with N2, a constant–current regulator feeds up to 145 mA from combinations of +130, 0, −48 and −130 volts onto the line unless the line is powered externally via an LBO bay.

The received line spectrum, as with other "N" terminals, is the opposite of that leaving the terminal: low–group receive with high–group send, etc. A low–group incoming signal is frogged into the high group; a high–group signal is accepted directly. Build–out pads in 10–dB steps account for short cable sections. After bandpass filtering and preamplification, receiving slope adjustments of +11 to −11 dB are available. The 24–channel signal then undergoes level regulation based on the total incoming power. The regulating element is a field–effect transistor rather than the thermistor used in earlier designs. The signal is then split in a hybrid to feed the receive sides of the two channel group modems.

Because of the need for precision, especially in applications using the N3–L junction discussed in Chapter 9, and because of the economies of bulk generation, all carriers for a group of up to 12 terminals come from a common carrier supply shelf. The shelf, in turn, is slaved to the master frequency supply in the office. The shelf produces 12 channel carriers, two channel–group carriers, and a group carrier.

The compressor unit in N4 is an integrated circuit rather than a pack of discrete components. Where an overall circuit is built up from channels on two carrier systems connected back–to–back, tandem companding operations are undesirable. As a result, a switch option disables the compandors at the tandem–connection point.

The carrier group alarm feature normally operates independently for the two channel groups, but can be tied to only group 1 if needed for compatibility with a distant terminal of a particular manufacture. It operates like the CGA in N2, using a "handshake" of 2600–Hz tones and signal–to–noise ratio checks in restoring a failed system to service. If the carrier signal fails coming toward a terminal, the outgoing signal is squelched so that the distant terminal will also recognize the failure.

The N4 terminal design provides a "test modem" unit that allows loop–back testing of a terminal independently of the distant terminal.

Other Members of the Short–Haul Analog Carrier Family

The N2 and N4 carrier systems are used in this text as examples of the final 12– and 24–channel developments for short–haul use [5]. However, a large number of earlier and related items, both carrier systems and individual equipment items, have been used in the communications industry [6]. Some relevant examples are described below. They illustrate the flexibility inherent in short–haul analog carrier.

N1 Terminal. This was the original "N" 12–channel terminal, circa 1950. Comparable electrically to the later N2 terminal, it allowed three 12–channel systems to terminate in an 11–1/2 foot bay.

ON Junction. This equipment item was a frequency/level converter to be installed at the junction of a carrier open–wire line and an N–carrier repeatered cable. It allowed a tandem combination of open–wire and cable line facilities. It thus permitted gradual replacement of open wire that had been channelized with "O" terminals without making those terminals obsolete.

ON1 Carrier System. This development combined O–carrier terminal equipment with a frequency converter derived from the ON junction. It allowed 20 voice channels (5 four–channel groups) to operate on an "N" repeatered line. It thus reduced the costs of long carrier systems below those that could be obtained with 12–channel N1 operation.

ON2 Carrier System. A refinement of ON1, this system used "O" terminals to provide 24–channel transmission (six four–

channel groups) on an "N" repeatered line. ON2 was widely installed on long routes before the N3 and N4 24–channel terminals became available.

ON Radio Combiner. This multiplexer unit allowed either two or four ON–type carrier systems to operate over microwave radio facilities. The result was up to 48 or 96 channels, with the low initial cost and modular growth plan of the O–type terminal.

ON/K System. This special arrangement translated the basic frequency range of an ON–type carrier system to the spectrum above 60 kHz. It made it possible to add ON carrier to cables that were already fully equipped for K–carrier operation in the 12–to–60–kHz range. While usable only in the restricted cases where "K" facilities were already in place, it avoided a sizable amount of cable construction. ON/K involved specialized repeaters placed in the existing "K" repeater huts, which were normally about 17 miles apart. The resulting ON repeater spacing was extraordinarily long.

N3 Terminal. This equipment, a sizably improved 24–channel terminal, provided a replacement for ON2 equipment circa 1965. Some of its components (e.g., compandors) were the same as those of the N2 terminal. The N4 terminal replaced N3 in turn, providing the culmination of design progress in short–haul analog terminals.

Program Terminals. Five–kilohertz program service was originally available in the N1 terminal via a special plug–in channel unit that used double–sideband transmission, preempted three channel slots, and relied on external compandors and equalization equipment. A separate program terminal later became available, combining the channel–unit function with a compandor, equalizers, and control functions. It could be connected to the line side of any terminal in the "N" family.

Wideband Facilities. When commercial 40.8–kb/s wideband data transmission first appeared circa 1965, a set of channel units was made available to plug into an N2 terminal. It preempted six of the voice channels. Special terminals were introduced later that connected directly to an "N" repeatered line. The resulting carrier system provided one two–way wideband data channel at 19.2, 40.8, or 50 kb/s, plus two voice circuits.

N3-L Junction. As discussed in Chapter 9, this unit allowed the use of broadband analog carrier facilities (radio or coaxial cable), in combination with N-carrier repeatered lines, to build 24-channel carrier systems. The systems could employ combinations of N3 terminals, N4 terminals, and A-type channel banks.

Automatic Deviation Regulator. Before the N2 repeater was available with its provisions for sophisticated equalization of the carrier line, transmission deviations caused by temperature changes were troublesome on very long "N" systems. An automatic regulator was used occasionally in these cases. Operating from the 12 carriers on the line, it provided automatic control of slope, bulge, cubic, and quartic distortions. It was installed in a central office, typically at the midpoint of the carrier system, with separate units handling the two directions of transmission.

Non-"N" Systems. Most of the short-haul analog carrier plant is based on the "N" and "O" designs. However, other designs were applied to some degree. One system comparable to ON2 used two 12-channel groups with single-sideband modulation, with all 24 carriers transmitted. Another provided 24 channels on a double-sideband basis in the 68-to-476-kHz band. Others supplied circuits by using frequency modulation of 20 carriers between 16 and 336 kHz, or of 24 carriers between 44 and 412 kHz. Some of these systems were usable on open wire as well as cable.

References

1. Coy, J. A. and E. K. Van Tassel. "Type-O Carrier Telephone," *Communications and Electronics*, Vol. 71 (Jan. 1953), pp. 428-437.

2. Perkins, E. H. "The N2 Repeatered Line," *Proceedings of the National Electronics Conference*, Vol. 22 (1966), pp. 457-462.

3. Boyd, R. C. et al. "The N2 Carrier Terminal," *Bell System Tech. J.*, Vol. 44 (May/June 1965), pp. 731-822.

4. Bleisch, G. W. et al. "The N3 Carrier System," *Bell System Tech. J.*, Vol. 45 (July/Aug. 1966), pp. 767-894.

5. Freeman, R. L. *Telecommunications Transmission Handbook*, Second Edition (New York: John Wiley and Sons, Inc., 1981), pp. 108–109 and 123–125.

6. Members of Technical Staff. *Transmission Systems for Communications*, Fifth Edition (Murray Hill, NJ: AT&T Bell Laboratories, Inc., 1982), pp. 287–288, 293, 343–347, and 453–454.

Chapter 12

Coaxial Carrier Systems

Coaxial cables are expensive but the transmission quality of the coaxial line (low loss, minimal noise, negligible crosstalk) accommodates many thousands of voice–frequency channels. As a result, the investment per channel–mile of coaxial systems is relatively low. Use of these systems was historically economical for a large cross–section of message channels accompanied by a rapid growth of demand. They are used primarily in the long–haul plant over distances from a few hundred to about 4000 miles [1]. The L5E system, an expanded version of the L5 system, represents the highest development of coaxial cable transmission. It is described in some detail in this chapter.

While the design and operation of undersea cable systems are similar to those of the L–type systems [2] in many ways, the submarine environment leads to significant differences. These differences affect the design of multiplex and other terminal equipment as well as the transmission line. Repeatered undersea cable systems are in use throughout the world. Those best known in North America are designated SA, SB, SD, SF, and SG.

12-1 ENGINEERING OF LAND COAXIAL SYSTEMS

The engineering of coaxial systems requires detailed knowledge of the transmission medium, the interactions between the medium and system components, the environment, and operating procedures. Consideration must be given to such elements of cable route selection as availability of right of way, the need to cross or avoid natural and manmade obstacles, and reliability requirements on "hardening" against natural or manmade disruption. The relationship between repeater spacing rules and route selection is also an important consideration in engineering a route.

Other aspects of route engineering include access for maintenance and possible undesirable induction from power transmission lines along the route.

Transmission Medium

The standard coaxial cable unit has a nominal diameter of 0.375 inch. It consists of a copper wire 0.1003 inch in diameter (about 10–gauge) centered in a copper tube having an inside diameter of 0.369 inch. In CCITT terms, this is a "2.6/9.5" cable, based on the two diameters in millimeters. The center conductor is held in place by polyethylene disks about an inch apart along the cable. The copper tube is formed from a flat strip 0.012 inch thick. The strip has serrated edges that interlock when it is formed into a tube. The secondary transmission constants of the line and the way the coaxial units are combined with single and paired interstitial wires into a cable are covered in Chapter 2.

Early cable designs provided only six or eight coaxial tubes, often with a group of 19–gauge wire pairs in the same sheath for short–haul carrier use. Later installations featured 12, 18, 20, or 22 tubes. The 18–tube design was used to meet duct–size limitations in metropolitan areas.

Cable designs with increased numbers of coaxial units had little effect on transmission characteristics except to increase the stranding factor, that is, the ratio of the length of coaxial unit to the length of cable. This factor differs for each cable type because of changes in cable lay or twist.

Electrical Factors. A number of electrical parameters related to cable design have significant, if not major, effects on transmission design. These parameters include the characteristic impedance of the coaxial unit, the power factor, and the breakdown voltage.

The characteristic impedance of these coaxial units is 75 ohms. While the impedance normally varies only slightly, physical discontinuities in the cable can cause significant departures from the nominal value. For example, lightning, back–filling operations, or shifting of the soil may produce dents in the cable. If a dent is deep enough to short–circuit the coaxial conductors, the unit must naturally be repaired. A nonshorting dent may cause an echo impairment due to the resulting impedance discontinuity. Because splices also cause such minor discontinuities, splice distances were randomized to avoid systematic buildup of echoes. Resplicing with improved connectors was often necessary in upgrading earlier cables for use with the later, higher–capacity coaxial systems. As a result of the stranding operation in manufacture, minute recurring deformities in the outer conductor may be produced and may cause departures from the expected transmission characteristic over a narrow range of frequencies whose wavelength is related to the stranding factor.

The power factor of a coaxial is a minute variation of the phase relationship between signal current and voltage. The variation, which tends to be a linear function of frequency, is caused by changes in the parallel leakage (conductance) between conductors. Although the power factor is negligible at low frequencies, it causes a departure of a few tenths of a decibel per mile from the expected square–root–of–frequency loss characteristic at high L5E frequencies, which approach 70 MHz and must be corrected. A nominal correction is made in each repeater. Finer–grained variations are corrected by equalizers placed along the line. The effect is relatively constant with time but can vary significantly from one vintage of cable to another.

Repeaters along a coaxial route are powered from central main stations over the center conductors of the coaxial units. In some cases, the required voltages are high enough to approach the voltage breakdown point of the polyethylene disk dielectric or of the gas in the hollow tube. As a result, corona (incipient voltage breakdown between conductors due to ionization) may form, especially where slivers or other sharp edges of the inner or outer conductor protrude into the dielectric region between the conductors. Power voltages must be held below the corona point to prevent the generation of circuit noise. Burrs or sharp edges discovered in factory or preservice corona tests may sometimes be burned out by application of suitable high voltage. Where high ac voltages were required for long power–feed sections in the L3 system, corona was controlled by filling the coaxials with sulphur hexafluoride, a heavy gas with high dielectric strength, rather than the usual dry air. The later systems use dc powering, which relieves the problem of peak voltages found with ac.

Survey of Systems

The principal features of the original and the existing coaxial systems are shown in Table 12–1. All of the systems follow the general design principles in Chapter 10. These principles became refined as successive systems were developed.

Table 12–1. Coaxial System Features

| System | Usual Cable Sizes (Units) | Repeater Stations | | Protection |
		Housing	Spacing (Miles)	
L1	4–8	Huts	8	1:1
L3	8–12	Huts	4	Multiline
L4	12–20	Manholes	2	Expanded
L5, L5E	12–22	Manholes	1	Digital control

(a) System Features

System	Nominal Bandwidth (MHz)	Comparable CCITT System (MHz)	Channels Per Coaxial Pair	4000-Mi. Noise Objective (dBrnc0)
L1	2.8	2.6	600	44
L3	8	–	1860	44
L4	17	–	3600	40
L5	57.5	60	10800	40
L5E	61.5	–	13200	40

(b) Service Features

System	Repeater Technology	Repeater Circuit	Equalization and Control	Power
L1	Electron tube	Parallel tubes, soldered in	Bumps & dynamic – local, out–of–service	60 Hz
L3	Electron tube	Single path, plug–in	Cosine & dynamic – local, out–of–service	60 Hz
L4	Solid-state	Single path, printed wiring	Bumps & dynamic – remote, in–service	DC
L5, L5E	Solid-state	Parallel transistors, hybrid IC, thin film	Bumps & dynamic – local, out–of–service	DC

(c) Design Features

Several trends may be identified by examining Table 12–1. For example, the pressure to provide increasingly larger channel cross-sections can be seen in the growth in size of cables shown in Table 12–1(a) and by the increase in channel capacity shown in Table 12–1(b). Thus, a fully developed early L1 route might provide only 1200 circuits, whereas L5E can provide up to 132,000. Improved performance is also apparent from the noise objective, 4 dB more stringent, applied to L4 and L5 systems relative to L1 and L3.

As indicated by the principles in Chapter 10, a sizable increase in the bandwidth of an analog carrier system must be accompanied by reduced repeater spacing to preserve signal–to–noise performance. Table 12–1(a) shows that the nominal repeater spacing was halved for each successive system; thus, upgrading from one system to another involved reuse of repeater sites and was relatively straightforward.

To minimize the effects of system failure and to facilitate maintenance, coaxial carrier systems in North America operate with one pair of coaxial units reserved in each cable for maintenance of service. The original L1 systems used one spare for each working facility. The two lines were fed in parallel; the receiving end switched manually or automatically from working to spare on demand. With the L3 system and cables having 8 or 12 coaxial units, one–for–one protection switching was deemed uneconomical and became unnecessary because of the improved reliability of electronic components. So one–for–three and one–for–five protection switching systems were designed. This arrangement was adapted for L4 systems so that nine working systems could be protected by automatic switching of a single spare line.

The control tones for L3 and L4 switching are carried in the band between 280 and 300 kHz. Because this frequency range is unusable in L5, a redesign was necessary. This need, added to advances in technology, resulted in use of digital control signals in L5. The system lets the standby line protect up to ten working lines.

Methods of design and construction of equalizers have evolved, as has the method of powering remote repeaters. The need for relatively frequent adjustment of L3 equalizers led to the desire for remote adjustment of L4 equalizers on an in–service basis. The L4 system, however, demonstrated the innate stability of solid–state circuits; the remote control feature was not considered necessary for L5. The transition from ac to dc powering of remote repeaters was made feasible by the low power consumption of solid–state devices.

Most modern systems are "hardened." Cables are buried about four feet underground. Repeaters are housed underground in manholes designed to withstand earthquakes or nondirect nuclear blasts. Main stations are placed well below grade. These buildings are shielded against electromagnetic–pulse effects. In the most hardened locations, the equipment is shock–mounted. Life support systems are provided to permit maintenance forces to work in the building for a month or more in the event that attack makes it necessary to seal the building. The routes themselves bypass major cities, using side legs to reach downtown from facility junctions on the outskirts.

Route Engineering. The spacing of line repeaters along the route is determined by the system signal–to–noise objectives. Spacing rules provide some flexibility in locating repeater sites without significantly affecting performance. The application of these rules is an important factor in determining the right of way. In extraordinary cases, at unusually wide river crossings, it has been possible to "stretch" repeater spacings by using special coaxial units as large as 7/8 inch.

Environment. The problems of route selection and right–of–way determination can be complicated by environmental factors in addition to those already mentioned. Temperature, terrain, building design and construction, and equipment designs all interact in ways that can affect cost and performance. For example, if a cable is laid in the median strip of a divided highway in a southern area and the median lacks trees, ground temperature around the buried cable can be higher than estimated in system design and regulation range can be insufficient. When recognized, these hazards can be overcome and thus figure in route selection and engineering.

12-2 THE L5E CARRIER SYSTEM

The earlier coaxial systems (L1, L3, L4) are of relatively little current interest, so these systems are not described in detail. The larger channel capacities, 10,800 channels per coaxial pair for L5 and 13,200 for "L5 extended," are provided by the multiplex arrangements described in Chapter 9. The increased capacity of L5E was possible because the L5 line equipment provided slightly more bandwidth than was needed for 10,800 channels. A closer-packed arrangement of mastergroups in the multiplex equipment and a slight increase in top frequency provided the additional channels. It was considered feasible to abandon filter–type arrangements for blocking and branching jumbogroups because of a relative decline in the costs of multiplex equipment that would perform equivalent drop–and–add functions. The result was a sizable gain in convenience of growth and rearrangement.

To achieve a satisfactory line design for L5E, the transmission design and layout, maintenance arrangements, protection switching features, and limitations of power distribution to remote repeaters had to be considered. Each of these aspects of line engineering imposes certain limitations on the achievable system performance.

Transmission Layout

The transmission design of L5E specifies the placement of repeaters and the provision of regulators and equalizers at strategic locations. As previously discussed, these design features are interrelated and dependent on the signal–to–noise objective. The objective is 40 dBrnc0 for voice–grade channels 4000 miles long. Of this objective, 39.4 dBrnc0 is allocated to the high–frequency line, the rest to terminal equipment.

Frequency Allocations. The L5E spectrum from 3.252 to 64.844 MHz is provided by mastergroup and multimastergroup translators as shown in Figure 9–7. The frequencies of line pilots used for switching and fault location, and of the synchronization signal used by the multiplex terminals are shown in Table 12–2.

Repeater Designs and Spacing Rules. The repeaters are installed along the cable route according to the hierarchical pattern

289

Table 12-2. Control Signals in L5E Systems

Signal Function	Frequency (MHz)	
Fault location	1.590	68.600
	1.600	68.650
Equalization	2.976	42.880
	21.956	66.048
Switch control	68.760	68.780
Synchronization		2.048

illustrated in Figure 12-1. The simplest or basic repeater is installed at nominal 1-mile intervals to compensate for line loss. At a maximum of 7 miles, a regulating repeater is installed to correct line-loss variations caused primarily by cable-temperature changes. At the midpoint of a full-length power-feed span, a maximum distance of 37.5 miles, an equalizing repeater is used to correct fixed and variable deviations that occur along the line in addition to temperature effects. (The equalizing repeater may be omitted from short spans.) These three types of repeater are housed in pressurized watertight apparatus cases in manholes. This differs from European practice in which small numbers of repeaters may be buried directly.

Power for manhole-mounted repeaters is supplied from power-feed stations, usually underground, spaced up to 75 miles apart. A transmitting repeater or receiving repeater, depending on the direction of transmission, terminates each coaxial line at the power feed station.

The control circuits and switches for the protection line are located up to 150 miles apart. Thus, a switching span may encompass two power-feed sections. Main stations that supply power but no protection switching are called power-feed main stations. Where power feed and protection switching are found, the station is called a switching power-feed main station. The most complex stations provide power feed, protection switching, and such operating features as signal and pilot administration, transmission surveillance, and multiplexing. This type of station is termed a terminal station when it terminates a side leg or a terminal main station when it is a junction station along a backbone route.

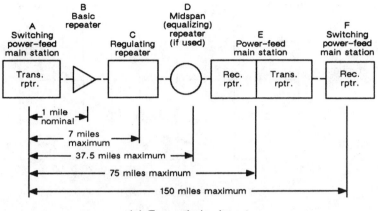

(a) Transmission layout

Function	A	B	C	D	E	F
Fixed equalizer	X	X	X	X	X	X
Adjustable equalizer						
Automatic	X		X	X	X	X
Manual	X				X	X
Power feed	X				X	X
Protection switching	X					X

(b) Station and repeater features

Figure 12-1. L5E system switching span.

Basic Repeater. Transmission performance of the L5E system is dominated by basic repeaters because they occur at 1–mile intervals and because basic repeater circuits are included in higher–ranking repeaters. Thus, about 4000 basic repeaters are used in a system of maximum length. Stringent requirements apply to gain characteristics, noise figure, power capacity, linearity, return loss, and temperature stability.

The basic repeater provides a fixed gain to compensate (within $\pm$ 0.15 dB) for the attenuation of 1 mile of cable at 55°F, as shown in Figure 12–2. (The repeater gain actually compensates

291

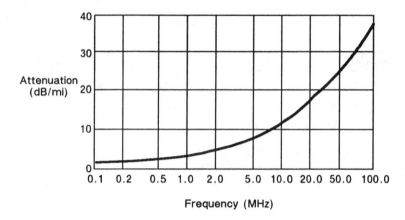

Figure 12-2. Attenuation–frequency   characteristic   of 0.375–inch coaxial unit.

for 1.006 miles of coaxial unit; the added gain provides margin for variations in cable length due to "snaking" in the trench and due to the cable's stranding factor.)

Expressed in decibels, the gain varies essentially as the square root of frequency; it is thus approximately 6.9 dB at 3.1 MHz and 31.5 dB at 65 MHz. A wider band, from 1.6 to nearly 70 MHz, is also controlled but less precisely. A block diagram of the repeater is shown in Figure 12–3.

Repeaters must withstand the high voltages to ground that result from series–string powering. They include circuits for separating the operating and signal powers at the input and recombining them at the output. They are protected against lightning and other high–voltage surges by the low–frequency networks shown in Figure 12–3. The earth–ground filters shown in the figure isolate the earth ground, which is required in the outer wall of the repeater housing for personnel safety, from the circuit ground within the repeater.

A line build–out (LBO) network in each basic repeater has a loss equivalent to that of a given length of cable. It is used to reduce the gain of the repeater in steps of 0.1 mile from 0 to 0.5 mile. Thus, there are six repeater codes corresponding to the overall gains provided. This feature allows flexibility in repeater

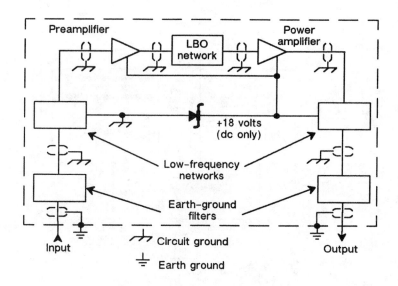

Input

Circuit ground

Earth ground

Output

Figure 12-3. Basic repeater.

spacing. The LBO network is placed electrically between the low–noise input amplifier and the high–power output stage.

Regulating Repeater. As shown in Figure 12–4, the regulating repeater contains all of the circuits of the basic repeater, a second LBO network, and circuits that perform pre– and postregulation. These additional circuits have zero insertion loss at nominal temperature and repeater spacing.

As discussed in Chapter 10, there is a significant signal–to–noise advantage in splitting the regulation about equally between the transmitting and receiving ends of a line section. This is accomplished, for the transmission deviations caused by cable temperature changes, by the use of two independent regulating networks. The preregulator, located in the transmitting portion of the repeater, responds directly to changes in earth temperature near the repeater. The temperature sensor is a thermistor buried at the same depth as the cable. The mapping circuits convert the nonlinear resistance versus temperature of the thermistor into a linear function of regulating network loss controlled by temperature. The actual gain is then controlled by the indirectly heated thermistor in the regulator network.

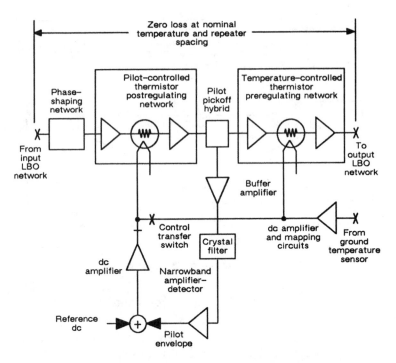

Figure 12–4. Regulator circuits of regulating repeater.

Postregulation is performed by the pilot–controlled network in the receiving portion of the regulator. The signal at the pickoff hybrid is amplified and the narrowband crystal filter selects the 42.88–MHz pilot. This pilot is again amplified, detected, and compared with a dc reference voltage. The difference between the two, the error signal, is amplified and used to heat the thermistor of the postregulator to control the overall repeater gain.

In a line on which the 42.88–MHz pilot is lost, the regulating repeaters could all be driven to their maximum gain, causing large unequalized misalignment. This action would introduce high gain to signals and noise in the affected line and could overload carrier spans well beyond the affected section. To prevent this overload, the regulators contain a transfer circuit. Upon loss of pilot, the control of the postregulator is transferred to the ground–temperature sensor. The imperfect adjustment that results is far less harmful to performance than loss of control.

The phase–shaping network in the receiving portion of the regulating repeater introduces a nonlinear phase–frequency characteristic in the transmission band. Due to the linear phase–frequency relationship of a repeatered line, certain third–order intermodulation products add in phase from repeater to repeater. Thus, the combined amplitudes of these products tend to be proportional to 20 log n, where n is the number of tandem repeaters. With the phase–shaping networks, the accumulation of intermodulation products becomes proportional to about 15 log n or a little less.

Equalizing Repeater. In addition to the circuits and features of a basic and a regulating repeater, an equalizing repeater contains several networks that equalize an L5E line approximately so as to limit signal–to–noise penalties due to misalignment. Equalizing repeaters are needed in long power–feed sections, as mentioned previously, depending on the length of the section and the cable vintage.

One of the networks used in the regulator portion of an equalizing repeater is a fixed deviation equalizer designed to compensate for the difference between the average gain of 22 repeaters and the nominal loss of 22 miles of line. This number of repeater sections approximates the average length of an equalizing repeater section. This equalizer is applied at equalizing and main–station repeaters. (Where an equalizing repeater is not used, a deviation equalizer is incorporated in the regulating repeater.) The residual deviations are partially corrected by manually adjustable "E1" equalizers. These, plus higher–ranking equalizers, are intended to minimize the mean–squared error in the line's frequency response after equalization.

The networks of the E1 equalizer are continuously adjustable over a limited loss range. The adjustment introduces a "bump" of loss over a limited frequency band. Ten such bumps are used at an equalizing repeater. A very narrow bump is also centered at the 42.88–MHz frequency of the regulating pilot. The network loss characteristics are illustrated in Figure 12–5(a). As shown in Figure 12–5(b), a number of the bump networks are connected in series with the amplifiers; four of the bumps are in the feedback loops of these amplifiers. Test access is available at the

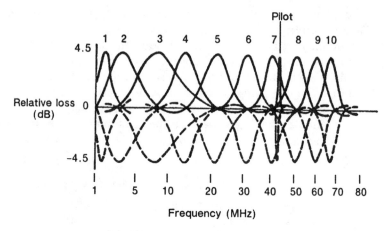

(a) Network loss characteristics

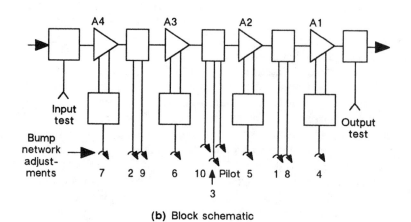

(b) Block schematic

Figure 12–5. E1 equalizer.

input and output to facilitate measurement of the system attenuation–frequency characteristic.

Main–Station Repeater. Each L5E main station contains the transmitting and receiving components of basic and regulating repeaters and, in addition, E1 and E2 equalizers. The E1 equalizer is functionally the same as that at an equalizing repeater but it is packaged for mounting in a central–office bay instead of a manhole apparatus case. The E2 equalizer resembles the E1 in a number of ways. It has bumps of loss over 18 narrow frequency bands to supplement the E1 equalizer bumps and provides fine-grained equalization of the L5E frequency band. Each loss bump is continuously adjustable over a range of ± 3.5 dB. In a 150-mile switching span, the E1 and E2 equalizers together can equalize the band from 1.6 to 66 MHz to within ± 0.4 dB.

The E2 equalizer contains seven amplifiers and six intermediate two-bump equalizer networks. Six of the amplifiers also contain bump networks in their feedback circuits. E2 equalizers are not used at power-feed stations or intermediate power-feed main stations. A dynamic (pilot-controlled) equalizer, the E3, is used in receiving main-station repeaters. It is controlled by line pilots at the four equalization frequencies listed in Table 12-2.

The transmission variations that are corrected by the E3 equalizer are primarily due to temperature changes that affect repeater gain. The temperature within a manhole changes from season to season and rises as additional lines are equipped. In addition, the regulator networks in the repeaters that compensate for cable-loss changes match the desired loss imperfectly; the error increases with the amount of compensation. The E3 equalizer addresses these errors by supplying two bumps centered on the 2.976- and 66.048-MHz pilot frequencies. The corrections are determined by digital circuits that hold the last-established setting of the equalizer in the event of the loss of pilots.

Main-Station Administration Equipment. At every main station, equipment is provided to interconnect line and terminal equipment. The terminal equipment includes multiplex terminals, branching filters to split multimastergroups between two or more converging routes, distribution circuits for line pilots and the synchronizing signal, protection switches, transmission surveillance and fault-location equipment, restoration access arrangements, multimastergroup trunk circuits, and line connecting equipment. The line connecting equipment is mounted in a transmit-receive bay with transmitting and receiving repeaters. These bays are used in three arrangements, one for power-feed main stations, one for switching power-feed main stations, and one for terminal stations and terminal main stations.

Maintenance and Reliability

Since L5E has such large circuit capacity, probability of failure and outage time must be minimized. As in other broadband systems, many circuits are duplicated and automatically switched. Access points are available for testing and emergency restoration. Features important in L5E include aspects of line maintenance and administration, a special protection switching system, a transmission surveillance system with added fault–location features, and four–wire order wires of advanced design.

Line Maintenance and Administration. Many features of L5E line operation are important for maintenance and administration. Among the most significant are the equalization system and the procedures for repeater replacement.

Equalization System. The individual components of the equalization system, described previously, are the fixed, manually adjustable, and automatically controlled equalizer networks. The equalizers are set at the time of installation and occasionally thereafter. For later adjustments, service is removed from the line under adjustment by operation of the protection switch.

Repeater Replacement Procedures. The dc power is supplied to manhole–mounted repeaters over the center conductors of the coaxial units. Removal of a repeater, for test or replacement, opens the power loop. Special means are therefore provided to maintain power continuity. The method is illustrated in Figure 12–6. At the input and output of each repeater, twin jacks are provided. When a repeater is to be unplugged from its apparatus case, the bridging pads are removed from the twin jack assemblies and a coaxial patchcord is plugged into the vacant jacks. This action bypasses the repeater and provides dc continuity through the patchcord. The repeater can then be removed without shutting down the power. In addition, the twin jacks provide a connection for fault–location tones that can be applied through the bridging pads to the repeater at input and output. The pads are of relatively high impedance to minimize bridging loss.

Protection Switching System. The L5 and L5E systems use their own one–for–ten protection switching system. As previously mentioned, the frequencies used in earlier systems for control

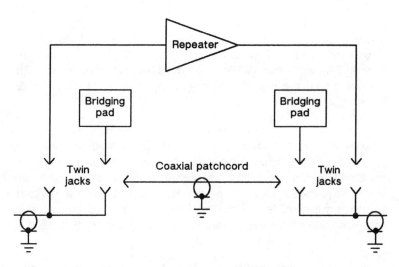

Figure 12–6. Manhole repeater patching.

information between switching points are unsuited for use in the L5E system. The L5/L5E protection system must be relatively immune to line noise and line hits (short–duration outages) because a signalling error can cause a service failure due to improper switch activation. The system was designed for gradual growth with minimum initial investment because it would be unusual to equip all coaxial units simultaneously at the time of cable installation.

Two criteria initiate an automatic transfer of service to the protection line. If the amplitude of the 42.88–MHz pilot departs by 5 dB or more from its nominal value at the receiving end of a switching span, a detector circuit calls for a switch. The received signal power is another criterion for switching. If the power exceeds a preestablished threshold, a switch is also initiated. In both cases, the completion of the switch depends on many conditions.

After the need for a switch has been indicated, the operation of circuits at both ends of the switching span must be properly sequenced and coordinated. These functions are accomplished by a signalling system that uses frequency shift keying of line signals at 68.76 and 68.78 MHz to communicate between the two ends of the span. The data rate is 2 kb/s. Switch commands are coded into a total of 39 digital code words, each seven bits in length with a parity bit. At the receiving end, the two signals are detected independently. With no errors, the two signals are complementary on the high-frequency line and identical at the detector output in the receiver.

The coded signals are normally transmitted over all equipped coaxial units in the switching span although, in some cases, the signals are transmitted over only one working line or over the standby line. The signalling receiver is normally connected to the lowest-numbered working line on which signals are transmitted. Controls are provided so that service may be switched manually to the standby line when required. In general, the manual controls override any automatic switch.

Transmission Surveillance. The complexities of L5E system operation require sophisticated equipment to make transmission measurements and to identify the location of faulty remote repeaters and main-station equipment. These functions are carried out by a transmission surveillance system (TSS). Units of this major support system for L5E include a transmission surveillance center (TSC), transmission surveillance auxiliary (TSA) units, a status reporting and control system, switched access networks, precise programmable transmission measuring equipment, and a minicomputer.

Many of the surveillance functions of the TSS are carried out automatically under the control of the minicomputer. In addition, manual override of the automatic features is possible to enable special measurements.

The TSC is located strategically at an L5E main station from which remote control of TSA units may be exercised. All automatic operations of the TSS originate at the TSC. Remote TSA units at other main stations are controlled by the TSC. At the TSC and each TSA unit, a switched access network is arranged to connect to selected measuring points and to the fault-location system from which troubles at remote repeaters can be identified and isolated. Transmission of data and control signals between the TSC and TSA units is by the status reporting and control system. The latter system is time-shared to provide TSC-TSA communication along with such other services as alarm surveillance at remote locations.

Transmission Measurements. The test equipment located at L5E main stations measures pilot levels in all systems operating through the main station and in all multiplex equipment at the station. The test equipment is programmed to make such measurements automatically and to report the results back to the TSC upon command for computer analysis.

In addition to pilot–level measurements, the test equipment can also be programmed to make attenuation–frequency measurements between distant locations and to transmit the results to the TSC. Measurements of this type must be made out–of–service; thus, the status reporting and control system switches service to the protection line during tests.

Remote Status and Control. Alarm polling is the principal function of the status reporting and control system. Typically, all remote stations under surveillance by a status–reporting central station are polled during a 2– to 4–second interval. Polling continues automatically until interrupted by a request for such operations as remote switching or data collection and transfer. When the alarm–polling function is so interrupted, it automatically takes precedence but performs a polling cycle at least once every 30 seconds in order to update the alarm status throughout the system.

Fault Location. As shown in Table 12–2, there are two low and two high fault–location frequencies in the L5E spectrum. Oscillators, normally inoperative, are located in each manhole apparatus case. The fault–location oscillators may be remotely activated and connected to the input and output of the repeater under test; one low–frequency and one high–frequency signal is connected to the input and one of each is connected to the output. The amplitudes of the signals are adjusted to be equal at the output when the gain of the repeater is normal. Thus, measurement of these signal amplitudes provides a sensitive indication of the operation of the repeater. The process is complicated at regulating and equalizing repeaters, especially in evaluating high–frequency gains, because repeater gain varies with cable temperature. However, tables are provided so that the variations in gain can be taken into account.

The TSS operates the fault location oscillators on an in–service basis. Control signals and power for the oscillators are transmitted over interstitial wires in the coaxial cable.

Order Wires. Coordination of maintenance and repair work is supported by an order–wire system that provides voice communication among all manholes and main stations. It uses interstitial pairs in the cable with four–wire transmission. To reduce transmission losses, the pairs are usually loaded with 44–mH inductors at repeater points ("Q44" loading) as described in Chapter 2. Gain and signalling are included.

Power System. A simplified block diagram of the L5E power–feed system is shown in Figure 12–7. The power converters change either 24 or 140 volts dc to the required dc line feed voltage. The converters are located at main stations along the route at distances up to 75 miles. The dc is fed to the coaxial units through power separation filters that combine (or separate) the power and signal. The dc comes from constant–current feed circuits that regulate at 910 mA. In normal installations, the voltage to ground at each end of a power–feed section may be as high as 1150 volts; end–to–end, the maximum voltage differential is thus as high as 2300 volts. In special cases, these voltages may be as high as 1250 and 2500 volts respectively.

Power feeds to the coaxial units for the two directions of transmission are basically independent. A failure of power feed for one direction of transmission operates the protective grounding circuit in Figure 12–7, leaving the unaffected direction in operation. The protective grounding circuit also operates under other trouble conditions such as abnormal dc earth potentials, a nearby lightning strike, or high 60–Hz induction.

Where a coaxial route is less than 37.5 miles long, the converters at one end of the section are omitted. Converters can be controlled remotely from the central location of the status reporting and control system.

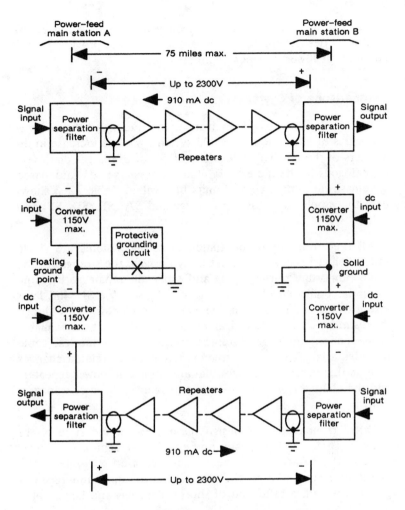

Figure 12-7.   Power-feed system.

12-3 ENGINEERING OF UNDERSEA CABLE SYSTEMS

The transmission design principles of undersea coaxial carrier systems are similar to those applied to land systems. The greatest differences derive from differences in the environment. These are manifested in installation and repair methods, system equalization, efficiency of usage of the line, and reliability considerations [3]. After the first repeatered undersea system was installed

303

in 1950, a new design emerged about every six or seven years. Each new design represented a significant step in providing more channels at lower cost per channel–mile.

Comparisons of Systems

Among the technological advances that increased the channel capacities of later undersea cable systems was the increase in diameters of the coaxial cables. The effect of the larger diameters is analogous to the increase in channel capacities of land–based systems from adding coaxial units in a cable. Table 12–3 shows data that apply to the systems designated SA, SB, SD, SF, and SG.

All the cables used for analog undersea systems are single solid–dielectric coaxials. In the early designs, the strength of the cable (important during laying and especially repair work) came from the outer sheathing. In the cable used for SD and later systems, the strength is in the center conductor. This design makes more efficient electrical and structural use of the available cross–section; for a given tensile strength, the armorless cable provides a larger coaxial diameter. Other cable–related changes include the increased voltages that are applied to power repeaters and the change from four–wire to equivalent four–wire transmission.

Other comparisons of design parameters of the systems are given in Table 12–3. Repeater and equalizer spacings were shortened as the bandwidth of the system increased. In spite of the increasing bandwidth in the later systems, maximum repeater gain decreased, a reflection of shorter spacings and larger cable diameters.

A significant advance in physical design was accomplished when the flexible (or articulated) repeater housing of the SA and SB systems was replaced by a rigid housing. The nonflexible case was made possible by improved techniques for handling the cable and repeaters on shipboard. The changes in design required development of entirely new cable handling machinery for cable ships. In electrical design, better control of feedback loops became possible and overall system performance improved accordingly.

Table 12-3. Comparison of Undersea Systems

Characteristic	System Designations				
	SA	SB	SD	SF	SG
Coaxial diameter (inches)	0.460	0.625	1.0	1.5	1.7
Type of cable (deep sea)	Armored	Armored	Armorless	Armorless	Armorless
Maximum dc voltage	500	2600	6000	4200	7000
Cables per route	2	2	1	1	1
Transmission mode	4W	4W	Equiv 4W	Equiv 4W	Equiv 4W
Repeater spacing (nautical miles)	36	38	20	10	5
Equalizer spacing (nautical miles)	None	200	192	192	150
Maximum gain (dB)	65	62	50	40	41
Active devices	Tube	Tube	Tube	Transistor	Transistor
Repeater housing	Flexible	Flexible	Rigid	Rigid	Rigid
Maximum length (nautical miles)	125	2200	3850	4000	4000
Number of channels	24	36	138	845	4000
Channel spacing (kHz)	4	4	3	3	3
Top frequency (MHz)	0.12	0.17	1.1	6.0	30.0
Systems installed (nautical miles)	120	10,020	21,040	17,800	7,790

Design Features

While the transmission design principles are the same in undersea cable systems as in land coaxial systems, a number of details differ significantly. One is the requirement for extraordinary reliability (typically an allowance of four component–related failures for the whole cable span in 20 years), which requires both careful design and the use of "clean room" techniques in manufacture.

One environmental effect that favors undersea system design is the stability of deep–water temperature, which makes dynamic regulation unnecessary. What little change does occur can usually be corrected by the adjustment of shore–end equalizers, which give about equal amounts of pre– and postequalization. In the SG system, shore–controlled adjustable undersea equalizers are installed about every 700 nautical miles to compensate for possible cable aging effects. The stability of the medium also permits the allocation of smaller signal–to–noise misalignment margins than in land systems.

The economic advantages of equivalent four–wire transmission led to a repeater configuration in which a single amplifier is used for both directions of transmission. The frequency bands for the two directions are separated and combined by directional filters in each repeater. The configuration used, shown in Figure 12–8, results in a large number of filters of identical design being connected in tandem. To assure satisfactory transmission,

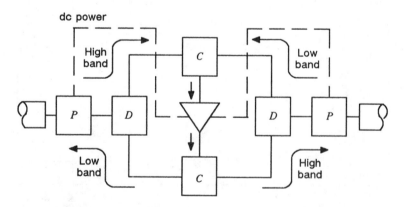

P = Power separation filter
D = Directional filter
C = Combining network

Figure 12–8. Equivalent four–wire repeater.

particularly as regards the attenuation–frequency characteristics of the system, the design and manufacturing requirements imposed on these networks are quite stringent.

The line powering arrangement for single–cable systems uses earth return, with voltage applied at both ends to minimize stress on the cable. The line power circuits are designed to accommodate the large and varying earth potentials that arise during magnetic storms.

Since the cost of undersea cable systems is dominated by the cost of the repeatered line, every effort is made to use the medium efficiently. Thus, the voice–channel spacing in these systems is 3 kHz rather than the 4 kHz used for land systems. The 3–kHz spacing is made possible by the use of channel filters with sharper cutoff characteristics, by a double modulation process, and by a reduction of approximately 200 Hz in the voiceband. The resulting passband is about 250 to 3100 Hz. In addition, the capacity of certain undersea systems is increased substantially by the use of time–assignment speech interpolation (TASI) equipment at the terminals. These channels, of course, do not exhibit the objectionable time delay inherent in satellite transmission; neither do the fiber–based digital undersea systems that are currently emerging.

The unique characteristics of undersea systems lead to the evaluation of signal–to–noise design parameters not usually important in land systems. The use of equivalent four–wire transmission, the stability of the environment, the effects of repair work, the loading effects of 3–kHz channelization and of TASI, and the differences in speech volume of overseas callers all complicate the analysis in design. These factors are further complicated by the international division of responsibility among private and government agencies regarding design, manufacture, operation, and ownership.

Installation. The entire process of laying cable, connecting repeaters to the cable, and equalizing the system is most efficient when the process is continuous. Cable, repeaters, and equalizers are stored on shipboard according to careful plans; the repeaters and equalizers are prespliced at proper places along the cable so as not to interrupt the process of laying. Initially, the land–end cable section is installed using armored shallow–water cable buried in a trench to protect it from anchor and sea damage. Connections to the cable for power sources and transmission test equipment are immediately established on shipboard and at the shore end. Measurements of the system transmission characteristics are then made continuously as the cable and repeaters are laid on the sea bottom. The equalizer characteristics required are based on these measurements. The equalizers, installed at intervals shown in Figure 12–8, are called ocean block equalizers. Appropriate equalizer networks are switched in or out of the transmission path before the equalizer is sealed. The process requires computer–controlled test equipment, which is used intensively during the laying process.

Maintenance. Cable repairs involve unique transmission problems. Aside from the difficulties of locating damaged or severed cable or a defective repeater, repairs usually result in the addition of a length of cable of about twice the depth of the water at the repair location, depending on the available slack in the cable. In shallow water the loss of this added cable can often be absorbed; in deep water, a repeater must be added.

References

1. Freeman, R. L. *Telecommunications Transmission Handbook*, Second Edition (New York: John Wiley and Sons, Inc., 1981), pp. 109–119, 418–445, and 639–645.

2. Members of Technical Staff. *Transmission Systems for Communications*, Fifth Edition (Murray Hill, NJ: AT&T Bell Laboratories, Inc., 1982), pp. 81–83, 288–289, and 376–379.

3. Schenck, H. H. and L. Waldrick. *1984 World's Submarine Telephone Cable Systems*, NTIA–CR–84–31 (Washington, DC: National Telecommunications and Information Administration, 1984).

Telecommunications Transmission Engineering

Section 4

Digital Systems

The rapid expansion of digital transmission systems (facilities and terminals), together with similar expansion of switching systems, has made it possible to provide all–digital networks. The goal of pervasive digital connectivity in the public switched network will be achieved soon. In only a few years the capabilities of transmission systems have leap–frogged over the ubiquitous 1.544 Mb/s DS1 system on copper pairs to optical fiber systems capable of 1.7 Gb/s (and higher). Such progress includes new electrical and optical hierarchies. To use the capabilities of this high–bit–rate transport efficiently, digital operation at DS3 level (44.736 Mb/s) is common and higher rate building blocks are becoming available. The expanding digital technology makes new services possible and provides better quality transport more economically than ever before.

This section discusses pulse code modulation (PCM) transmission systems, fiber optics, digital hierarchies and associated topics, and the older digital metallic–pair lines.

Chapter 13 covers the basic PCM technology. It discusses the underlying principles of sampling, quantizing, companding, coding, and formatting. DS1 superframe, extended superframe (for 64–kb/s clear channel capability) and low–bit–rate voice (LBRV) are illustrated. Zero–code substitution methods for DS1 are described. Application to metallic–cable line, digital loop carrier, and integrated services digital network (ISDN) are discussed.

Chapter 14 considers fiber optic transport systems capable of 1.7 Gb/s (and higher). The general characteristics of optical transmitters, lasers and light–emitting diodes, and optical diode receivers are illustrated and American National Standards Institute (ANSI) standard information on optical interfaces is given. The chapter also provides a current methodology for the design of an optic transport system. An optical fiber undersea cable system (TAT–8) is described, including its digital circuit multiplication system. This system uses LBRV and digital speech interpolation to increase the number of voice channels that can be served by five to one.

Chapter 15 covers the electrical and optical digital hierarchies, their bit–stream formats, and the associated multiplexers and channel banks. It illustrates the ANSI electrical hierarchy for DS0 through DS4 levels, their formats, and zero–code substitutions. Asynchronous and synchronous operating modes, synchronous transmission (SYNTRAN), and synchronous optical network (SONET) capabilities are discussed. ANSI optical hierarchical levels, OC–1 through OC–8 (2488.32 Gb/s) are noted and the basic optical carrier format for the synchronous transport signals is presented.

Chapter 16 describes the several older metallic–pair digital transmission lines for transporting DS1 through DS4 levels. This includes the T1, T1 outstate, T1C, T1D, T1G, T2, and T4M designated lines. The chapter also discusses the electrical characteristics of the lines, the repeaters, line layout rules, etc.

Chapter 13

PCM Transmission Systems

This chapter on pulse code modulation (PCM) contains four parts. The first discusses the basic concept of PCM and the processing that is required in the terminals, such as sampling, quantizing, coding, framing, etc., to provide the basic digital line DS1 format (1.544 Mb/s). Other topics covered are low–bit–rate voice (LBRV) coding, DS1 superframe and extended superframe (ESF) formats and 64–kb/s clear–channel capability (64CCC). Part 2 covers the use of PCM digital loop carrier (DLC) in the loop–feeder plant on existing cable pairs or on optical fibers. Part 3 discusses providing capability for integrated services digital network (ISDN) services. Basic and primary access facilities are described. Finally, Part 4 discusses the transmission–delay effects that are commonly found in digital processing.

General

A pulse transmission system may be defined as a carrier system in which the unmodulated carrier is a series of regularly recurrent pulses. Modulation of the carrier may take the form of varying any of several pulse parameters such as amplitude, duration, position in time, or presence. Thus, the modulation methods are called pulse amplitude modulation (PAM), pulse duration modulation (PDM), pulse position modulation (PPM), and PCM. Only PCM lends itself well to digital processing and to the technique of regeneration used in the line repeaters of a digital system. This technique is used to reconstruct and retime pulses that have been impaired by transmission over an imperfect medium. It requires the line input pulses to be discrete in time, amplitude, and duration. Although the need to regenerate the transmitted signal is a requirement imposed by transmission line parameters, the signal processing required to achieve a suitable line format takes place in the terminal equipment.

311

In PCM, the carrier is modulated by the insertion or removal of pulses in time slots of the unmodulated carrier to form a code that represents some characteristic of the modulating signal. Voiceband message signals are processed in digital terminal equipment designed to transform each channel signal from an analog to a digital format (coding), to multiplex a number of such coded signals into a line pulse stream by time–division–multiplex (TDM) techniques, and to provide timing and synchronization so that the individual message signals can be extracted and restored closely to their original analog forms at the receiving terminal. Digital data transmission requires the TDM and the timing and synchronization functions.

Most digital systems are designed so that the line signals are regenerated at every repeater (i.e., they are amplified, equalized, retimed, and reshaped to eliminate the effects of noise and distortion). This produces one of the major advantages of PCM transmission, i.e., the nonaccumulation of line impairments. In rare cases, a mixture of analog and digital repeaters may be used. In these cases, the signal is amplified and equalized at analog repeater points. Regenerative repeaters are used only where required to eliminate the signal impairment accumulated over several analog repeater sections.

Message signals are represented by a stream of binary pulses that are identical in amplitude, shape, and duration. This pulse stream may be further processed (coded) to make it more suitable for transmission over the transmission line. Although incurred on a per–line–section basis, the attenuation, distortion of shape or duration, and induced interference are all virtually eliminated by each regenerative repeater, thus producing a nearly unimpaired line signal for transmission to the next repeater. Exceptions are errors in pulse regeneration and random variations (jitter) in the time positions of pulses, which can cause errors and slips in the digital domain and random phase modulation in the analog domain. Jitter accumulates in successive repeaters and is kept small by design.

As digital transmission systems have come into common use, the administration of network signals has led to the development of a digital signal (bit–rate) multiplex hierarchy (covered in Chapter 15) analogous to that found in analog (bandwidth) systems. In addition, an integration of digital transmission and switching technology has evolved that interacts in many ways with the digital multiplex hierarchy.

13-1 PROCESSING IN A PCM TERMINAL

The terminal equipment processes one or more input analog and/or digital signals to produce a composite digital stream suitable for transmission over the digital line to a distant terminal where the processes are reversed. It must perform a number of functions in processing voiceband signals. These functions include filtering, amplitude sampling, coding, timing, framing, synchronizing, and multiplexing. As parts of the coding process, quantizing and instantaneous companding functions, or equivalent, are performed on voice signals. In addition, signalling functions may be incorporated. Where appropriate, digital data signals may be interleaved to enable the simultaneous transmission of combinations of data and processed speech signals.

Sampling, Quantizing, and Companding

It can be shown that a bandlimited signal can be represented accurately by pulse–amplitude samples taken at regular time intervals at a rate equivalent to at least twice the bandwidth. Furthermore, it can be shown that the original signal can be recovered from these samples with no loss of information [1].

A simplified illustration of the entire PCM process is given in Figure 13-1. A very short segment of a speech wave and the PAM pulse samples of the segment are shown in Figures 13-1(a) and (b). In Figure 13-1(c), a 4-bit binary PCM code, PCM-4, is illustrated as representing the amplitudes of the PAM pulses. Figure 13-1(d) shows that the binary signal is commonly converted to a bipolar signal for line transmission: 0s in the binary signal are 0s in the bipolar signal but 1s in the binary signal are transmitted as alternate positive and negative pulses in the bipolar format. In practice, however, there is an inversion of the binary signals so that the PCM word representing an idle signal is translated to an all 1s bipolar signal. This provides for continuing synchronization. Figures 13-1(e), (f), and (g) show the processes necessary to recover the original signal from the line signal.

313

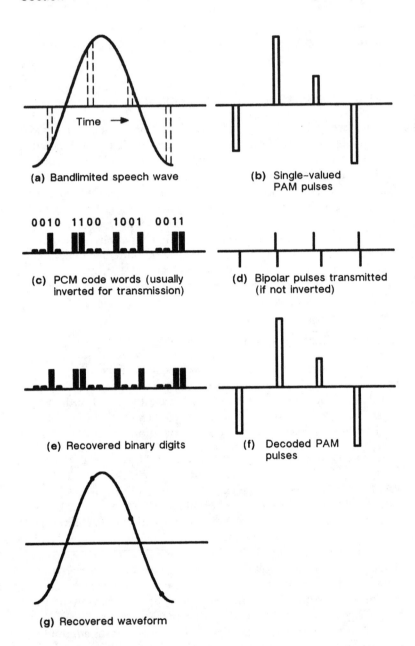

(a) Bandlimited speech wave

(b) Single-valued PAM pulses

0010 1100 1001 0011

(c) PCM code words (usually inverted for transmission)

(d) Bipolar pulses transmitted (if not inverted)

(e) Recovered binary digits

(f) Decoded PAM pulses

(g) Recovered waveform

Figure 13-1. Signal processing in digital transmission.

A single value is used to represent each PAM sample since the sampling time is very short compared to the sampling interval. The total allowable amplitude range of the sample is divided into increments (quantized) to be used for discrete signal representation from sample to sample. The number of steps and their size are significant parameters in the accuracy of the representation.

Figure 13-2 illustrates the action of a quantizer in which the total input amplitude range is divided into 16 uniform steps. The transfer characteristic of such a quantizer is illustrated in Figure 13-2(a). The diagonal dashed line shows the linear input/output signal relationships that would exist without quantization. The heavy "stairstep" shows that for a step, s, of input signal amplitudes between x_j and x_{j+1}, the output signal has a constant value y_j. As shown, the incremental values for the output signal represent uniform quantization steps between the minimum and maximum values that the input signal can attain.

The difference between the quantized output signal and the output signal without quantization is represented as the error signal in Figure 13-2(b). The power contained in this error signal is called quantizing noise, which can be determined and used for evaluating the resulting signal-to-distortion ratio for this noise.

Figure 13-2(c) shows how a full-load sine-wave signal would be represented with such a uniform quantizing arrangement. For a sine wave having an amplitude in excess of the full-load value, distortion due to overload would be observable at the peak values of the wave. For signals smaller than full load, the signal-to-distortion ratio would deteriorate because the quantizing steps would represent relatively large amplitude variations. The latter observation suggests a method, variously called instantaneous companding and nonlinear coding, to be used for improving the signal-to-distortion ratio for low-amplitude signals since these are prevalent.

The transfer characteristic of a nonuniform companding quantizer is chosen so that more amplitude steps are used to represent small amplitude variations. Such a quantizer is illustrated in Figure 13-3(a). Figure 13-3(b) shows that less quantizing noise is generated by small signals than by large signals. The selection of a quantizer characteristic to satisfy the signal-to-distortion

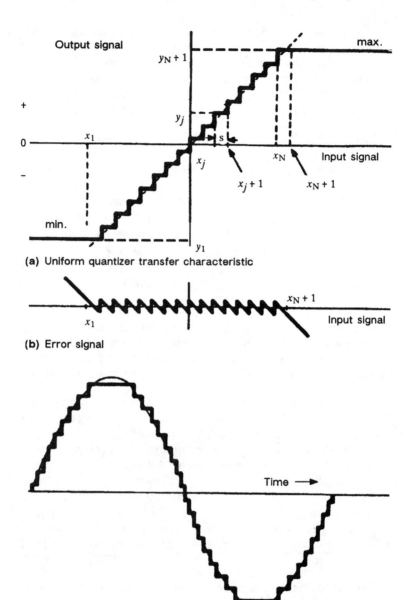

(a) Uniform quantizer transfer characteristic

(b) Error signal

(c) Quantized full-load sine wave

Figure 13-2. Characteristics of a uniform quantizer.

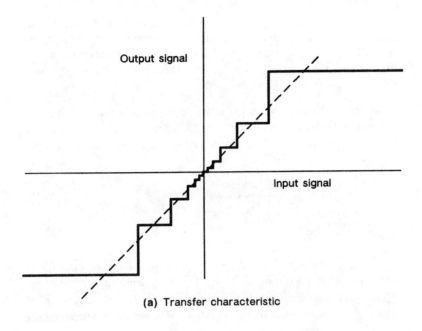

(a) Transfer characteristic

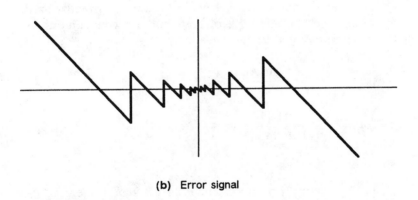

(b) Error signal

Figure 13-3. Characteristics of a nonuniform quantizer.

objectives for the types of signal to be transmitted is made during the design of the system. Where speech is the signal type of greatest interest, a near-constant signal-to-distortion ratio in

decibels is desirable over a wide range of speech signal amplitudes. Such a condition is theoretically achievable by the provision of a modified logarithmic compression characteristic, which
may be closely approached in practice by the use of modern
solid–state circuits.

There are two methods [2] that are commonly used to provide
a modified logarithmic compression characteristic. The first is the
μ – law used in North America and Japan, as represented by the
equation:

$$F(x) = \pm \ \frac{\ln(1+\mu|x|)}{\ln(1+\mu)}, \ -1 \le |x| \le 1 \qquad (13-1)$$

where μ = 255.

For large x (high signal), $F(x)$ approaches a logarithmic function; for small x (low signal), $F(x)$ approaches a linear function.
The μ –law ideally produces an improvement of about 30 dB in
signal–to–distortion ratio for small signals versus a linear (non-
compressed) characteristic.

The other method is the A–law used in Europe [standardized
by the European Conference of Posts and Telecommunications
(CEPT)] represented by the equation:

$$F(x) = \pm \ \frac{1 + \ln A|x|}{1 + \ln A} \ \frac{1}{A} \le |x| \le | \qquad (13-2)$$

$$F(x) = \pm \ \frac{A|x|}{1 + \ln A} \ 0 \le |x| \le \frac{1}{A}$$

where A = 87.6.

The A–law ideally produces about 24–dB improvement in signal–to–distortion ratio for small signals versus a linear characteristic.

Pulse Code Modulation

To facilitate regeneration in the line repeaters, the quantized
amplitude samples just described must be transformed into a

pulse format that permits regeneration. For this purpose, it is desirable that the pulses be identical in amplitude, shape, and duration. In addition, the pulses must appear in the signal at predictable times and must be controlled in a manner that permits them to be interleaved with other signal pulses, i.e., to be time-division multiplexed. Therefore, the amplitude of each sample is converted to a series of fixed–amplitude, precisely timed pulses (a binary word) by the process of PCM.

The number of quantizing steps used after pulse–amplitude sampling has a direct effect on the selection of the PCM code. A unique binary code must be used to represent each quantized amplitude. The number of binary digits necessary thus directly depends on the number of amplitude steps to be represented over the total range of the quantizer.

For speech transmission, it has been found satisfactory to sample speech at 8000 times a second and provide 255 amplitude steps. If each amplitude is to be represented by a binary number, eight bits is the minimum word length that can be used to represent all of the amplitude steps. The process of coding an amplitude sample as a binary word may be accomplished in many ways and by a variety of circuit arrangements.

One method of coding has been called "easily digitally linearizable coding" for the μ –255 (or for the A–law) compression characteristic [2]. This characteristic can be approximated closely by four straight segments of different slopes for positive values as shown in Figure 13–4 and four more for negative values (not shown). Each segment has 16 quantizing steps. The steps are equal within each segment and all step sizes are multiples of the smallest step. This arrangement permits direct digital processing. As the positive and negative segments nearest the origin are colinear, the compression characteristic is referred to as the 15–segment approximation. Using this compression method, the 8–bit μ –255 PCM code word representing a channel amplitude sample is composed of: 1 bit for polarity as an above–zero or below–zero reference, 3 bits for the segment (1 of 8) and 4 bits for the quantizing step within the segment (1 of 16) to provide for the 256 codings ($2 \times 8 \times 16$). Subtracting one for the

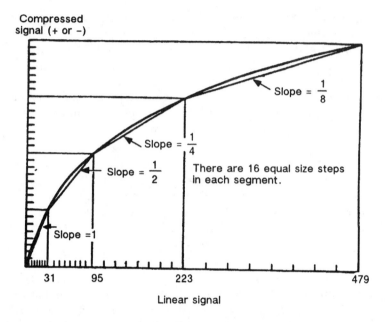

Figure 13–4. First four segments of straight–line approximation to μ–255 compression curve.

redundant zero codes leaves 255 amplitude steps, hence, the
μ –255 designation.

Low–Bit–Rate Voice

Low–bit–rate voice is a digital coding technique that reduces
the bit rate needed for transmitting voice or voiceband data to
less than the full PCM rate of 64 kb/s. A tutorial on coding
speech at low bit rates over a range of 64 kb/s down to 4 kb/s has
been presented by Reference 3 and is briefly reviewed in the
following. LBRV is usually the result of voice processing to reduce the redundancies in speech, to provide adaptive quantization and pitch extraction, and then to code the processed signal
in a perceptually efficient manner. Quality, bit rate, complexity,
and delay are some significant factors that are affected by the
processing and coding.

Quality suffers as the bit rate is reduced, but this effect can be
lessened to some degree by the complexity of the processing (at

320

increased cost), which in turn increases the processing delay. LBRV designs usually are based on waveform coders and vocoders. Waveform coders employ algorithms to produce an output that approximates the input waveform. Vocoders, in essence, digitize a compact description of the spectrum of the input in several frequency bands, including extraction of the pitch component of the speech signal. Transmission occurs at very low bit rates but with poor quality.

Some of the promising techniques for better quality are: (1) adaptive differential PCM, for coding rates of 32 and 16 kb/s, where a combination of adaptive quantization and adaptive prediction of the speech wave is employed, (2) adaptive subband coding, for rates of 16 kb/s to 8 kb/s, where speech is separated into frequency bands and each is coded with different strategies to suit some predictive measure of the input spectrum and the properties of hearing, (3) multipulse linear predictive (hybrid) coding, for rates of 8 kb/s to 4 kb/s, where a suitable number of pulses are supplied to optimize the excitation information for a speech segment (an improvement over the two–state excitation of a vocoder) and to supplement linear prediction of the segments, and (4) stochastically excited linear predictive coding (LPC), for rates of 4 kb/s to 2 kb/s, where the coder stores a repertory of candidate excitations, each a stochastic sequence of pulses, and the best match is selected.

A rough comparison of the promising code types, from PCM using 64 kb/s as the highest bit rate and quality level, down to current vocoders at 2 kb/s with poorest quality, is shown in Table 13–1. The table indicates that as the bit rate is decreased by half in each step, the complexity increases by ten in terms of estimated millions of processing instructions per second (except for an LPC vocoder), the delay increases, and the quality deteriorates from high to synthetic (poor). Curves of the perceived speech quality based on subjective laboratory tests of high– and low–complexity coders are shown in Figure 13–5. It is apparent that the quality (mean opinion score) falls off rapidly as the bit rate is decreased below about 16 kb/s. It is expected, however, that continued research into new coding techniques will provide more promising results.

321

Table 13-1. Comparison of Low–Bit–Rate Speech–Coding Schemes

Coder Type	Bit Rate (kb/s)	Complexity (MIPS*)	Delay (ms)	Quality
PCM	64	0.01	0	High
ADPCM	32	0.1	0	High
Adaptive subband coding	16	1	25	High
Multipulse LPC	8	10	35	Communication
Stochastically excited LPC	4	100	35	Communication
LPC vocoder	2	1	35	Synthetic

*Estimated million instructions per second.

A version of an available design for LBRV, adaptive differential pulse code modulation (ADPCM), requires 32 kb/s and provides up to 48 high–quality voice channels (without channel signalling) instead of 24 (with signalling) within the DS1 (1.544–Mb/s) digital stream. Channel signalling for LBRV is handled by a common–channel signalling (CCS) method or by devoting four channels out of the 48 to signalling (discussed below in this chapter under "Low–Bit–Rate Voice Bundled Format and Application"). In addition to separation of signalling, however, there are restrictions on tandem–connecting links and voiceband data transmission.

The perceived quality of speech produced by waveform coders at varying digital coding rates was measured in subjective tests [3] with many listeners. The speech quality for vocoders and hybrid coders is estimated based on informal listening tests at several laboratories. A mean opinion score (MOS) of 5 is considered excellent, 4 is good, 3 fair, 2 poor, and 1 bad. In all tests, a standard telephone bandwidth of 3.2 kHz was maintained.

Adaptive Differential PCM. The reduction in bit rate for the LBRV channel is made possible by using ADPCM techniques and fast digital processing. A brief description of this technique

Subjective quality
(mean opinion score)

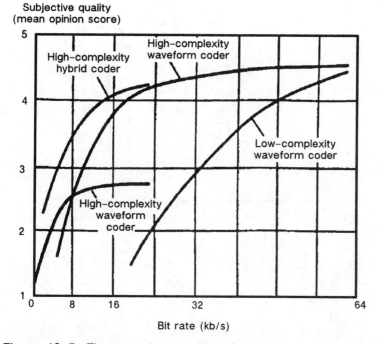

Bit rate (kb/s)

Figure 13-5. The perceived quality of speech produced by coders at various coding rates.

begins with the analog–to–digital conversion of the voiceband signal into the μ–law PCM format. This is converted into uniform PCM and a difference signal is obtained by subtracting an estimate of the immediately previous sample of the input signal from the current sample of the input signal. The difference signal is then assigned four binary bits by a 15–level adaptive quantizer. To make an estimate of the previous signal, the 4–bit quantizer output is passed through an inverse adaptive quantizer, an adaptive predictor, and a reconstructed–signal calculator, which are used to form the estimate. The 4–bit binary word of the adaptive quantizer output (one bit for sign and three for magnitude) is the signal to be transmitted. A simplified block diagram of the LBRV encoder/decoder is shown in Figure 13–6, with 64–kb/s PCM on one side and 32–kb/s ADPCM on the other.

A detailed description and the ADPCM coding algorithm is contained in Reference 4, as based on a U.S. standard [5]. This

323

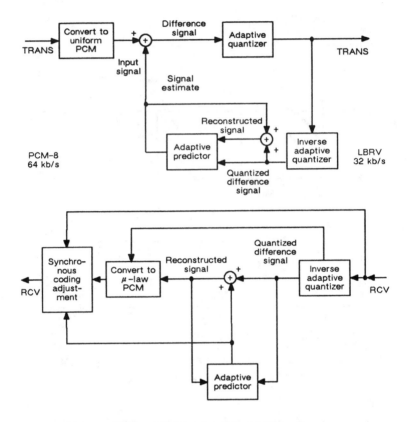

Figure 13-6. LBRV—simplified block diagram.

material replaces the text of Recommendation G. 721 of CCITT Volume III.3, Red Book (1984) for North American use. The newer algorithm is a modified version of the CCITT recommendation to resolve problems with the older 202–type data modems and with zero–code restraints on the transmitted signal. The application of LBRV in the network [6] is under continuing study as it requires special administration because of link compatibility, signalling provisions, data limitations, restrictions on the number of tandem coding/decoding steps and other problems. It is gaining use in private networks to minimize the cost of long–haul interswitch trunks derived from rented DS1 channels that are thereby capable of providing 48 circuits without signalling, or 44 circuits with signalling. It is also available for use in DLC systems.

Digital Data Signal Processing

To provide flexibility for digital transmission systems, the terminal equipment must be able to process digital data as well as voice signals. The required processing does not include amplitude sampling or companding, but the digital signals must be inserted into the bit stream in a way that satisfies data transmission requirements and, at the same time, is compatible with digital line transmission. Furthermore, if the digital signals are to be multiplexed with other digital signals or with digitized speech signals, they must be processed so that the format is compatible with multiplexing, framing, timing, and synchronization functions throughout the system. Digital data transmission requires bit integrity—no change in the transmitted *1* or *0* bit signal.

A number of types of terminal equipment that meet these complex requirements are available. They commonly handle digital data at rates of 2.4, 4.8, 9.6, 19.2, and 56 kb/s, either with or without a lower–speed secondary channel included in the data stream.

Multiplexing. Interleaving or sequencing the pulses that represent the signal amplitudes of different channel signals into a single continuous bit stream is called time–division multiplexing. The process involves timing, synchronization, and framing.

Timing. All of the major logical processes in a digital system terminal depend on accurate timing of the pulses associated with each signal and with the multiplexing of the coded signals into a single pulse stream. In most terminals, the transmitter timing is provided by or derived from a single clock circuit that distributes a stream of pulses with a highly precise and stable repetition rate. The sampling and coding functions are controlled by this timing signal so that all pulses are properly related regarding repetition rate, width, and position in a time sequence.

Receiver timing is derived from the incoming bit stream. This allows the receiver pulse detector circuits to follow timing "wander" or "jitter" that may be present on the stream. When the received digital data is to be passed on, a buffer is provided to hold the data until read–out. If the write–in and read–out data rates were different, the buffer could become overfilled or underfilled and transmission errors would be introduced.

325

Synchronization. For satisfactory performance, digital transmission and switching circuits must be properly synchronized with one another. In the originating terminal, this function is fulfilled by the timing signal previously discussed. Where the function of the equipment is to multiplex digital signals from different sources, it is necessary to ensure that all sources are in synchronism or to adjust the rates of the incoming signals before multiplexing. Because of the importance of synchronization, the clock circuits in both cases must be extremely reliable and must produce timing signals with great precision.

Framing. Detailed methods of multiplexing and demultiplexing digital signals vary from system to system. However, one feature is shared by all. The pulse stream of multiplexed signals must be organized so that the pulses associated with each specific signal can be identified and separated from the other signals in the stream. This is accomplished by organizing the pulse stream into *frames*. The separation of one signal from the others is then accomplished by counting pulse positions relative to the beginning of a frame. In this manner, code words representing the elements of each signal can be extracted from the combined bit stream and reassembled into a single stream of pulses associated with a particular channel signal. This procedure also permits the identification of the most significant digit in a code word.

Loss of framing may be caused by line errors that alter the framing pattern and cause the receiver to react falsely. This condition is called a *misframe*. The mean time between misframes even under conditions of high error rate must be made long to prevent excessive loss of information, while the time required to reframe must be kept very short.

The PCM words (8-bit coding) and a synchronizing bit are assembled into basic frames that in turn are grouped into a superframe of 12 basic frames or, more recently, into an extended superframe format of 24 basic frames. The ESF allows new features that are described later in this chapter.

Basic Frame

The full-rate basic frame organization for the eight-bit PCM signals from each of 24 voiceband channels is shown in Figure

13–7. Each frame of 125 µs length (sampling rate of 8,000 Hz) consists of an F–bit for synchronization and 192 (24 × 8) bits for the 24 PCM channels, or 193 bits per frame. This is repeated 8000 times per second to form a 1.544–Mb/s serialized bit stream, DS1.

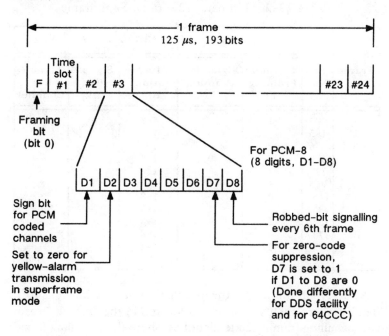

Figure 13-7. Basic DS1 frame organization (PCM-8).

Provisions for robbed–bit signalling, discussed later, and for the yellow alarm sent from a remote out–of–service terminal are shown.

Superframe

Twelve basic frames are assembled into a serial superframe format [7], as shown in Table 13–2. The table indicates the bit assignments for synchronization, terminal and signalling channel framing, the information bits for the PCM channels, and the robbed–bit A and B signalling channels. The eight information bits are assigned the first through eighth bit positions except that the eighth bit (least significant) is "robbed" in frames 6 and 12 for the A and B signalling channels. A modest increase in message channel noise due to robbing bits is discussed later in this chapter under "Robbed–Bit Signalling."

Table 13–2. Format: 12–Frame Superframe

Frame No.	Bit No.	F Bits		Bit Use Per Time Slot		
		Terminal Framing Ft	Signalling Framing Fs	Inform- ation Bits	Signal- ling Bit	Signal- ling Channel
1	0	1	–	1–8	–	–
2	193	–	0	1–8	–	–
3	386	0	–	1–8	–	–
4	579	–	0	1–8	–	–
5	772	1	–	1–8	–	–
6	965	–	1	1–7	8	A
7	1158	0	–	1–8	–	–
8	1351	–	1	1–8	–	–
9	1544	1	–	1–8	–	–
10	1737	–	1	1–8	–	–
11	1930	0	–	1–8	–	–
12	2123	–	0	1–7	8	B

After synchronization, the terminal frame coding bits (F_t) identify where each superframe is located in the DS1 bit stream. The signalling framing code identifies where the signalling frames 6 and 12 are located. When the signalling channel is not used, the signalling bit is left in the 1 or 0 state or may be used to indicate that data is being transmitted.

Extended Superframe Format

Newer digital terminals provide for the ESF [8,9], which is shown in Table 13–3, by extending the superframe from 12 to 24 frames. This format allows the full 64 kb/s of each channel to be used as information bits (clear–channel capability) and divides the F–bit pattern of 8 kb/s previously assigned for basic terminal and signalling framing into three subchannel assignments. These are:

(1) 2 kb/s for terminal framing

Table 13-3. Extended Superframe Format

Frame No.	Bit No.	F-Bits			Bits Use Per Time Slot		Signalling Options			
		Frmg. Pattern	Data Link	CRC Code	Information	Rbd. Bit Sgnlg.	T	2	4	16
1	0	–	M1	–	Bits 1-8	–	–	–	–	–
2	193	–	–	C1	Bits 1-8	–	–	–	–	–
3	386	–	M2	–	Bits 1-8	–	–	–	–	–
4	579	0	–	–	Bits 1-8	–	–	–	–	–
5	772	–	M3	–	Bits 1-8	–	–	–	–	–
6	965	–	–	C2	Bits 1-7	Bit 8	–	A	A	A
7	1158	–	M4	–	Bits 1-8	–	–	–	–	–
8	1351	0	–	–	Bits 1-8	–	–	–	–	–
9	1544	–	M5	–	Bits 1-8	–	–	–	–	–
10	1737	–	–	C3	Bits 1-8	–	–	–	–	–
11	1930	–	M6	–	Bits 1-8	–	–	–	–	–
12	2123	1	–	–	Bits 1-7	Bit 8	–	A	B	B
13	2316	–	M7	–	Bits 1-8	–	–	–	–	–
14	2509	–	–	C4	Bits 1-8	–	–	–	–	–
15	2702	–	M8	–	Bits 1-8	–	–	–	–	–
16	2895	0	–	–	Bits 1-8	–	–	–	–	–
17	3088	–	M9	–	Bits 1-8	–	–	–	–	–
18	3281	–	–	C5	Bits 1-7	Bit 8	–	A	A	C
19	3474	–	M10	–	Bits 1-8	–	–	–	–	–
20	3667	1	–	–	Bits 1-8	–	–	–	–	–
21	3474	–	M11	–	Bits 1-8	–	–	–	–	–
22	4053	–	–	C6	Bits 1-8	–	–	–	–	–
23	4246	–	M12	–	Bits 1-8	–	–	–	–	–
24	4439	1	–	–	Bits 1-7	Bit 8	–	A	B	D

Notes:

1. C1 to C6 cyclic-redundancy-check code.

2. Option T—Transparent mode (bit 8 used for information—no signalling bits) for 64CCC.

3. Option 2—2-state signalling (channel A).

4. Option 4—4-state signalling (channels A and B).

5. Option 16—16-state signalling (channels A, B, C, and D).

6. Data link may be subdivided, see text.

329

(2) 2 kb/s for cyclic redundancy check, CRC–6 (an in–service block–error check)

(3) 4 kb/s for a data link, or 2 kb/s for zero–byte time–slot interchange (ZBTSI) [10] plus 2 kb/s for a data link.

In brief, it has been found that item (1) provides sufficient input for rapid synchronization. Item (2) provides for a CRC–6 in–service block–error check [11] of one or more errors in the extended superframe of 24 basic frames. It can be shown that this error–detection code is capable of detecting 98.4 percent of all superframes containing errors. The information can be used for many features such as false–framing protection, protection switching, and performance monitoring. The data link of item (3) is used to send alarm signals, control signals, and performance reports via two formats: (1) bit–oriented signals of repeated assigned code words and (2) message–oriented signals. The bit–oriented signals carry priority codes (such as yellow alarm) and command and response codes (such as loop–back and protection switching). The message–oriented signals carry performance-monitoring information (such as no events, CRC error, and severely errored framing).

For ZBTSI, the 4–kb/s data link is divided into two 2–kb/s channels [10]. The first channel, made up of M1, M3, M5, M7, M9, and M11 bits, is used for ZBTSI functions. The second channel, made up of the other M bits, is used for the above ESF data link information, but at the reduced rate of 2 kb/s.

Robbed–Bit Signalling

The basic DS1 frame bit organization (Figure 13–7) shows the bit assignments, including the robbed bit used for signalling. The superframe format of 12 basic frames shown in Table 13–2 indicates that the A and B signalling channels are provided by bit 8, the least significant bit, borrowed from the information bits in every six frames. This provides for four–state signalling capability. When not used for signalling, the robbed bit may be left as a 0 or a 1 or used for data purposes. With such signalling, only 56 kb/s is readily available for unconstrained information transport.

The ESF of Table 13–3 shows the bit assignment for 24 basic frames and the signalling options. In the transparent mode all eight bits are used for traffic. Other options using robbed bits provide for a 2–, 4–, or 16–state signalling channel. Two– and four–state signalling modes are commonly used in a pre–ESF environment; the 16–state mode is, in essence, reserved for future use.

Robbed–bit signalling increases the noise in the message channel. If signalling frame integrity is maintained (remains in the same original frame) the noise is increased by about 1.8 dB [2], equivalent to PCM–7 5/6 coding. However, integrity is not maintained through most cross–connection and switching systems. Instead, reframing often results in the original signalling bits in the frame being frozen as 0s or 1s and new signalling frames assigned, with the new signalling bits overriding the message bits. In tandem connections, this effect can theoretically increase the message channel noise up to 6 dB, equivalent to PCM–7 coding [2]. Using clear–channel capability and CCS avoids this condition.

64–kb/s Clear–Channel Capability and Zero–Code Substitution

64CCC is defined as using the full 64 kb/s that is assigned to each channel. It is provided for by the transparent mode, option T, in the ESF of Table 13–3. In this mode, channel signalling must be provided by other means (out–of–slot or common–channel). This allows the full 64 kb/s to be used for transport.

When 64CCC is provided, there is a possibility that a line pulse pattern, all zeros, may be transmitted that will not keep line or other regenerators in synchronism. The 1.544–Mb/s DS1 stream requires: (1) an average pulse density of one in eight and not more than 15 consecutive zeros [4] and (2) at least n ones in every $8(n + 1)$–bit window where $n = 1$ to 23.

There are several ways to meet this condition. One interim way is to establish and administer a mix of robbed–bit channels and only a few clear channels. The success of this passive method depends on the bit statistics of the channels involved. A better method, commonly used, is to employ an active zero–code substitution technique that replaces a string of eight 0s in the transmitted bipolar line pattern with a distinctive word containing *1*s, which can be detected at the receiving end to enable restoration of the original word. One such method has been labeled B8ZS, for bipolar with eight–zero substitution. It will recognize any string of eight contiguous zeros and substitute a bipolar–violation pattern as shown in Figure 13–8. The bipolar violation occurs because the substituted code starts with the same polarity as the last one bit. Successful application of B8ZS requires that the directed violation pattern be recognized only for zero substitution and not as an indication of errors. For example, older multiplexers, T1–type protection switches, and other equipment may have a violation monitor and removal function that would interpret the B8ZS code as having four logic errors and two violations instead of eight zeros.

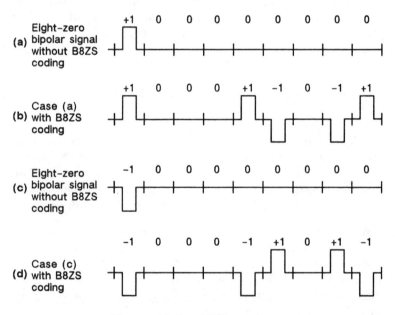

Figure 13–8. B8ZS coding.

Another method is the previously mentioned ZBTSI technique. In brief, this method involves buffering the scrambled PCM stream and searching for all–zero octets that combine with adjacent octets to violate the density or ones requirement noted above. When this condition is found, the all–zero octet is flagged and replaced by an inserted address code containing ones to ensure meeting the requirements. At the other end, the flag and code are recognized and the zero octet is restored to its original state.

The application of one ZBTSI method entails a delay of four frames of the DS1 signal and uses 2 kb/s of the ESF data channel. The delay would result in an additional round–trip delay of 1.0 ms per encode/decode pair and several pairs in tandem would reduce the voice grade–of–service because of increased talker–echo impairment. The ZBTSI method, however, does not interfere with using bipolar violation for error detection, now employed by existing multiplexers and by some DS1 test equipment to measure bit error ratio. Long–range network planning, however, favors the B8ZS method to avoid the delay.

Low–Bit–Rate Voice—Bundled Format and Application

A line format for LBRV is a four–bundle–frame format [4,5] to provide 44 LBRV channels and four signalling or "delta" channels over a DS1 bit stream. The F–bit framing pattern is the same as that employed in DS1 superframe or ESF format. The basic LBRV frame (125 μs) is shown in Figure 13–9, which shows the grouping of four bundles, each having 11 LBRV channels and one delta channel. Each channel contains only four bit assignments for ADPCM 32–kb/s channels. The delta channel in each bundle is used for signalling and alarms, signalling channel alignment, a CRC–6 cyclic redundancy code for block–error detection, and a data link for each bundle. The delta 1 channel bit assignments for bundle 1 are shown in Table 13–4.

LBRV Application. Specialized applications of LBRV are under way. There are two major equipment units, the channel bank and the LBRV transcoder. The channel bank converts voiceband channels into a pair of LBRV DS1 1.544–Mb/s bit streams organized, as shown in Figure 13–9, into 44 transport channels and four delta channels for signalling, etc.

The transcoder converts the two DS1 bit streams, each for two full–rate (64 kb/s) digroups of 24 channels, into one LBRV DS1 bit stream for the 48 channels as noted above. The

333

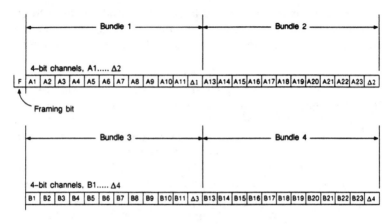

One 125-μs frame of 193 bits consists of a framing bit and four bundles.
A1 ⟶ A11, A13 ⟶ A23 are channels associated with full-rate digroup A
B1 ⟶ B11, B13 ⟶ B23 are channels associated with full-rate digroup B
Δ1 Delta channel associated with bundle 1, etc.

Figure 13-9. LBRV DS1 frame organization.

voice-frequency (VF) performance requirements and objectives specified in References 6 and 7 apply to LBRV channel banks until addressed specifically for LBRV.

Generally, the application of LBRV will require detailed administration for end-to-end compatibility of transmission and operations support. Voiceband data transport is limited, typically to 4800 b/s, and the number of PCM/LBRV/analog codings is also limited.

A typical application for private branch exchange (PBX) tie trunks is shown in Figure 13-10.

Formation of Line Signals. The 50-percent duty cycle, bipolar, alternate-mark-inversion, electrical DS1 line signal is made up of the elements discussed above, i.e., coded information pulses, signalling pulses, and framing pulses. Signals at higher line rates include control bits, parity bits for error detection, and communication bits for administrative uses. The format of this combined signal must satisfy the requirements of the transmitting and receiving terminal equipment as well as those of the repeatered line.

Table 13-4. LBRV-Delta-1 (Δ1) Channel Bit Assignments

Frame	Bit Position				Frame	Bit Position			
Number	45	46	47	48	Number	45	46	47	48
1	A1	A2	0	U1	13	C1	C2	1	U13
2	A3	A4	1	U2	14	C3	C4	0	U14
3	A5	A6	0	CRC1	15	C5	C6	1	CRC4
4	A7	A8	1	U4	16	C7	C8	0	U16
5	A9	A10	0	U5	17	C9	C10	1	U17
6	A11	M1	1	U6	18	C11	M3	0	U18
7	B1	B2	0	CRC2	19	D1	D2	1	CRC5
8	B3	B4	1	U8	20	D3	D4	0	U20
9	B5	B6	0	U9	21	D5	D6	1	U21
10	B7	B8	1	U10	22	D7	D8	0	U22
11	B9	B10	0	CRC3	23	D9	D10	1	CRC6
12	B11	M2	1	U12	24	D11	M4	0	U24

Notes:

1. Bit position numbering within a frame begins with 0. Δ1 occupies the above bit positions of the 193-bit frame and carries signalling data for trunks 1-11 of associated digroup A.

2. The A, B, C, and D signalling channels are included in this table in bit positions 45 and 46 for the 16-state signalling mode of operation. In the 4-state mode, the channel A signalling bits are repeated in the C channel, and the channel B signalling bits are repeated in the D channel. M1, M2, M3, and M4 are bundle alarm bits.

3. Bits in position 47 are for signalling channel alignment.

4. U bits are an interterminal bundle data link for future use, set to *1* at present.

5. Δ2, Δ3, and Δ4 have similar formats, except that:

   a. Δ2 occupies bit positions 93, 94, 95, and 96 and carries signalling data for trunks 13-22 of digroup A.

   b. Δ3 occupies bit positions 141, 142, 143, and 144 and carries signalling data for trunks 1-11 of digroup B.

   c. Δ4 occupies bit positions 189, 190, 191, and 192 and carries signalling data for trunks 13-22 of digroup B.

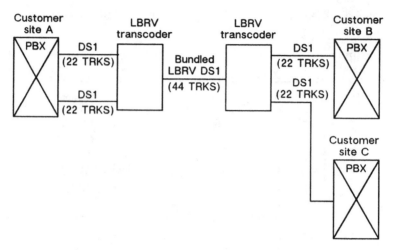

Figure 13-10. LBRV application example.

The basic need is to establish the line repetition rate. This involves the entire system, line, and terminal equipment, and establishes or influences many of the other basic system interrelationships. The factor that most influences the line rate is the number of channels to be provided, i.e., how many DS0s are to be carried.

Other system requirements must be satisfied. To avoid unwanted variations in average signal voltage (baseline wander) while keeping the regenerative repeaters simple and inexpensive, it is desirable to use a bipolar electrical line signal, as illustrated in Figure 13-1(d), in which the dc and low-frequency components are negligible. The way to satisfy these requirements is tailored to each specific system.

Demultiplexing and Decoding. At the receiving end of a digital transmission system, the inverse of the processes used at the transmitting end must be provided. Logic circuits, operating on information contained in the framing code, steer the pulses associated with each channel through appropriate gates to separate them from the other channel signal pulses.

The signalling pulses are removed from the pulse stream and directed to signalling conversion circuits. The PCM pulses are converted to PAM samples, which are then passed through low-pass filters to recover the original analog signal. The received–signal decoding process, in general, uses a simpler circuit design than that of the transmitter coding process.

13-2 DIGITAL LOOP CARRIER

The use of PCM DLC or integrated digital loop carrier (IDLC) in the loop–feeder plant has become widespread in recent years. The application is from end offices to remote terminals containing cable cross–connection facilities. The line facilities may be repeatered cable pairs in existing cables, optical fibers with appropriate multiplexers, or other suitable media. Transmission, signalling, and other functions are provided for various message-telephone services and for special services.

DLC Arrangements

Several DLC arrangements are possible. One older loop–feeder arrangement for analog switching, shown in Figure 13–11, provides, at both ends, VF interfaces and conversions to digital form for transmission.

Other DLC arrangements are covered in Reference 13, which presents the functional criteria and features needed for the customer services that are provided. The reference covers a number of topics including:

(1) System description and application information

(2) Transmission and supervision criteria for single and multi-party service, digital data, universal voice grade use, etc.

(3) Signalling and supervision criteria for loop–start, ground–start, reverse–battery, ringing, etc.

(4) Basic voice–grade analog transmission criteria

(5) Transmission facility (metallic pair and DS1) interfaces, with protection lines and maintenance features.

Analog Transmission Criteria

Some of the voice–grade analog transmission criteria follow.

(1) Echo return loss (ERL) is to be greater than 18 dB and singing return loss (SRL) is to exceed 10 dB.

337

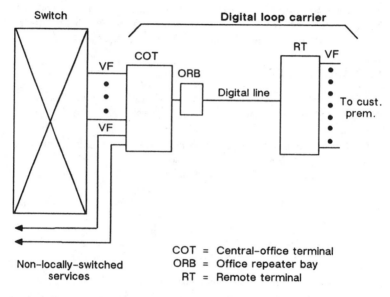

Figure 13–11. Digital loop carrier for loop feeder.

(2) Total loss, end–office terminal to network interface on customer's premises, is not to exceed 8 dB. The office impedance is 900 Ω and the customer's interface is 600 Ω.

(3) DLC system loss is not to exceed 2 dB at 1004 Hz in either direction.

(4) Frequency response at 400 Hz and 2800 Hz is to be within –0.5 dB (less loss) and +1.0 dB of loss at 1004 Hz with signal level of 0 dBm0 applied.

(5) Amplitude tracking of 1004–Hz loss relative to an input signal level of 0 dBm0 is to be within ±0.5 dB over an input range from –37 to +3 dBm0.

(6) Idle–channel noise at either end is not to exceed 20 dBrnc0.

(7) Peak–to–average ratio (PAR) is to be 90 or greater with a –13 dBm0 input level.

(8) Crosstalk between channels of the DLC is to be –65 dBm0 or less in the disturbed channel with a single–frequency

signal of 0 dBm of 200 Hz to 3400 Hz applied to the disturbing channel.

DLC Interface Criteria

Some of the criteria for DLC transmission facility interfaces are:

(1) The jitter transmitted from the DLC into the DS1 line facility is to not exceed 0.2 μs.

(2) The DLC is to tolerate jitter received from the DS1 line facility within the limits shown in Figure 13–12.

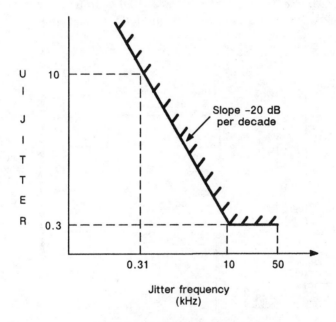

Unit interval (UI) for DS1 = 0.648μs

Figure 13–12. DS1 input jitter tolerance.

(3) An option for 64CCC is to be provided, including a zero–byte suppression technique and CRC–6 error–detection coding.

(4) Standard DS1 pulse shapes, levels, line formats, etc., are to be used.

A DLC arrangement for digital switching offices, shown in Figure 13–13, provides DS1 rate interfaces to the end office and digital or voice–frequency interfaces at remote distribution points. This is labeled IDLC because the DLC is integrated into the switch fabric without a CO terminal. Generic requirements, objectives, and interfaces for the IDLC are given in Reference 13 in terms of functions. This includes requirements and options for customer services, end–to–end voice transmission, coin, digital data capability, digital (DS0) cross–connection, ISDN capability, digital bridging, DS1 extensions, etc. Requirements for supporting interfaces to the digital network such as for synchronization, jitter, frame format, maintenance, and alarms are presented. Some of these are addressed in the following sections.

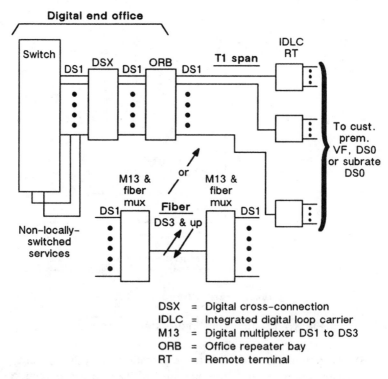

DSX = Digital cross-connection
IDLC = Integrated digital loop carrier
M13 = Digital multiplexer DS1 to DS3
ORB = Office repeater bay
RT   = Remote terminal

Figure 13–13. Integrated digital loop carrier for loop feeder.

Many of the criteria for voice–grade transmission are the same as noted above. The round–trip delay allocated to the remote terminal (RT) from its analog interface to the DS1 line is 1.0 ms or less. For RT to RT connections through the serving switch, 99 percent are to have echo delays less than 6.5 ms. Other connections are covered by Volume 1, Table 7.40 of the LSSGR [14]. The IDLC is to provide for full–duplex digital–data transmission at synchronous rates of 2.4, 4.8, 9.6, and 56 kb/s. Digital–data transmission is covered in Volume 3, Chapter 17.

ISDN Service

For this service, the IDLC–ISDN interface standard is being finalized. It will provide for a full duplex data transmission throughput rate of 144 kb/s from the digital subscriber line (DSL), equivalent to a digital subscriber line. The 144 kb/s will be assigned to two 64–kb/s B channels and one 16–kb/s D channel (for signalling or control information and packet data.) ISDN is discussed in Part 3 of this chapter.

Carrier Serving Area

DLCs are used in a systematic approach to deployment in the loop–feeder plant by means of a carrier serving area (CSA) plan. The CSA is the geographic area around a remote DLC terminal that serves the metallic lines, or digital subscriber lines to customer premises in that area, as described in Chapter 3 and in Chapter 5 of Volume 3. A typical CSA serves 400 to 2000 lines. The size of the area depends on the length allowed for the distribution cables, which must be no longer than 12 kft.

13-3 INTEGRATED SERVICES DIGITAL NETWORK

ISDN refers to the integration of communications services for transporting voice, data, and packet data over digital facilities. The ISDN plan [15,16] provides customer interfaces for access to the digital network via ISDN switches, all of which operate in a synchronous full–duplex manner. The standard interfaces include basic–rate access and primary–rate access. Basic–rate access involves a single DSL operating over a metallic loop. Primary–rate access operates at DS1 bit rate over a digital carrier and provides many channels, such as those needed for a digital PBX. The DSL is described in Chapter 3.

Performance Objectives

The error–ratio objectives (CCITT) for ISDN are given in Volume 1, Chapter 26, Part 4.

ISDN Basic–Rate Access

The access to the ISDN digital switch or network for a single line is at a 144–kb/s rate to transport two clear 64–kb/s bearer (B) channels and a 16–kb/s delta (D) channel noted previously. The access path is defined as extending from the 144–kb/s T network termination located on the customer's premises to the network node that processes the D channel or performs ISDN switching functions for the B or D channels. The various interfaces and reference points, determined by standards committees, are shown in Figure 13–14. The U interface is at the DSL line rate (160 kb/s, the sum of the 144–kb/s throughput rate plus 16–kb/s overhead), and the R and S interfaces are for B and D channel terminations, respectively.

There are several path configurations for transporting the ISDN basic access service from the T interface to the ISDN digital office. Some of these are shown in Figure 13–15 and involve the DSL and IDLC facilities. Path (c) employs digital multiplexers that must keep the B and D channel grouping and bit integrity intact. Digital cross–connections must also preserve this grouping.

If basic–rate access is provided via a DS1 carrier of 24 channels (1 through 24), a proposed channel and bit assignment for the ISDN B and D channels is shown in Figure 13–16. Three 64–kb/s time slots, channels 1, 2, and 3, denoted B1, DP, and B2, are assigned for ISDN access transport. The DP (D plus) channel bit assignment provides for the 16–kb/s ISDN D channel. Other DP bit assignments provide for spare, alarm,

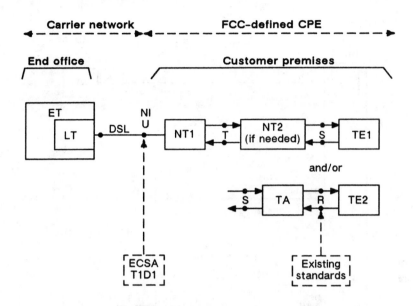

CCITT I-Series Recommendations Terminology

DSL	=	Digital subscriber line
ET	=	Exchange termination
LT	=	Line termination
NT	=	Network termination
TA	=	Terminal adaptor
TE	=	Terminal equipment
R, S, T, U	=	Reference points

USA & FCC terminology

CPE	=	Customer-premises equipment
ECSA	=	Exchange Carriers Standards Association
NI	=	Network interface
T1D1	=	Standards committee under ECSA

Figure 13-14. ISDN basic-rate access interfaces.

clear-channel indication, and a *1* bit to meet the ones-density requirement.

The functions and requirements for the line termination (LT) unit for the ISDN end office and for the customer-premises network termination 1 (NT1), are given in Reference 16.

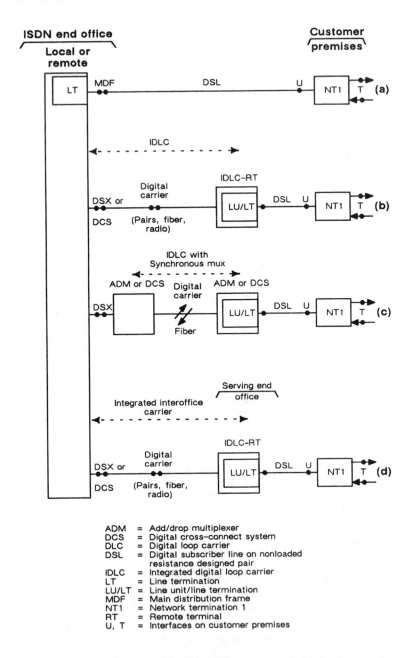

ADM   = Add/drop multiplexer
DCS   = Digital cross-connect system
DLC   = Digital loop carrier
DSL   = Digital subscriber line on nonloaded
         resistance designed pair
IDLC   = Integrated digital loop carrier
LT   = Line termination
LU/LT = Line unit/line termination
MDF   = Main distribution frame
NT1   = Network termination 1
RT   = Remote terminal
U, T   = Interfaces on customer premises

Figure 13-15. ISDN basic-rate access examples.

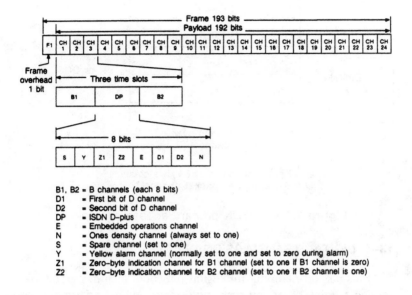

B1, B2 = B channels (each 8 bits)
D1   = First bit of D channel
D2   = Second bit of D channel
DP   = ISDN D-plus
E   = Embedded operations channel
N   = Ones density channel (always set to one)
S   = Spare channel (set to one)
Y   = Yellow alarm channel (normally set to one and set to zero during alarm)
Z1   = Zero-byte indication channel for B1 channel (set to one if B1 channel is zero)
Z2   = Zero-byte indication channel for B2 channel (set to one if B2 channel is one)

Figure 13-16. ISDN basic-rate access on DS1.

ISDN Primary-Rate Access

This multichannel access from a digital PBX to the ISDN switch or cross-connection is at the DS1 line rate. It will transport [17]:

(1) 23 B channels and a D channel

(2) 24 B channels if the associated D channel is not needed in the same DS1

(3) up to four H0 channels each of 384 kb/s, or

(4) one H1 channel of 1536 kb/s.

A simple example of this access is shown in Figure 13-17. The B channels are clear 64-kb/s channels with zero-code substitution as previously described. The current interface requirements are contained in Reference 18, which is discussed in Volume 3, Chapter 18 on access services.

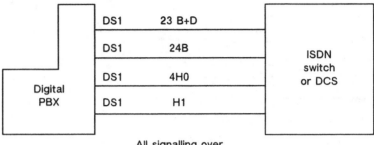

All signalling over
D channel

B = Bearer channels of 64 kb/s clear
D = Signalling and packet channel

Figure 13-17. ISDN primary access example.

13-4 DIGITAL TRANSMISSION DELAY

Transmission planning for digital networks includes grade–of–service studies based on loss, noise, and echo impairments as discussed in Volume 1, Chapters 24 and 26. With PCM–8 or ADPCM–4 digital networks, the loss is set to a fixed value for voiceband transmission. The noise is relatively low and is also fixed (for a single coding/decoding). The major impairment remaining is due to echo, which depends on two main factors: the return loss at the point of reflection and the echo–path time delay.

The reflection is normally at the digital end office where the four–wire digital connection is terminated in a two–wire analog loop. The echo path delay is the round–trip delay through the network from end office to end office. The time delay depends on the delay of the network elements and the media employed for transmission.

The effect of reducing echo by providing a higher return loss by better loop matching is discussed in Volume 3, Chapter 2, on the region digital switched network transmission plan.

As more digital processing is used to provide intelligent functions in switching and other network elements such as cross–connections, reduced bit–rate units, multiplexers, and channel banks, more signal delay is introduced into a connection. When delay becomes excessive, echo cancellers (described in Volume 3, Chapter 8, Part 3) with adequate delay range are needed to reduce echo to very low levels.

Some one–way delays are shown in Table 13–5 for a few kinds of digital element.

Table 13–5. Digital Network Elements—One–Way Delay

Element	Delay
Digital switch (Digital to digital) Channel banks (pair at 1000 Hz)	500 μs
D4 type 2W & 4W	370
D5 type 2W	970
4W	790
ISDN (NT1 and DSL line unit)	1000 max.
ADPCM coder/decoder	250–1000
B8ZS coder/decoder	5
ZBTSI coder/decoder	500
T1 line	7.8 μs per mile
Optical fiber	8.4 μs per mile
Radio (free space)	5.3 μs per mile

References

1. Members of Technical Staff. *Transmission Systems for Communications*, Fifth Edition (Murray Hill, NJ: AT&T Bell Laboratories, Inc., 1982), pp. 109–110.

2. Bellamy, J. C. *Digital Telephony* (New York: John Wiley and Sons, Inc., 1982), pp. 99–109.

3. Jayant, N. S. "Coding Speech at Low Bit Rates," *IEEE Spectrum* (Aug. 1986), pp. 58–63.

4. *Low Bit Rate Voice (LBRV) Terminals*, Technical Reference TR–TSY–000210, Bellcore (Iss. 1, Sept. 1986).

347

5. *ANSI T1.301–1987*, "Digital Processing of Voice–Band Signals—Algorithm and Line Format for 32–kb/s Adaptive Differential Pulse–Code Modulation (ADPCM)" (New York: American National Standards Institute, 1987).

6. *ANSI T1.501–1988*, "Network Performance—Tandem Encoding Limits for 32 kb/s Adaptive Differential Pulse–Code Modulation (ADPCM)" (New York: American National Standards Institute, 1988).

7. Bell System Technical Reference PUB 43801, *Digital Channel Bank—Requirements and Objectives*, American Telephone and Telegraph Company (Nov. 1982), with Addendum TR 43801A (Jan. 1985).

8. *Extended Superframe Format (ESF) Interface Specification*, Technical Reference TR–TSY–000194, Bellcore (Iss. 1, Dec. 1987).

9. *ANSI T1.403–1989*, "American National Standard for Telecommunications—Carrier–to–Customer Installations, DS1 Metallic Interface Specification" (New York: American National Standards Institute, Feb. 1989).

10. Draft of ANSI, *Report T1X1.4/87–702R4*, "American National Standard on Formats for the North American Digital Hierarchy" (New York: American National Standards Institute, 1987).

11. Smith, J. W. and A. B. Sripad. "Performance of Cyclic Redundancy Check Code in the New 1.544 Mb/s Extended Framing Format," *Globecom 1984 Conference Record* (Atlanta, GA: Nov. 1984), Vol. 2.

12. *Functional Criteria for Digital Loop Carrier Systems*, Technical Advisory TA–TSY–000057, Bellcore (Iss. 4, June 1988).

13. *Integrated Digital Loop Carrier System Generic Requirements, Objectives and Interfaces*, Technical Reference TR–TSY–000303, Bellcore (Iss. 2, Rev. 2, Sept. 1989).

14. *LSSGR, LATA Switching Systems Generic Requirements*, Technical Reference TR–TSY–000064, Bellcore (Iss. 2, July 1987), Vol. 1.

15. "ISDN Basic Access Transport," *Digest of Technical Information*, Special Report SR–TSY–000104, Bellcore (Iss. 2, May 1987), Vol. 4.

16. *ISDN Basic Access Transport System Requirements*, Technical Advisory TA–TSY–000397, Bellcore (Iss. 2, May 1987).

17. *ISDN Primary Rate Interface for SPCS–to–PBX Signalling*, Technical Advisory TA–TSY–000035, Bellcore (Iss. 1, Mar. 1985).

18. *High–Capacity Digital Special Access Service—Transmission Parameter Limits and Interface Combinations*, Technical Reference TR–NPL–000342, Bellcore (Iss. 1, June 1989).

Chapter 14

Fiber Optics

In recent years, the rapidly expanding fiber optic technology for telecommunications has made it possible to transmit light pulses at enormously high rates over optical fibers. In just a few years, single–wavelength fiber optic systems in the field have gone from a capability of 45 Mb/s over a span of 1.5 miles in 1977 to 1.7 Gb/s over a span of 45 miles in 1987. With rapid advances, even higher bit rates are imminent in commercial systems. Laboratory experiments have reported transmitting 4 Gb/s over 64 miles of optical fiber with direct modulation [1] and 73 miles with external modulation [2].

This chapter briefly notes the advantages of fiber optic transmission, reviews its rapidly expanding capabilities and discusses the general characteristics of fiber optic transmitters and receivers. (The fiber itself is described in Chapter 2, Part 6, where some important systems design considerations and requirements are noted.) A methodology is presented for applying fiber optic systems, and typical parameters for a 1.7–Gb/s optical line are shown. Also noted is the application to the loop–feeder plant with the view of reducing costs because of the short spans that are involved. The chapter briefly describes the transmission parameters of the TAT–8 undersea fiber optic system together with the interworking arrangements for connections between two dissimilar digital networks, the North American and European. The chapter ends with a brief note on basic maintenance needs.

14-1 FIBER OPTICS

Fiber optic systems have the potential to transport huge amounts of information reliably and economically. Such systems have been and are being applied in all parts of a telecommunications network including the loop–feeder or carrier serving areas and are being field–tried for loops. The application of fiber optics to a national network has enhanced digital transmission capabilities and will eventually provide for a universal digital network for transporting all kinds of information—voice, data, TV, etc.—at low cost.

In addition to the greater transport capability, fiber optics has the following advantages over radio or conductor forms of transport: greater distances between repeaters, negligible crosstalk interference or noise coupling in the fiber cable, better security in the medium, high–voltage isolation (such as for cables into electric power stations), small size versus capability, lightning immunity for all–dielectric, plastic–sheathed cables, no common ground between the ends, immunity to electrical noise in the central office, etc. There may be, however, some fiber degradation due to thermal and pressure effects from an explosive lightning stroke in a nearby conductor. Some disadvantages of fiber optics are: the fiber requires extremely pure materials in manufacture, fiber splices with low losses are difficult to make without special tools because of the need for precise alignment, and the electronics are still vulnerable to temperature and radiation effects. Since fiber cannot carry electric current, a paralleling copper wire to supply power to repeaters is needed in some applications such as transoceanic service.

A fiber optic system consists of an optical fiber cable connecting a light source and receiver. If the system range (length) is limited by fiber attenuation or dispersion, regenerative repeaters are necessary. Low–loss light propagation is usually in the infrared region, 0.8 to 1.6 micrometers (μm). Fiber design considerations are discussed in Chapter 2, Part 6.

Fiber systems have evolved rapidly through research and development since early application in the late 1970s. In general terms, the first generation of such systems may be characterized by operation at about 0.82 μm with then–available semiconductor light sources and detectors. Multimode silica fibers of 3– to 4–dB/km loss were used with AlGaAs (aluminum gallium arsenide) injection lasers or GaAs light–emitting diodes (LEDs) and photodiode detectors. They transmitted at about a 45–Mb/s rate initially, but were quickly replaced with a 90–Mb/s system. Three 90–Mb/s bit streams could be multiplexed onto the same

352

fiber. The main application was for short interoffice trunking and an important route in the Northeast Corridor. (The capacity of this corridor has increased with advances in technology.)

The second generation operated in the 1.3-μm region for lower loss and less pulse broadening from dispersion in the fiber. An InGaAsP (indium gallium arsenide phosphide) laser operating at room temperature was used for long spans and an LED for short spans over multimode fibers. A positive–intrinsic–negative (PIN) type photodiode detector became available and bit rates up to about 100 Mb/s were possible. Of historical interest was the introduction in late 1982 of the Fiber SLC® Carrier System in the loop distribution plant. This system could operate at the DS3 line rate (44.736 Mb/s) at a wavelength of 1.3 μm over a multimode fiber with an LED source and a PIN (FET) detector. Non-repeated operation up to 12 miles was possible.

The third generation operated at about 1.3 μm, initially, over single–mode fiber with a narrow–spectrum laser source with either a PIN diode detector or an avalanche photodetector diode (APD). Bit rates of several hundred Mb/s were provided with repeater spans of more than 30 miles with upgrading to rates of about 1.7 Gb/s. Later developments provided for operation at 1.55 μm where the loss of silica fiber is the lowest.

A brief overview of recent research progress in lightwave technology is given in Reference 3. This generally discusses the ongoing progress in fiber, transmission bandwidth, single–frequency lasers and optical receivers to provide greater bandwidth over long spans. The reference includes curves that show experimental sensitivities of noncoherent (direct) detection and coherent (heterodyne) detection. It also includes a plot of the results of long–distance experiments (noncoherent) on distance versus bit rate as limited by system loss and laser spectral width, as reported in England, Japan, and the U.S. The best observed results appear close to the theoretical limits.

Most fiber systems in use today operate at speeds of 139, 405, 417, or 565 Mb/s. Older and lower–capacity facilities use 45

SLC is a registered trademark of AT&T.

Mb/s; newer and upgraded systems use 810, 1180, or 1700 Mb/s, with 2400 Mb/s in prospect.

14-2 FIBER OPTIC TRANSMITTERS

Optical transmitters of current design convert on–off electrical signals into pulsed optical signals and couple these signals into the fiber for transmission. Efforts are being pursued to integrate the optics and associated electronics monolithically in order to provide for higher–bit–rate transmission. It appears that the associated electronics may limit the operating bit rate.

The two major kinds of semiconductor transmitter, LEDs and lasers [4,5], have the necessary characteristics such as size, conversion efficiency, coupling efficiency, speed, electrical amenability, environmental resistance, and reliability. Some of the these are discussed in the following.

Light-Emitting Diodes

LEDs are either surface emitters or edge emitters. The surface–type emission pattern is typically $120° \times 120°$; usable emission occurs at currents of 100 mA. The peak power coupled into multimode fiber is about –10 to –20 dBm; into single–mode fiber, –27 to –37 dBm. The spectral (noise) width of the emission is about 35 to 50 nm for short wavelengths and about 80 to 120 nm for long wavelengths. The edge–emitting diode has a more directive emission pattern, typically $120° \times 30°$, so the power coupled into the fiber is up to 10 dB greater than for surface emitters. The spectral width is about 30 to 90 nm over the band of interest. The LED structure is similar to that for lasers and care must be taken to prevent unwanted laser action.

Figures 14–1(a) and 14–1(b) depict edge– and surface–emitting LEDs [5]. The spectral width of the LED source and the dispersion characteristic of the fiber limit the bandwidth that can be used.

Current LEDs have a typical pulse rate limit of 30 to 100 Mb/s with special designs extending the range to several hundred

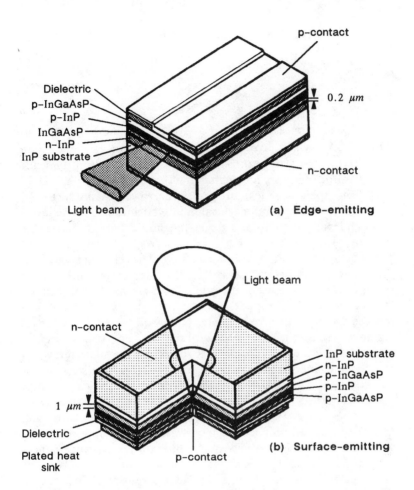

Figure 14-1. LED structures.

Mb/s. The LEDs are operated with a small forward bias (low light emission) to overcome a turn–on delay. Also, as the output optical power varies with dc voltage and with temperature, the power supply is usually regulated and temperature compensation of the LED is required. A thermoelectric cooler (part of the package) may also be used to stabilize the LED temperature over a reasonable range of temperature differences between the diode and the ambient. Mature LED designs have superb reliability with extrapolated mean time to failure at 70°C of 1 to 10 Mhr

355

(shorter at elevated temperatures), where 1 Mhr is about 100 years.

Lasers

Semiconductor lasers have a typical emission pattern of $30° \times 30°$; which provides for higher coupling efficiency than for LEDs. They give peak powers of -10 to $+10$ dBm, typically near 0 dBm, coupled into either multimode or single–mode fibers. The spectra (lines) are much narrower than for LEDs, ranging from 3 to 5 nm for typical multi–longitudinal–mode lasers to much less than 1 nm for a single–longitudinal–mode laser. The structure of a current multimode laser is shown in Figure 14–2(a). It relies on mirrors formed by cleaved crystal facets at each end of the optical cavity [5]. In this design, the emitted spectrum, 3 to 5 nm wide, is made up of a group of lines with the lines separated by the mode spacing of the cavity. Efforts to narrow the spectrum to permit greater bandwidth and repeater spacing have resulted in other structural designs. The structure of an internal distributed–feedback laser to reduce the spectrum width to a few megahertz is shown in Figure 14–2(b). The structure of an external–cavity laser [5] to reduce the spectral width to only a few kilohertz is shown in Figure 14–3. This design is typically 20 to 30 times longer than the internal design. The latter two lasers appear to be promising for the next generation of optical systems to use the inherent capability of the fiber and to advance coherent transmission techniques. Multimode laser operation produces mode–partition noise where the relative intensity of the various modes fluctuates, with the total optical power remaining constant, and degrades system performance. Single–mode lasers eliminate this noise. Single–frequency lasers would ideally reduce the dispersion bandwidth impairment to only that associated with the spectrum produced by the modulation. Another bandwidth impairment is laser chirp, which is a frequency change in the laser output caused by "on" and completely "off" signalling. The change effectively increases the undesired spectral lines. This effect can be suppressed by always keeping the laser in the light–emitting state and changing the light intensity for signalling. These impairments and other noise sources (including reflection–induced noise) are discussed in Reference 6.

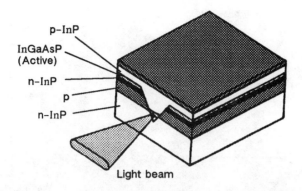

(a) Cleaved crystal facets at each end of the optical cavity

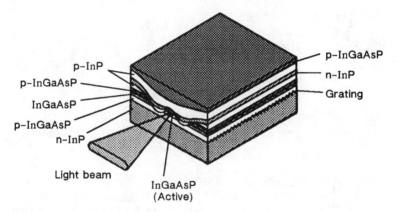

(b) Grating for internal distributed feedback for narrowing of spectrum

Figure 14–2. Laser structures.

14–3 FIBER OPTIC RECEIVERS

Optical receivers of current design are coupled to the fiber as a unit. They convert on–off light pulses by photodetection into electrical signals, which are then processed by associated electronics to provide the output data stream. As discussed in Chapter 2, currently there are two kinds of photodetector diode, the PIN and the APD type. A theoretical comparison [5] at 156 μm of the two photodiode types is indicated in Figure 14–4. It

357

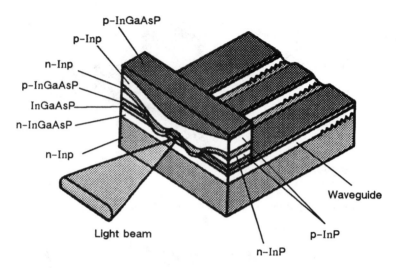

Figure 14-3. The integrated, external-cavity distributed Bragg reflector laser for single wavelength and narrow line width.

shows that, for a bit error ratio (BER) of 10^{-9}, the APD type can detect a lower optical signal power than the PIN type by about 10 dB.

A recent comprehensive review of the progress of photodetectors and receivers up to late 1985 has been presented in Reference 7. This reference includes design formulations for receiver sensitivity, noise, frequency response, dynamic range, and other operational terms for various semiconductor diodes. The reference also summarizes the results of laboratory experiments that were reported in current literature on receiver sensitivities. These are shown in Table 14-1; they do not yet reach the theoretical values. An ideal receiver would offer good sensitivity (low received power for 10^{-9} BER), wide dynamic range, relatively low cost to make and operate, reliability, low dependence on temperature, etc. None of the diodes in Table 14-1 has all of the ideal characteristics. For example, the APD (middle column) has highest sensitivity and good dynamic range but is difficult to produce. The photoconductor has poorer sensitivity but is simpler and has the potential to be integrated with low-noise amplifiers.

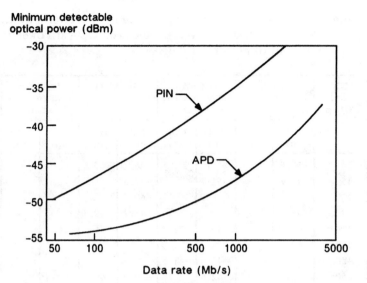

Figure 14-4. Minimum detectable (time-average) optical power versus data rate for APD and PIN photodiodes.

It is expected, however, that advances will provide improved receivers with integrated optic and electronic circuits.

14-4 DIGITAL FIBER OPTIC SYSTEMS

Typical digital fiber optic system requirements and objectives for both single-mode and multimode fiber optic systems for use within an exchange carrier area are covered in Reference 8. This applies to interoffice systems and loop-feeder systems in which protection switching sections range from 5 miles to about 250 miles. Transmission design parameters are specified for the worst-case values and for statistical values. The reference applies to forming a system (terminals, repeaters, and cable) from separate suppliers or to a complete, integrated system from a single supplier.

Several pertinent topics concerning system design considerations and performance requirements are discussed in the

Table 14-1. Summary of Experimental Receiver Diode Sensitivities (Average Received Optical Power P, in dBm, for 10^{-9} BER)

Bit rate (Mb/s)	InGaAs PIN		InGaAs SAM/SAGM APD		Ge APD		InGaAs Photocond- uctor	
	1.3 μm	1.55 μm	1.3 μm	1.55 μm	1.3 μm	1.55 μm	1.3 μm	1.55 μm
34	-52.5				-46	-55.8		
45	-49.9		-51.7		-51.9			
100					-40.5			
140	-46				-45.2	-49.3		
274	-43		-45	-38.7		-36		
320	-43.5							
420			-43	-41.5				
450			-42.5		-39.5	-40.5		
565					-33			
650	-36							
1,000			-38	-37.5	-28		-34.4	
1,200	-33.2	-36.5						
1,800			-31.3		-30.1			
2,000				-36.6		-31		-28.8
4,000				-32.6				

SAGM = Separated absorption, grating, and multiplication regions

SAM = Separated absorption and multiplication regions

following. The major design items for an optical regenerator section are indicated in Figure 14-5.

Terminal Equipment

This equipment includes fiber optic terminals and regenerators, jumper cable, connectors, frames, wavelength–division multiplexers, etc. These are located in central–office–like environments where all equipment is to remain operational with moderate controls on temperature and humidity [9]. The reference includes other equipment and building requirements such as heat dissipation limits, grounding, electromagnetic

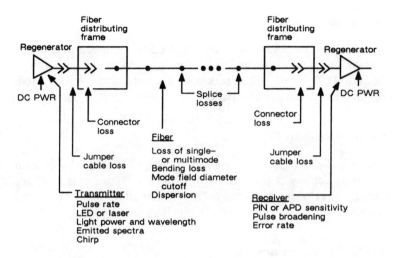

Figure 14-5. Regenerator section—major design considerations.

compatibility, electrostatic discharge, etc. that involve equipment design and application.

Line Signal

Line signals are usually in the form of return to zero (RZ) or non–return–to–zero (NRZ) pulses. The RZ pulses usually have an average 50–percent duty cycle, which is a fraction of time that the light source is "on" compared with the assigned time slot. For "off," the light from the LED is turned off, whereas the lasers are only dimmed (NRZ) to about 10 dB below the "on" light.

Line signals are also used for clock recovery. The clock recovery circuit requires a minimum number of transitions between 0s and 1s and only short runs of consecutive 1s or 0s. To meet these conditions, line signals are usually scrambled to provide a good balance between 0s and 1s.

Cross-Connection Interfaces

These electrical interfaces are required for connection to other circuits and for measuring transmission performance, usually at DS1 to DS3 levels. Interfaces and allowable connecting cable lengths are discussed in Chapter 26.

Alarm Indication Signals

These digital signals are used to prevent alarms and protection switching activity beyond the span where a failure exists. These signals, previously known as "blue," "inhibit," "all Is," and "keep-alive" signals, are detailed in Reference 10.

Availability Requirements

These are used for the design of protection switching. The availability requirement is derived from a transmission objective of 99.98-percent availability for a two-way 250 mile (400-km) DSX-1 to DSX-1 connection (prorated with length). Unavailability (outage) is defined as any time period one second or longer where the BER of any individual channel (DS1, DS1C, DS2, or DS3) is greater than or equal to 10^{-3}. This equates to a maximum outage time of 105 minutes per year. For a similar connection between DSX-3s, the allocated maximum outage time is 79 minutes per year, which correlates to a maximum outage of 0.32 minute per year-mile. Other requirements relating to per-DS1 availability, versus simultaneous failure of groups of DS1s, are given in Reference 10.

Equipment Reliability Requirement

The mean time between failures (MTBF) of optical transmitter and receiver circuit packs must be a minimum of four years.

Error Performance Requirements

This is a measure of in-service transmission performance in terms of BER, errored seconds, and burst-errored seconds with the following definitions [11].

(1) BER is the ratio of the number of bits in error to the total number of bits transmitted during a measurement period (a series of one–second intervals).

(2) An errored second is any one–second interval containing at least one error.

(3) A burst–errored second is any errored second containing at least 100 errors.

Forward–looking requirements [11] for error performance, which are given below, are for one–way systems of 250 miles in length. As with availability, performance of shorter systems is prorated in direct proportion to route mileage.

(1) The BER at DSX–1, DSX–1C, DSX–2 or DSX–3 interfaces must be less than 1×10^{-9}, excluding all burst–errored seconds.

(2) Burst–errored seconds, other than those caused by protection switching induced by equipment failures, should average no more than four per day at the interfaces noted above.

(3) For systems interfacing at the DS1 level, the long–term percentage of errored seconds (measured at the DS1 rate) should not exceed 0.14 percent. This is equivalent to 99.86–percent error–free seconds. While no errored–second requirement is given for the DS1C and DS2 rates, any DS1 channel carried in a DS1C, DS2, or higher–rate channel must meet the DS1–rate errored–second requirement.

(4) For systems interfacing at the DS3 level, the long–term percentage of errored seconds (measured at the DS3 rate) should not exceed 1.0 percent. This is equivalent to 99.0–percent error–free seconds.

Protection–Switching Performance

Automatic protection–switching systems are used to increase system availability by replacing a failed facility with a standby facility. Four parameters are important:

(1) Time required to detect the failure

(2) Time required after detection to complete the switch from the failed facility to the standby

(3) BER threshold for initiation

(4) Protection–switch reliability.

At DS3 rate or higher, the maximum detection time for fiber optic systems to determine that the BER threshold is exceeded is

BER	Time
10^{-3}	10 milliseconds
10^{-4}	100 milliseconds
10^{-5}	1 second
10^{-6}	10 seconds
10^{-7}	100 seconds

Upon initiation, switching time is not to exceed 50 ms. The other two parameters are included in References 10 and 11 as well as in requirements on system transient response (recovery from a temporary disturbance), where the input or line–rate signal is interrupted and recovery is required within a stated time after restoration.

Jitter

Jitter is timing variations in the digital stream and is usually measured at DS1 through DS3 multiplexer levels (not at optical carrier levels) because multiplexers are the significant sources. Jitter requirements are included in Chapter 15, Part 4.

Transmission Delay

This is an important transmission parameter. The one–way transmission delay over a 100–mile system with no intermediate terminal must not exceed 1.0 ms and is directly prorated with length. (The delay of a 100–mile fiber by itself is about 0.8 ms.) The consequence of delay on the transported signal is covered in other chapters.

14-5 TRANSMISSION SYSTEM DESIGN METHODOLOGY

The methodology [8] for design of a fiber system provides a procedure to determine if the system or regenerator section will meet system BER requirements when operating over the length of the section involved. To determine this, calculations are made based on known performance data of fiber, transmitter and receiver with allowances for WDM devices, splices, connectors, and margin (usually 3 dB). The calculations will show that system needs are met, or are limited by loss or by dispersion (pulse broadening). There are several steps in this process. The terms are defined below:

(1) Determine the BER requirement based on section length from BER $\leq$ (2.5×10^{-11}) length (km).

(2) Select the receiver parameters P_R, P_D, Δt_{max} from receiver characteristics corresponding to the required BER from step (1).

The terms used in this procedure are defined as follows, where the worst case is generally the two–sigma value:

(a) P_R is the receiver sensitivity value at the operating wavelength in terms of worst case (at end of life) of the input optical power, in dBm, of a 50–percent mark density signal to achieve the appropriate BER. It is measured on the line side of the receiver connector. This value should take into consideration imperfections in the light source such as extinction–ratio variation (optical power ratio of ones to zeros), imperfections in the receiver circuit such as increases in leakage current, and possible light reflected back to the laser.

(b) P_D is the maximum dispersion power penalty in dB, which includes: (1) the worst–case required increase in receiver input power, which accounts for average pulse broadening due to fiber dispersion and is related to the time–averaged transmitter spectrum causing intersymbol interference (errors), and (2) mode–partition noise caused by rapid

365

pulse–shape fluctuations due to changes in the longitudinal modes of the laser. P_D corresponds to a specific BER and $\Delta_{t_{max}}$.

(c) $\Delta_{t_{max}}$ is the maximum allowable rms pulse broadening in nanoseconds that a detector can receive and meet the required BER.

(3) Calculate the section gain, G, and loss. If $G - L$ is equal to or greater than zero, the section design is not limited by loss.

(a) G is the system gain. It is determined from $G = P_T - P_R - M - U_{WDM} -$ jumper cable loss (if significant): $\sum N_j\, U_j$, where

P_T is the worst case of the end–of–life average output optical power in dBm that is coupled into a test jumper cable on the line side with 50–percent mark density. The test cable is to be at least 2 meters long and have a 5–cm loop.

P_R is defined in (a) above.

M is system margin, usually taken as 3 dB.

U_{WDM} is the worst–case loss of WDM equipment (if used, at both ends), including additional connector losses and effects of temperature, humidity, and aging.

The last term in the equation is the sum of connector losses other than those included in P_T and P_R, respectively.

(b) L is the fiber cable loss and is determined from $L = l(U_C + U_\lambda) + N_S(U_S)$ where

$l =$ length of spliced cable in kilometers including allowance for cable repair,

U_C = end-of-life cable loss, dB/km at 23°C at nominal wavelength,

U_λ = the largest increase in cable loss in dB/km at 23°C over the wavelength of expected operation versus that at the nominal wavelength,

N_S = the number of splices in cable of length l plus allowance for repair splices,

U_S = maximum allowable splice loss (in dB/splice).

(4) Calculate the end-to-end pulse broadening in terms of time: $\Delta_t = (\Delta\lambda)\ (D)\ (l)\ (.001)$ where $\Delta\lambda$ is the rms spectral width of the transmitter, in nm, D is the fiber dispersion coefficient at the nominal wavelength in picoseconds/nm-km, and l is the fiber length in km. If Δ_t is equal to or less than the $\Delta_{t_{max}}$ limit of the receiver, then the section design is not limited by dispersion. Reference 8 (Appendix 3) indicates a method to determine the worst-case dispersion over a range of wavelengths.

(5) If the results of parts (3) and (4) are satisfactory, the section design is acceptable.

(6) The maximum receiver input power in dBm must be specified. An optical attenuator may be required to meet this requirement on short line sections.

Currently, most fiber optic systems convert DS3 signals into optical signals for transmission over the fiber and reconvert to DS3 signals at the far end. A simple block diagram of one end of this conversion process is shown in Figure 14-6 for a 1.7-Gb/s optical line. The functions of the conversion equipment may include: synchronization, framing, scrambling, zero-code suppression, bit stuffing, performance monitoring and reporting, fault-location, DS3 protection switching, optical line protection switching, etc. The fiber for the protection line should preferably be in a different cable than the fiber for the service lines and over a different route. The extra circuits and lines used for protection are not shown in the figure. A protection circuit may be used to protect a number, N, of service circuits where N is a matter of

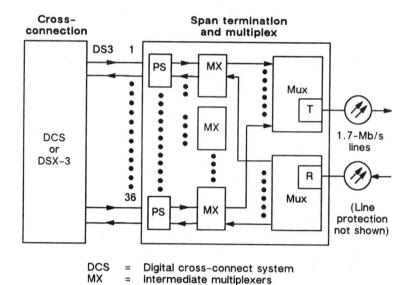

DCS = Digital cross-connect system
MX = Intermediate multiplexers
PS = Protection switch per DS3 channel
R = Optical receiver
T = Optical transmitter

Figure 14-6. DS3 connections to an optical fiber line.

engineering and economic judgments. For example, DS3 channels may be fully protected on a 1 × 1 arrangement and the optic line on a 1 × 7 arrangement (one protection line for seven service lines).

Typical optical line parameters operating in the 1.3-nm wavelength region are shown in Table 14-2. The transmitter is assumed to be a laser with a narrow spectrum and the receiver is an avalanche detector. For such a detector there is a maximum received optical power that, if exceeded, is destructive. For short ranges or for testing, it may be necessary to use an optical attenuator to reduce the received level to within operating range.

14-6 OPTICAL INTERFACE STANDARD

An American National Standards Institute (ANSI) standard for optical interfaces [12] has been developed by the T1 Committee (T1X1.4) of the Exchange Carriers Standards Association

Table 14-2. Typical Optical Line Parameters

Wavelength: 1.3 nm (nom.)
Bit rate: 1.7 Gb/s (nom.)
Code: unipolar NRZ
 	
Transmitter:
    Power (laser): −3.5 dBm
    Spectral width (half−power): 0.5 nm
 	
Receiver sensitivity: −32 dBm (for BER = 10^{-11})
 	
Power penalties:
    Dispersion: 0 dB (not limiting)
    Reflection: 0.5 dB
 	
Office losses: 2.5 dB
 	
Loss margin: 3.0 dB
 	
Maximum outside plant losses:
    0.46 dB/km (0.74 dB/mile)
 	
Maximum allowable dispersion: 3.4 ps/nm/mile
 	
Maximum repeater spacing:
    30 miles (more with lower losses)

(ECSA) to promote compatible widespread use of optical technology. The standard applies to interconnection at a connector, splice, or cross−connection of fiber optic systems operating at 1.31− or 1.55−μm nominal wavelength. It covers the optical parameters at such interfaces, as shown in Figure 14−7 at a patch panel, in order to ensure that equipment from different manufacturers is compatible. A family of standard optical carrier (OC) rates, with either return−to−zero or non−return−to−zero pulses, is given in Table 14−3 as integer multiples of 51.840 Mb/s [13]. These rates and the multiplex formats that produce them are discussed in greater detail in Chapter 15. The optical parameters are based on a performance objective of 1 × 10^{-10} BER for a regenerator section length of 40 km or less with an allowance of 1 dB power penalty due to dispersion. A standard operating

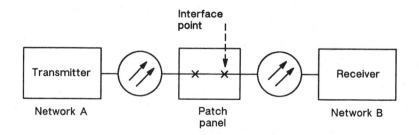

Note: X indicates a connector location.

Figure 14-7. Optical interface.

Table 14-3. Standard Optical Carrier Rates

OC	Mb/s
OC-1	51.840
OC-3	155.520
OC-9	466.560
OC-12	622.080
OC-18	933.120
OC-24	1244.160
OC-36	1866.240
OC-48	2488.320

condition is specified with electrical inputs fully loaded and driven by pseudorandom data.

The interface optical parameters for nonrepeatered section lengths of 25 km or less and for lengths 25 to 40 km that are covered are (1) return loss, (2) laser spectral characteristics, (3) power levels, and (4) pulse shape. Other parameters, such as for connectors, splices, and optical fiber cable, are covered by many references (mostly EIA-455-series) noted in the standard.

Return Loss

The optical return loss at any interface point must be 20 dB or more.

Spectra

The spectral width requirements are indicated in Tables 14-4 and 14-5 for multimode and single-mode operation. These

Table 14-4. Spectral Requirements—1.31– and 1.55–μm Multilongitudinal–Mode Lasers

		Maximum Δλm† (nm)		
Section Length	Rate	Band A 1.30-1.32 & 1.54-1.56 μm	Band B* 1.285-1.330 & 1.525-1.575 μm	Band C** 1.27-1.34 μm
25 km or less	OC-1	30	30	30
	-3	15	15	5
	-9	10	7	5
	-12	8	5.5	3.5
	-18	6	3	2.5
25 to 40 km	OC-1	25	25	
	-3	10	10	
	-9	7.5	4.5	
	-12	6	3.5	
	-18	4	2	

*   Outside band A

** Outside band B

†   Δλm   is the one-tenth-maximum spectral width of an optical source. It is the greatest difference in nm between the wavelength of the last mode on each side having one-tenth the amplitude of the peak mode and the wavelength of the peak mode.

Table 14-5. Spectral Requirement—1.31– and 1.55–μm Single–Longitudinal–Mode Lasers

Operating band	1.28 to 1.34 μm and 1.525 to 1.575 μm
Max. spectral width*	$\Delta\lambda_{15} \leq 1.0$ nm
Side–mode suppression ratio**	≥ 25 dB

*   Full width at 15 dB below peak power of central wavelength.

** Ratio of optical power in dominant mode to power in most significant side mode under fully modulated conditions.

values are compatible with present fibers and sources, i.e., 1.31–μm lasers on single–mode fibers and 1.55–μm lasers on dispersion–shifted single–mode fibers. The requirements were made more stringent for lasers with central wavelengths further from the fiber zero–dispersion wavelength because of dispersion–caused limitations.

Power Levels

There are three ways of setting the power level at an interface: a jointly engineered level for mutual satisfaction or, for sections of 25 km or less, a dynamic level and a fixed–power midpoint level. The dynamic level, in effect, prorates the loss according to length. The fixed power establishes power levels at the midpoint of section design. Only the midpoint values will be given here; these minimum values are shown in Table 14–6.

Table 14–6. Fixed–Power Midpoint Values

Level	Minimum Power
OC–1	–21 dBm
OC–3	–20
OC–9	–17.5
OC–12	–17
to	
OC–48	

Pulse Shape

Pulse shape requirements for single– and multi–longitudinal–mode lasers are shown in Figure 14–8 to define the terms and in Table 14–7 for the values. Included is the value of the extinction ratio, which is the average optical energy of a logic–one level to that of a logic–zero level. The ratio should be ten or more to provide adequate detection.

14-7 FIBER SYSTEMS IN THE LOOP NETWORK

Fiber optic systems are being applied widely to provide circuits from end offices to loop distribution points. Generally in this area

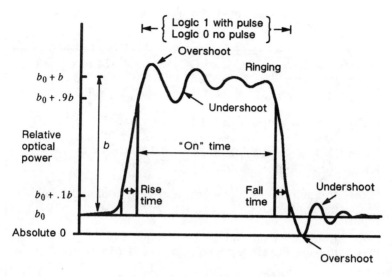

Extinction ratio = average optical energy of
logic "1" to "0"

(See Table 14-7 for values.)

Figure 14-8. Optical pulse shape parameters.

the span lengths are short and it is not necessary to design for the lowest loss. As a result, costs can be reduced as, for example, less expensive fiber or an LED instead of a laser might be used. Reference 14 reports of ongoing work on optimizing the design process for fiber loop–feeder systems and to improve techniques for designing loop fiber systems. The process involves determining the optimum bit rate based on minimizing costs that depend on bit rate and cable fiber counts, determining the optimum value of fiber loss, splicing loss, and system gain, and then selecting components to meet system requirements. Examples of the process for 45–, 90–, and 135–Mb/s facilities covering several economic scenarios and growth forecast profiles are given.

14-8 FIBER OPTIC UNDERSEA CABLE SYSTEMS

Just recently, fiber optic transmission systems for undersea facilities have been placed in service. Such systems have been

Table 14-7. Values for Pulse Parameters Shown in Figure 14-8.

Carrier rate:	OC-1 to OC-18	OC-24 to OC-48
(a) Rise time	≤ T/3*	≤ T/3
Fall time	≤ T/3	≤ T/2

(b) Overshoot of a logical "1" ≤ 1.0 b
   Undershoot of a logical "1" ≤ 0.3 b
   Overshoot of a logical "0" ≤ 1.0 b
   Undershoot of a logical "0" ≤ 0.2 b

(c) In addition, for non-return-to-zero coding the following applies:

   Rise time + on time ≤ 1.05T and ≥ 0.9T
   Ringing Frequency ≤ 2/T for OC-1 to OC-48

(d) Also, for return-to-zero coding the following applies:

   Rise time + on time + fall time ≤ 2/3 T
   Ringing frequency ≥ 3/T for OC-1 to OC-18
   Ringing frequency ≥ 2/T for OC-24 to OC-48

(e) Extinction ratio = 10 dB or more

*T = Bit period

designed to provide low-cost, high-quality digital facilities for international connections. This new technology is an improvement over the older analog cable technology. It is expected that expansion of undersea network paths hereafter will normally be by digital means.

The eighth transatlantic telecommunication system (TAT-8), which began service in 1988 for connections among the USA, England, and France [15,16,17], employs a lightwave system of three fiber pairs to span over 5800 km of ocean. The cable includes a mid-ocean branching point. The major transmission design characteristics of this system, the AT&T SL280 undersea lightwave system, and the North American service-interfacing arrangements are briefly discussed in the following.

The lightwave system was designed for a 25–year life and had been field– and service–tested previously in a 120–km undersea connection in the Canary Islands. The system provides for 3780 digital channels (each 64 kb/s) per fiber for a total of 7560 channels for the two service fiber–pairs contained in the undersea cable, with one additional pair in each direction for protection. To increase the number of effective voice channels that can be served, bit compression and speech interpolation are employed via a digital circuit multiplication system (DCMS). Service reliability is increased by the protection fiber–pair span line and by redundant transmitter sources in the regenerators. The round–trip delay for TAT–8 is about 65 ms, whereas for satellite facilities the delay is about 480 ms (DCMS adds to the delay of the facility itself). These delays involve the need for echo cancellation to avoid echo impairment in a connection, as discussed in other chapters.

The single–mode optical fiber is based on silica–oxide glass with depressed cladding, with zero dispersion at the operating wavelength near 1.30 μm. Transmission is at a line rate of 295.6 Mb/s (designated 280 Mb/s) and the fiber loss including splices and cabling is about 0.39 dB/km. Physically, the undersea deep-water cable containing the three fiber pairs, a copper cylinder (for power supply to repeaters) and steel strength members, is only 21 mm in diameter, versus 43 mm for the SG analog system.

The optical transmitters are InGaAsP laser diodes with controlled constant average output pulses of about -1.5 dBm over a median life of 10^6 hours. The optical receivers are PIN photodiodes of the same elements with a sensitivity of about -36 dBm for a BER of 10^{-9} or better. Included in the receiver portion of the repeater is a channel equalizer to shape the received pulses to a Nyquist I cosine rolloff characteristic with b=1, which provides for good eye–openings for pulse detection and balance between noise sensitivity (narrow detector bandwidth) and jitter tolerance (wider detector bandwidth). Retiming and automatic gain control circuits are also included. The latter is to keep the pulse amplitude for the decision circuits at a constant average value.

The repeater spans are designed to have an end–of–life BER performance of 1×10^{-9} or better. Usually, 10 dB of margin is used in the loss budget for the spans in determining the length of cable allowed in the span, which is usually greater than 50 km.

Digital Circuit Multiplication System

DCMS uses two techniques to increase the number of voice channels that can be served by effectively reducing the bit rate required for each channel. The low–bit–rate voice (LBRV) technique (see Chapter 13) using only 32 kb/s per voice channel allows for a 2 to 1 multiplication factor. A digital speech interpolation technique of assigning the silent intervals in speech to the active speech of another channel provides an additional 2.5 factor. This provides an overall multiplication factor of 5 to 1. Of course, the factor depends on the signal activity of each channel. Some disadvantages are: interpolation cannot be used for digital data channels and LBRV channels may limit the voiceband data rate to 4800 b/s. Further gradual reduction of the 32–kb/s LBRV bit rate to 16 or 8 kb/s may be possible for infrequent short–time overload intervals where some impairment is acceptable. The DCMS on the American side also includes the conversion between the American and European digital systems for the compressible channels. A functional diagram of the DCMS is shown in Figure 14–9. The conversion for noncompressible signals also takes place in the multiplex system converter located on the American side.

Service reliability of the system has been increased by redundant transmitter lasers via an optical switch in the regenerator. This service–protection redundancy is controlled by operation and maintenance functions of the undersea terminals.

The undersea system interfaces with the North American Standard (NAS) digital hierarchy at the U.S. end and the hierarchy established by the European Conference of Posts and Telecommunications (CEPT) at the other end. The two digital hierarchies are shown in Table 14–8. For compatibility reasons, a hybrid hierarchy (CCITT Red Book, Recommendation G.802) was formed and is shown in Table 14–9. For TAT–8 the digital connection to the 280–Mb/s (nominal) lightwave system is two 140–Mb/s (nominal) inputs, each providing 1890 channels, for a total of 3780 channels of 64 kb/s with CEPT A–law coding for the voiceband channels.

376

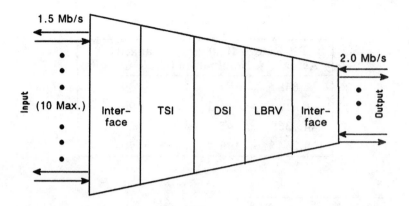

DSI = Digital speech interpolation.
LBRV = Low-bit-rate voice (ADPCM) coder-decoder.
TSI = Time-slot interchange.

Figure 14-9. Simplified DCMS for voice.

Table 14-8. Hierarchies and Capacities

North American (NAS)		European (CEPT)	
Bit Rate (Mb/s)	No. of VF Circuits	Bit Rate (Mb/s)	No. of VF Circuits
1.544	24	2.048	30
6.312	96	8.448	120
44.736	672	34.368	480
139.264	2016	139.264	1920

The interworking arrangement [18] between the NAS and CEPT standards is shown in Figure 14-10. The 140-Mb/s bit stream at the terminal to the underwater systems is converted to 45 Mb/s for transport to the American international switching center where conversion to the 1.5-Mb/s basic NAS μ - law format takes place. As shown on the figure, the compressible voice and data channels are kept separate from noncompressible channels where digital integrity is required.

377

Table 14-9. Hybrid Hierarchy

| Bit Rate (Mb/s) | | Capacity |
Actual	Nominal	(64-kb/s Circuits)
2.048	2	30
6.312	6.3	90
44.736	45	630
139.264	140	1890

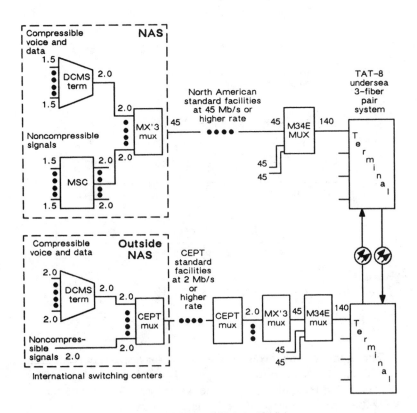

MX'3 = Multiplexer 2 Mb/s to 45 Mb/s
M34E = Multiplexer 45 Mb/s to 140 Mb/s
MSC = Multiplexer system converter

Figure 14-10. Digital interworking for TAT-8.

14-9 MAINTENANCE

Computer–aided administration, maintenance, and surveillance systems are in wide use. These receive trouble reports, direct the transfer of service to standby facilities, and perform diagnostic routines to aid in isolating the trouble.

The basic maintenance requirements for a digital transmission system are filled by equipment capable of detecting errors in or loss of the line signal, determining the location of a faulty repeater, and transferring service (manually or automatically) from a failed line to a standby line. These functions are fulfilled by equipment of various degrees of sophistication depending on the length of the systems and on the number of voice circuits that can be affected by failure.

In some systems, when a complete loss of signal is detected, service is switched automatically to another line and the alarm indication signal is substituted on the defective line; thus, subsequent spans do not respond to the trouble condition. This procedure, in effect, provides isolation of gross troubles to a span.

Fault–location procedures usually take the form of inserting a signal in the defective span with intentional violations of the code format. These violations are introduced at an audio rate and a voice–frequency signal is returned on a maintenance pair in such a manner that the defective repeater can be identified.

References

1. Gnauk, A. N., B. L. Kasper, et al. "4–Gbits/s Transmission Experiment Over 103 km of Optical Fiber," *IEEE Journal of Lightwave Technology*, Vol. LI–3, No. 5 (Oct. 1985).

2. Eisenstein, G., S. K. Korothy, et al. "4–Gbits/s Transmission Experiment Over 117 km of Optical Fiber," *IEEE Journal of Lightwave Technolgy*, Vol. LI–3, No. 5 (Oct. 1985).

3. Li, T. "Advances in Lightwave System Research," *AT&T Technical Journal*, Vol. 66, No. 1 (Jan./Feb. 1987).

4. Kaminow, I. and S. E. Miller, Editors. "Interoffice Transmission Systems," *Optical Fiber Telecommunications II* (San Diego, CA: Academic Press 1988), Chapter 19.

5. Dixon, R. W. and N. K. Duta. "Lightwave Device Technology," *AT&T Technical Journal*, Vol. 66, No. 1 (Jan./Feb. 1987).

6. Agrawal, G. P. and T. M. Shen. "Computer Simulation and Noise Analysis of the System Performance of 1.55 μm Single–Frequency Semiconductor Lasers," *IEEE Journal of Lightwave Technology*, Vol. LI–5, No. 5 (May 1987).

7. Bain, M. and T. P. Lee. "Optical Receivers for Lightwave Communication Systems," *IEEE Journal of Lightwave Technology*, Vol. LI–3, No. 6 (Dec. 1985).

8. *Digital Fiber Optic Systems—Requirements and Objectives*, Technical Advisory TA–TSY–000038, Bellcore (Iss. 3, Apr. 1986).

9. *Network Equipment–Building System (NEBS) Generic Equipment Requirements*, Technical Reference TR–EOP–000063, Bellcore (Iss. 3, May 1988).

10. *Alarm Indication Signal Requirements and Objectives*, Technical Reference TR–TSY–000191, Bellcore (Iss. 1, May 1986).

11. *Transport Systems Generic Requirements (TSGR): Common Requirements*, Technical Reference TR–TSY–000499, Bellcore (Iss. 1, Dec. 1987).

12. *ANSI T1.106–1988*, "American National Standard for Telecommunications—Digital Hierarchy—Optical Interface Specifications; Single Mode" (New York: American National Standards Institute, 1988).

13. *ANSI T1.105–1988*, "American National Standard for Telecommunications—Digital Hierarchy—Optical Interface Rates and Formats Specifications" (New York: American National Standards Institute, 1988).

14. Garbanati, L. F., R. C. Menendez, and R. B. Misra. "Optimal Design of Fiber Systems in the Loop Network," International Symposium on Subscriber Loops and Services (Tokyo, Japan: Sept./Oct. 1986), pp. 309–314.

15. "Suboptic," International Conference on Optical Fiber Submarine Telecommunication Systems, Sessions 1 to 13 (Paris, France: French Ministry of Telegraph and Telephone Administration, Feb. 1986), pp. 18–21.

16. Runge, P. K. and P. R. Trischitta. "The SL Undersea Lightwave System," *IEEE Journal on Selected Areas in Communications*, Vol. SAC–2, No. 6 (Nov. 1984).

17. Adl, A., T. A. Chien, and T. C. Chu. "Design and Testing of the SL Cable," *IEEE Journal on Selected Areas in Communications*, Vol. SAC–2, No. 6 (Nov. 1984).

18. Dinn, N. F., D. M. Garvey, and A. G. Weygand. "Digital Interconnection of Dissimilar Digital Networks," *IEEE Communications Magazine*, Vol. 24, No. 4 (Apr. 1986).

Chapter 15

Digital Hierarchies, Formats, Multiplexers, and Channel Banks

Digital systems have become the mainstay of telecommunications to meet the ever–increasing needs of modern society. Such systems provide the best available method of transporting information accurately and economically; their quality for voice is unparalleled. Digital systems, both transmission and switching, are being installed at a rapid pace to provide for the exploding expansion of digital connectivity. From a modest beginning with the T1 carrier transmission system operating at a bit rate of 1.544 Mb/s over metallic pairs, the technology has advanced to fiber optic systems operating at rates of 1.7 Gb/s or more via a hierarchy of optical bit rates.

This chapter covers the digital and optical bit–rate hierarchies and the associated bit–stream formats that are employed in digital systems. It describes various formats for the older asynchronous multiplex designs and for the newer synchronous technology such as SYNTRAN (synchronous transmission) and SONET (synchronous optical network). Included is a brief review of American National Standards Institute (ANSI) standards on optical rates and formats.

The digital multiplexers that are needed for networking are discussed with reference to system requirements and objectives. The chapter discusses digital channel banks where the conversion takes place between digital and analog domains and indicates some requirements.

15-1 THE DIGITAL HIERARCHY

The digital network has been planned, for economic and other reasons, to connect communication paths of low capacity or bit rate to paths of higher bit rates via multiplexing. A hierarchy of transmission rates called digital levels has been established. These are designated by digital signal (DS) numbers that increase in rate from DS0 to DS4.

The rates of the hierarchical ladder are not usually integral multiples because bits are added to facilitate multiplexing and other functions.

The digital multiplex units used to translate from one digital signal level to another are designated by prefix M (for multiplex) or more recently by DM (for digital multiplex) followed by designations of the associated digital levels. For example, M13 multiplex equipment is used to multiplex several DS1 signal levels into a DS3 level and to demultiplex a DS3 level down to several DS1 levels. The DS1 level is the basic building block produced by pulse code modulation (PCM) channel banks and digital switches.

The hierarchical bit–rate levels (serialized streams) associated with the multiplex designations and their application are shown in Figure 15–1. Optical carrier bit rates are covered later. At each level, each bit must be identified and the bit pattern structured in an organized format to provide the many functions required. The format of the bit stream depends on the method of multiplexing, the message signal, framing technique, and signalling information. It is necessary to standardize the format to ensure that the signal is compatible with the terminal equipment used at the ends of the facility. Also, the pulse shape of the transmitted signal must satisfy the interconnection and transmission requirements imposed by the transmission facility used. The latter requirements are expressed in terms of signal characteristics observed at a digital signal cross–connect (DSX). Included are such parameters as the transmission rate, the pulse shape, the location in the bit stream of parity bits required by the transmission system, and the allowable number of consecutive zeros.

15-2 ASYNCHRONOUS FORMATS

Initially, in the evolving digital network, synchronization of all the network elements to the same reference bit rate was not

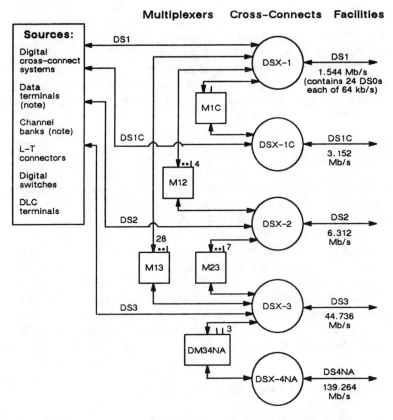

Figure 15-1. Digital hierarchy.

available. To accommodate slightly different or varying rates, techniques were developed for asynchronous multiplexing. Asynchronous multiplexers perform several basic functions including positive "bit stuffing" (to increase the bit rate slightly), which is used to synchronize lower-rate signals for translation into the desired higher-rate output [1]. The several low-speed signals are bit-interleaved, inverted, and may be scrambled (if needed) to balance zeros and ones. Various overhead bits (such as stuffing, stuffing indicator, condition indicator, framing, alarm, maintenance, and parity) are added to the information bits, and the bit streams are formatted to form the high–speed output signal. Zero–code suppression techniques of adding or forcing ones, or of rearranging long strings of zeros, are provided to ensure sufficient pulse–density energy in the bit stream for continuous synchronization of line regenerators. Demultiplexing returns the signals to the original bit–stream format when the substituted code is removed.

The DS1 Signal

The DS1 signal is a nominal 1.544–Mb/s bit stream produced by PCM digital switches, digital loop carrier (DLC) terminals, and channel banks, where 64 kb/s is assigned to each of 24 channels. As discussed in Chapter 13, the bit–stream rate is 64 kb/s times 24, the number of channels, plus 8 kb/s for framing to make up the output signal. The DS1 bit–stream assignments are shown in Table 13–2 of Chapter 13 for the superframe format (robbed–bit signalling), and on Table 13–3 for extended super-frame format, which provides, with zero–code substitution, clear–channel capability. The line signals are bipolar, alternate–mark–inverted, 50–percent duty–cycle pulses.

DS1 Zero–Code Substitution

To provide continuous synchronization, the DS1 signal should have: (1) an average pulse density of one in eight and not more than 15 zero bits in succession, and (2) at least n ones in every $8(n+1)$ bit window where $n = 1$ to 23. Older systems merely set the least significant bit, bit 7, to "one" if all eight bits (including the signalling bit 8) in a byte were zero (zero–code suppression). This would create a small amount of noise when the channel was decoded at the far end because the bit was not corrected. Some newer systems are capable of coding and decoding a bipolar with eight–zero–substitution (B8ZS) code for use in DS1 signals when eight zeros are found. The code inserts bipolar violations that are recognized by receiving multiplexes as B8ZS coding and the zeros are restored in the signal. The B8ZS capability must be used at both terminals and all intermediate multiplexers before this feature can be realized. If a zero–byte time–slot interchange

(ZBTSI) is employed instead, no multiplex change is required. These two methods are described in Chapter 13 under the heading "Clear Channel Capability."

The DS1C Signal

Two DS1 signals are combined to form a DS1C signal but, as received, they are generally not synchronized with one another nor with the new DS1C signal of 3.152 Mb/s.

Pulse Stuffing

The synchronization of the two DS1 signals to make them alike in repetition rate and of a rate suitable for incorporation into a single DS1C bit stream is accomplished by *pulse stuffing*. In this process, time slots are added to each signal in sufficient quantity to make the signal operate at a precise rate controlled by the clock circuit in the transmitter. Pulses are inserted (or stuffed) into these time slots but carry no information. Thus, it is necessary to code the signal so that these noninformation bits can be recognized and removed at the receiving terminal. The DS1C signal format is shown in Figure 15–2.

The DS1 signals, received from the DSX–1 cross–connect frame as bipolar signals, are first converted to unipolar form. The two signals are multiplexed by interleaving them bit–by–bit.

The multiplexed bit stream is next scrambled, to control the energy statistics of the bit stream, in a single–stage scrambler. This signal is then combined (multiplexed) with a control–bit sequence that permits the proper demultiplexing and the deletion of stuffed bits from the two signals at the receiving terminal.

Each control bit precedes a block of 52 bits from the multiplexed DS1 signals, 26 bits from each. The control bits form a repetitive sequence 24 bits long that, with the information bits associated with each control bit, defines a 1272–bit block called an M frame. This control–bit sequence may be regarded conveniently as a digital word whose individual bits are distributed in the composite pulse stream. Each 24–bit control sequence (or word)

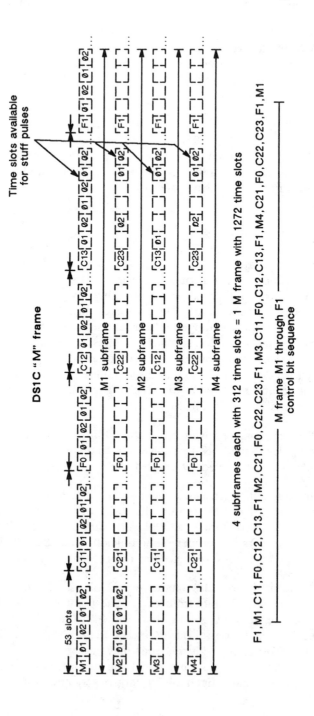

Figure 15-2. Organization of DS1C signal bit stream.

is made up of three subsequences designated M, F, and C. The entire sequence is shown in Figure 15–2. The symbol $\emptyset$ is used with subscripts to show how the information bits from the two DS1 signals are interleaved.

The M sequence consists of four bits designated $M1$, $M2$, $M3$, and $M4$. They are the first, seventh, thirteenth, and nineteenth bits in the 24–bit sequence and define the start of four 318–bit subframes in the 1272–bit M frame. The M sequence may be written $0\ 1\ 1\ X$. The first three bits, $0\ 1\ 1$, are used to identify the M–frame format. The fourth bit, X, is used as a maintenance signalling channel to transmit receiving–terminal alarm conditions to the transmitting terminal. A 1 indicates no alarm while a 0 indicates the presence of an alarm at the receiving terminal.

The F sequence is made up of alternate $1s$ and $0s$ ($F1 = 1$ and $F0 = 0$) that appear at the beginning of every third 52–bit information sequence, i.e., as every third bit in the 24–bit control sequence. This code is used at the receiving terminal to identify the scrambled input signals and the control–bit time slots.

The C–bit sequence is used to identify the presence or absence of stuff pulses in the information–bit positions of each subframe. There is a sequence of three C bits in each subframe. If a stuff pulse is to be inserted during the subframe, the C bits are all $1s$. Otherwise, they are all $0s$. The stuffed time slot is the third information bit following the third C bit in the subframe. Stuffing for one DS1 signal occurs during the first and third subframes and for the other during the second and fourth subframes of an M frame. The maximum stuffing rate is 4956 b/s for each DS1 signal; the nominal rate is 2264 b/s.

The processes described above are carried out in the transmitting terminal. All must be reversed at the receiving terminal in order to restore the original DS1 signals.

In its transmitted form, the DS1C signal is bipolar with a 50–percent duty cycle. The component DS1 signals and the DS1C signal are converted to a binary (unipolar) form for processing within the multiplex equipment. Thus, bipolar violations in any of these signals are eliminated.

389

The DS2 Signal

The DS2 signal is primarily of historical interest, having been superseded by DS3 for growth purposes. At this level, an M12 multiplex unit is used, as indicated in Figure 15-1, to combine four DS1 signals into a single bit stream. The 6.312-Mb/s DS2 signal is made up of the combination of these four DS1 signals and a number of control, framing, and stuff bits.

Synchronization of the four DS1 signals is necessary because, as with T1C, these signals may have originated from different sources having independent and unsynchronized timing clocks. Synchronization is accomplished by adding stuff pulses to each signal so that all four are of the same rate, which is determined by a common timing clock at the multiplex unit.

All of the information and control bits for the far-end demultiplexer are carried within an 1176-bit frame, which is divided into four 294-bit subframes, as shown in Figure 15-3.

The information slots that are interwoven in the stream are labeled $\emptyset$. The control-bit word, dispersed throughout the frame, begins with an M bit. The four M bits are transmitted as $0\ 1\ 1\ X$ where the fourth bit may be used as an alarm indicator. When no alarm condition exists at the transmitting end of the section, a 1 is transmitted; when an alarm is present, a 0 is sent. The $0\ 1\ 1$ sequence for the first three M bits is used in the receiving circuits to identify the frame.

Within each subframe two other sequences are used for control purposes. Each control bit is followed by a 48-bit block of information of which 12 bits are taken from each of the four DS1 signals. These are interleaved sequentially in the 48-bit block. The first bit in the third and sixth blocks is designated an F bit. The F bits are a $0\ 1\ 0\ 1$ . . . sequence used to identify the location of the control-bit sequence and the start of each block of information bits.

The stuff-control bits are transmitted at the beginning of each of the 48-bit blocks numbered 2, 4, and 5 within each subframe. When these control bits, designated C, are $0\ 0\ 0$, no stuff pulse is present; when the C bits are $1\ 1\ 1$, a stuff pulse has been added in the stuff position.

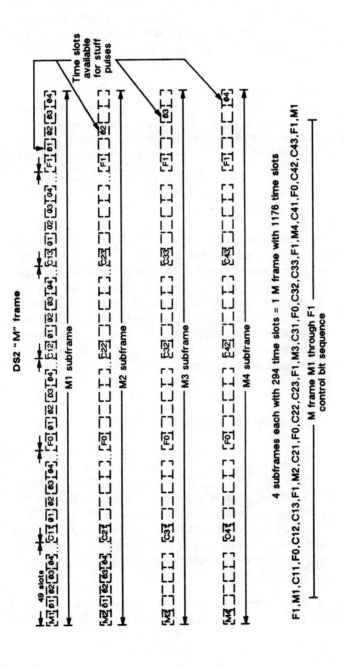

Figure 15–3. Organization of DS2 bit stream.

391

The stuff bit positions are all assigned to the sixth 48–bit block in each subframe. In subframe No. 1, the stuff bit is the first bit after the F1 bit; in subframe No. 2, the stuff bit is the second bit after the F1 bit, and so on through the fourth subframe. The nominal stuffing rate is 1796 b/s for each DS1 input signal. The maximum is 5367 b/s.

Prior to multiplexing in the M12 multiplex unit, input signals 2 and 4 are logically inverted. This is done to improve the ones–and–zeros balance of the output DS2 signal. At the output of the M12 unit, the multiplexed signal is unipolar. It must be converted to a bipolar format with a 50–percent duty cycle for transmission.

DS2 Zero–Code Substitution

The format used at the DS2 level for zero–code substitution is called bipolar with six–zero substitution (B6ZS). If there is no sequence of 0 bits longer than five, the signal remains true bipolar. However, if a sequence of six $0s$ occurs, the format is modified. If the last pulse before the six $0s$ was positive, the code substituted for the six is $0+-0-+$; if the pulse before the six $0s$ was negative, the code substituted is $0-+0+-$. In both cases, bipolar violations occur in the second and fifth bit positions of the substitution. These violations are recognized at the receiver so that the proper sequence of six $0s$ can be substituted.

The DS3 Signal (Asynchronous)

A DS3 signal is usually generated within the M13 by two steps of multiplexing. As indicated above, combinations of up to four DS1 signals are processed to form a DS2 signal. Then, as many as seven DS2 signals may be multiplexed to form the DS3 signal. In demultiplexing, the inverse two–step process is carried out. Internally, these signals are all in a polar format so that there can be no bipolar violation. The output DS3 signal is in a modified bipolar format with three–zero substitution (B3ZS) and the usual 50–percent duty cycle.

The pattern of subframe, frame, and control bits for the 44.736–Mb/s DS3 signal is formed in much the same manner as that described for the DS1C and DS2 levels in the hierarchy. The DS3 signal is partitioned into frames of 4760 bits. Each frame is divided into seven subframes, each having 680 bits. Note that the number of subframes corresponds to the number of DS2 signals formed within the multiplex unit. Each subframe, in turn, is divided into eight blocks of 85 bits. The first bit in each block is used as a control bit with the remaining 84 bits available for information. This format is outlined in Figure 15-4, which indicates the information slots designated as $\emptyset1$ through $\emptyset4$ and the various control slots.

The initial bits in successive subframes are X, X, P, P, $M0$, $M1$, and $M0$. The first time slot in each of the first two subframes, designated as an X bit, may be used for alarm or other operations purposes. However, the two X bits in a frame must be the same, either $0\ 0$ or $1\ 1$.

The first time slots in the third and fourth subframes are designated as P bits. These are used to convey parity information relating to the 4704 information time slots following the first X bit in the previous frame. If the modulo-two sum of all information bits is 1, $P\ P = 1\ 1$; otherwise, $P\ P = 0\ 0$.

The first time slots in subframes 5, 6, and 7 are designated M bits. These three time slots always carry the code $0\ 1\ 0$, which is used as a multiframe alignment signal.

In each subframe, blocks 2, 4, 6, and 8 carry F bits. These are transmitted in the first time slot of each of these blocks as a $1\ 0\ 0\ 1$ code. The code is used as a frame-alignment signal to identify all control-bit time slots.

The first time slots in subframes 3, 5, and 7 carry bits to indicate the presence or absence of a stuff pulse in the subframe. The bits designated $Ci1$, $Ci2$, and $Ci3$ are the stuffing-indicator bits for the ith subframe where i is any number from 1 to 7. In the C-bit positions, a $1\ 1\ 1$ code indicates that a stuff pulse has been added; a $0\ 0\ 0$ code indicates that no stuff pulse has been added. One stuff pulse per subframe may be added in the eighth block. The stuffing time slot is the first information time slot in that block for the DS2 signal that corresponds numerically to the subframe, i.e., the ith time slot in the eighth block of the ith

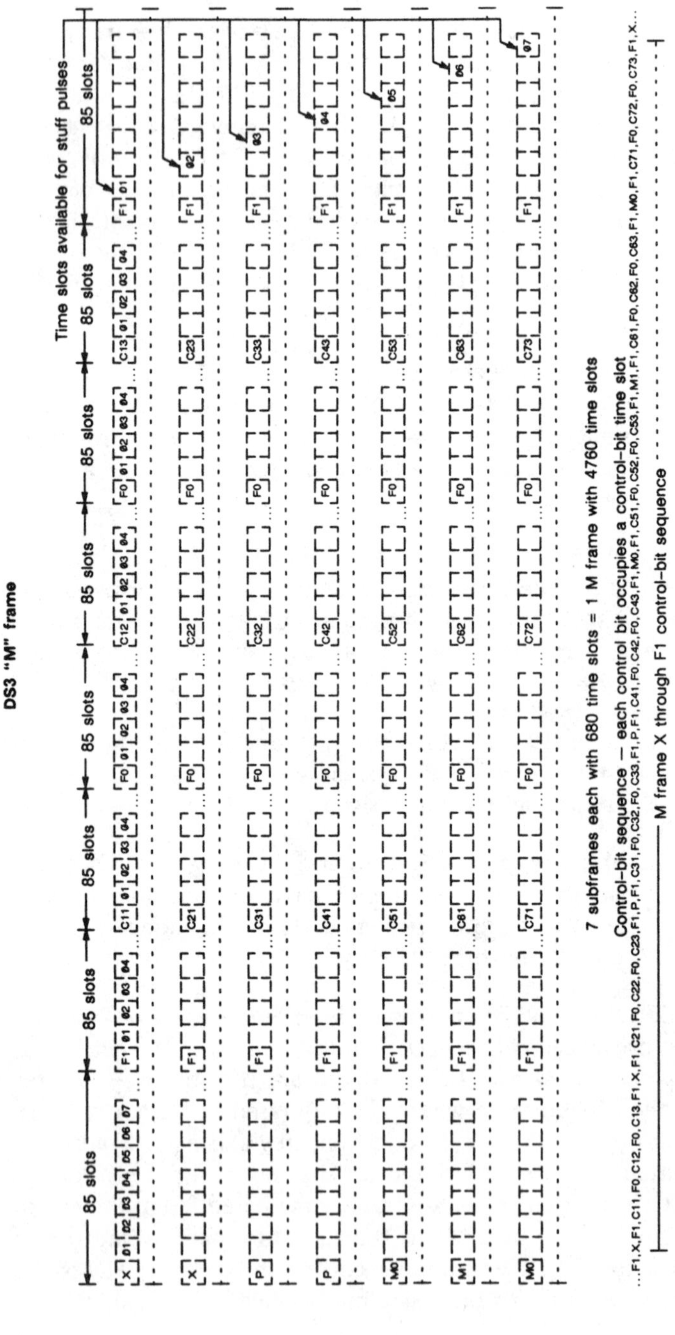

DS3 "M" frame

Time slots available for stuff pulses

85 slots | 85 slots | 85 slots | 85 slots | 85 slots | 85 slots | 85 slots | 85 slots | 85 slots | 85 slots

7 subframes each with 680 time slots = 1 M frame with 4760 time slots

Control-bit sequence — each control bit occupies a control-bit time slot

...F1,X,F1,C11,F0,C12,F0,C13,F1,X,F1,C21,F0,C22,F0,C23,F1,P,F1,C31,P,F1,C31,F0,C32,F0,C33,F1,F1,C41,F0,C42,F0,C43,F1,M0,F1,C51,F0,C52,F0,C53,F1,M1,F1,C61,F0,C62,F0,C63,F1,M0,F1,C71,F0,C72,F0,C73,F1,X,...

M frame X through F1 control-bit sequence

Figure 15-4.　DS3 signal format.

subframe. The nominal and maximum stuffing rates per
6.312–Mb/s input are 3671 b/s and 9398 b/s, respectively. The
6.312–Mb/s signals appear internally in the multiplex unit. Each
is a DS2 signal made up of four multiplexed DS1 signals in a
manner similar to that used in the M12.

DS3 Zero-Code Substitution

The B3ZS format for zero–code substitution is one in which
any three consecutive $0s$ in the polar signal are replaced by a
sequence that produces a bipolar violation. Each block of three
consecutive $0s$ is removed and replaced by $B\ 0\ V$ or $0\ 0\ V$ where
B represents a pulse conforming with the bipolar rule and V represents a pulse violating the bipolar rule. The choice of $B\ 0\ V$ or
$0\ 0\ V$ is made so that the number of B pulses between consecutive V pulses is odd.

Following is an illustration of B3ZS coding that assumes the
polarity of the last pulse transmitted previous to the three successive $0s$ was negative. Case 1 assumes that an odd number of
pulses has been transmitted since the last bipolar violation; case 2
assumes an even number of pulses.

Binary signal: 1 0 1 0 0 0 1 1 0 0 0 0 0 0 00 1 0 0 0 1 ...

B3ZS signal

Case 1 (odd): + 0 - 0 0 V+ - B 0 V B 0 V 0 0 + 0 0 V- ...
               + 0 - 0 0 - + - + 0 + - 0 - 0 0 + 0 0 + - ...

Case 2 (even): + 0 - B 0 V- + B 0 V B 0 V 0 0 - 0 0 V+ ...
               + 0 - + 0 + - + - 0 - + 0 + 0 0 - 0 0 - + ...

If the last pulse had been positive, the resulting B3ZS signals
would be the inverse of those shown.

The DS4NA (North American) Signal

A DS4NA signal is generated by multiplexing three asynchronous DS3 signals together and resulting in a bit stream of 139.264
Mb/s [2]. This is a recent proposed designation by a T1 working
party of the Exchange Carriers Standards Association (ECSA).

The proposed DS4NA format is shown in Figure 15–5. The DS4NA signal is made up of M frames having 954 time slots composed of six M subframes of 159 slots each. The figure indicates the designation of the time slots for information and other purposes such as stuffing, parity, etc. The line signals are polar, alternate–mark–inverted, non–return–to–zero pulses.

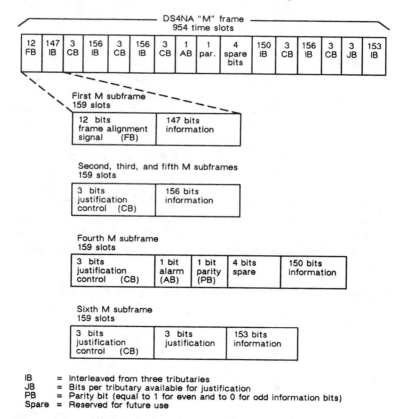

IB   = Interleaved from three tributaries
JB   = Bits per tributary available for justification
PB   = Parity bit (equal to 1 for even and to 0 for odd information bits)
Spare = Reserved for future use

Figure 15–5. DS4NA frame structure.

The DS4 Signal (Asynchronous)

The DS4 signal has not received wide use. It is formed by multiplexing six 44.736–Mb/s DS3 asynchronous signals, using pulse–stuffing synchronization, to produce the 274.176–Mb/s

DS4 signal. The DS4 signal is a polar binary signal. Logical *1* bits are positive pulses and logical *0* bits are negative, both with 100–percent duty cycle.

In DS4, the basic digital block consists of 4704 time slots called a superframe. Each superframe is divided into 24 frames of 196 time slots each and each frame is divided into two subframes of 98 slots each. In each subframe, the first two time slots are used for control bits and the remaining 96 slots are used for information.

This organization of the bit stream is shown in Figure 15–6. The symbol $\emptyset$ is used with subscripts to show how the information bits from the six DS3 signals are interleaved on a bit–at–a–time basis according to the input numbering order.

In the time slots designated M and $\overline{M}$, X and $\overline{X}$, and C and $\overline{C}$, collectively called S bits, each of the bits with an overscore is the complement of the companion bit without overscore. Bits M_1, M_2, and M_3 are used to align the superframe and are always coded *1 0 1*. Thus, $\overline{M_1}$, $\overline{M_2}$, and $\overline{M_3}$ are always coded *0 1 0*. The bits designated X and $\overline{X}$ may be used for signalling, maintenance, and operations information. The X bits must be coded *0 0 0*, *1 1 1*, *0 0 1*, or *1 0 0* but may be changed within that constraint to convey system information. The bits $C_iC_iC_i$ are used as a stuffing indicator word for each DS3 input i. The word *1 1 1* indicates that the ith input has been stuffed in that superframe and *0 0 0* indicates that there has been no stuffing in that superframe. The complementary C and $\overline{C}$ bits are used as the demultiplexer for two–bit error correction. The time slot used for stuffing DS3 input i is the eighth $\emptyset_i$ slot occurring after the last C_i bit in the superframe.

The nominal stuffing rate is 27,429 b/s per DS3 signal; the maximum is 58,286 b/s.

The bits designated P are parity bits used in error detection. Bit P_1 is a parity bit taken over all odd–numbered information bits in the two frames immediately preceding P_1. Bit P_2 is a parity bit taken over all even–numbered information bits within the same two frames. Bit P_1 or P_2 is a *0* if the number of counted *1s*

One DS4 superframe

Frame no.	Assigned time slots			
	←— 2 —→	←—— 96 ——→	←— 2 —→	←—— 96 ——→
1	$M_1\overline{M}_1$	$\emptyset_1\emptyset_2\emptyset_3\emptyset_4\emptyset_5\emptyset_6\emptyset_1\emptyset_2$...	P_1P_1	$\emptyset_1\emptyset_2\emptyset_3\emptyset_4\emptyset_5\emptyset_6\emptyset_1\emptyset_2$...
2	$M_2\overline{M}_2$	$\emptyset_1\emptyset_2\emptyset_3\emptyset_4\emptyset_5\emptyset_6\emptyset_1\emptyset_2$...	P_2P_2	$\emptyset_1\emptyset_2\emptyset_3\emptyset_4\emptyset_5\emptyset_6\emptyset_1\emptyset_2$...
3	$M_3\overline{M}_3$		P_1P_1	
4	$X_1\overline{X}_1$		P_2P_2	
5	$X_1\overline{X}_1$		P_1P_1	
6	$X_1\overline{X}_1$		P_2P_2	
7	$C_1\overline{C}_1$		P_1P_1	
8	$C_1\overline{C}_1$		P_2P_2	
9	$C_1\overline{C}_1$		P_1P_1	
10	$C_2\overline{C}_2$		P_2P_2	
11	$C_2\overline{C}_2$		P_1P_1	
12	$C_2\overline{C}_2$		P_2P_2	
13	$C_3\overline{C}_3$		P_1P_1	
14	$C_3\overline{C}_3$		P_2P_2	
15	$C_3\overline{C}_3$		P_1P_1	
16	$C_4\overline{C}_4$		P_2P_2	
17	$C_4\overline{C}_4$		P_1P_1	
18	$C_4\overline{C}_4$		P_2P_2	
19	$C_5\overline{C}_5$		P_1P_1	
20	$C_5\overline{C}_5$		P_2P_2	
21	$C_5\overline{C}_5$		P_1P_1	
22	$C_6\overline{C}_6$		P_2P_2	
23	$C_6\overline{C}_6$		P_1P_1	
24	$C_6\overline{C}_6$	$\emptyset_1\emptyset_2\emptyset_3\emptyset_4\emptyset_5\emptyset_6\emptyset_1\emptyset_2$...	P_2P_2	$\emptyset_1\emptyset_2\emptyset_3\emptyset_4\emptyset_5\emptyset_6\emptyset_1\emptyset_2$...

24 frames each with 196 time slots = 1 superframe with 4704 time slots

Figure 15-6. DS4 signal format.

is even and 1 otherwise. The P bits are transmitted as identical pairs.

The information bits of the DS4 signal designated $\emptyset_i$ are scrambled before being combined with control bits. This is accomplished by modulo–two addition of the information bits to the bits of a pseudorandom sequence. Each bit of the pseudorandom sequence, which has a signalling rate of 137.088 Mb/s (one–half the DS4 rate), is used to scramble two information bits. The even–numbered information bits are added (modulo–two sum) to the corresponding pseudorandom bits and the odd–numbered information bits are added to the complement (logically inverted sequence) of the pseudorandom bits.

15-3 SYNCHRONOUS FORMATS

SYNTRAN—DS3

In recent years the dominant growth of digital transmission has been at the DS3 (44.736–Mb/s) level via fiber optics and digital radio. With the asynchronous multiplexers operating at the DS3 level, adding or dropping a constituent DS1 or DS0 level meant that the entire DS3 level had to be demultiplexed to make the change and then multiplexed back to DS3 level.

Synchronous multiplexing with a restructured DS3 format provides a more efficient method of accessing the DS1 or DS0 levels of this DS3 signal. This would also encourage direct DS3 termination on digital cross–connect and switching systems and would simplify maintenance access. As stuffing bits are not needed, such time slots (totaling 1.2 Mb/s of capacity) can be used for other overhead functions. The restructured DS3 format is called SYNTRAN [3,4,5].

The advantages of the SYNTRAN format are graphically shown by Figure 15–7, which indicates in simple form that once the framing signal is known, the order of the DS1 or DS0 bits is known; they can be accessed directly. The asynchronous format does not offer this certainty.

Some possible applications of SYNTRAN are shown in Figure 15–8. These take advantage of the capability to add or drop directly from the DS3 level, of the direct DS3 interface with a switch or digital cross–connect, and of the simpler direct DS3–to–DS1 shift in digital level.

The SYNTRAN DS3 format offering DS1/DS0 direct access is more complicated in order to be comparable with the

Asynchronous

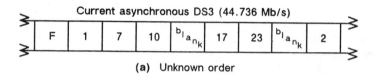

(a) Unknown order

SYNTRAN

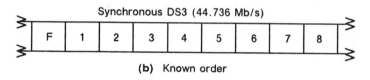

(b) Known order

F = Framing   Number = Consistent DS1s

Figure 15-7. Comparison of DS3 frames.

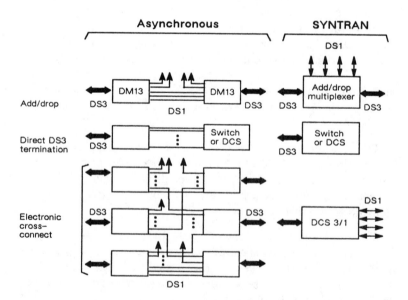

Figure 15-8. Asynchronous   operation   compared   with
SYNTRAN.

asynchronous DS3 format noted earlier. SYNTRAN retains the
same bit rate (44.736 Mb/s) and the same M frame length of
106.4 μs. Easy identification of DS0 channel bytes, however,
requires an 8–kHz frame repetition rate or a 125–μs frame
structure. It can be noted that 699 M frames occupy the same
time interval as 595 frames of 125 μs, which is then defined as
the synchronous superframe [4,5].

The DS3 SYNTRAN format bit organization is shown in Figure
15–9 for one M frame. A simplified description follows. Upon
completion of framing, X is found. Information bytes B_n, each of
eight bits b_0 through b_7 from the 28 constituent DS1s, follow X.
Some B bytes are reserved for carrying DS1 framing bits and
some for out–of–slot signalling for clear–channel (64–kb/s) DS0
operation. The C bits are used for several purposes including a
CRC–9 in–service performance monitor for each 3–M–frame
block and a data link. The CRC–9 code detects all single–bit
errors, all error bursts of length less than 10 bits, and 99.8 percent of error bursts greater than 10 bits long. This supplements
the parity check contained in the P bits. The P, F, M, and X bits
are not changed from those defined for the DS3 signal format
noted earlier. References 4, 5, and 6 provide details on
SYNTRAN and its applications.

SONET

This conceptual term is an acronym for synchronous optical
network [7]. The need for this concept became evident as fiber
optic systems materialized with ever–increasing bit–rate capacity
and proliferated in the network. Before SONET, to reach a
higher bit–rate level, several DS3 bit streams were multiplexed
together and various overhead channels and bit stuffing techniques were employed in order to use the available fiber capacity.
As this resulted in different rates and formats, the terminals of
one supplier could not communicate optically with another. An
expanding fiber optic technology along with the introduction of
new systems without standardization can result in a fragmented
optical network because the constituent systems are incompatible. It was realized that standard formats and signals would be
necessary to provide for a flexible network [7] with direct optical
interface to digital switching systems [8].

401

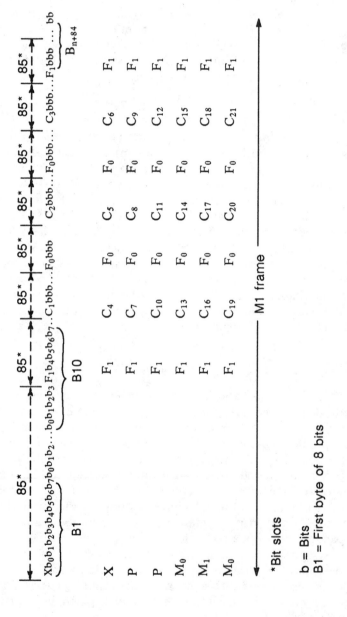

Figure 15-9. M-frame structure for synchronous DS3 format, SYNTRAN.

Work to prepare optical standards is being carried out by the T1 Technical Committee of the ECSA under auspices of the ANSI. Two ANSI standards on digital–hierarchy optical interfaces, rates, and formats are discussed in Parts 5 and 6 of this chapter.

15-4 DIGITAL MULTIPLEXERS

Time–division multiplexers [9] are used to combine a number of lower–bit–rate signals into a higher rate signal to increase transmission efficiency. The process is reversed to return to the lower rate. The capability of direct low–rate interchange of the component signals of the high–rate level may be provided as well as add/drop functions. Digital cross–connects were used originally at DS1 level to allow rearrangement of lines and terminals to provide routing flexibility and test access. Cross–connects are discussed in Chapter 26.

Multiplex and cross–connect functions, however, are frequently combined into one terminal. These functions are described more fully in the following.

Functions

In addition to multiplex level translations (such as DS1 to DS3) and direct interchange of component signals, the functions of digital multiplexers may include zero–code substitution, add/drop capability, condition monitoring, performance monitoring, alarm control, internal protection switching, operations system interfaces, etc.

Level translation involves processing the signals and requires synchronization to a common reference–frequency source to derive timing information. To combine asynchronous signals, the bit–stuffing technique described earlier is used to bring the lower near–rate signals into synchronization. The reference source must be very stable and accurate. It is connected throughout the network as indicated in Volume 1, Chapter 19. Elastic stores and phase–locked loops are used to provide basic timing for multiplexing circuits. The elastic stores are needed to correct for small short–time variations such as jitter in recovered timing derived from the reference source.

Zero–code substitution such as B8ZS or ZBTSI (covered earlier in this chapter and described in Chapter 13) is required to provide sufficient signal energy to keep regenerators running in synchronism.

Add/drop capability allows the extraction of a lower–rate signal from a higher–rate through signal at an intermediate point and the replacement of this signal with another that originates at that intermediate point. Condition monitoring is associated with detection of: loss–of–signal, out–of–frame, bipolar violations, cyclic redundancy check (CRC) errors, parity errors, alarm indication, internal failure, control indication, etc. Performance monitoring is the collection of performance data in reference to a threshold such as error rate.

Alarm actions define what alarms are activated, inhibited, or released, and what control and indication signals are needed for major or minor alarms. Protection switching may be provided in order to meet limits on outages due to equipment or other failures. Standby units with automatic switching and restoral are normal at DS2 level and above.

Operations systems connections are usually employed to provide remote centralized surveillance and control of terminals and facilities.

Requirements and Objectives

Several references, as indicated below, give requirements on digital multiplexers for asynchronous and synchronous signals to cover the various digital and optical hierarchical levels.

Asynchronous

The multiplexers for asynchronous DS1 through DS3 signals are shown in Figure 15–1 as M1C, M12, and M13. The requirements and objectives for such multiplexers are covered in

Reference 10. The reference covers specifications on interfacing; on multiplexing features and functions such as zero–code substitution, monitoring, and add/drop; and on operational requirements such as condition and performance monitoring, protection switching, and jitter limits. More recent jitter requirements are discussed later in this chapter under "Jitter," and are covered in Reference 11.

Synchronous—SYNTRAN DS3

The synchronous DS3 add/drop multiplex (ADM3/X) provides an interface between DS3 (SYNTRAN) signals and DS1 signals. Both sets of signals will be synchronized to the same or equivalent reference source. Optionally, provision can be made to multiplex synchronous DS1C and DS2 signals. The requirements and objectives for this multiplex are covered in Reference 12. These are similar to those noted above.

There are two transmission modes of operation—byte–synchronous and bit–synchronous. The byte mode allows direct access to both DS0 and DS1 signals in the DS3 stream. This mode is required when DS0 access and cross–connection capability, and direct SYNTRAN DS3–to–switch interfaces are needed. The bit mode allows direct access only to DS1 signals within the DS3 stream. A simple configuration of the multiplex for terminal and add/drop conditions is shown in Figure 15–10.

SONET

A bit–rate hierarchy has been established for the synchronous optical network [7]. The associated optical carrier signal (OC–N) and the equivalent electrical synchronous transport signal (STS–N) hierarchies are shown in Table 15–1.

Multiplexers are used to provide interfaces between signals of different bit–rates in the existing network and SONET. The generic requirements and objectives for SONET add/drop multiplex (SONET ADM) are contained in Reference 13. As discussed in Part 6 of this chapter, the virtual tributary (VT) structure of the STS–N bit–stream format is included. This

405

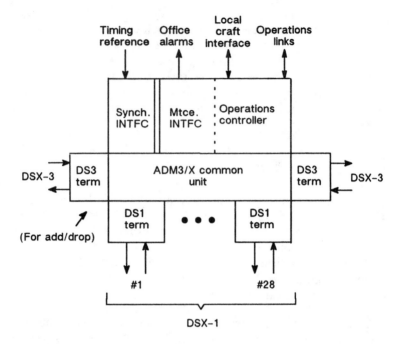

Figure 15-10. ADM3/X   terminal   and   add/drop configuration.

Table 15-1. Standard Rates (ANSI)

Optical Carrier	Synchronous Transport Signal	Line Rate (Mb/s)
OC-1	STS-1	51.840
OC-3	STS-3	155.520
OC-9	STS-9	466.560
OC-12	STS-12	622.080
OC-18	STS-18	933.120
OC-24	STS-24	1244.160
OC-36	STS-36	1866.240
OC-48	STS-48	2488.320

format is used to transport sub–DS3 signals (DS1, DS1C, DS2) over the optical system. The main features of the multiplexers that are covered by the reference include the following:

— DS1/DS3 electrical interfaces (for asynchronous and synchronous signals)

— OC–N fiber interfaces

— DS1/DS3/OC–N multiplexing

— DS1/DS3 add/drop capability

— Remote and local operations interface

— SONET operations channels.

Optional features include special multiplexing such as for DS1C and DS2, cross–connect capability, access and test capability, and facility protection switching. Reference 13 also includes requirements on network compatibility; on transmission synchronization, jitter, and delay; and on SONET transmission modes and maintenance. A simple configuration of the multiplex for terminal and add/drop conditions is shown in Figure 15–11. It is conceptually similar to the SYNTRAN ADM3/X, but is optically oriented rather than solely electrical.

Jitter

Jitter is the result of the timing variations in the digital stream produced by terminals and regenerators, which can cause errors. Jitter requirements [11] apply to network (carrier or user) interfaces and digital equipment to ensure meeting the network requirement. The network output–jitter limits are shown in Table 15–2. Digital–equipment jitter requirements are in terms of tolerance, transfer, generation, and amplification (enhancement) for tandem equipment. Current requirements are for two categories of equipment.

Category 1 includes terminal options that perform an asynchronous multiplex function. Examples of transport network elements (NEs) that fall under category 1 equipment are add/drop

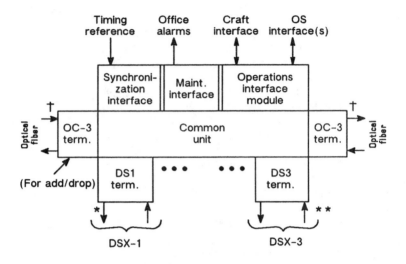

* Shown with DS1, but DS1C and DS2 terminations may be provided.

* * Shown with DS3, but OC-1 terminations may be provided.

† Shown with OC-3, but higher level terminations may be provided.

Figure 15-11. SONET   VT   ADM—terminal   and   add/drop configurations.

multiplexers (ADMs), digital radio terminals, and fiber optic terminals (excluding terminals that function solely as digital repeaters or regenerators).

Category 2 includes equipment whose behavior regarding timing jitter is governed exclusively by its input timing recovery circuit. Examples of transport NEs that fall under category 2 equipment are digital cross–connect systems (DCSs), terminals of a DLC system, repeaters for metallic cables, and regenerators for optical fiber cables.

The definitions of the jitter terms and their requirements are as follows.

Jitter Tolerance. Input jitter tolerance is defined as the *maximum* amplitude of sinusoidal jitter at a given frequency that, when modulating the signal at an equipment input port, results in

Table 15-2. Limits for Network Output Jitter

Level	Filter Band *	Jitter †
DS1	10 Hz – 40 kHz	5.0
	8 kHz$^\#$ – 40 kHz	0.1
DS1C	10 Hz – 40 kHz	5.0
	1.5 kHz$^\#$ – 40 kHz	0.1
DS2	10 Hz – 60 kHz	3.0
	3 kHz$^\#$ – 60 kHz	0.1
DS3	10 Hz – 400 kHz	5.0
	30 kHz$^\#$ – 400 kHz	0.1

* Lower and upper cutoff frequencies shown; rolloff of
20 dB/decode.

$\dagger$ Peak-to-peak unit intervals, measured over at least 1
min.

\# This is the jitter half-bandwidth of a typical timing extraction circuit as given by $F = f_0/2Q$, where f_0 is
the line rate and Q is the Q-factor of the timing extraction circuit.

no more than two errored seconds cumulative, where these errored seconds are integrated over successive 30–second measurement intervals, and the jitter amplitude is increased in each succeeding measurement interval.

Figure 15–12 shows the input jitter tolerance mask that applies
to category 1 equipment. The requirement must be met for the
extreme (plus *and* minus) allowable input bit–rate offset values.
Figure 15–13 shows the input jitter tolerance mask that applies to
category 2 equipment.

Jitter Transfer. The transfer of jitter through an individual
unit of digital equipment is characterized by the relationship between the applied input jitter and the resulting output jitter as a
function of frequency. For equipment in which a linear process
describes the transfer of jitter from the input to the output port,
the jitter transfer function is defined as the ratio of the output
jitter spectrum to the applied input jitter spectrum.

Input jitter
(time slots, peak-peak)

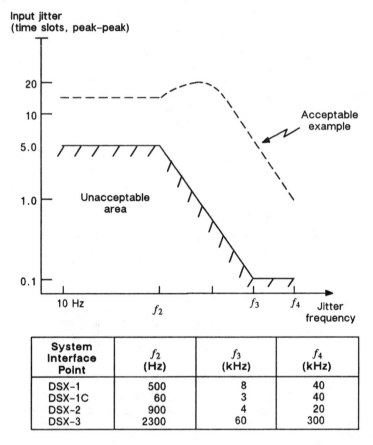

System Interface Point	f_2 (Hz)	f_3 (kHz)	f_4 (kHz)
DSX-1	500	8	40
DSX-1C	60	3	40
DSX-2	900	4	20
DSX-3	2300	60	300

Figure 15-12. Category 1 equipment—sinusoidal input jitter tolerance.

Figures 15-14 and 15-15 show the jitter transfer functions for category 1 and category 2 equipment.

Jitter Generation. Jitter generation is defined as the process whereby jitter appears at the output port of an individual unit of digital equipment in the absence of applied input jitter.

When looped back at the high-speed rate (whether a standard interface exists at the higher rate or not), category 1 equipment must produce less than 0.3 unit interval (UI) of rms timing jitter and less than 1.0 UI of peak-to-peak timing jitter at the output

410

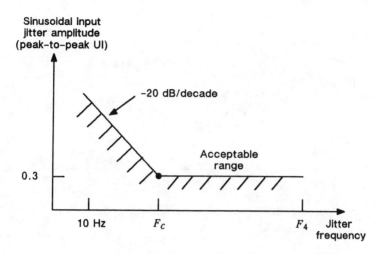

Interface Rate	F_C (kHz)	F_4 (kHz)
DS1	6.43	40
DS1C	1.31	40
DS2	2.63	20
DS3	22.3	300
HR*	$\dfrac{R}{2000}$	Under study

*HR denotes any level above DS3 whose
corresponding bit rate is R.

Figure 15–13. Category 2 equipment—sinusoidal input jitter
tolerance.

of the terminal receiver. The measurement interval must include
all frequencies between 10 Hz and F_4 of the network interface
jitter requirement (Table 15–2). This requirement applies over
the entire range of permissible input bit–rate offsets.

Jitter–generation requirements for category 2 equipment are
currently under study.

411

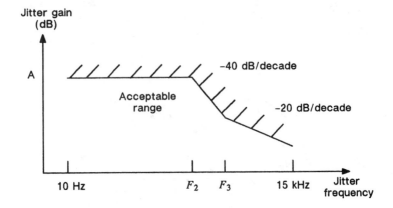

Demultiplexer Rates*	A (dB)	F_2 (Hz)	F_3 (kHz)
DS2–DS1	0.5	350	2.5
DS3–DS1	0.1	350	2.5
DS3–DS1C	0.1	350	2.5
DS3–DS2	0.1	500	2.5
HR1–DS3+	0.1	1000	#
HR3–HR2++	0.1	1250	#

* This implies demultiplexing from the higher level to the lower level.

+ HR1 denotes any level above DS3.

++ HR3 and HR2 denote levels above DS3, where the rate corresponding to HR2 is less than or equal to 140 Mb/s.

The rolloff between F_2 and 15 kHz is 20 dB/decade.

Figure 15–14. Category 1 equipment—desynchronizer jitter transfer.

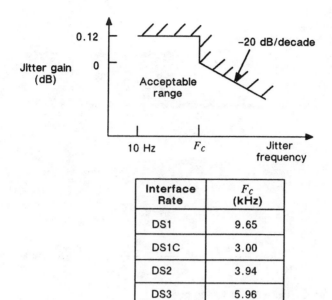

Interface Rate	F_c (kHz)
DS1	9.65
DS1C	3.00
DS2	3.94
DS3	5.96
HR*	$\dfrac{R}{1600}$

*HR denotes any level above DS3
whose corresponding bit rate is R.

Figure 15–15. Category 2 equipment—jitter transfer.

Jitter Enhancement. The basic requirement for jitter amplification is that a system of up to 250 miles in length, when subjected to sinusoidal input jitter as indicated by the template of Figure 15–16, will output less than 5.0 UI of peak–to–peak jitter, measured over a 30–second interval, with a measurement bandwidth from 10 Hz to at least 40 kHz. To simulate a 250–mile connection adequately, the circuit should incorporate at least 12 multiplex/demultiplex operations. While performing a jitter enhancement test, the input bit–rate offset should be adjusted within its allowable range to the point where output jitter is maximized.

15–5 OPTICAL HIERARCHY

There are two ANSI standards on digital–hierarchy optical interfaces, rates, and formats [14,15]. The standards consider

413

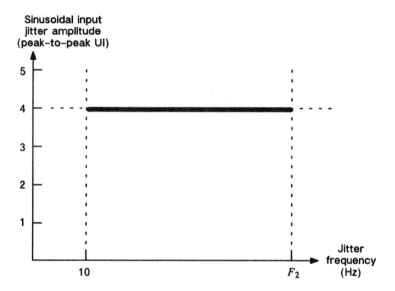

*Refer to Figure 15-14 for frequency F_2
(Use row in table with appropriate lower demultiplexer rate)

Figure 15-16. Tandem jitter enhancement—sinusoidal input template.

optical carrier interfaces for a regenerator *section*, a *line* (including sections and line terminals) and a *path* (including multiplexers, lines, and sections). This terminology is illustrated in Figure 15-17. An example showing optical carriers connected to regenerators, multiplexers, and cross-connect equipment, making up sections, lines, and paths is illustrated in Figure 15-18.

The standards define a synchronous optical hierarchy to cover various multimegabit line rates needed to transmit highly structured bit-stream formats incorporating payload information bits and overhead bits.

The basic optical carrier signal is defined as OC-1, having a bit rate of 51.840 Mb/s (level 1). A byte-interleaved multiplexing plan provides for a family of standard line rates, defined as N times the basic rate of $N \times 51.840$ Mb/s, as Table 15-1 illustrates for the selected values of N. The table also shows the corresponding electrical signal, STS-N, which has the same bit rate

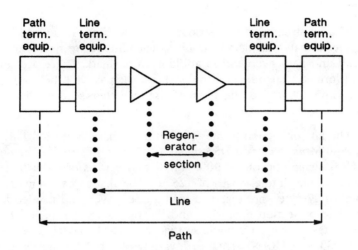

Figure 15-17. Definition of section, line, and path.

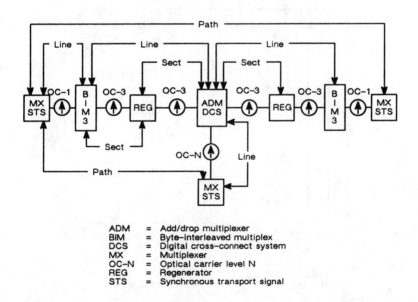

ADM	=	Add/drop multiplexer
BIM	=	Byte-interleaved multiplex
DCS	=	Digital cross-connect system
MX	=	Multiplexer
OC-N	=	Optical carrier level N
REG	=	Regenerator
STS	=	Synchronous transport signal

Figure 15-18. Section, line, and path examples.

as the optical level. A discussion of the bit-stream formats follows.

15-6 OPTICAL FORMATS

The bit streams of the various signal levels are organized into frame formats that detail the bit assignments for transport overhead and path overhead in addition to payload. There are several formats depending on the payload, such as DS3, below–DS3 or above–DS3, and the area of use, whether section, line or path.

The line or section frame format for the basic STS–1 signal of 51.840 Mb/s to carry a DS3 signal is shown in Figure 15–19. The STS–1 signal consists of 90 columns and 9 rows of 8–bit bytes, giving a total frame length of 125 μs. The first three columns, a total of 27 bytes, are reserved for transport overhead needed for the line or section operation and the rest is for the payload of 783 bytes. Provision is made so that the STS–1 may carry a DS3 (or DS3 SYNTRAN) signal or a variety of sub–DS3 signals such as DS1, DS1C, DS2, or European–style 2.048–Mb/s signals.

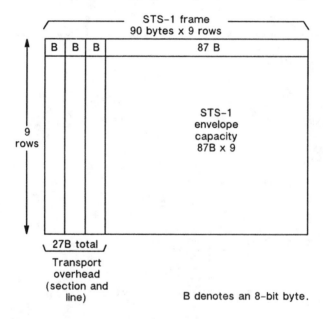

Figure 15-19. STS–1 frame (125 μs).

The frame formats for the STS–1 signal to carry the sub–DS3 payload are called virtual tributary structure. It was developed for efficient carriage and switching of these sub–payloads. There are two modes of VT operation: locked and floating. The locked mode simplifies interfacing in distributed 64–kb/s switching, while floating mode minimizes delay in distributed VT switching. The VT formats are too numerous to be included here.

The path frame format for the STS–1 to carry DS3 or sub–DS3 in a path is called STS–1 synchronous payload envelope. It requires path overhead, 9 bytes, in addition to transport overhead, 27 bytes, leaving 774 payload bytes. This frame format is shown in Figure 15–20.

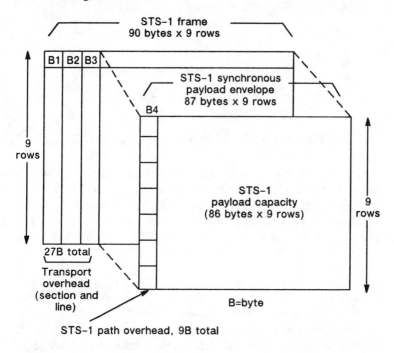

Figure 15–20. Illustration of STS–1 frame, synchronous payload envelope and payload capacity.

The frame format for an STS–N signal is formed by bit–interleaving the N constituent STS–1 signals. This format, shown in Figure 15–21, is a developed version of the STS–1 frame in Figure 15–19.

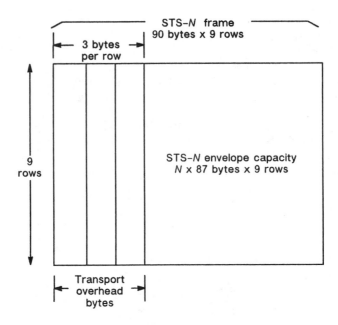

Figure 15-21. STS-N frame (125 μs).

Service paths that require higher rates than STS-1 are mapped into consecutive STS-1 frames as a concatenated STS-Nc whose constituents are kept together. The STS-Nc synchronous payload envelope and payload capacity are shown in Figure 15-22. The STS-Nc signal must be multiplexed, switched, and transported through the network as a single entity.

Many topics, such as timing, synchronization, data communication, and data protocols, are covered by the ANSI standards. Included are payload format mappings, which are considered for asynchronous and synchronous signals as shown in Table 15-3. To promote understanding, details on overhead and transport functions and byte assignments are explained by four layers, each higher level requiring the services of all the following lower levels in this list: photonic (no added overhead), path, line, and section layers. The layers involve consideration of framing, scrambling, error-monitoring, synchronization, multiplexing, maintenance, protection switching, order-wire, data communications, etc. functions.

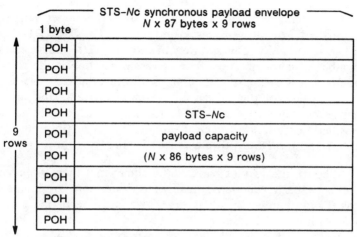

POH = Path overhead

Figure 15-22. STS-*Nc* synchronous payload envelope and payload capacity.

Table 15-3. Payload Mappings in the ANSI Standard [15]

Signal Rate	Asynchronous	Synchronous Bit	Byte
DS1	X	X	X
DS1C	X		
DS2	X		
2.048 Mb/s	X	X	X
DS3	X		X

15-7 PCM CHANNEL BANKS

The processing of voiceband signals such as speech and data for transmission over digital facilities is accomplished by equipment designated as D–type channel banks. The many functions of these banks include interfacing with various analog circuits on the customer side and a standard digital signal, DS1, on the network side. Other basic functions include filtering, sampling, quantizing, coding, multiplexing, synchronizing, framing, and formatting at the transmitter and the inverse of most of these at the receiver.

419

Over the years a succession of D–type banks has become available as technology has advanced. The earlier types requiring manual adjustment were designated D1A, D1B, D1C, D1D, D2, D3, D4, and DCT, plus a variety of comparable terminals from a number of manufacturers. The newest generation is the remote microprocessor–controlled and software–adjusted D5–type, which is part of the D5 Digital Terminal System, and an enhanced version of D4 with D5 features. This section will include a generic description of the ubiquitous D4–type (introduced in 1976) and the D5–type (introduced in 1984).

Although the various banks differ somewhat, they all perform the same basic functions. Each of one or more groups of 24 voiceband channel signals is processed into one or more DS1, 1.544 Mb/s, pulse streams. As described in Chapter 13, Part 1, each channel is sampled 8000 times per second. PCM processing codes the samples into 8–bit words, and the words are formatted into the DS1 signal. The number of channels can be almost doubled if the low–bit–rate voice (LBRV) techniques (coding the samples with 4–bit words—Chapter 13, Part 1) is used.

The interface between analog circuits (information and signalling) and digital circuits in the channel banks is provided by plug–in channel units. Many different types of D4 channel unit are available to provide for the transmission of message, special, and program service circuits; for the many signalling arrangements used; for two–wire or four–wire operation; and for Dataports. The functional diagram of a typical two–wire D4 channel unit is shown in Figure 15–23. The figure shows the conversion from two–wire to four–wire operation via a hybrid, the features for adjusting the sending and receiving gains via switched pads, and the −8.5/+4.0 transmission level points (TLPs). Some detail on digital processing and timing functions are shown in Figure 15–24.

The D4 Channel Bank

The last manually adjusted and most versatile of the D–type banks is the D4. It provides basically the same functions as those described for other D–banks but is arranged to operate in any one of four different line formats (modes) that permit its use with

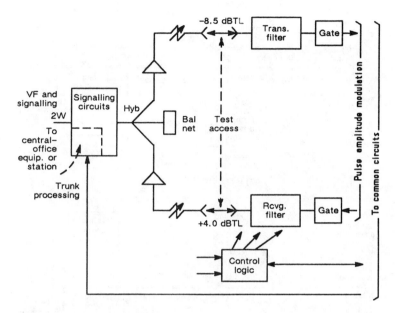

Figure 15–23. Channel–bank unit (two-wire)—functional
diagram.

DS1, DS1C, DS2, or dedicated fiber facilities by the selection of
appropriate plug–in equipment. Each D4 bank provides for the
transmission of up to 48 channel signals. About a 2–to–1 reduction in size and per–channel power dissipation has been realized
in the D4 bank relative to the earlier D3 bank, which was improved over *its* predecessors.

Operating Modes. Figure 15–25 illustrates the five operating
modes of the D4 channel bank. Mode 1 is used with a DS1C line
facility, usually T1C, operating with D4 channel banks at both
ends. For this mode, the DS1C line interface units, LIU–1, are
used to multiplex two DS1 binary signals and then transform the
composite binary signal to the bipolar format required for transmission. They also include the bank clock circuits and the looping circuits used for single–ended testing and insert control bits
required at the distant receiving bank. The mode 1 signal provides synchronous digroup operation that *cannot* be demultiplexed to DS1 by an M1C multiplex unit nor can it be multiplexed to the DS3 level. As a result, it is not widely used.

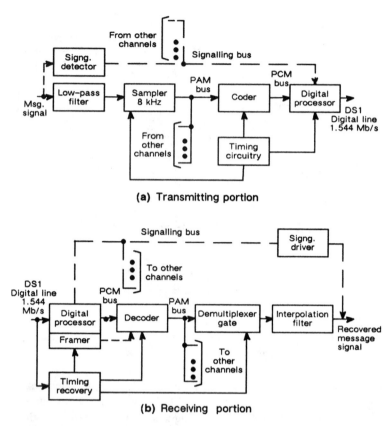

(a) Transmitting portion

(b) Receiving portion

Figure 15–24. Typical channel–bank unit—processing diagram.

Mode 2 may be used with a DS1C facility, usually T1C, having a D4 bank at one end and another mode 2 system or an M1C multiplex unit at the other. The DS1 terminals of the M1C multiplex unit may be connected to any source/sink equipment providing the proper interface such as a D1D, D2, D3, or D4 bank, or to a digital switch. The LIU–2 performs functions similar to those of the LIU–1 in mode 1, but operates asynchronously with a synchronizer/desynchronizer (SYNDES) unit to add or delete control and stuff pulses the same way as in the M1C multiplex unit.

In mode 3, the D4 bank can be used with any two DS1 facilities, no matter how derived. The interface with the lines is

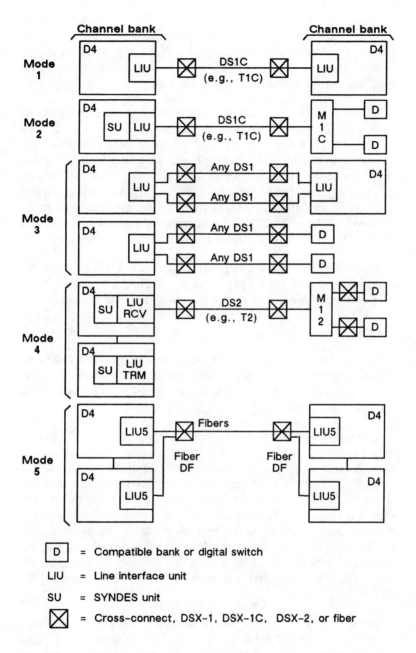

Figure 15-25. D4 channel-bank operating modes.

provided by LIU–3 circuits, which deliver DS1 signals for transmission. The mode 3 operation terminates any equipment providing proper interface such as another D4 bank, DCS, or digital switch. The two halves of the D4 are independent, and may be used for carrier systems to two distant offices.

Mode 4 operation requires a combination of two D4 banks to form a 96–channel bit stream for transmission over a DS2 facility, usually a T2 line. The far end of the transmission line may terminate in another D4 bank arranged for mode 4 operation or, as shown, it may terminate in an M12 multiplex unit, which may in turn be connected to any of a variety of channel banks. In the D4 banks, an LIU–4T unit controls the transmitting circuits in the two banks and an LIU–4R unit controls the receiving circuits. Each LIU must operate with a SYNDES unit.

Mode 5 operation is comparable to mode 4 except that the combined pair of banks produces a 96–channel optical signal that connects directly to a pair of dedicated optical fibers. It is not widely used, given the normal use of fibers at much higher speeds.

Besides the operating modes described above, the D4 bank can be equipped with a low–bit–rate coder unit as part of its common equipment. It then places 44 or 48 LBRV–coded channels on one DS1 facility.

Operating Features. Signal processing within the D4 bank is based on the use of two digroups of 24 channels each. These are designated A and B and the channels for each are designated 1A through 24A and 1B through 24B. These channels are sampled sequentially (D4), alternate sequentially (D1D), or by the D2 sampling sequence. The selection is based on the sequence in the channel bank used at the far end of the line. Timing is accomplished by clock circuits in the line interface units and may be controlled independently by an internal clock or dependently by using external timing via the building integrated timing supply (BITS).

While Figure 15–25 primarily illustrates ordinary voiceband applications, the D4 bank also provides direct access to a PCM bus, transmitting and receiving, for use by those special channel units that need it. Thus, digital data may be entered directly onto the PCM bus, as in the Dataport channel units. Additionally, program channel units that contain their own PCM coders may operate directly into the PCM bus, allowing for unusual bandwidths (e.g., 15 kHz) or expanded coding levels.

A D4 maintenance bank consists of channel–bank equipment that is kept operating in a looped condition. It is monitored for alarm conditions and tested for tone transmission by a maintenance–bank test set. These and other tests ensure the availability of replacement plug–in units known to be in good working order. The bank also provides channel–unit test capability for use in isolating troubles and for ensuring channel–unit integrity when a channel is to be added to a working bank. The maintenance bank is optional equipment.

The D4 bank has been extensively deployed in the telephone plant over the years and has found diverse applications on customer premises as well, either supplied by the exchange carrier or treated as customer–premises equipment and used in conjunction with DS1 high–capacity services. In addition, T1 network managers, which include D4–style voice–and–Dataport functions as well as digital cross–connect features, central monitoring and control, and other capabilities, are in growing use as part of customer-built networks.

The Enhanced–D4 and D5 Channel Banks

The D5 channel bank is part of the D5 Digital Terminal System [16] that, because of the ease in preparing circuits for service operation, is used mostly for special–services circuits that involve customers' loops. The enhanced–D4 system is based on retrofitting D4 banks with microprocessor control and special channel units. Generally, there is no manual adjustment on these banks for setting signalling options, gain, equalization or balance functions or for carrying out local testing. Instead, these functions are electronically programmable and set or carried out by the central system control using a microprocessor to administer the operation, provisioning, and maintenance functions for the banks. Data for prescription settings can be entered into the system or, for improved operation, a transponder can be used on the line at the customer's premises to obtain accurate loop transmission data automatically and program the units for service. The transponder is a small portable unit that works in conjunction with the central system. In response to the system controller, the loop's transmission characteristics are measured and the channel unit's gain, equalization, and balance are accurately set to optimum values accordingly. A simplified diagram of the interconnections of the D5 system processor to other functional units is shown in Figure 15–26; the enhanced–D4 structure is similar. Dedicated links connect the processor into systems as shown. Nonvolatile memory is usually employed to protect against power failures. Diagrams of typical automated four–wire and two–wire channel units with control and data connections to the system processor are shown in Figures 15–27 and 15–28, respectively.

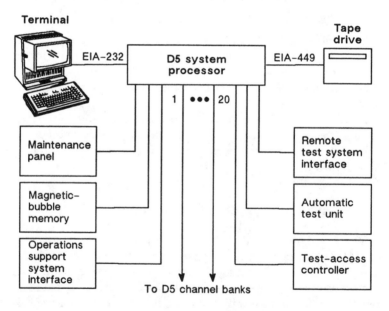

Figure 15–26. D5 digital terminal system processor interconnections.

The automation provided by these digital terminal systems allows better integration with several operations and maintenance centers for improved system operations and control. The integration is shown symbolically in Figure 15–29.

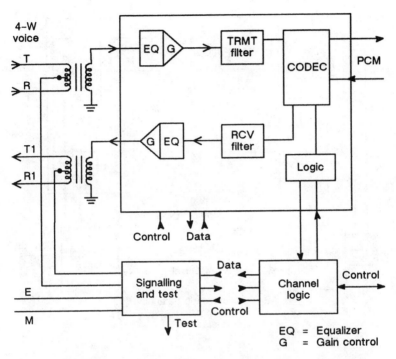

Figure 15-27. Automated four-wire channel unit.

D4 and D5 Dataports for Digital Data

In addition to having plug-in channel units used for message and special services, the D4 and D5 banks offer several channel units [17] for the transport of 2.4, 4.8, 9.6 (subrates) and 19.2– and 56–kb/s data signals for the Digital Data System (DDS). A Dataport unit translates a data signal to a DS0 signal rate by repeating the data rate (except for the 56–kb/s rate) to achieve the 64–kb/s rate, labeled DS0A. If subrate multiplex units are used, the data is not repeated but rather a number of subrate data signals are multiplexed together to achieve the 64–kb/s rate, labeled DS0B.

In both cases the resulting 64–kb/s signals are translated into assigned channels in the DS1 bit stream. Zero–code substitution techniques to provide adequate pulse density on the line are employed to prevent all zeros, which are possible in data transport,

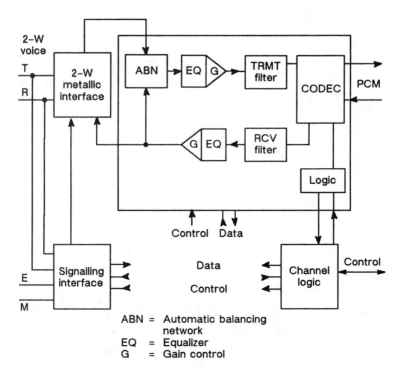

ABN = Automatic balancing
      network
EQ = Equalizer
G   = Gain control

Figure 15–28. Automated two–wire channel unit.

from appearing in the 64–kb/s time slots. The bank thus provides a mix of voice and data services.

Unlike the earlier DDS equipment arrangement having designated bays of equipment, a newer arrangement uses half of a D4 channel–bank mounting with Dataport, subrate multiplexer, and other plug–in units to form a digital data bank. This sharing of equipment frames provides a simpler and more economical DDS arrangement. Application is described in Volume 3, Chapter 17.

The D5 channels (and other comparable products) have options for clear–channel (64–kb/s) operation with the B8ZS zero–code suppression technique to provide sufficient pulse density and for integrated services digital network (ISDN) operation. Some products provide a ZBTSI option for pulse density. The B8ZS and ZBTSI techniques are described in Chapter 13, Part 1.

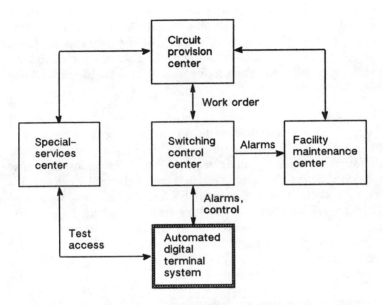

Figure 15-29. Integration of the automated digital terminal
systems with operations and maintenance
centers.

Requirements for the Dataport channel–unit functions are
given in Reference 18.

15-8 DIGITAL CHANNEL-BANK REQUIREMENTS AND OBJECTIVES FOR VOICEBAND SIGNALS

Some digital channel banks sample and convert each of 24
separate voiceband signals into a PCM bit stream of 64–kb/s per
channel and then serialize the 24 digitized channels into the
1.544–Mb/s 12–frame superframe format or into the 24–frame
extended superframe format shown in Chapter 13 in Tables 13–2
and 13–3. Other banks sample the voiceband signals and serialize the signals into a common pulse amplitude modulation
(PAM) bus and then encode and organize them into the
12–frame or 24–frame format. The banks also reconvert the digital stream into voiceband signals. Signalling and alarm information is provided by the banks. This section will give some voice-
frequency (VF) requirements and objectives for digital terminal

banks taken from Section B of Reference 19, which also contains general characteristics, including maintenance and alarm features; VF operating characteristics, including transmission levels and office cable compensation; signalling characteristics for the many types of voice channel provided; and testing procedures and arrangements.

The banks are designed so that many types of two–wire and four–wire VF channels can be provided by options or various plug–in modules reflecting different transmission levels, two–wire or four–wire, and signalling requirements. The following transmission requirements are common to most channel types and refer to channel banks measured back–to–back. Test signals of 1000 Hz are avoided because false framing and small gain variations are possible when the test signal is a precise subharmonic of the sampling frequency. Thus a test signal of 1004 Hz is commonly used.

Channel Attenuation vs. Frequency

The boundaries for this characteristic are shown for four–wire and for two–wire, receive and transmit, in Figures 15–30 and 15–31.

Loss and Loss Stability

The ranges of loss adjustment are given in the reference and depend on the designated transmission level at the point of connection and office cable compensation. The loss stability objective at a frequency between 1004 and 1020 Hz and at 0.0 dBm0 is within ± 0.5 dB after 20 years.

Tracking

Tracking is defined as a deviation from input to output in reference to 1004 Hz at 0 dBm0. With an input from −37 dBm0 to +3 dBm0 the maximum deviation shall be 0.5 dB. When averaged over 20 or more banks the deviation shall be less than 0.25 dB.

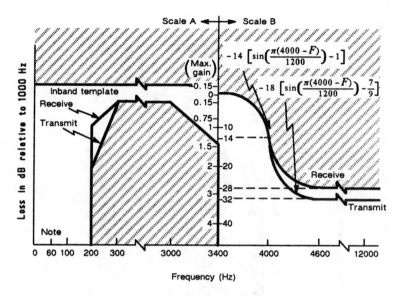

Note: Loss at 60 Hz ≥ 14 dB in the transmit direction.

Figure 15-30. Four-wire frequency response template requirement.

Four-Wire Impedance

The return loss measured at 1004 Hz shall be 28 dB minimum. At any other frequency between 300 and 3000 Hz, the return loss shall be 23 dB minimum.

Two-Wire Return Loss

The two-wire return loss against 600 ohms or 900 ohms, as appropriate, with a loop resistance of 25 ohms inserted between the two-wire channel unit and measuring set and with a four-wire channel unit at the far end shall be: echo, 28 dB minimum; singing, 20 dB minimum. For two-wire applications with two-wire toll switches, the return loss shall be: echo, 33 dB; singing, 20 dB.

431

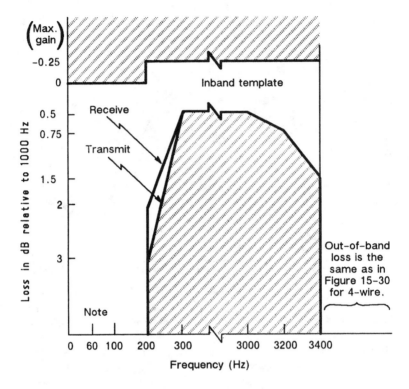

Note: Loss at 60 Hz ≥ 20 dB in the transmit direction.

Figure 15–31. Two–wire frequency response template requirement.

Four-Wire Transhybrid Loss

Based on the test arrangement of Reference 19, this loss is: echo, 34 dB minimum; singing, 20 dB minimum.

Crosstalk

The channel bank shall meet crosstalk requirements with any of the channels as a disturbing channel and any other as the disturbed channel with a 0–dBm0 signal of 0 to 4 kHz on the disturbing channel. For each setup as shown in Figure 15–32 for

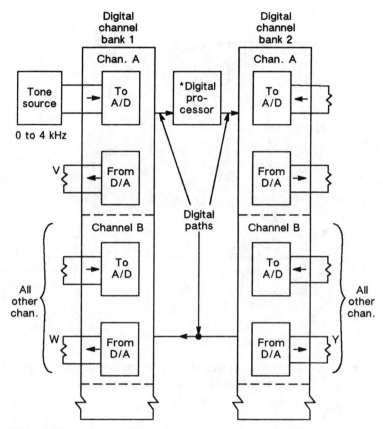

*Used to force all ones in receiver for disturbing channel.

Notes:
1. Channel A is the disturbing channel.
2. Channel B is the disturbed channel.
3. Terminate disturbed channels in appropriate impedances.
4. Set tone source over a range of frequencies 0 to 4 kHz at 0 dBm0.
5. Measure at ports V, W, and Y with a tuned meter.

Figure 15-32. Crosstalk measurement connections.

the major transmit and receive contributions, the equal level crosstalk coupling loss at points V, W, and Y shall be greater than that shown in Figure 15–33. Procedures for other crosstalk paths (transmit and receive ports) are noted in Reference 19. The losses for these paths are to be at least 6 dB greater than shown in the figure.

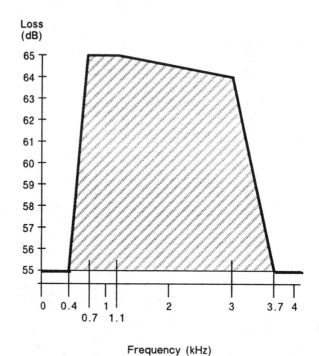

Figure 15–33. Minimum equal level crosstalk coupling loss, transmit and receive contributions.

Longitudinal Balance

The longitudinal balance when measured per the methods of *IEEE Std. 455–1976* shall meet the following requirements:

Frequency (Hz)	20 log (Vs/Vm) – dB min.	
	Two–Wire	Four–Wire at –16 TLP
200	58	74
500	58	74
1000	58	74
3000	58	69

Idle–Circuit Noise

Idle–channel noise for VF in to VF out shall not exceed 23 dBrnc0 (objective, 20). For the transmit or receive section alone, the noise shall not exceed 20 dBrnc0 (objective, 17).

Signal–to–Distortion Ratio

The overall signal to distortion shall be measured with a notched filter in the output path to attenuate the input test tones to well below levels of the distortion noise. The requirements are for input frequencies of 1004 to 1020, 304, and 2996 Hz.

Input Level (dBm0)	Minimum Signal–to–Distortion Overall (dB)
0 to –30	33
–40	27
–45	22

Single–Frequency Distortion

The overall requirement with a 0–dBm0 input shall be as follows:

Input	Output
Sweep from 0 to 12 kHz	–28 dBm0 or less at any other frequency
Select a tone between 1004 and 1020 Hz	–40 dBm0 or less at any other frequency, 0 to 4 kHz

Peak–to–Average Ratio

Peak–to–average ratio (PAR) is described in Volume 1, Chapter 21. For channel banks, each VF channel shall have a PAR rating of 94 minimum.

References

1. Fleury, B. "Asynchronous High Speed Digital Multiplexing," *IEEE Communications Magazine*, Vol. 24, No. 8 (Aug. 1986).

2. Draft of ANSI, *Report T1X1.4/87-753*, "American National Standard for the Fourth Hierarchical Level (DS4NA)" (New York: American National Standards Institute, 1987).

3. Ritchie, G. R. "SYNTRAN—A New Direction for Digital Transmission Terminals," *IEEE Communications Magazine*, Vol. 23, No. 11 (Nov. 1985).

4. Ballart, B., J. O. Eaves, L. A. Ferrara, and G. R. Ritchie. "Restructured DS3 Format for Synchronous Transmission (SYNTRAN)," *Globecom 1984 Conference Record* (Atlanta, GA: Nov. 1984).

5. *Synchronous DS3 Format Interface Specification*, Technical Reference TR-TSY-000021, Bellcore (Iss. 1, June 1984).

6. *ANSI T1.103-1987*, "American National Standard for Telecommunications—Digital Hierarchy—Synchronous DS3 Format Specifications" (New York: American National Standards Institute, 1987).

7. *Synchronous Optical Networks (SONET) Fiber Optic Transmission Systems, Requirements and Objectives*, Technical Advisory TA-TSY-000755, Bellcore (Iss. 1, Nov. 1987).

8. *Digital Switch Interface Generic Requirements*, Technical Advisory TA-TSY-000782, Bellcore (Iss. 1, Mar. 1988).

9. Members of Technical Staff. *Transmission Systems for Communications*, Fifth Edition (Murray Hill, NJ: AT&T Bell Laboratories, Inc., 1982), Chapter 29, "Digital Multiplexers."

10. *Asynchronous Digital Multiplexers, Requirements and Objectives*, Technical Reference TR-TSY-000009, Bellcore (Iss. 1, May 1986).

11. *Transport Systems Generic Requirements (TSGR): Common Requirements*, Technical Reference TR-TSY-000499, Bellcore (Iss. 1, Dec. 1987).

12. *Synchronous DS3 Add–Drop Multiplex (ADM 3/X), Requirements and Objectives,* Technical Reference TR–TSY–000010, Bellcore (Iss. 1, Feb. 1988).

13. *SONET Add–Drop Multiplex Generic Requirements and Objectives,* Technical Reference TR–TSY–000496, Bellcore (Iss. 1, Sept. 1988).

14. *ANSI T1.106–1988,* "American National Standard for Telecommunications—Digital Hierarchy—Optical Interface Specifications; Single Mode" (New York: American National Standards Institute, 1988).

15. *ANSI T1.105–1988,* "American National Standard for Telecommunications—Digital Hierarchy—Optical Interface Rates and Formats Specifications" (New York: American National Standards Institute, 1988).

16. Albert, W. G., T. J. Ciaccia, J. C. Ghiloni, Jr., P. G. St. Amand, and R. P. Snicer. "Special–Service Circuits: D5 Delivers Them Faster and Easier," *Bell Laboratories Record,* Vol. 63 (Mar. 1985).

17. Aprille, T. J. and C. A. Siller. "Data Transmission with D4 and D5 Digital Channel Banks," *Conference Record,* IEEE International Conference on Communications (1987).

18. *Digital Channel Banks—Requirements for Dataport Channel Unit Functions,* Technical Advisory TA–TSY–000077, Bellcore (Iss. 3, Apr. 1986).

19. Bell System Technical Reference PUB 43801, *Digital Channel Bank, Requirements and Objectives,* American Telephone and Telegraph Company (Nov. 1982).

437

Chapter 16
Digital Transmission—Metallic Lines

A number of digital lines using two wire pairs or two copper–tube coaxials are used to transmit the electrical signals of the digital hierarchy at DS1 level and above. Regenerative repeaters are installed at specified intervals along the line to amplify, retime, and regenerate the pulses for transmission to the next line or office repeater or to a terminal.

This chapter describes the metallic digital lines and repeaters that have been used in the network, although fiber optic systems (Chapter 14) are quickly supplanting such systems. In comparison, optic systems have enormous capacity and are free from interference due to crosstalk. Digital loop–feeder and integrated services digital network (ISDN) basic–rate and primary–rate access facilities, including the digital subscriber line, are discussed in Chapters 3 and 13.

16–1 DIGITAL LINE FUNDAMENTALS

Metallic digital–transmission systems, such as T–type carrier using electrical signals, produce a stream of discrete pulses, generated in the terminal equipment, that must satisfy certain requirements imposed by the repeatered transmission line. In all cases, the line signals are impaired by the transmission medium. These impairments are overcome by repeaters placed at regular intervals along the transmission path. In addition, the line equipment must be arranged so that impairment limits are not exceeded.

Performance Objectives

The current performance objectives [1] for T1 carrier in metropolitan areas (assuming the number of tandem repeater sections is 50, maximum) has been that 95 percent of end–to–end systems must have bit error ratios of less than 10^{-6} (i.e., one error or less in 10^6 bits). From this it was determined that the objective for one repeater section is that 99.9 percent of the sections must have bit error ratios of less than 10^{-6}. The end–to–end objectives are under study by standards committees with an eye toward tighter limits, such as a very small percentage of one–minute intervals with a bit error ratio worse than 1×10^{-7}, and other criteria.

Electrical Signal Characteristics

Most wire–pair digital systems transmit bipolar or modified bipolar signals because, with them, the average values of dc components are minimum and the design of repeater circuits is thus facilitated.

Line Repetition Rate. Digital systems involve the transmission of a signal having a fixed repetition rate. For signals above DS1 in the hierarchy, the rate is determined by limitations imposed by the transmission medium and by the number of bits added for framing, synchronization, and other administrative functions. Multiple signals from the lower levels of the hierarchy or other sources are then fitted into the bit stream as efficiently as possible.

These considerations have led to standard line rates that were originally derived to satisfy the requirements of a particular transmission system type. These rates, now designated DS1 (1.544 Mb/s), DS1C (3.152 Mb/s), DS2 (6.312 Mb/s), DS3 (44.736 Mb/s), and DS4NA (139.264 Mb/s), form the current digital multiplex hierarchy. They are not integrally related because bits are added to each signal to control the multiplexing process and for other service functions. Chapter 15 contains information on rates and formats.

Signal Coding Format. A number of coding techniques may be used for the line signal. In the electrical domain, the bipolar format, or a code modification such as bipolar with zero substitution, is usually used because dc and very–low–frequency signal components are virtually eliminated and because the

440

concentration of energy in the signal is shifted down to one-half the bit frequency. The shift of energy to the lower frequency reduces crosstalk coupling, reduces the required bandwidth, and makes the design of timing recovery circuits more practical. In many other signal formats, the energy is concentrated at much higher frequencies or exhibits a nearly flat spectrum to very high frequencies. The elimination of dc components permits transformer coupling between transmission conductors and repeaters, and facilitates the design of threshold decision circuits by controlling baseline wander.

Many factors enter into the choice of code for the transmitted signal for a specific system. Code characteristics may be used to measure the performance of the repeatered line, to derive timing information, to minimize crosstalk, and for a number of other functions. The optimum for each system is the code that provides satisfactory performance most economically and coordinates most practicably with other systems that operate in the same cable.

Transmission Line Signal Impairments

The transmission of electrical digital signals from one repeater to another introduces a number of impairments that must be corrected at each repeater. These impairments include loss, distortion, random noise, impulse noise, and crosstalk. In addition, timing jitter introduced by the regenerative repeaters tends to accumulate from repeater to repeater.

Loss and Distortion. As in any transmission system that uses wire pairs or coaxial conductors as the transmission medium, the principal impairments are the loss and the attenuation/frequency distortion (Figures 16-1 and 16-2) introduced by the cable conductors. These impairments attenuate and distort the pulses and eventually make them unrecognizable. The pulses must be restored to the point where detection circuits can recognize the presence or absence of a pulse in each time slot. The impairments are overcome at repeater points by an amplifier/equalizer that introduces gain/frequency characteristics that approximate the inverse of the loss/frequency curve of the transmission conductors. These corrections must be made before the regeneration

Attenuation constant (dB/mile)

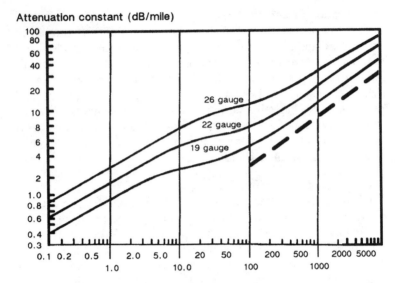

Frequency, f (kHz)

Note:　Dashed line shows slope proportional to $\sqrt{f}$.

Figure 16-1. Attenuation of typical telephone cables at 55°F.

Attenuation constant
(dB/mile)

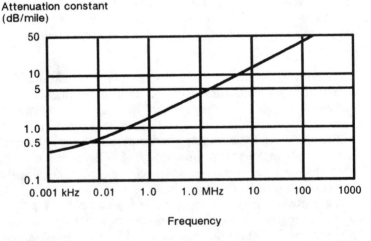

Frequency

Figure 16-2. Attenuation of typical 0.375-inch coaxial cable.

process, generally by an automatic line build–out circuit in the equipment.

Noise. As with any other type of system, digital system application must be considered from the point of view of thermal noise, impulse noise, and crosstalk. These impairments are controlled by specification of repeater spacings and cable–pair usage for the two directions of transmission. However, since regeneration eliminates noise accumulation from repeater to repeater, it is possible to consider these phenomena on a per–repeater basis to a far greater extent in digital system design than in analog systems. A characteristic of digital systems is that they perform extremely well up to a critical value of the signal–to–noise ratio and then deteriorate rapidly when that critical value is passed. Thus, margin must be provided to preserve a satisfactorily low error rate.

These qualitative statements regarding error impairment in digital signal transmission apply quite well where the noise has predictable characteristics and is of a known amplitude. However, these attributes are not always applicable where impulse noise is controlling. Impulse noise consists of large amplitude peaks that occur unpredictably in infrequent bursts against a relatively quiet background. The most common sources of impulse noise are the switching transients that occur in telephone central offices and lightning.

Switching transients are most interfering in those sections of cable closest to electromechanical central offices. They are induced, by cable–pair crosstalk, into digital system pairs from voice–frequency (VF) pairs where those are still used. Control of such transients is achieved by maintaining cable–pair balance to minimize the effects of longitudinal induction and by designing the repeater sections adjacent to central offices to be shorter than nominal. Thus, signal attenuation is reduced and a higher signal–to–noise ratio is maintained. Also in interoffice applications, digital systems and VF circuits are usually segregated in different cables or in different cable units (binder groups) to reduce the probability of induced transients or crosstalk.

Impulses caused by lightning surges tend to be induced longitudinally in the cable pairs. Thus, the effects of such surges are minimized by maintaining a close impedance balance from each conductor to ground (longitudinal balance).

Electrical Crosstalk

Crosstalk between cable pairs and in regenerator apparatus cases is a limiting impairment in the application of digital transmission systems over wire–pair cables. The limitation results from the juxtaposition within the cable sheath of the two directions of transmission and the crosstalk coupling at the repeaters. Near-end (NEXT), far–end (FEXT) and apparatus–case (ACXT) crosstalk paths are shown in Figure 16–3. The cable is made up with binder groups of pairs, called units. Crosstalk occurs, with

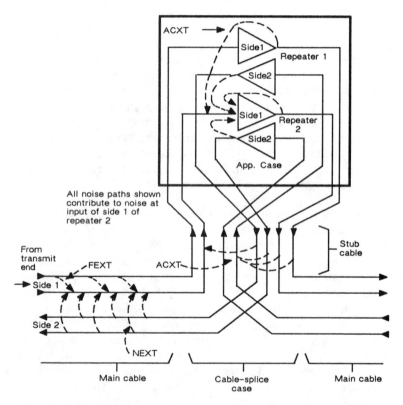

Figure 16–3. Crosstalk coupling paths for intermediate–repeater sections.

decreasing intensity, between pairs within the same unit, pairs in adjacent units, and pairs in nonadjacent units. For systems having both directions of transmission in the same or adjacent units, the limitation is due to NEXT. When the two directions are in nonadjacent units, or in separate or screened cables, the limitations may be due to FEXT or ACXT.

Because regenerative repeaters are used in digital systems, crosstalk impairments do not accumulate from one repeater section to the next. Averaging techniques used in the analysis of analog systems cannot be used in digital systems. In digital systems, a single repeater section with a slightly lower than acceptable signal–to–noise ratio significantly degrades the error performance of the entire chain of repeater sections.

The distribution of the pair–to–pair equal level coupling loss (ELCL) in cables has been found to be log–normal. Capacitance balance between pairs is measured during manufacture. When limits are exceeded, cables are rejected. Since there is a correlation between capacitance unbalance and crosstalk coupling, the distribution of coupling losses tends to be truncated at the low–loss end. A representative distribution of pair–to–pair ELCL, for pulp cable measured at 3 MHz, is shown in Figure 16–4. Crosstalk coupling loss at frequencies other than 3 MHz can be inferred from known relationships between crosstalk loss and frequency. Crosstalk loss decreases with frequency at 6 dB per octave for FEXT and approximately 4.5 dB per octave for NEXT.

In a multipair cable, a given pair receives crosstalk interference from many other energized pairs. Probability theory can be used to obtain the distribution of crosstalk coupling as the power sum of many interferers. The resulting distribution is again log–normal. Figure 16–5 illustrates the modeled distributions of NEXT and FEXT when 49 pairs of a 50–pair cable unit crosstalk into one pair. Because of the effect of transmission level point (TLP) differences, NEXT can be far worse than FEXT.

Figure 16–6 illustrates the relationship between crosstalk coupling loss and the number of interferers. Because of random addition, the effective coupling loss decreases about 3 dB when the number of interferers doubles. The minimum FEXT shown represents the 99.9–percent limit of the distribution and does not

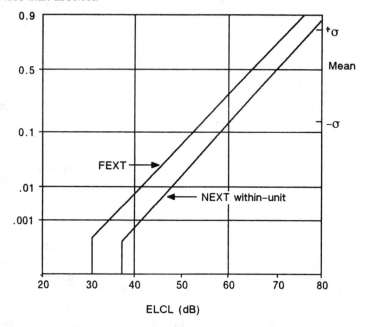

Figure 16–4. Pair–to–pair ELCL at 3 MHz for 1000 feet of a 50–pair unit of 22–gauge pulp cable.

reflect the truncation of the original pair–to–pair ELCL distribution.

The results of a field measurement program on crosstalk [2] are shown in Figure 16–7 for installed DS1 systems in terms of noise power margin in decibels above the noise power that would produce an error rate of 10^{-3}. The figure indicates that at the design point of 0.1 percent, the lowest margin was due to ACXT but was still satisfactory. Improved repeater cases to reduce ACXT would enhance the margin by about 11 dB. Performance then would be limited by FEXT, or the additional margin could be allocated to increase the fill. (Low–crosstalk cases were made available to address this opportunity.)

Crosstalk in paired cables can be reduced by changing cable design to reduce the pair loss and the capacity coupling (causing

446

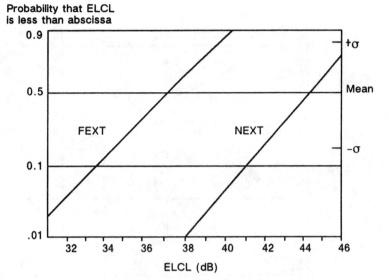

Figure 16-5. Power sum of crosstalk interference from 49 pairs.

the crosstalk). Screening to partition the cable pairs into two groups, one for all transmitting pairs and the other for all receiving pairs, is a particularly effective way to reduce crosstalk between directions of transmission.

Signal Reflections. The transmission distortions that occur in digital systems all tend to produce intersymbol interference. Signal reflections, which contribute to this type of impairment, are a result of impedance discontinuities that may arise from many sources. To prevent the generation of reflections, the terminating impedances of repeater and terminal circuits are designed to match the impedances of connecting transmission lines or other equipment. However, there are many other sources of reflections, such as gas plugs and splices, that must be controlled if system performance is to be satisfactory.

Gas plugs are used in wire–pair cables at points where they enter central–office buildings and at maintenance–area boundaries. A gas plug is an airtight seal, usually formed from epoxy resin forced into the cable sheath, that allows application of gas

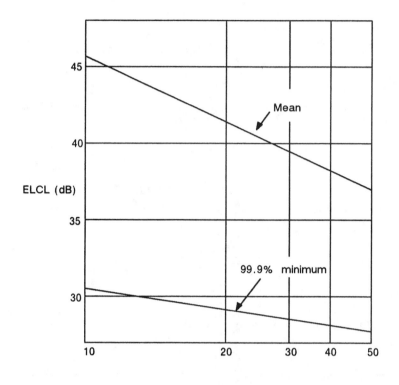

Figure 16–6.   Power sum of interfering signals due to FEXT.

pressure between plugs to prevent moisture accumulation. The electrical effect of the plug is to add capacitance concentrated at the plug, thus creating a discontinuity in the impedance of the cable pairs. Repeater spacings are made short where gas plugs are used in order to accommodate the added capacitance. Splices in cable pairs also introduce impedance discontinuities and capacitance unbalance in the transmission paths, which can increase echoes and crosstalk.

Changes of gauge and insulation at points where different types of cable are spliced together also cause impedance discontinuities and echoes. In addition, bridged taps, used extensively in the loop plant but rarely in the trunk plant, can also produce echoes.

448

Margin (dB)

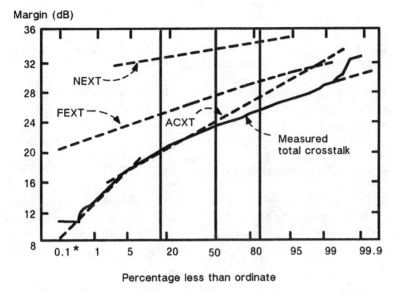

Percentage less than ordinate

*Design point at 0.1%

Figure 16-7. Predicted service margins due to NEXT, FEXT, and ACXT.

They are routinely removed when converting an existing cable to digital span lines.

Repeater Characteristics

The regenerative repeaters placed along a digital transmission line perform operations that result in an authentic replica of the signal transmitted from the previous repeater or system terminal. These functions include: amplification and equalization of the received signal, the generation of an internal timing or clock signal, the slicing of the incoming signal and deciding whether a pulse is present in each time slot, and the regeneration of discrete pulses in the proper time slots to form the original line signal. To support these functions, there must also be circuits to power the repeater and to protect the repeater from lightning or other surges.

A regenerative repeater is usually ac–coupled to the transmission line by transformers. Such coupling permits the powering of

449

the repeater from direct current carried on the transmission conductors and isolates the repeater from low–frequency noise on the line. However, it effectively removes any dc or low–frequency components from the signal.

A common technique used to deal with this is to place restrictions on the coding of the transmitted signal to reduce the dc and low–frequency content. A less common technique, quantized feedback, involves the incorporation of circuits in each repeater to restore the dc and low–frequency signal components. Only minor coding restrictions are then imposed.

Timing. The regenerated signal transmitted from a repeater must be accurately timed to maintain the proper intervals between pulses and pulse width. Timing information is usually extracted from the line signal after it has been equalized and amplified.

The processes of timing and regeneration lead to a signal impairment called *jitter*, the appearance of pulses at timing intervals different from ideal. Jitter, which can be regarded as a random phase modulation of the pulse stream, can cause errors at the receiver. From some sources, jitter adds systematically while from others it adds randomly or nonsystematically. Systematic effects degrade the pulse train in the same way at all tandem repeaters. Examples are intersymbol interference, pulse–width differences, and clock threshold offsets. Nonsystematic jitter sources include the mistuning of clock circuit filters and crosstalk from other systems. In a long chain of repeaters, jitter performance is usually dominated by systematic effects.

Regenerator Circuits. A fundamental function of the regenerator is to examine the incoming signal during each pulse interval and to determine if a pulse is present in that interval. This function is carried out after the signal has been amplified and equalized.

Most regenerative systems transmit bipolar signals. Such signals can have (in a pulse interval) one of three states: positive, zero, and negative, usually designated +, 0, −. The threshold circuits are gated to admit the line signal at the middle of each pulse interval. If the signal is positive and exceeds a positive

450

threshold, it is recognized as a positive pulse. If it is negative and exceeds a negative threshold, it is recognized as a negative pulse. If it has a value between the positive and negative thresholds, it is recognized as a *0* (no pulse).

When either threshold is exceeded, the regenerator is triggered to generate a pulse of the appropriate duration, polarity, and amplitude. In this manner, the distorted input signal is reconstructed as a new output signal for transmission to the next repeater.

Surge Protection and Power. Operating power for line repeaters is generally supplied by direct current transmitted over the signal conductors. The dc and ac signals are separated and recombined at the repeater terminals. A dc voltage is derived from the line current as it passes through zener diodes in the repeater.

In many locations, it is necessary to protect the repeater circuits against damage by lightning or power surges. Primary protection is provided by gas tubes or by carbon blocks that limit longitudinal surges to a maximum of about 1000 volts peak. Secondary protection is provided by a serial connection of parallel, oppositely poled diodes bridged across each conductor pair. With a current–limiting resistor in series with each conductor, surge currents are limited to a peak value of about 50 amperes.

Transmission Line Layout

Regenerative repeaters are distributed along a transmission line at distances that are determined by a number of interrelated phenomena. With the initial designs of DS1 digital systems, a 6000–foot objective was established for repeater spacings on 22–ga cable (about one–half of this when adjacent to switching offices) so that underground vaults and other facilities previously used for loading coils could be reused for regenerative repeaters. Most digital systems using wire–pair media are designed for this nominal spacing. Repeater spacing can be increased to about 15 kft with special cable (low loss/low crosstalk) and repeaters.

Most DS1 systems are organized so that up to 25 repeaters can be housed in one apparatus case at each location. This arrangement affords efficient space use in manholes or on telephone poles.

Amplification and Equalization. Sufficient repeater amplification must be provided to compensate for the losses of the transmission line and repeater circuits, such as equalizers, which are ahead of the pulse detector circuit. Automatic line build–out networks are used so that the overall channel characteristic between two repeater points approximates a raised–cosine characteristic that, with the transmitted pulse characteristic, meets the Nyquist I criteria for pulse transmission.

System lengths have been generally constrained by maintenance considerations. In most cases, the overall length is divided into spans that are defined as the distances between central–office buildings. These spans are specified in terms of the maximum distance over which repeaters can be powered from central–office power supplies. In addition, it is convenient to regard spans in terms of maintenance and operating functions and the related equipment in the buildings at their ends.

16-2 T-TYPE DIGITAL LINES

The repeated metallic lines have all been designated as T–type digital lines, T1 through T4M. The designations and corresponding signals are indicated in Table 16–1. Over the years, the T1 and T1 outstate (T1OS) lines of basic DS1 rate have been extensively deployed and are still being applied in those areas where a modest number of channels are to be provided by digital carrier, or growth is slow, or DS1 transmission is needed through existing loop cable. The higher bit–rate T1C, T1D, T148, 9148, T1G, and T2 lines have had relatively low usage and the T4M is no longer in service.

The layout of T–type lines is based on repeater spacings established by line equalization and loss, crosstalk and other interferences, and the provision of adequate margins [3]. Line spans that encompass a number of repeater sections are based on satisfying operations and maintenance considerations and on supplying power.

Table 16-1. Digital Carrier Lines and Signals

Line Type	Cable	Fac. Rate	No. of Chan. (64 kb/s)	Line Rate (Mbaud)	Line Format
T1, T1OS	Pairs	DS1	24	1.544	Bipolar-RZ-AMI
T1C	Pairs	DS1C	48	3.152	Bipolar-RZ-AMI
T1D	Pairs	DS1C	48	3.152	Duobinary (3 level)- scrambled
T148C and 9148	Pairs	DS1C	48	2.361	Ternary 4B3T
T1G	Pairs	DS2	96	3.22175	Quaternary 2B1Q
T2	Low-cap pairs	DS2	96	6.312	Bipolar-RZ-AMI
T4M	Coaxial	DS4	4032	274.176	Polar-NRZ- scrambled

RZ　　= Return to zero
AMI　 = Alternate mark inverted
2B1Q　= See Table 16-2 (2 bits per quaternary level)
4B3T　= Groups of 4 binary bits encoded into 3 ternary bits
NRZ　 = Non-return to zero

The provision of fault-locating facilities, maintenance spare lines, and protection switching arrangements are other aspects of digital line application that must be considered.

Zero-Code Substitution

To provide enough energy to keep accurate clock recovery at the repeaters, sufficient *1*s must be sent or a zero-code substitution technique provided by the digital terminals is necessary, as discussed in Chapters 13 and 15. For T1 systems, the usual code is B8ZS (bipolar with eight-zero substitution) and for T2, B6ZS (bipolar with six-zero substitution).

Performance

Most T lines are engineered and maintained to meet an end-to-end error rate of 10^{-6} bits at the DS1 level under worst-case operating conditions. Typical performance is much better. More stringent tests are made for T lines used in the Digital Data System.

16-3 THE T1 DIGITAL LINE

The first digital line (ca. 1961) and the one that is in most common use is part of the 24-channel T1 Digital Transmission System. The initial field of application was primarily to provide switched network trunks between central offices up to about 50 miles apart, instead of VF trunks. The T1 line has also been found economical for loop feeder applications such as those discussed in Chapters 3 and 13.

While T1 was initially limited to a maximum length of about 50 miles by operation and maintenance considerations, it is routinely used up to 100 miles or so with present maintenance plans and is technically suitable for distances of up to 200 miles. The T1OS digital line, covered in Part 3 of this chapter, is such an application.

The DS1 signal transmitted over a T1 carrier line has a repetition rate of 1.544 Mb/s and uses a bipolar, 50-percent duty cycle format. It must contain no more than 15 consecutive 0s and have a pulse density of n pulses in every window of $8(n+1)$ time slots. These constraints on signal characteristics must be applied in the system terminal equipment and are necessary to ensure satisfactory operation of regenerative repeaters located along the line. Zero-code substitution techniques are described in Chapter 15.

Transmission Media

A wide variety of multipair exchange cables may be used for T1 systems. These include polyethylene-insulated conductor (PIC) and pulp-insulated copper-pair cables of 19, 22, 24, 25, and 26 gauge. The two directions of transmission can be carried in the same cable provided they are in different cable units, or binder groups, in order to control crosstalk between systems. Engineering rules [4,5] specify the way such separation must be accomplished. Within these rules, a limit is imposed on the number of pairs that can be used as T1 lines without shortening the repeater spacing. If additional fill is needed at full spacing, the two directions of transmission can be carried in separate cables or in cables with shielding between binder groups to provide enough isolation so that the cable fill of T1 lines is equivalent to that obtained by using separate cables. Such cables are called screened cables.

Great care must be taken in all applications to ensure that cable pairs have been checked for satisfactory operating conditions. All bridged taps, load coils, and line build—out networks must be removed. In digital loop carrier and customer—premises applications, loop cables are generally not operated under gas pressure and are therefore relatively exposed to impairment due to moisture. A cable route from the central office to a remote area is usually made up of mixed gauges. Binder—group integrity may be lost since it was historically less important in the loop plant than in the trunk plant. All of these factors must be examined and the cable upgraded where deficient if the T1 line is to operate satisfactorily.

Repeater Spacing

The spacing between T1—type wire—pair line repeaters is nominally 6000 feet for 22—gauge cable. This distance was chosen to match the distance between load points on H88—loaded cables that could be reused for carrier. The distance is comparable on 25—gauge low—capacitance pairs, and much longer (10—11 kft) on 19—gauge trunk cable. In loop plant, with its fine gauges and frequent route junctions, the spacing may be much shorter than 6000 feet. The spacing between the office and the first line repeater is short, nominally 2900 feet, to match the end section spacing of a loaded cable and to reduce the effects of central—office impulse noise.

T1 Repeater

The T1 system uses two general types of repeater, called line and central—office repeaters. Line repeaters, designed for outside—plant environments, have two regenerators arranged for either one or two directions of transmission. These repeaters are generally assembled in apparatus cases that house 25 repeaters (50 regenerators). The other type, designed for use in central–office repeater bays (ORBs), contains circuits to regenerate the signals on only one line. Thus, two such regenerators must be used at each intermediate central–office repeater point for a complete two–way system. However, where a T1 line terminates, only a single central–office repeater is used in the receiving direction, as the transmitted signal has just been generated. Other differences between line and central–office repeater de-signs relate to powering and maintenance features. Power is fed from central offices to the remote repeaters, while the office repeaters may be powered locally or from the line power loop.

Figure 16–8 shows a typical digital line repeater. Its major functions are equalization, pulse detection, clock recovery, and pulse regeneration [5,6]. It also provides conversions from the line to circuit format and vice versa, surge protection, fault location, powering from the line, and other functions. Error rate and eye diagrams, pulse shaping, timing, and line coding are

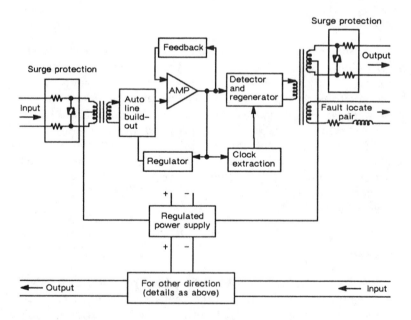

Figure 16-8. Typical digital line repeater.

discussed in Reference 4. Office repeaters are designed to deliver the standard DSX–1 signal level to cross–connect equipment through up to 655 feet of office cable.

For equalization, the automatic line build–out (ALBO) network and the feedback amplifier equalize the cable characteristic to restore the received pulse to the best shape for detection, considering intersymbol interference, noise, and timing jitter. The pulse regulator keeps the equalized received pulse at a constant amplitude for clock recovery and detection.

For clock recovery, the clock extraction network may perform several functions on the pulses such as equalization, rectification, and filtering to select the timing component. The filtering technique may be either a high–Q tuned circuit (for DS1 rates), a crystal filter, or a phase–locked loop (higher Q for higher rates). The timing signal is then processed to produce sharp timing pulses. Recovering the clock from the incoming pulse code modulation (PCM) pulses is called "self–timing."

The timing pulses provide the means for setting the sampling window (eye) of the threshold detector circuit, which determines the presence or absence of a received pulse. When a received pulse is detected, the pulse regenerator is activated and transmits the regenerated pulse. The timing (fixed width) of these pulses is controlled by gating on the clock pulse.

Modern repeaters are designed so that in the absence of an input signal, the repeater does not produce a free–running output signal which, in the past, could disturb other systems.

Powering is provided via the "phantom" path of the two cable pairs, using a constant current of 140 or (in modern units) 60 mA. Power feeding from the central office(s) at the ends of the span involves combinations of −48, −130, and +130 volts.

Timing Jitter. Timing jitter is defined as instability in the recovered clock. It appears in the regenerated pulse timing. Changing pulse patterns in the received PCM serial bit stream, intersymbol interference, and noise at each repeater or terminal generate timing jitter. Jitter accumulates systematically, primarily because the same pulse pattern appears at each repeater. With standard PCM coding, high-frequency jitter in excessive amounts above 4 kHz causes interchannel crosstalk and lower frequency jitter causes distortion within the channels. Also, for DS1 rates, the distortion due to jitter of about 1.4 μs (about two unit intervals) approaches the distortion due to quantizing noise. Jitter interface requirements are included in Chapter 15, Part 4.

T1 Line Layout

The repeatered lines in interoffice T1 are laid out as span lines, i.e., the transmission lines from a DSX-1 cross-connect frame (or an ORB) in one power-feed central office to a DSX-1 cross-connect frame (or an ORB) in the next power-feed central office. A span line provides both directions of transmission. Maintenance lines, order wires, and fault-location lines between central office buildings are provided on a span line without regard to system terminal locations. The DSX arrangement also provides a convenient administrative unit for system assignment and maintenance. As a universal fixed-level point for cross-connections, it provides a flexibility that is unavailable in analog short-haul carrier systems.

With 22-gauge cable, the maximum distance between power feed points is approximately 36 miles with modern low-power repeaters. Many factors, such as cable gauge, aerial or below-ground installation, and length of end sections, affect the exact spacing of power feed points. In some cases, remote power feed points are located between central-office buildings.

Regenerative repeaters are housed in apparatus cases located along the cable. These cases may be mounted in manholes, on pedestals, or on telephone poles. Stub cables are connected to the apparatus cases at the factory and connections are made to transmission cables by splicing. Single-cable and two-cable operations require different splicing patterns.

Repeaters are designed for optimum performance at a cable loss of approximately 31 dB at 772 kHz (the peak of the power spectrum), which is equivalent to a cable length of about 6000 feet for 22-gauge pulp-insulated cable and other commonly used cable types. Engineering rules specify the permitted departures from the nominal spacings to accommodate environmental conditions along the route. For example, it was mentioned earlier that the first repeater spacing out of a central office may be short to overcome the effects of impulse noise originating from switching transients.

Cables are designed and manufactured in various ways, as described in Chapter 2. Some are made up of bundles of conductor pairs called binder groups. Earlier types are made up of layers of conductor pairs. Splicing rules determine the extent to which the integrity of the binder groups and layers is maintained. The intersystem crosstalk performance of the cable depends heavily on these factors and on the vintage of the apparatus cases; engineering rules specify which conductor pairs may be used under various circumstances. System performance objectives can be met with confidence only when these rules are closely applied in the layout of systems.

One or more powered span lines are reserved as maintenance lines. These are used to carry service while maintenance is being performed on working lines or to restore service in the event of working–line failure. T1 systems can be equipped with automatic protection switching.

Where a T1 span extends to a customer's premises, for use with 1.5–Mb/s digital service or ISDN primary–rate access, the span terminates at the customer's network interface rather than an ORB. The customer supplies an FCC–registered channel service unit or ISDN equivalent (NT1) that provides basic ORB functions. Part of the 772–kHz cable loss of the last section of the span is allocated to customer–supplied premises cabling.

Maintenance Considerations

Three characteristics of the T1 line signal can be used by monitoring equipment for in–service maintenance purposes. These are: (1) proper bipolar alternate–mark–inverted line code with a zero–code substitution (if employed), (2) correct line rate of 1.544 Mb/s, and (3) proper pulse density (specified previously). The detection of bipolar violations in the bit stream is a common test but the test equipment must be compatible with the type of zero–code substitution used in order to avoid interpreting intentional violations as errors. When violations are excessive, an error report may be generated and protection switching may be initiated. A loss–of–signal alarm should be initiated when 100 to 250 consecutive zeros are detected in the received signal (after zero–code conversion back to original). Line monitors may be used as part of an automated carrier surveillance system with programmed fault–analysis features.

An out–of–service aid to T1 system maintenance is the fault–location system used to identify which repeater section is causing line troubles. An H88–loaded fault–location pair is required for lines accommodated by each set of apparatus cases (25 repeaters) in each span to provide fault–locating facilities for up to 12 repeater locations. Each location is assigned an interrogation frequency that corresponds to the passband of a common filter connected to each repeater in an apparatus case.

When fault location is carried out, the line under test is removed from service. A fault location test set is used to transmit a test signal from the DSX–1. This test signal includes many bipolar violations, giving a strong VF component that passes through the repeaters and is picked off by the fault–location filter at each repeater point. The test signal is changed to correspond in frequency with the passband of the filter at the repeater under test. The VF signal is returned to the test location over the fault–location pair and is measured by the test set. The faulty repeater section is identified when its single–frequency signal is weak or absent.

A number of other out–of–service tests are employed for T1 system maintenance. These include measurements of transmission pair losses and bipolar violations with a quasi–random bit stream as well as tests of repeater performance.

An order wire is provided on interoffice spans to expedite maintenance. It requires a loaded pair that parallels the digital line. Typically, the order–wire pairs are loaded with 88–mH coils installed in repeater apparatus cases or spliced into the line, as required. Access to the order wire is provided at each repeater location and at both ends of the span. The order wire provides both point–to–point communication and access to the switched message network to aid in maintenance activities. Battery for talking and signalling on the order wire is provided through the order–wire panels located in the central offices at both ends of the span. This panel may be located at the DSX–1 cross–connect frame or ORB.

16-4 THE T1 OUTSTATE DIGITAL LINE

The T1OS (outstate) line uses regular T1 carrier terminals but permits the installation of much longer systems than are possible with conventional applications. The increased length is made possible by the application of more stringent engineering rules to permit operation with up to 200 repeaters in tandem, as well as the use of automatic protection switching. The maximum length of a system, nominally 200 miles, is a function of the quality of individual repeater sections and the permissible repeater spacings. These spacings are dictated by the need to maintain signal amplitudes at values that permit processing by the repeaters and to maintain an adequate signal–to–interference ratio so that errors are few. Screened or dual cables are used whenever possible to eliminate the effects of near–end crosstalk.

16-5 THE T1C DIGITAL LINE

The central office and interoffice outside–plant environments for which the 48–channel T1C (T1 conversion) system was developed are similar to those of the 24–channel T1 system. As a result, there are many similarities between the two systems. The same repeater spacings may be used for T1C, thus facilitating the conversion from T1 to T1C. In addition, the bipolar 50–percent duty cycle signal format is used by both systems and the same transmission media can be used. Regeneration, powering, and maintenance functions are also similar.

While the signal format in the T1C system is similar to that in the T1 system, it differs in one major respect—repetition rate. The T1C system is designed to provide 48 voice–grade channels. To accommodate these channels, the line repetition rate in T1C is 3.152 Mb/s, more than twice the 1.544–Mb/s rate of the T1 system. This greater channel capacity is the main advantage of the T1C system over T1 since much more efficient use is made of cable conductors and ducts. However, the higher cable loss due to the higher frequency of operation requires higher sensitivity in the repeaters and more attention to crosstalk control. T1C is not normally used in loop cables for these reasons.

Transmission Media

The T1C system can generally be used with the same media used for T1 systems, although there is a limitation in the maximum number of pairs that can be equipped in single bidirectional cables. However, with the greater channel capacity of the T1C system, a net channel gain of more than 50 percent can be realized over T1 operation. With two–cable or screened–cable operation, cable pairs can be fully used (with the usual pairs reserved for order wires and fault–locating functions) and a two–to–one increase in capacity per system can be realized with T1C operation.

Crosstalk effects are controlled by strict application of engineering rules regarding segregation of cable pairs, selection of binder groups, and shielding of splices.

T1C Repeater

A T1C regenerator [7] is conceptually similar to the T1 unit in Figure 16–8. The ALBO network and the equalizing amplifier can compensate for cable characteristics and loss in the range of 10 to 53 dB as measured at 1.576 MHz, the peak of the power spectrum. Timing is accomplished by extracting the 3.152–MHz component from the signal by means of a crystal filter.

T1C Line Layout

The design of the span lines for T1C systems is functionally equivalent to that for T1 systems. Repeater spacing rules, maximum route distances, and the number of repeaters housed in an apparatus case are all similar, but T1C rules are more restrictive in setting repeater spacings adjacent to central offices. Up to 250 repeaters, however, can be operated in tandem for T1C.

16-6 THE T1D DIGITAL LINE

Systems exemplified by the 48–channel T1D 3.152–Mb/s system are used for refitting interoffice T1 span lines to increase the number of systems that can be operated in single bidirectional cable, where the more economical T1C systems cannot be used due to near–end crosstalk limitations. This limitation has been made less stringent for T1D, and for the similar systems T148 and 9148, by changing the format of the line signal to reduce the frequency range of its energy spectrum, which reduces the influence of crosstalk. The T1D line format is a duobinary code [8] of three levels, zero, plus, and minus. With this coding, the signal power spectrum peaks at dc with a zero at half the signal rate. Most of the spectrum is contained within one–fourth of the signal rate. This is unlike the T1C signal format (also for 48 channels), which has a spectral peak at half the signal rate. Thus, as the frequency of the band covered by the spectrum for T1D is reduced, the influence of similar–system crosstalk due to capacity coupling between cable pairs is reduced and more T1D systems can be operated in the same cable than T1C systems. However, because susceptibility to interference also has been shifted to lower frequencies, T1D is more sensitive to VF interference and central–office impulse noise than T1C. Up to 200 T1D repeaters can be operated in tandem.

16-7 THE T1G DIGITAL LINE

The 96–channel T1G 3.22175–Mbaud (or 6.4435 Mb/s) system almost doubles the cable capacity over that of T1C lines with few additional engineering restrictions [9]. This was made possible by using a line coding that carried the 96 channels but produced about the same power frequency spectrum as the 48–channel T1C system. The line coding is quaternary (four level), i.e., 2 bits per symbol as shown in Table 16–2. (This code is conceptually similar to the digital subscriber line code in Chapter 3, but the code assignments of the four levels are different.) With the same spectrum, the same crosstalk rules apply and the capacity can be doubled. Up to 200 repeaters can be operated in tandem. Unlike other systems, the T1G span terminating system includes multiplexers that are cabled directly to a DSX–1. As a result, each T1G span line is accessed at the DSX as four DS1s.

Table 16-2. T1G Line Coding (2B1Q)

Binary Bits	Quaternary Level
11	+3 V
01	+1
00	−1
10	−3

The system includes error monitoring at each line repeater and automated fault–location features.

16-8 THE T2 DIGITAL LINE

The extension of digital transmission techniques to distances well beyond a metropolitan area was first realized with the development of the T2 system, which provides 96 DS0 channels for transmission over distances up to about 500 miles with special low–capacitance cable. The required terminal equipment includes D–type channel banks or digital switches with an M12 multiplex unit, or D4 channel banks operating in mode 4 as described in Chapter 15, Part 7.

The T2 system design is similar to the T1 system design in a number of ways. However, there are also substantial differences in signal format, transmission media, repeater design, line layout, and maintenance procedures.

Signal Format

The bit–stream format of the T2 line signal is bipolar, return–to–zero (50–percent duty cycle) with alternate mark inversion. The repetition rate is 6.312 Mb/s. The substitution of the special (B6ZS) code for any succession of six 0s guarantees the presence of enough pulses in the signal to maintain repeater clock operation. It introduces bipolar violations that are used at the receiving terminal as an indication that the special code is to be removed from the signal.

Transmission Media

Although certain of the cables used for T1 and T1C transmission could be used for T2, the higher losses due to the higher repetition rate and the excessive crosstalk would make repeater spacings uneconomically short. To overcome this problem, a special low–capacitance (LOCAP) cable was designed specifically for use with the T2 system. Cables of this design included 27, 52, or 104 conductor pairs of 0.039 μF/mile capacitance. The conductors are dual–expanded polypropylene–insulated 22–gauge copper. Separate cables must be used for opposite directions of transmission. These cable pairs exhibit less loss and lower crosstalk coupling than do conventional cable pairs.

T2 Regenerator

As with other systems, a T2 regenerator [10] performs the functions of pulse reshaping, retiming, and regeneration. A selection of plug–in equalizers must be made to match repeater gain to the LOCAP cable loss in the preceding repeater section. Timing circuit operation is based on the characteristics of the pulse stream. A monolithic crystal filter with a very narrow passband extracts the clock signal.

Line Layout

Repeaters are housed in apparatus cases that may be mounted in underground vaults or on poles. Each apparatus case can house up to 24 one–way regenerators. A protection switching system is provided in which one protection line can protect up to 23 working (or service) lines. The two directions of transmission are protected independently.

Normally, the maximum repeater spacing with underground or buried air–core LOCAP cable is 15,000 feet. This maximum spacing is adjusted downward for sections adjacent to a central office or for those containing aerial cable. Individual repeater sections are engineered to meet a design–number objective similar to that for the T1OS system. The objective for a maximum length system of 250 repeaters is that the error rate should not exceed one error in 10^7 bits in 95 percent of all lines.

16-9 THE T4M DIGITAL TRANSMISSION SYSTEM

The T4M line was designed to carry DS4 signals in an intercity or metropolitan area facility. It took advantage of the transmission characteristics of coaxial cable to provide much greater channel capacity than that possible over paired cable. While no longer in service, it is included here as an example of a particular technology.

Signal Format

T4M transmitted the DS4 signal of the digital hierarchy at 274.176 Mb/s; this rate accommodated 168 multiplexed DS1 signals or 4032 DS0 channels. The system used the 100–percent duty cycle (non–return to zero) unipolar signal because it used the information–carrying capacity of the digital line more efficiently. Figure 16–9 shows unipolar (50–percent duty cycle), bipolar, and T4M unipolar signals for comparison. An analytical comparison of the bipolar and the T4M formats indicated that the T4M format had better error–rate performance [3]. However, scrambling was necessary to allow practical repeater designs.

Transmission Medium

The T4M system was designed to operate over 0.375–inch diameter coaxial cable units. Cables were manufactured with up to 22 of these coaxial units. An 18–unit cable was used in 3–1/2 inch cable ducts, commonly found in older duct runs under city streets, and a 22–unit cable in more modern 4–inch cable ducts. Thus, large channel requirements were fulfilled by T4M systems.

T4M Regenerator

A block diagram of the major functions of the T4M regenerator [11] is shown in Figure 16–10. These are similar to those described previously for the T1D repeater except for the quantized–feedback function used to control dc wander caused by the missing or attenuated dc and low–frequency components of the received signal.

After information signals and power were separated at the input, an equalizer compensated for gross signal distortion

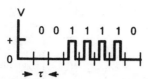

(a) Unipolar signal (50% duty cycle)

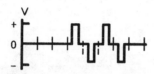

(b) Bipolar signal with alternate pulse
inversion (50% duty cycle)

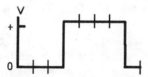

(c) T4M Unipolar signal (100% duty cycle)

τ = time slot

Figure 16–9. T4M signal–format comparison.

introduced by the transmission medium. An ALBO circuit then compensated for temperature changes and for variations in regenerator spacing within a broad range defined by the regenerator code used.

The decision circuit recognized the presence of positive or negative pulses and produced new undistorted pulses. These functions were carried out with the help of the timing and control circuit to provide accurate sampling of the pulse stream in the decision circuit.

The quantized–feedback circuit completed the reshaping of the signal prior to the decision circuit. Filtering resulted in a prescribed attenuation of low–frequency components, which

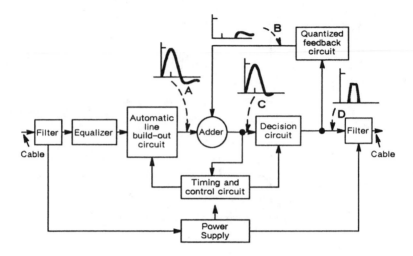

Figure 16–10. T4M regenerator.

produced a negative tail as shown at A in Figure 16–10 (for an isolated pulse). In brief, the quantized feedback circuit inverted the tail, as shown in B, and fed it back at the right time to the decision–circuit input to cancel the unwanted tail. The resulting signal, at C, contained only a negligible amount of intersymbol interference and permitted the generation of a new pulse of the desired characteristics, as shown at D. The new pulse stream and power feed current were recombined at the output for transmission to the next regenerator.

Line Layout

The spacing between T4M regenerators, nominally one mile, could be as much as 5700 feet. System length was limited primarily by powering and maintenance considerations.

References

1. *ANSI T1.403–1989*, "American National Standard for Telecommunications—Carrier–to–Customer Installations, DS1 Metallic Interface Specification" (New York: American National Standards Institute, Feb. 1989).

2. Kaup, T. C., D. G. Leeper, A. K. Reilly, and P. E. Scheffer. "T1 Carrier Measurements—Field Measurement Results," *Bell System Tech. J.*, Vol. 60, No. 6 (Jul./Aug. 1981).

3. Members of Technical Staff. *Transmission Systems for Communications*, Fifth Edition (Murray Hill, NJ: AT&T Bell Laboratories, Inc., 1982), Chapter 30.

4. Bellamy, J. C. *Digital Telephony* (New York: John Wiley and Sons, Inc., 1982), Chapters 4 and 7.

5. Cravis, H. and T. V. Crater. "Engineering of T1 Carrier Repeatered Lines," *Bell System Tech. J.*, Vol. 42, No. 2 (Mar. 1963), pp. 431–486.

6. Mayo, J. S. "Bipolar Repeater for Pulse Code Modulation Signals," *Bell System Tech J.*, Vol. 41 (Jan. 1962), pp. 25–47.

7. Anuff, A. et al. "A New 3.152 Mb/s Digital Repeater," *Conference Record*, IEEE International Conference on Communications (June 1975), Vol. 3, pp. 39–10 to 39–13.

8. Lender, A. "The Duobinary Technique for High–Speed Data Transmission," *IEEE Transactions on Communications and Electronics*, Vol. 82 (May 1963), pp. 214–218.

9. Azaret, J. O. et al. "New, Improved T–Carrier Doubles Capacity, Cuts Costs," *AT&T Bell Laboratories Record*, Vol. 63 (July 1985), pp. 26–31.

10. Tarbox, R. A. "A Regenerative Repeater Utilizing Hybrid Integrated Circuit Technology," *Conference Record*, IEEE International Conference on Communications (1969), pp. 46–5 to 46–10.

11. Waldhauer, F. D. "A 2–Level 274 Mb/s Regenerative Repeater for T4M," *Conference Record*, IEEE International Conference on Communications (June 1975), pp. 48–13 to 48–17.

Telecommunications Transmission Engineering

Section 5

Radio Systems

Microwave systems modulated by digital signals provide a significant amount of the new facilities being installed in interoffice telecommunications networks. The design of these systems, which allows direct interconnection with emerging digital networks, is based on the latest solid–state technology. There are rapid advances in providing systems with more digital capacity in a restricted radio spectrum allocation.

Microwave systems carrying analog frequency division multiplexed signals currently have little application for new facilities. However, some analog microwave systems installed over the past 35 years remain in service. These remaining analog microwave routes are rapidly being converted to digital.

Radio remains the only viable medium for providing effective mobile communications. New technologies and additional frequency allocations provide a society on the move with a mobile service equivalent to the telephone service provided by the conventional public telecommunications network.

Chapter 17 contains a general discussion of the design features of both digital and analog terrestrial microwave radio systems. A brief description of application trends is followed by a characterization of the transmission medium and its impairments. The general transmission layout of radio terminal and repeater equipment is then outlined. The chapter concludes with a consideration of system performance criteria with emphasis on methods for meeting service reliability objectives.

Chapter 18 covers the engineering of terrestrial microwave systems and the routes they traverse. Common–carrier radio–frequency bandwidth allocations and the way these bands are channelized are discussed in detail. The chapter describes the criteria for choosing a specific type of system as well as how those choices relate to the type of application. It also discusses methods of selecting a route and determining the repeater sites in relation to terrain characteristics, atmospheric and path transmission aberrations, and intersystem and intrasystem interference control. Governmental jurisdictions related to microwave route engineering are also noted.

Chapter 19 provides descriptions of common terrestrial analog microwave systems. The system descriptions include various application and design features.

Chapter 20 discusses digital microwave techniques and the characteristics of generally available terrestrial digital systems. It describes special techniques for modulating high–density digital signals onto the radio carriers. The availability and application of adaptive equalizers are covered, as well as the application of digital microwave to digital termination services. The chapter concludes with a view of future trends in digital microwave technology.

Transmission over domestic microwave satellite telecommunications facilities is discussed in Chapter 21, which highlights the differences between satellite and terrestrial microwave systems.

The section concludes with Chapter 22, which covers a number of existing and proposed mobile telecommunications systems. Much of the chapter is devoted to cellular mobile technology, which provides the dominant service in this category. The chapter also describes conventional mobile systems, radio paging, proposed universal digital portable communications, and the application of mobile–type systems in providing service to fixed stations in remote areas.

Chapter 17

Terrestrial Microwave System Design Features

A wide variety of both frequency–division and time–division multiplexed (FDM and TDM) signals are transmitted over terrestrial microwave radio systems in the telecommunication network. The microwave radio frequencies allocated by the Federal Communications Commission (FCC) for common–carrier use include bands near 2, 4, 6, 11, 18, 22, 28, 31, and 39 GHz. These frequency allocations strongly influence many aspects of microwave radio system engineering, design, transmission layout, field of application, and operation. Signals are transmitted on radio channels within the common–carrier bands when and as authorized by the FCC. The channel spectrum of the available bands is used to full capacity in some geographic areas by transmitted multiplexed signals. To eliminate the need for guard bands between the radio channels and thereby maximize usage of the spectrum, the signals in adjacent channels are usually transmitted with orthogonal polarizations.

The state of the technology at the time of the introduction of microwave systems to the telecommunication network over 40 years ago dictated frequency modulation (FM) as the dominant mode of transmission for the analog baseband signals. The standardized channelizing of the common carrier frequency bands was based on the capabilities of these FM systems. Technological advances have greatly increased the circuit–carrying capability of these FM systems within the standardized bands. In the mid 1970s, single–sideband amplitude modulation (SSBAM) systems, which accomplish even greater spectrum efficiency, were introduced. While these SSBAM systems carrying analog baseband signals make efficient use of the frequency spectrum, they do not realize the economies of direct connection to the telecommunication network's digital switching machines and digital transmission facilities.

473

As digital facilities became prevalent in the network, microwave systems were introduced to carry digital baseband signals. While these initial digital microwave systems allowed the coveted direct digital network interconnection, the modulation techniques used allowed only a very limited number of voice channels within the allocated bandwidth. Because of the poor spectrum utilization of these systems, the FCC authorized only limited application. More recently, technological advances have led to sophisticated modulation schemes, such as quadrature amplitude modulation (QAM), which allow the digital microwave systems to provide equivalent voice channels within the allocated bandwidth comparable to the number provided in available FM systems. The economies realized by these high–capacity systems have assured the installation of digital systems on virtually all new microwave installations. These high–capacity digital systems are replacing analog systems on a programmed basis as the network becomes more and more digital.

The principal components of any microwave radio system are the transmission medium, terminal equipment, repeaters, and entrance facilities. Numerous interactive design considerations must precede the careful integration of these components in providing facilities that interconnect and meet the performance criteria of the telecommunications network.

17-1 THE TRANSMISSION MEDIUM

In microwave radio systems, the transmission medium may be regarded as including the atmosphere, the transmitting and receiving antennas at repeater points and terminals, and the waveguide components that connect the antennas to the repeater or terminal equipment. The general characteristics of these components of the medium are discussed in Chapter 2. The effects of these characteristics on system design features depend somewhat on the frequency bands transmitted, the nature of the radio repeaters, and the performance requirements appropriate to the field of application.

Transmission Medium Impairments

The control of transmission impairments is quite different depending on their origin, whether in the atmosphere, antennas, or waveguides. In every case, the methods used to control and minimize the effects of impairments continue to evolve as performance criteria become more stringent [1].

Microwave radio transmission normally requires a line–of–sight path between transmitting and receiving antennas. When the atmosphere is well mixed and adequate clearance is provided between the line–of–sight path and potential obstacles, the transmission loss is highly predictable and stable. However, when different strata of atmospheric temperatures and humidities exist, components of the direct signal and reflections interact to reduce or increase the net received signal amplitude. This phenomenon is called fading.

Fading that covers the entire frequency spectrum of a route is referred to as flat fading. Dispersive or multipath is a type of fading that is frequency–selective, affecting only one or two radio channels at any one time. The depth of fade varies widely and, in some instances, causes a complete failure of transmission in one or more channels for short periods of time. Due to the characteristics of frequency modulation, FM analog systems can tolerate different amplitude levels across a single transmitter channel. However, SSBAM and high–capacity digital systems are very vulnerable to amplitude variations within a channel. Various techniques are used to compensate for the effects of fading and to prevent loss of service.

Systems that operate at frequencies higher than 10 GHz, where raindrop size is an appreciable fraction of a wavelength, encounter variations in attenuation due to absorption and scattering. Service may be seriously impaired by heavy rainfall. The repeater spacings for such systems tend to be shorter than in lower frequency systems and are thus less susceptible to multipath fading. At 18 GHz and above, rain attenuation and scattering are the dominant media impairments.

Antenna impairments result from using an unsuitable antenna type, departures from design specifications, damage, or improper orientation. An antenna commonly used for terrestrial microwave radio transmission is the horn reflector [2]. This antenna provides high gain, a narrow transmitted beam, the ability to transmit both horizontal and vertical signal polarizations, and a wide bandwidth that permits the simultaneous transmission of signals in the 4–, 6–, and 11–GHz bands. Other systems may be equipped with parabolic "dish" antennas. If the proper feed method is selected, this type of antenna can also be used for simultaneously transmitting two polarizations in one or two frequency bands.

The wide bandpass characteristic of the horn reflector results in little delay distortion across the allocated frequency bands. At the frequencies for which it is designed, the horn reflector confines the bulk of the radiated energy to a beam two degrees wide or less. The transmitting and receiving antennas must be precisely aligned because departure from proper alignment causes excessive path loss, increases the delay distortion significantly, and reduces the cross–polarization discrimination.

Microwave antennas are usually mounted at or near the tops of high buildings or towers to provide adequate clearance in the line–of–sight paths. Horn reflector antennas are usually connected to the radio repeater or terminal equipment by circular waveguide of such a diameter (2.81 inches) that it can transmit 4–, 6–, and 11–GHz signals of both horizontal and vertical polarizations. Parabolic antennas are generally fed by rectangular or elliptical waveguide to a point near the antenna where there is a transition to the antenna feed arrangement.

The major sources of impairment in the waveguide portion of the transmission medium are the joints between waveguide sections, connections to the antenna feedhorn, waveguide bends, flexible waveguide sections, and system–combining networks. The impedance discontinuities that may occur at these points result in system degradation. Thus, stringent return–loss requirements are imposed on all individual waveguide sections and components. For this reason, the mechanical alignment of all the pieces that make up a waveguide system must be precise. Irregularities due to foreign matter inside the waveguide or to dents or other imperfections on the inside surface must also be avoided.

17-2 TERMINALS AND REPEATERS

A diagram of a generalized microwave terminal is illustrated in Figure 17–1 with (a) showing the transmitter and (b) the

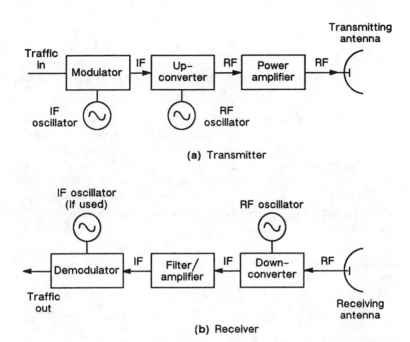

(a) Transmitter

(b) Receiver

Figure 17-1. Generalized microwave terminal.

receiver. Input telecommunication traffic enters the transmitter and is modulated by an intermediate frequency (IF). An IF is used in microwave systems because it is not usually practical to provide the necessary amplification at microwave frequencies for the low-level signals at the receiver input. Amplification at IF (nominally 70 MHz), however, is practical and economical. The IF is upconverted to a microwave carrier frequency and, after going to a transmitter power amplifier, is transmitted via the antenna. The received signal enters the antenna and is mixed with a radio-frequency (RF) carrier to produce the IF. After filtering and amplification, the IF enters the demodulator, which recovers the output baseband telecommunication traffic.

With the exception of filter responses and output drive levels, analog and digital microwave terminals are very similar, from the transmitter IF through the transmission medium to the receiver IF. The major differences between analog and digital microwave systems occur in the modulators and demodulators. Analog

477

systems generally use conventional FM techniques to modulate/ demodulate an IF with an analog baseband signal. Digital microwave systems, on the other hand, generally use techniques such as quaternary phase shift keying (QPSK) or QAM to modulate the IF with a baseband digital signal.

Figure 17–2 shows a diagram of a generalized microwave repeater. The signal is received by the microwave antenna, filtered, and downconverted to IF (again nominally 70 MHz). After either amplification or regeneration (depending on whether it is an analog or a digital system) at IF, the signal is again upconverted to RF. The RF signal is then amplified and transmitted. A duplicate set of equipment is required for the other direction of transmission.

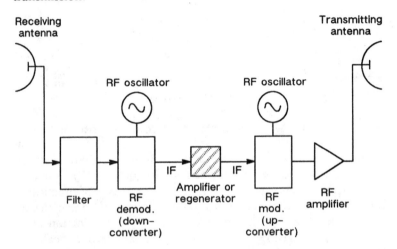

Figure 17–2. Generalized microwave repeater.

Where an obstruction prevents a direct microwave path between two points, it is sometimes possible to establish a passive repeater to redirect the microwave beam. The most common type of passive repeater is a flat "billboard" metal reflector, which acts as a microwave mirror. Line–of–sight paths with adequate clearance must be established between the passive repeater and each of the end points.

A generalized arrangement for using a common antenna for microwave transmitters and receivers sharing the same path is shown in Figure 17–3. This arrangement, which can be used at both terminals and repeaters, uses selective bandpass filters and ferrite waveguide circulators.

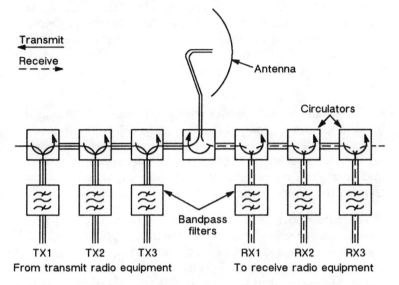

Figure 17–3. Generalized common antenna arrangement.

Modern terrestrial microwave terminal and repeater equipment is all solid–state with the exception of a traveling wave tube amplifier, which is required in some applications. Many systems that once used triode or klystron tubes have been refitted to solid–state microwave amplifiers. This equipment and some microwave systems that deviate from the generalized models shown are discussed in some detail in Chapters 19 and 20.

17–3 ENTRANCE FACILITIES

Radio–frequency circuits and equipment are usually located in proximity to the associated antennas, but are often physically removed from signal sources for the radio system. In metropolitan areas, associated microwave transmitting and receiving equipment is located nearby on one of the highest floors of the building. Other equipment, such as multiplex, is likely to be located on one of the lower floors of the structure or even in a nearby building; the radio equipment and signal sources may thus be several hundred feet apart. In suburban and rural areas, the antennas are normally mounted on high towers with the RF equipment at the base of the tower. The distance to the signal source is typically several hundred feet and may be eight miles or more in extreme cases. The facilities that interconnect the baseband signal sources, called "entrance facilities," must be designed to meet stringent transmission, reliability, and operating requirements.

The signals transmitted over microwave radio systems originate in various types of equipment. The design of entrance facilities depends on the characteristics of the source equipment as well as on the characteristics of the signals. Sources include multiplex and connector equipment, video circuits, digital cross–connect frames, and direct connections from other systems.

The baseband signals most commonly transmitted on microwave radio systems are those generated in the FDM and TDM equipment described in Chapters 9 and 15. Similar signals are also used as radio system inputs by connection from an adjacent or intersecting broadband route. In this case, the signal may be a composite signal made up of a portion of a signal from another route and of signals generated in local multiplex equipment. Filters, combining networks, and separating networks are arranged to form a signal spectrum compatible with the radio system involved.

In some microwave terminal locations, it is undesirable to use the normal transmission mode because of existing or potential interference problems. One such situation may occur where a radio route terminates at the earth station of a satellite communications system. The terrestrial system may induce excessive interference into the satellite system. Another situation may occur where a radio route traverses a congested urban area in which new building construction may obstruct the transmission path. Alternate routing of the radio path may be expensive or perhaps impossible. In these cases, the radio system might be terminated at the last repeater before the normal terminal. The last section would then consist of an entrance link to the terminal location. Sometimes an IF entrance link on fiber or coaxial cable is the most economical solution.

Analog Entrance Links

Analog baseband wire–line entrance link (WLEL) equipment is available to satisfy the needs where microwave radio systems carry FDM signals. This WLEL provides a wide range of options that make it applicable to most analog microwave radio systems under a variety of loading and operating conditions. Figure 17–4 gives a simplified schematic of a WLEL arrangement.

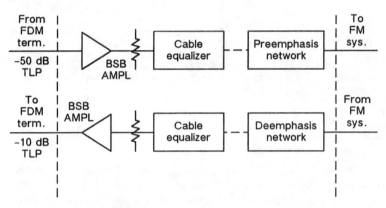

Figure 17–4. Simplified schematic of a baseband wire–line entrance link.

The amplifiers, equalizers, and other frequency–dependent components have been designed to operate with a number of cable types having insertion losses that increase in proportion to the square root of frequency. Components are selected for compatibility with the type and length of cable to be used and with the channel capacity of the radio system being served. Entrance links may include intermediate repeaters as well as terminal equipment located at the multiplex and radio ends. Typical distance limits, as shown in Table 17–1, depend on cable types and channel capacity of the served radio system.

Digital Entrance Links

On light–route digital microwave systems where a DS1 rate is applied to the radio, a T1 line provides a practical, economical entrance facility. There are several entrance link options for the more common heavy–route digital microwave systems that accept

Table 17-1. Length Limits for a Typical WLEL

Cable		Nonrepeatered WLEL (miles)		Repeatered WLEL (miles)
Description	Z (ohms)	1200 Channels	1800 Channels	Up to 1800 Channels
724-type unbalanced	75	0.5	0.5	NA
754-type balanced	124	0.5	0.5	NA
16 PEVL balanced	124	2.81	1.92	3.84
0.375-in coaxial unbalanced	75	5.85	4.0	8.0

one or more DS3 rate signals. Solid dielectric coaxial cable can be used to transmit the DS3 signal up to 900 feet. Long DS3 links can be provided by 45-Mb/s fiber optic systems. Details of these fiber optic systems are covered in Chapter 16.

Video Entrance Links

Satisfactory digital transmission of broadcast-quality video signals generally requires a digital line rate of DS3 or higher and the transmission of high-quality video in a digital format requires special arrangements that are still emerging. Many video circuits therefore are carried on analog microwave. Entrance links for these analog video microwave systems normally use one of the baseband video transmission systems described in Chapter 6.

17-4 PERFORMANCE CONSIDERATIONS

The determination of a transmission layout of microwave radio systems that meet performance objectives involves many considerations. Among these are transmitter power output, receiver noise figure, and route layout to provide line-of-sight transmission with adequate clearance from obstacles. Achievable noise and bit error performance, system bandwidth, adequate channel capacity, and RF channel allocations also need to be considered. In addition, transmission and reliability objectives consistent with system application must be well documented and properly applied. This documentation requires continuing analysis of definitions and measurement methods [3].

Radio repeater spacings are determined primarily by line–of–sight path clearance, the signal strength required at the receiver, and the geographical locations of points where access is needed for connection to multiplex equipment or other systems. In relatively flat terrain, an increase in path length dictates an increase in antenna tower height, which is thus an economic factor in repeater site selection. Transmitter power output and antenna gain similarly affect the economics of selection, but the performance of radio systems is not as sensitive a function of the repeater spacing as the performance of cable systems. The primary reason for this lies in the transmission medium. Cable loss is measured or expressed directly in dB per mile; doubling a length of cable multiplies its loss in dB by two. On the other hand, radio path loss varies as 20 times the log of the path length. Therefore, doubling a path length increases its loss only 6 dB. It follows, then, that there is greater flexibility in the choice of repeater spacings in a radio system than in cable systems where a specific spacing is determined by repeater performance, transmission characteristics of the medium, and system noise requirements. In a radio system, the problem involves tower economics, geography, fading or rain attenuation, interferences, and system noise or bit error requirements. These factors result in typical 4– and 6–GHz microwave repeater spacings of 20 to 30 miles and shorter spacings at 11–GHz and above.

Noise and Bit Errors

The concept of establishing optimum signal amplitudes between an overload and a noise "floor" (discussed in Chapter 10, Part 3) is applied in the design of microwave radio systems as well as in the design of analog wire transmission systems. However, bandwidth, repeater spacing, and signal–to–noise ratio are not nearly as closely related in radio systems as in wire systems.

483

The maximum signal amplitude may be considered in terms of the radiated power of the RF wave. Limits on transmitted power and frequency deviation are imposed by the Rules and Regulations of the FCC.

The minimum allowable RF signal amplitude at the input to a repeater is set by the receiver noise floor. This noise floor depends on a combination of the noise at the input to the receiver and the random noise generated within the repeater.

A system is designed to operate with a "normal" signal at the receiver that is 35 or 40 dB above a minimum received signal that renders a message circuit unusable. System signal/noise and bit error performance are defined on the basis of this normal signal. Automatic gain control (AGC) circuits in the receiver compensate for differences between this normal signal and the minimum signal, and allow a system to stay in service during atmospheric fades that do not drop the signal below the minimum level. Thus the difference between the normal level and the minimum level is defined as fade margin.

Fades of magnitude less than the fade margin will gradually deteriorate signal/noise performance, thus increasing message channel noise on analog systems. Figure 17–5 shows the gradual increase in message–circuit noise on an analog microwave path as the received signal drops from the normal level to the minimum usable level. The figure also shows that error performance (and thus voice–channel noise) does not deteriorate on a properly equalized digital microwave system until the fade margin is reached. Thus, there is little forewarning on digital systems as the fade approaches the point where all circuits are lost.

The noise performance of analog microwave systems is often evaluated experimentally by a technique called noise loading. This technique may be used to determine system performance. The performance of digital microwave systems can be evaluated experimentally by applying fade simulation along with additive noise while measuring bit errors.

Service Continuity

Several protection switching arrangements are used at terminals and repeaters to provide continuity of service when received

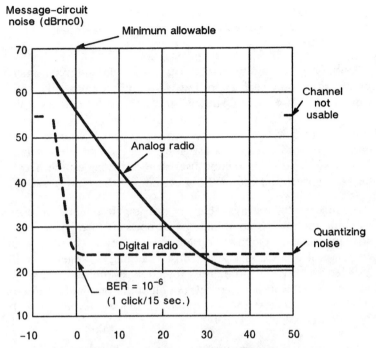

Figure 17-5. Effects of microwave signal on message-circuit noise.

signals drop below the minimum level allowable. They operate automatically to protect against equipment failure and atmospheric fading. They may also be controlled manually to facilitate maintenance of working radio channels, to provide for part-time or incidental television transmission of special events, or to effect emergency broadband restoration. In some arrangements, automatic switching is initiated by AGC circuits; in others, the switching is initiated by an increase of noise beyond an established threshold level, or by the loss of RF carrier power. Digital microwave systems usually switch on the loss of framing or excessive bit errors. The protection channel may be at a different position in the RF spectrum than the channel in trouble (frequency diversity switching), or may be at the same frequency as that of the channel in trouble but received from a separate antenna system at a different height (space diversity), or may be on the same frequency but use a separate antenna feed from a different azimuth (angle diversity).

Frequency Diversity Switching. Since fading phenomena usually affect only certain portions of the microwave radio spectrum (one or two radio channels) at a time, automatic switching arrangements are often used to transfer service during deep fades from the assigned RF channel to a protection channel. This mode of operation requires assigning a portion of the available microwave band to protection use; stringent rules established by the FCC govern the use of the spectrum for these purposes [4].

Arrangements are available to provide frequency diversity switching for various combinations or portions of microwave radio transmission systems. Those most commonly used operate over several repeater sections. Most switching arrangements are designed to provide intraband protection switching (where the protection and working channels are all at the nominal 4–, 6–, or 11–GHz frequencies); however, some provide interband switching called crossband diversity.

Some protection arrangements switch at IF while others are arranged to protect an entire radio channel from baseband input to baseband output, including entrance links and radio terminal equipment. Systems are available in which a protection channel protects just one working channel; others are available in which one protection channel protects several working channels.

Figure 17–6 shows a simplified diagram of a typical frequency diversity switching arrangement in which one protection channel protects two working channels in a single repeater switching section. The received signals of all channels are monitored at the output of the receivers. Substandard performance on either of the working channels results in the control logic initiating a switch to the protection channel. The process is reversed when the monitoring equipment detects that the affected channel is again operating better than the accepted threshold (revertive switching). Note that the transmitter switch is initiated over a control channel that must be independent of the channel being protected. This independence can be assured by using an external facility or a separate protection scheme for the control channel.

The switch threshold is set to anticipate a worsening problem before it develops into an outage; a make–before–break switch then assures no service interruption.

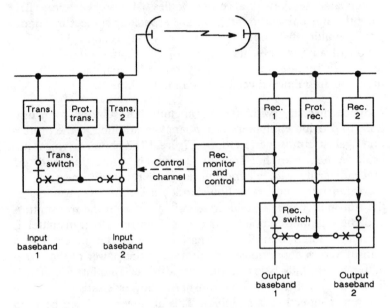

Figure 17-6. Simplified diagram of a typical 1:2 frequency diversity switching arrangement.

Space Diversity and Hot–Standby Switching. Frequency congestion and FCC rules, which limit the permissible number of frequency diversity protection channels, make space diversity a viable technique for application on some routes or paths. The effectiveness of space diversity switching depends on the exploitation of the structure of the electromagnetic fields of a radio wave at the receiving point in a point–to–point radio repeater section. Two vertically separated receiving antennas are mounted on the same tower. The regular antenna is usually mounted near or on the top of the tower, with the diversity antenna mounted lower. The outputs from the two antennas are combined in a proper phase relationship. The nature of fading phenomena is such that only on rare occasions does a signal suffer from destructive multipath interference at both antennas when they are properly spaced [5,6]. Horizontal antenna separation will

487

produce the same advantage, thus horizontal space diversity is sometimes also a viable option [7].

Repeater sections that cross bodies of water or very flat, smooth, and barren countryside are especially subject to atmospheric multipath fading. These sections may require the optimization of antenna heights. High–capacity digital microwave systems may require space diversity on individual paths within a multihop frequency diversity switching section.

Space diversity switching may include hot–standby configurations to provide equipment redundancy in addition to the protection against atmospheric fading. Figure 17–7 shows a typical microwave hop with hot–standby equipment protection and 1:1 space diversity with all transmitters and receivers operating on the same frequency. The hot–standby switching arrangement at the transmitter uses a solid–state switch between the transmitters and the channel combining network. The unused transmitter is normally routed to an RF termination. The output power of both transmitters is continuously monitored. If the power of the transmitter in use falls below normal by a preset amount, a switch is initiated and, if the standby transmitter power is satisfactory, the antenna connection is switched. This arrangement may be used in either a revertive (return–to–normal) or nonrevertive mode. Manual switching and lockout can be made by means of a switch

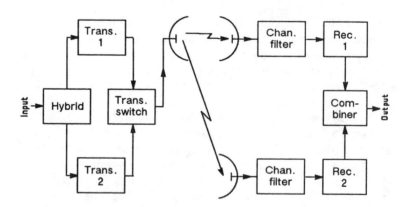

Figure 17–7. A typical 1:1 space diversity and hot–standby switching arrangement.

control circuit. At the receiver location, the signals from the regular antenna and the diversity antenna are applied to separate channel filters and receivers. From the receivers, they are applied simultaneously to a combiner, which maintains proper phase relationships during fading conditions.

Angle Diversity. It has recently been demonstrated that angle diversity using a dual–beam parabolic antenna can be effective in reducing the effects of multipath fading [8]. In angle diversity, two antenna beams are slightly separated in their vertical elevation. The performance improvement is a result of the difference and variation of the phase and amplitude of the two signals as a consequence of their different angles of arrival. In addition to using a dual–beam antenna, angle diversity can be attained by similar antennas side by side with slightly different elevation angles. Antennas at the same elevation with different radiation patterns produce similar results [7].

With appropriate combining and switching techniques, angle diversity can provide performance improvement over more conventional space diversity arrangements on routes where the performance is limited by frequency–selective fading. This performance advantage, combined with the economies of a single antenna, suggest that angle diversity may be more frequently employed for future systems' applications.

References

1. Coutts, R. P., M. Liniger, and W. D. Rummler. "Multipath Fading Channel Models for Microwave Digital Radio," *IEEE Communications Magazine*, Vol. 24, No. 11 (Nov. 1986), pp. 30–42.

2. Friis, R. W. and A. S. May. "A New Broadband Microwave Antenna System," *Electrical Engineering* (June 1958), pp. 502–506.

3. Greenstein, L. J. and M. Shafi. "Outage Calculation Methods for Microwave Digital Radio," *IEEE Communications Magazine*, Vol. 25, No. 2 (Feb. 1987), pp. 30–37.

4. Federal Communications Commission. *Rules and Regulations, Title 47, Code of Federal Regulations, Part 21*

(Washington, DC: U.S. Government Printing Office, Oct. 1987), Section 21.100(c).

5. Bullington, K. "Unlocking the Secrets of Microwave Propagation," *Bell Laboratories Record*, Vol. 50 (Jan. 1972), pp. 8–13.

6. Vigants, A. "Space Diversity Engineering," *Bell System Tech. J.*, Vol. 54 (Jan. 1975), pp. 103–142.

7. Gardina, M. F., T. C. Lee, and S. H. Lin. "Diversity Protections for Digital Radio—Summary of Ten–Year Experiments and Studies," *IEEE Communications Magazine*, Vol. 26, No. 2 (Feb. 1988), pp. 51–64.

8. Alley, G. D., A. J. Giger, and E. H. Linn. "Angle Diversity on Line–of–Sight Microwave Paths Using Dual–Beam Antennas," *Conference Record*, IEEE International Conference on Communications (1987), pp. 0831–0841.

Chapter 18

Terrestrial Microwave System Engineering

Facility planning studies based on forecasts of network growth and restructuring or specific orders for wideband services often indicate the need for new point–to–point microwave radio systems and routes. Engineering studies are then used to determine the radio–frequency (RF) band to be used and the type of system to be installed. Most new systems are installed on the many existing microwave routes. However, if a new route is required, specific locations of terminal and intermediate stations must be determined.

In addition to these overall studies, much detailed work is required to establish the specific route and to determine the system layout along the route. In this aspect of the work, studies must be made of both real and potential interferences into the new system from outside sources and by the new system into existing systems. On new routes, specific repeater sites must be selected and the required heights of antenna towers determined. Consideration must also be given to reliable sources of ac power and accessibility for maintenance.

18-1 OPERATING FREQUENCIES AND SYSTEM CHARACTERISTICS

The Federal Communications Commission (FCC) has allocated frequency bands for common–carrier transmission use at nominal frequencies of 2, 4, 6, 11, 18, 22, 28, 31, and 39 GHz. The total allocations and the maximum per–channel bandwidth are shown in Table 18–1. Systems are generally available for use in each of the available bands through 22 GHz. Currently there is increasing application in the bands above 11 GHz.

2-GHz Band

Common-carrier system signals are limited to two 20-MHz wide bands between 2.110 and 2.180 GHz. The limited telephone channel capacity, the complications of sharing the frequency band with other users, and FCC-imposed limitations on 2-GHz systems have made these allocations relatively unattractive to exchange carriers. However, low-capacity systems are in use to provide light-route facilities to remote areas and alarm facilities for other systems. These systems are available from several suppliers.

Table 18-1. Common-Carrier Frequency Allocations

Band (GHz)	Band Edges (GHz)	Total Bandwidth (MHz)	Maximum Per-Channel Bandwidth (MHz)
2	2.11 - 2.13	20	3.5
	2.16 - 2.18	20	3.5
4	3.7 - 4.2	500	20
6	5.925 - 6.425	500	30
11	10.55 - 10.68	130	2.5
	10.7 - 11.7	1000	40
18	17.7 - 19.7	2000	220
22	21.225 - 22.975	750	100
31	31.0 - 31.3	300	50
39	38.6 - 40.0	1400	50

4-GHz Band

With a 20-MHz-per-channel limit in the 500-MHz bandwidth, the 4-GHz band accommodates 12 two-way radio channels. The standardized frequency assignments for the 4-GHz band are illustrated in Figure 18-1. The two-way channels are numbered 1 to 12. The two frequency bands used for each channel are designated A and B, with A always assigned to the lower-frequency channel. At adjacent repeaters, transmitter and receiver assignments are interchanged. The frequencies shown at the right of the figure are the center frequencies of the

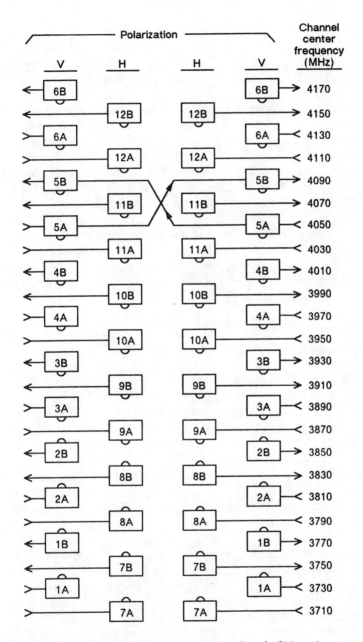

Figure 18-1. Standard frequency plan for 4-GHz microwave systems.

493

RF channels. In the figure, a half–round symbol on top of one of the channel symbols indicates that the receiver local oscillator is normally above the channel frequency; a half–round below denotes an oscillator below the channel frequency.

Long–haul common–carrier microwave routes (which started in the early 1950s) make extensive use of the 4–GHz band to the point of exhausting available 4–GHz frequency assignments in many major metropolitan areas of the United States. Coordination with satellite earth stations further limits the application of 4–GHz systems. Systems in operation are for the most part AT&T TD–type analog and digital systems.

Various suppliers now have digital microwave systems available with a capacity of up to two DS3 lines (1344 message circuits) in the 20–MHz channel bandwidth. These systems can be used in areas where frequency congestion is not a problem or to convert existing analog systems to digital.

6–GHz Band

The nominal 6–GHz band uses frequencies between 5.925 and 6.425 GHz. This 500–MHz band is divided into eight pairs of 30–MHz channels, which have for some time been used for analog frequency modulation (FM) microwave systems with capacity for up to 2400 message circuits. Later, analog single–sideband amplitude modulation (SSBAM) microwave systems have been applied with capacity for 6000 message circuits per allocated RF channel. Table 18–2 lists the normal standard 6–GHz channel assignments. Alternate 6–GHz frequency plans are available, which facilitate the resolution of interference problems.

Most recently, digital microwave systems in the 6–GHz band with a capacity of up to three DS3 lines (2016 voice channels) in the allocated 30 MHz of bandwidth have become available. These have become the predominant systems to be installed for common–carrier growth and the replacement of analog microwave systems. They are available from several suppliers and incorporate a number of options and features, as well as employ the latest solid–state microwave technology.

494

Table 18-2. Normal Standard 6-GHz Frequency Plan

Channel Designation	Frequency (MHz)	Channel Designation	Frequency (MHz)
11T	5945.20	21T	6197.24
12T	5974.85	22T	6226.89
13T	6004.50	23T	6256.54
14T	6034.15	24T	6286.19
15T	6063.80	25T	6315.84
16T	6093.45	26T	6345.49
17T	6123.10	27T	6375.14
18T	6152.75	28T	6404.79

11-GHz Band

The 11-GHz common-carrier band provides frequency space for 12 pairs of 40-MHz radio channels between 10.7 and 11.7 GHz. The standard frequency plan for these channels is shown in Table 18-3. Rain attenuation forces shorter repeater spacings for 11-GHz systems in most areas of the country, which tend to make the routes more expensive than those at 4 or 6 GHz. However, frequency congestion at the lower frequencies has resulted in considerable application of 11-GHz systems. Available analog FM microwave systems provide up to 2400 message circuits in the 40-MHz allocated bandwidth. However, virtually all new 11-GHz systems being installed are digital with capacity for three DS3 lines.

18-GHz Band

The spectrum allocated to common-carrier use at 18 GHz extends from 17.7 to 19.7 GHz. Pairs of 5-, 10-, 20-, 40-, 80-, and 220-MHz RF channels have been allocated by the FCC. With rain attenuation generally limiting the microwave hop lengths to less than 5 miles, these systems are generally more expensive than fiber optic systems; therefore, they have limited application. Less expensive, lower-capacity systems are being used as frequency congestion problems at 4, 6, and even 11 GHz

Table 18-3. Standard 11-GHz Frequency Plan

Regular Plan, Channel Pairs			
Channel No.	Frequency (MHz)	Channel No.	Frequency (MHz)
1P	10,755	2J	11,685
2P	10,955	1J	11,405
3P	10,995	4J	11,445
4P	10,715	3J	11,645
5P	11,155	6J	11,605
6P	10,875	5J	11,325
7P	10,915	8J	11,365
8P	11,115	7J	11,565
9P	11,075	10J	11,525
10P	10,795	9J	11,245
11P	10,835	12J	11,285
12P	11,035	11J	11,485

become more acute in the large metropolitan areas. The same pertains to 23 GHz, which is useful for cross–campus or inter-building applications over short hops.

18-2 CHOICE OF SYSTEM

Virtually all new routes use systems that carry digital signals in order to realize the economies of direct interconnection to digital facilities and switching machines. Economic factors involved with the installation of new switching systems as well as the activation of new digital networks such as the integrated services digital network (ISDN) are expediting the conversion of existing analog routes to digital. The selection of the type of digital system to be used requires engineering studies of route factors, type of application, and performance objectives. In addition, the selection of the RF band to be used interrelates with all other considerations and ultimately leads to the most appropriate system type.

Some of the route factors that influence the system choice include length, initial and ultimate channel capacity, interference or potential interference between intersecting routes, and the existence of other systems along the route. Geographical and environmental factors also influence the choice of system; for example, site–to–site antenna visibility or rain attenuation may be controlling factors. The system may require frequent or infrequent dropping and adding of channels at intermediate points. Error performance of the various systems, particularly regarding transmitter output power and the path losses that may be expected along the planned route, must be considered. The transmission band selected tends to determine the specific system choice but it must be chosen to satisfy all the other criteria.

The route length, required channel cross–section, and the existing or potential congestion of frequency bands all have an influence on system selection. In addition, the selection of a system may be influenced by corporate policy, which might dictate route diversity, the provision of a separate route, or use of a different type of transmission facility between the route terminals in order to provide greater service reliability or network survivability.

Additional capacity may possibly be provided on existing routes by under– or overbuilding. These terms are used to describe the addition of a second radio system sharing the land, buildings, towers, antennas, waveguides, and power supplies of the existing system. The new system must operate in a different portion of the radio–frequency spectrum. The existing route must be equipped with broadband (dual–frequency) antennas and band–combining networks. For example, a 6–GHz system might be added to a route already equipped with 4–GHz systems and an 11–GHz system might be used to overbuild an existing route equipped with 4– and 6–GHz systems.

The selection of the new system is influenced by the anticipated growth along the route as well as the immediate augmentation of service. Anticipated growth is especially pertinent since the FCC regulations impose stringent requirements on the ratio of protection channels to regular channels. Thus, selection is influenced by the total channel capacity required, its relation to the total system capacity, the ease with which the growth can be accommodated by equipping additional radio channels, and the costs associated with each of these factors.

In longer systems, performance and costs tend to be dominated by repeater equipment rather than by terminal and multiplex equipment. In shorter applications, repeater equipment has less influence on system performance and costs. Thus, the layout of the equipment is often dictated by the need for flexibility in dropping and adding circuits at intermediate points.

The selection of the RF band is made for consistency with all of the other route factors previously discussed. The overriding considerations are likely to be the result of propagation and interference studies and the interaction between these factors and the selection of suitable repeater sites. When the technical requirements have been satisfied, the final system selection is based on cost.

18-3 ROUTE SELECTION AND LAYOUT

The establishment of a final route layout for a new system and the precise specifications for locating each required repeater constitute the most important and, in some ways, the most difficult aspect of microwave system engineering. Signal propagation must be studied carefully to give reasonable assurance that the appropriate objectives can be met. Interference studies are made to give assurance that intra- and intersystem interferences are held to specific limits.

Repeater sites must be selected to satisfy transmission and interference requirements. After sites have been selected, antenna towers are designed and placed to satisfy operating and environmental requirements. In addition, governmental agencies exert considerable influence on radio system layout; the requirements imposed by these agencies must be met.

All of these facets of route selection and layout are highly interactive and requirements must all be simultaneously satisfied. The process is iterative and successive compromises must be made in order to establish a satisfactory overall system [1].

Site Selection

Route layout is started with a preliminary selection of several alternate radio repeater sites based on acceptable paths from all

498

existing terminals and proposed junctions with other routes. Proposed frequency selections are made based on the standard channelizing plans shown in Figures 18–1, Tables 18–2 and 18–3, and the frequencies already in use on adjacent routes. The normal frequency arrangement is the so–called two–frequency arrangement using a single antenna for each route direction from a terminal or intermediate repeater station. In the two–frequency arrangement, the same radio channel frequencies, one for transmitting and one for receiving, are used at each station for the opposite directions of a two–way radio channel. Signals in like–numbered channels received from opposite directions at a repeater station are horizontally and vertically polarized to minimize interferences. Channel pairs and polarizations are reversed at successive repeaters. The frequency selection is completed based on RF interference objectives, which involve complex relationships among many factors. Tabulation of these objectives are available for many combinations of signal loadings, RF stability, channel frequency separation, type of signal (digital, video, or frequency–division multiplexed), and application of preemphasis and deemphasis to the baseband signal. By properly accounting for output powers, antenna gains, antenna discriminations, path losses, and frequency separations, new paths that satisfy intersystem interference requirements may be established.

After the sites for the repeater stations closest to the terminals and junction points along the route have been tentatively selected, the other intermediate sites are similarly selected and a route layout map is prepared as illustrated in Figure 18–2. Note that the repeater sites are selected so that the route zigzags to minimize interferences from within the new system due to "overreach," the transmission from one station to another far removed. Overreach may occur as a result of unusual atmospheric conditions or lack of terrain blockage. In the preliminary selection of the intermediate sites, RF interference between the new route and other nearby or crossing routes must also be considered.

The factors that determine the desirability of a repeater site are numerous and varied. Among the most important are drainage, soil characteristics, visibility and grade of access road, exposure to hazards or undesirable neighboring property, proximity to major highways that might be subject to construction or

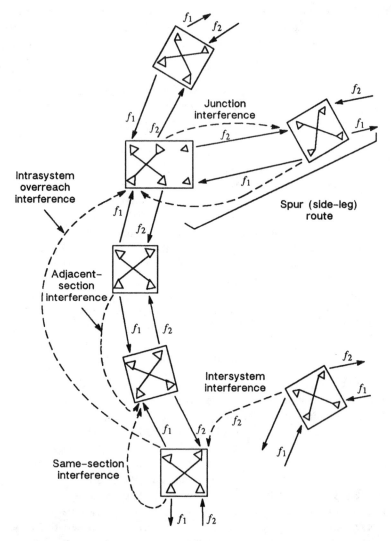

Figure 18–2. Microwave route layout showing interference paths.

relocation, possibility of flooding, area of land available, and relative location of power and telephone lines. Consideration must be given to local zoning and land–use laws and to legal requirements on building and tower construction.

After an option to buy or lease has been obtained, each site must be surveyed. Magnetic and true bearings must be shown and true north must be indicated to an accuracy of ± 1 degree. The spherical coordinates of the proposed tower location must be determined to an accuracy of one second of latitude and longitude. The survey results are used to check elevation of the tower location. Detailed information of this type and accuracy is required by the FCC for its records.

The size of the site depends on the type of station and the required height of the tower. Adequate consideration must be given to the type of construction to be used so that, to the extent possible, the buildings and tower blend into the surroundings. Adequate clearance must be provided between the buildings and abutting properties and highways or roads. Provision must be made for vehicle parking.

Where other criteria are satisfied equally, the final selection of a repeater site may well be related to accessibility for maintenance and availability of power for the repeater operation. Investigation and record should be made of unusual weather in the environs. The amount of snow and rain, wind characteristics, and range of temperatures may all have an impact on system operation and maintenance.

After the desired sites have been agreed upon from all points of view, site purchase activities are started. When title is obtained for all sites, construction work may be started provided approval has been obtained from the FCC for the construction of the route and, where necessary, from the Federal Aviation Administration (FAA) for tower construction.

Path Transmission Characteristics

When engineering a new microwave route, it is necessary to make transmission calculations and determine propagation effects that might be encountered. After preliminary sites have been chosen and a frequency and polarization plan selected, terrain profile studies and measurements must be made. Path propagation tests may be made along the route, studies of weather data must be undertaken, and fade margins must be determined.

Terrain Profile Studies. After preliminary selections of repeater sites have been made, it is necessary to determine the topographical characteristics of each path between proposed repeater sites. This type of information is needed to be certain that there is no obstacle in the path between stations and no point from which radio waves might be reflected to cause transmission impairment. When obstacles or objectionable reflection points are discovered, it may be necessary to change one or more of the proposed repeater sites.

Beam Bending. When the atmosphere is well mixed by convection or turbulence, standard atmospheric conditions are said to exist. Under these conditions, pressure, temperature, and water vapor content decrease with altitude. As a result, the dielectric constant of the atmosphere decreases monotonically with altitude, and microwave beams are curved downward by refraction. If the beam curvature corresponds to the curvature of the earth, the beam path can be represented graphically as a straight line relative to a flat earth. This observation suggests that a radio beam path may be represented by a straight line relative to an earth contour having a suitably adjusted radius or the earth may be represented as a flat surface with the beam paths depicted as curves adjusted to display the proper relationship to the flat earth's surface. In many radio engineering studies, it is convenient to adopt the former representation and to assume beam paths are straight. Earth contours may then be plotted relative to an earth radius that has been appropriately adjusted.

To accomplish this graphical representation, the earth's curvature must be assigned a value that makes allowance geometrically for the actual bending of the beam. The factor that relates the actual and fictitious earth radii, k, is only approximately constant in that the bending of the beam varies with the change in altitude. However, for the conditions involved in microwave system engineering, departures from constant gradient are small and may usually be neglected [2].

The factor k is defined for engineering purposes by

$$k = \frac{C_E}{C_F} = \frac{1/r_E}{1/r_F} = r_F/r_E \qquad (18\text{-}1)$$

where curvature, C, is the inverse of radius, r, and the subscripts E and F represent true earth and fictitious earth. Thus, k is the ratio of the fictitious earth radius to the true earth radius; it is sometimes called the effective earth radius factor.

A range of values of k, commonly used in most of the country, is given in Table 18-4. More extreme values are also used in some situations. The value of k is sometimes as low a 0.5 and, in certain coastal areas, sometimes assumes a negative value. The curvature $C_I = -0.5$ is normally used as the maximum engineering value for inverse curvature (upward bending) of a microwave beam. The corresponding value of k is 0.67. The curvature $C_O = 0$ represents an unbent beam. The corresponding value of k is 1.0. The value of $C_S = 0.25 \, C_E$ ($k = 1.33$) is used for beam bending in a standard atmosphere. The curvature C ($k = \infty$) represents the situation in which the beam is bent to follow exactly the earth's curvature; this value is usually taken as the maximum engineering value for downward beam curvature.

Table 18-4. Range of Values for k

Beam Curvature	Relative Fictitious Earth Curvature (C_F/C_E)	k
$C_I = -0.5 \, C_E$	$(C_E - C_I)/C_E = 1.5$	0.67
$C_O = 0$	$(C_E - C_I)/C_E = 1.0$	1.0
$C_S = 0.25 \, C_E$	$(C_E - C_S)/C_E = 0.75$	1.33
$C_E = C_E$	$(C_E - C_E)/C_E = 0$	∞

Figure 18-3, not drawn to scale, shows beam paths relative to real earth curvature and fictitious earth curvatures for a straight radio beam. The values of k are the same as those given in Table 18-4.

Atmospheric Variations. When near-standard atmosphere conditions exist for microwave radio transmission, $k = 1.33$. However, temperature, pressure, and water vapor gradients may vary from those associated with the defined standard

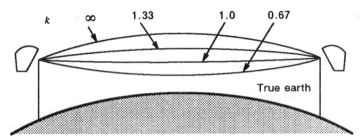

(a) Atmospheric beam bending between antennas

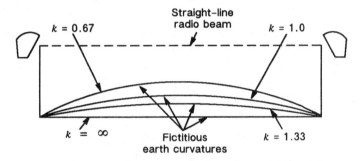

(b) Relative earth curvatures for straight radio beams

Figure 18-3. Beam-bending relationships.

atmosphere. Other values of k then apply and the atmosphere is referred to as nonstandard.

Other anomalies may occur. During quiet, hot summer evenings, the atmosphere may be stratified. In these cases, reflections or refractions may occur at the interfaces between layers and whole regions of the atmosphere may produce a focusing effect, sometimes called ducting. These are significant factors in producing fading of microwave signals.

At 11-GHz or higher frequencies, the signal attenuation caused by heavy rainfall becomes the dominant factor in determining the proper repeater spacing to meet the end-to-end reliability objective. The occurrence probability of heavy rainfall varies considerably with geographic location. Long-term ($\leq$ 20 years) probability distributions of point rain rates for more than 200 U.S. locations have been obtained for engineering radio

504

paths above 10 GHz. Microwave rain–attenuation models and radio–path design charts have been developed for engineering 11–, 18–, and 22–GHz radio paths based on the nationwide rainfall data base and microwave rain–attenuation experiments at many locations.

Path Profile. A profile plot of the earth's surface must be prepared for each path between proposed repeater sites. Figure 18–4 illustrates a path–profile sketch obtained from detailed topographic maps, aerial surveys, field surveys, or a national data base of digitized terrain heights. The profile is plotted on special graph paper, the vertical coordinate of which represents height above sea level. The other coordinate represents horizontal distance along the surface of the earth. The earth curvature is modified by k to permit the representation of the radio beam as a straight line between transmitting and receiving antennas.

In addition to the profile of the earth's surface, other obstructions and possible reflecting surfaces must be determined by field observation and plotted. For example, tree heights are designated by T in Figure 18–4. These heights are plotted with suitable allowance for growth. If a lake were located along the path, its presence would be appropriately noted as would an obstructing or reflecting building.

After allowance has been made for Fresnel zone clearances, as described in Chapter 2, the profile plots may be used for a tentative estimate of required tower heights at each of the repeater sites. Final determination is made after expected reflection or obstruction fading has been estimated or calculated for the chosen antenna heights. Computer programs are available that consider obstruction fading in determining the minimum tower height required to meet outage objectives.

Frequently, path profiles are drawn on rectangular graph paper and may be computer–generated. When this is done, a line representing the earth curvature is drawn. This line must simulate the earth curvature for the appropriate value of k. Templates or calculated clearances are sometimes used, typically for $k = 0.67$ or 1.33. Computer–generated profiles will provide clearances based on the k value selected. Clearances are measured relative to the earth's surface.

Actual elevations
in feet above
sea level

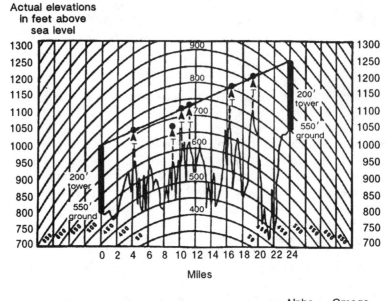

$k = 0.67$　　　　24　mile path　　From　Beta　to　Gamma

Route　　Alpha — Omega

Figure 18–4. Typical path profile sketch.

This method is particularly useful when the effects of different k values must be considered. It also eliminates the need for special graph paper.

Transmission Layout. Once the sites are located and antenna heights selected, free–space path loss can be calculated. Under standard atmospheric conditions, the ratio of the power emitted by an isotropic transmitting antenna to the power captured by an isotropic receiving antenna closely approaches the free–space loss (FSL). By definition, the FSL is restricted to the propagation of the path of a direct wave remote from the earth and its effects. This loss is calculated for each path by the formula

$$FSL = 36.6 + 20 \log d + 20 \log f \text{ dB} \qquad (18–2)$$

where d is the distance in miles between transmitting and receiving antennas and f is the frequency in MHz.

A combination of the characteristics of available microwave antennas, transmitter output power, and receiver options must be selected to compensate for the calculated free–space and waveguide losses for each path. Adequate fade margin above these losses, of course, must be included in the calculations and selections to ensure meeting performance objectives. Diversity protection arrangements are selected based on reliability calculations using available statistical data on fading, equipment failure rates, and repair times [3]. Finally, service channel options are chosen to supply the control circuits for the diversity arrangement. To meet reliability objectives on high–capacity digital systems, adaptive receiver equalizers are usually required in addition to diversity [4].

Path Testing. The best combination of antenna heights at the two ends of a repeater section may also be determined by path testing. In spite of the fact that the process is costly and time consuming, careful and effective path testing is sometimes undertaken on new routes, especially when profile studies and subsequent field surveys are judged to yield inadequate or questionable data regarding the heights of obstructions or the reflectivity of the path. The high costs may be justified by the fact that the correction of an error in antenna placement may force a very expensive project. For example, if the antenna must be moved after the initial installation, antenna weight and wind loading factors may require changes in tower design, and waveguide connections must be lengthened or shortened to accommodate the new antenna location. Furthermore, the antenna mounting platform is not readily movable.

Path tests usually involve the transmission of an RF signal between antennas mounted on temporary test towers erected at the two proposed adjacent repeater sites. Since the transmitted power and antenna gains are known, measurement of the received power may be used to determine the transmission loss between the two points. Regulations regarding signal transmission and tower construction established by the FCC and the FAA must be observed in conducting these tests. In addition, advance arrangements must be made for access to the sites and various work permits must be obtained. Provision must also be made for temporary power and for construction operations.

A temporary guyed tower, up to about 300 feet high, is erected at the location of each proposed permanent tower. Each temporary tower holds a vertical track on which is mounted a carriage that supports an antenna. The elevation and azimuth of the antenna can be adjusted by motors. The carriage also supports a transmitter or receiver and one end of the connecting power and control cable. The carriage may be raised or lowered by a winch whose cable feeds through a counter calibrated to indicate the height of the antenna. Controls, power supplies, and communications equipment are located in a van at the tower base.

With these test arrangements, the two antennas (one at each end of the path) may be raised and lowered in specified patterns. The transmission loss between the two sites is measured for each set of antenna positions. The resulting data, referred to as a height–loss run, may be used to determine antenna placement to minimize reflections and loss, to establish the location of reflection points, and to determine the value of the factor k at the time of measurement. The analysis of the data involves the application of the principles of optical geometry. Microwave signals obey the same fundamental laws as light waves.

The measurement of path loss is seldom made under conditions so ideal that true free–space is observed. Losses may be affected by reflections from terrestrial objects or from atmospheric strata and by diffraction at an obstruction located in or near the edge of the direct transmission path. However, with most microwave paths, earth effects can be minimized under normal conditions so that the path loss is essentially FSL. When path–loss measurements are made, the results may be compared with the FSL computed by Equation 18–2. Analysis is then necessary to determine the source or cause of the difference and to determine the best course of action if the departure from expected loss is excessive. The analysis, greatly aided by the data obtained from the height–loss run, involves the determination of reflection points and the phase lag of the reflected signal relative to the direct signal.

Many terrain factors must be taken into account in this analysis. The terrain may be slightly concave and, as a result, energy arrives at the receiving antenna by a number of independent paths. One or more of the reflected waves in such a case may be of larger amplitude than the direct wave.

Path–loss measurements should be made, as nearly as possible, under standard atmospheric conditions. Strata of temperature, moisture content, and pressure can cause reflections that are difficult to account for in analyzing test results. Variations during the test period are also difficult to analyze. When atmospheric conditions are stable but exactly standard (i.e., $k = 1.33$), measurements can be made successfully but test results must be used to determine the value of k at the time of test.

In certain cases, attenuated transmission in the presence of an obstacle in or at the edge of the direct path can be measured. Transmission takes place because of diffraction of the wave in the region beyond the obstacle. The phenomenon may be explained by the Huygens principle, which states that "every point on a wavefront may be considered to be a new source from which new wavelets issue." Thus, some rays are bent around the obstacle and no reflection is involved. This form of interference, called knife–edge diffraction, can often be overcome by suitable adjustment of antenna heights; such a phenomenon is inconsequential where there is sufficient clearance. Clearance of at least 0.6 times the distance to the first Fresnel zone is usually provided along the direct path to achieve loss that approximates FSL. More clearance is provided where fading conditions are likely to be encountered.

If path testing is not done, it is essential that detailed path measurements be made and some of the analysis detailed above made after construction but prior to placing the route in service. These measurements should be continued so that variations with time can be observed. At this point, solutions to path transmission problems would gravitate toward alternatives other than changing antenna height, such as adding space or angle diversity.

Interference Studies

Radio–frequency interference may originate in the impaired system (intrasystem) or in a system that parallels or crosses the impaired system (intersystem). Of concern are those interference patterns that relate to the route layout of microwave systems and to the selection of repeater sites [5]. In addition, these studies involve the frequency allocations used in the systems of interest [6].

The FCC requires that all interference problems be resolved before filing for a license. Thus, layout studies must be carried out well in advance of any preparations for actual route construction. Studies must cover a radius that could affect or be affected by existing routes. This radius is normally 125 miles; however, the coordination distance may extend to 200 miles along the azimuth of the antenna.

Where routes are lightly loaded and in areas that are uncongested with respect to radio system use, interference problems are often easily avoided by choosing frequency bands so that different radio channels are used in the potential interference situations. However, this solution often cannot be used, particularly if growth is considered.

There are a number of route layout relationships that involve the potential for causing intra– or intersystem interference. These include interferences between similar systems as well as interferences that may be induced by radar or satellite systems. These must all be related to the practice of transmitting and receiving at different frequencies in alternate sections. Some of the important sources of such interferences are illustrated in Figure 18–2, where the high and low channel frequencies are distinguished by the designations f_1 and f_2.

Intrasystem Interference. Three examples of intrasystem interference are illustrated in Figure 18–2: same–section, adjacent–section, and overreach interferences. For adjacent and same–section interferences, like frequencies but opposite directions of transmission are involved. In the illustration of overreach interference, like frequencies are involved but, in this case, the same directions of transmission are involved for the interference and the impaired channel. The impairment is an increase in channel noise and bit error ratio as a result of the impairment appearing as distortion of the RF signal.

For same–section interference, the path loss from transmitting to receiving antennas is very nearly the same for both impaired and interfering signals. The largest attenuation to the interfering signal results from the fact that the path involves transmission through one antenna from front to back. For adjacent–section interference, the impaired and impairing path lengths may be significantly different. Adjacent–section interference from the shorter section into the longer may be greater due to the lower attenuation in the shorter path. The largest attenuation to the interfering signal is the back–to–front discrimination of the receiving antenna in the impaired path.

For intrasystem overreach interference, the two major sources of attenuation to the interfering signal are the overreach distance, which approaches three (or even five) times the normal repeater spacing, and the directional discrimination of the transmitting and receiving antennas. The location of the repeater site and the resulting antenna orientation are thus important considerations in route layout and the control of overreach interference. In some cases, where the terrain is favorable, earth blocking may also be used to advantage; a repeater site may be chosen so that the overreach path is effectively blocked by a natural earth contour.

Intersystem Interference. Figure 18–2 shows two examples of intersystem interference that must often be considered in route layout studies. A junction between the main route and a spur is depicted near the upper part of the figure. If the spur is regarded as a separate system, perhaps being added to the layout after the main route has been in operation, the potential interferences between systems must be taken into account in locating the first spur station. Where path lengths are about equal, the path losses for interfering and impaired signals are nearly the same and the principal attenuation factors are those relating to antenna discrimination. Thus, relative orientation of the main route and spur antennas must be adjusted by location of the spur repeater to maximize the discrimination.

Another example of potential intersystem interference, shown in the lower portion of Figure 18–2, occurs when the route of one system approaches or crosses that of another. If the two routes cross, every effort must be made to have them cross at an angle exceeding 30 degrees so that both are benefited by maximum antenna discrimination or to locate the stations so that interference paths are blocked. Distances between repeater sites on the two routes are also important, as the longer path is generally more susceptible to interference due to higher path loss.

In some cases of intersystem interference, advantage can be taken of terrain characteristics. Where the terrain permits, terrain blockage may be used to advantage by appropriately locating one repeater site and thus introducing high attenuation in the interference path.

Potential intersystem interferences must be compared to other types of systems assigned to similar frequency bands such as systems of other carriers, satellite communications systems, and radar systems. In addition, where a system is to operate in proximity to a national border, the possibility of interference between systems on both sides of the border must also be considered.

Where a new installation takes the form of underbuilding or overbuilding, the same considerations of frequency coordination exist but there is less flexibility in finding solutions to problems than where a completely new route is being laid out. For example, all repeater sites and antenna orientations have been established and cannot economically be changed.

Terrain Scatter/Urban Scatter. Both intrasystem and intersystem interference can result from the scattering of radio waves that occurs as a result of the earth's reflective characteristics in the area where microwave beams cross. When this scattering takes place in rural areas, it is known as terrain scattering. When the scattering takes place in urban areas, it is called urban scattering. Urban scattering generally results from the reflective characteristics of various types of buildings and is particularly troublesome in the higher microwave frequency bands, 18–GHz and above. Considerable research is focused on characterizing and predicting urban–scattering effects.

Computer Aids. Centralized time–shared computer systems are used to record all pertinent information on microwave routes, repeater locations, frequency assignments, antenna data, interference patterns, etc. Access to this information is by remote data terminals located throughout the country for use in radio system engineering studies. A number of programs are available for computations and comparisons required in microwave–route engineering and layout. MRSELS (Microwave Radio and Satellite Engineering and Licensing System), which is maintained by Bellcore, is an example of a centralized package of programs for engineering microwave systems and making interference studies.

When information on a new route has been firmly established, it is added to the data stored in the computers. A vital step in the layout process involves a study of RF interference problems using programs designed to use the stored data.

18-4 GOVERNMENTAL JURISDICTIONS AND APPROVALS

Many aspects of common–carrier operations are subject to regulation by a variety of local, state, and federal agencies. By its nature, it is impossible to constrain radio transmission to specific geographical boundaries. Thus, all radio transmission is regarded as an interstate form of communication and is regulated by the FCC. However, there are aspects of route engineering other than those involving propagation that are subject additionally to the regulations of other government agencies.

Federal Communications Commission

The FCC has been granted jurisdiction over all forms of non-government radio communication within the United States. In exercising its role, the FCC, in cooperation with the State Department, coordinates specific radio matters with the corresponding organizations of neighboring countries and, where appropriate, with the International Telecommunications Union (Volume 1, Chapter 25).

During the preliminary engineering of a new route, if path testing is undertaken, temporary authority must be obtained from the FCC and the Commission must be kept informed of test activities and completion.

The license application must provide sufficient data to show that the project is in the public interest and will meet all FCC technical requirements. A maximum construction period of 18 months is allowed from the date the license is granted, and the

FCC must be notified that construction is complete before the station can be put in service.

Federal Aviation Administration

This agency, commonly known as the FAA, is concerned directly with the design and maintenance of towers or other antenna–supporting structures, especially those located less than 20,000 feet from airports or along heavily traveled air routes. FAA clearance must be obtained to erect such structures. The agency also specifies tower lighting and painting requirements. Regulations of the FAA are applied to temporary as well as permanent towers. When path testing is being done in support of propagation studies, the FAA must be kept advised of when such tests are started and completed if the erection of temporary towers is involved. The FAA must also be notified promptly of tower light failures, which prompts special alarming from remote locations.

Local Government Authorities

When the radio repeater sites are selected, permits must be obtained from local authorities for tower construction, building construction, hoisting, and access–road construction. Zoning and land–use ordinances that regulate such towers must be carefully considered and application must be made for variances from such ordinances when required.

References

1. *Engineering Considerations for Microwave Communications Systems* (San Carlos, CA: Lenkurt Electric Company, Inc., 1970).

2. Dougherty, H. T. "A Survey of Microwave Fading Mechanisms, Remedies, and Applications," *Environmental Science Services Administration (ESSA) Technical Report ERL 69–WPL4* (Washington, DC: U.S. Government Printing Office, Mar. 1968), pp. 369–387.

514

3. Chen, W. Y.–S. "Estimated Outage in Long–Haul Radio Relay Systems with Protection Switching," *Bell System Tech. J.*, Vol. 50 (Apr. 1971), pp. 1455–1485.

4. Chamberlain, J. K. et al. "Receiver Techniques for Microwave Digital Radio," *IEEE Communications Magazine*, Vol. 24, No. 11 (Nov. 1986), pp. 43–53.

5. Curtis, H. E. "Radio Frequency Interference Considerations in the TD–2 Radio Relay System," *Bell System Tech J.*, Vol. 39 (Mar. 1960), pp. 369–387.

6. Members of Technical Staff. *Transmission Systems for Communications*, Fifth Edition (Murray Hill, NJ: AT&T Bell Laboratories, Inc., 1982), Chapter 23.

Chapter 19

Terrestrial Analog Microwave Systems

With the introduction of microwave radio relay systems into the telecommunications network about 1950, a number of analog microwave systems were designed to transmit frequency–division multiplexed (FDM) signals carrying video and message circuits. The oldest of these designs used vacuum tubes with klystron microwave frequency generators. Later designs are based on all–solid–state technology, with a declining use of traveling wave tube power amplifiers for some applications. Technological advances in the design of the equipment, filters, waveguide arrangements, and antennas have increased the circuit capacity of the early frequency modulation (FM) systems more than threefold; however, the system configurations have remained basically the same. In the mid 1970s, single–sideband amplitude modulation (SSBAM) systems were developed, which provide more than twice the voice channel capacity of comparable FM systems and involve some deviation from the original FM design concepts.

Systems with repeaters that provide amplification at intermediate frequency (IF) without returning the signal to baseband are called heterodyne systems. They generally meet transmission objectives on circuits up to 4000 miles in length; hence, these have widely been referred to as long–haul systems.

On the other hand, systems that return the signal to baseband at each repeater are called baseband systems. Since demultiplexing to baseband at each repeater introduces additional noise, it was more practical to design these baseband systems to meet transmission objectives only on circuits of 250 miles or less, and, consequently, they were often termed short–haul systems. While baseband systems accumulate more noise per hop than heterodyne systems, they have an economic advantage on systems that require access to the baseband for frequent dropping and reinserting of circuits at intermediate points.

Most modern FM analog microwave systems use basic components that can be combined to provide either baseband, heterodyne, or a combination of the two modes. With the availability of these baseband/heterodyne systems, the classification of microwave systems as long–haul or short–haul has almost disappeared.

For over 25 years, analog microwave was the dominant facility installed to provide interexchange transmission facilities; however, the telecommunication network's evolution to digital has resulted in analog microwave's obsolescence. Nevertheless, the large number of embedded analog installations ensures that some analog microwave systems will remain in service for some time.

19-1 FM HETERODYNE SYSTEMS

While the distinction between short–haul and long–haul microwave radio systems has now virtually disappeared in application, a number of FM heterodyne systems were designed by various manufacturers to meet the requirements of 4000–mile transmission. Repeaters for these systems were designed to satisfy the signal–to–noise objectives established for long network trunks; system layouts were selected to favor infrequent dropping and adding of circuits along the route and to satisfy reliability criteria by the inclusion of multirepeater protection switching arrangements. FM heterodyne systems in the 4–, 6–, and 11–GHz common-carrier frequency bands generally use a 70–MHz IF and employ similar types of equipment component and configuration. Design variations have taken into account the 20–, 30–, and 40–MHz radio–frequency (RF) channel bandwidth limitations at 4, 6, and 11 GHz, respectively. These differences in bandwidth account for a maximum voice–channel capacity (meeting 4000–mile circuit noise objectives) of 1800 for 4–GHz systems and 2400 for 6– and 11–GHz FM systems.

Microwave radio systems are designed to meet noise objectives expressed in terms of the noisiest message channel during the busy hour. The current objective for a 4000–mile message trunk provided on heterodyne systems is 41 dBrnc0. The use of horn-reflector antennas along with basic system design are the major factors that allow the noise objective to be met. The horn reflector antenna permits simultaneous transmission of vertically and horizontally polarized signals in adjacent RF channels, and can transmit an extremely broad band of frequencies. It is presently being used at 2, 4, 6, 11, and 18 GHz and has been shown to be satisfactory at 30 GHz [1]. Waveguide dimensions must be appropriate to the frequency band or bands being transmitted.

The basic components of FM heterodyne microwave systems are the FM terminals, radio transmitters/receivers, and intermediate repeaters.

FM Terminals

The initial and final steps of modulation in FM microwave systems that use heterodyne (IF) type repeaters are performed by FM terminal transmitters and FM receivers. These units are often referred to simply as terminals.

Figure 19–1 is a block diagram of a typical FM terminal transmitter. The balanced baseband input signal (either video or broadband multiplex) is amplified and converted to an unbalanced signal in the baseband amplifier. This signal is applied to the deviator in which the signal voltage frequency modulates a 70–MHz oscillator. The output of the deviator is filtered to eliminate unwanted signal components and is amplified as required.

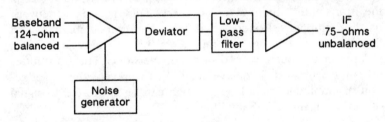

Figure 19–1. Block diagram of a typical FM terminal transmitter.

The noise generator may be used when multiplexed message signals are transmitted. It must be disabled when a television signal or a digital signal with very low frequency components is transmitted. The noise, confined to the band from 0 to 1 kHz, provides a random variation of the carrier frequency, called spreading. This causes certain tone interferences that may appear in other radio channels to be spread over several voice channels, thus making the interference more like random noise and substantially reducing the subjective effect of the tones.

Figure 19–2 shows a circuit arrangement typically used in an FM terminal receiver. The limiter is used to remove amplitude variations in the signal before demodulation in the discriminator.

Figure 19–2. Typical FM terminal receiver.

Microwave Transmitters and Receivers

Figure 19–3 is a block diagram of a typical heterodyne microwave transmitter with a traveling wave tube (TWT) power amplifier [2]. The incoming IF from the protection switching equipment is applied to the IF limiter amplifier, which removes essentially all amplitude modulation; the transmitter modulator converts the signal from the 70–MHz IF band to the appropriate RF channel frequency. The output signal from the transmitter modulator passes through the microwave distribution network to reach the transmitter microwave network. This bandpass network passes the upper sideband and reflects the lower sideband as well as other unwanted signal components that are dissipated in an isolator in the microwave distribution network. The transmitter microwave network is delay–equalized to prevent the introduction of amplitude modulation, which can be converted to signal distortion in the TWT amplifier.

The TWT input network provides an impedance match between the transmitter microwave network and the TWT amplifier by the use of an isolator. The input network also contains an attenuator for controlling the TWT input signal power. The test access port is available for measurement during this adjustment.

The TWT amplifier provides a signal power of typically +40 dBm (10 watts) at the output of the TWT output network, a microwave integrated circuit similar to the TWT input network. The output network contains a low–pass filter to suppress harmonics in the TWT output signal. The amplifier is powered by a dc–to–dc converter that generates the voltages required by the TWT.

The test access port is used during the measurement and adjustment of output power. The signal then enters the channel–combining filter where it is combined with other channel signals for transmission. The output of the channel–combining filter is transmitted to the antenna through system–combining networks not shown in Figure 19–3.

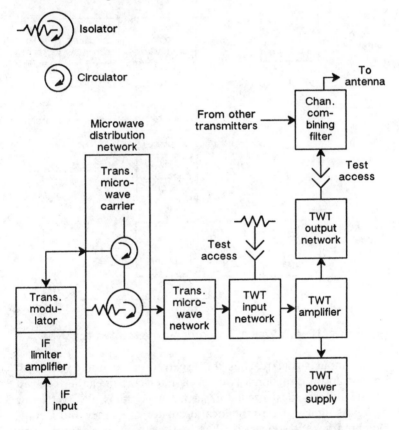

Figure 19–3. Typical heterodyne FM transmitter.

Figure 19–4 is a block diagram of a typical heterodyne microwave receiver. The received signal is carried from the antenna by waveguide through band–separating networks to the channel–separation networks shown in the figure. The selected channel is delay–equalized within this waveguide network to compensate for the delay distortion of the receiver channel–separating filter and the preceding transmitter channel–combining filter. The test access port that follows the separation network is the reference point for the received signal power.

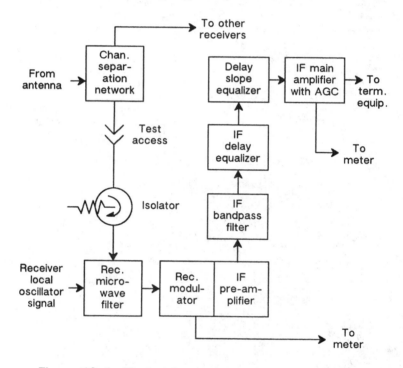

Figure 19-4. Typical heterodyne microwave receiver.

The input signal reaches the receiver modulator through an isolator and a directional filter. This filter combines the received signal and the local oscillator signal. It contains a very narrow bandpass filter tuned to the local oscillator frequency and a complementary band–rejection filter in the received signal path to prevent the local oscillator signal from reaching the receiving antenna. The narrow bandpass filter also suppresses noise and other spurious signals that may be present in the output of the microwave generator.

The receiver modulator converts the incoming microwave signal to a 70–MHz IF signal. Unwanted output signal components from the modulator are absorbed by the reverse loss of the isolator in the receive signal path; thus, they are prevented from reaching the receiving antenna. The modulator is followed by filters, equalizers, and amplifiers, which suppress unwanted out-of-band signal components, equalize delay distortion, and (with an adjustment pad) set the IF signal output power. The output IF signal is typically delivered to protection switching equipment.

Intermediate Repeaters

Figure 19–5 shows one direction of transmission through a repeater typical of those used in FM heterodyne microwave systems. Note that the basic transmitter and receiver are identical to the transmitters and receivers used at microwave terminals, which were just discussed.

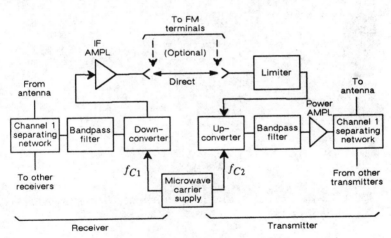

Figure 19–5. Microwave radio IF repeater.

After the received channel signal has been modulated to the IF band by the down–converter, it is amplified and connected directly to the limiter of the transmitting portion of the repeater. Thus, at repeater points the signal is not demodulated to baseband. A microwave carrier supply furnishes carriers at different frequencies, fc_1 and fc_2, to the up– and down–converters.

Transmitter output power for heterodyne repeatered systems ranges from 1 to 12 watts depending on system design.

Heterodyne system repeaters with a standard intermediate frequency band centered at 70 MHz typically have receiving and transmitting equipment for one two–way channel mounted in a single transmitter/receiver bay. Where the equipment is used at an intermediate repeater station, this bay serves one direction of transmission through the station. Where it is used at a main station, at which the protection switching section terminates, the receiver and transmitter are used for the two directions of transmission associated with one route direction [3, 4]. These arrangements are illustrated in Figure 19–6.

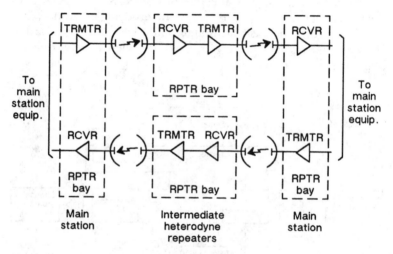

Figure 19-6. Typical heterodyne transmitter/receiver equipment.

System Layout

Heterodyne systems are laid out in accordance with the engineering considerations discussed in Chapter 18, which results in typical repeater spacings of 20 to 30 miles for 4– and 6–GHz systems, and 15 miles or less for 11–GHz systems. IF repeater switching sections usually include 6 to 9 intermediate repeater stations. Figure 19–7 is a block diagram of a typical switching

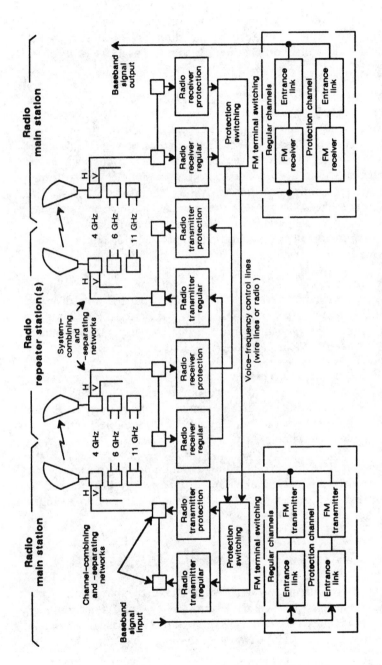

Figure 19–7. Typical heterodyne system layout for one direction of transmission in one switching section.

section including intermediate repeater stations. The radio transmitter, receivers, and transmission paths are usually installed with frequency–diversity protection–switching arrangements, which provide one protection channel for as many as 11 working channels.

When the route is shared with systems operating in other frequency bands, system networks must be used to combine or separate the 4–, 6–, and 11–GHz signals, vertically and horizontally polarized. These networks feed circular waveguide that carries the signals to or from the antennas. The RF channels in the band being used are connected to the system networks through channel–combining and –separating networks. These are waveguide filters that provide the bandpass and attenuation characteristics to permit combining, in a single rectangular waveguide, all of the vertically or horizontally polarized transmitting or receiving channel signals.

Early heterodyne systems used external facilities (wire–line or low–capacity microwave) for order wire, alarms, and diversity control circuits. Modern systems may use various means for inserting the service channel into the microwave IF, thus eliminating the need for external auxiliary circuits.

When required for circuit administration, the system layout may include FM terminals, wire–line entrance links (WLELs), and terminal switching arrangements as illustrated in Figure 19–7. These system components are often equipped with separate protection switching arrangements.

One or more RF channels may be equipped to transmit video signals. In such cases, television dropping may be required at intermediate repeater points and additional protection switches may be provided at those points.

19–2 FM BASEBAND SYSTEMS

FM baseband microwave systems make the baseband signal available at each intermediate repeater, generally for dropping/ inserting circuits. While such systems are economic for systems that require frequent circuit dropping or branching, the demodulation to baseband at each repeater increases the intermodulation noise to the point of limiting the system length. A number of FM baseband systems were designed by various organizations for application in the 2–, 4–, 6–, and 11–GHz bands to meet a 10 hop (250 mile) message noise objective of 35 dBrnc0. These systems have message–circuit capacities (meeting 250–mile noise objectives) varying from 96 in the 2–GHz band to as many as 1800 at 6 GHz.

In a baseband microwave transmitter, the baseband is applied directly to the frequency deviator of the RF generator [5]. Thus the microwave carrier is frequency–modulated by the baseband signal with no intermediate conversion to IF. However, in a baseband IF receiver, the recovery of the baseband signal is greatly facilitated by using an intermediate step of modulation similar to that of the typical heterodyne receiver. Figure 19–8 shows one direction of transmission through a microwave radio baseband repeater [5]. Signals are received by an antenna and transmitted through waveguide to the channel–separating network shown at the left of the block diagram. The desired signal is selected by a bandpass filter and connected to a down–converter, which translates the FM signal to an IF band centered at 70

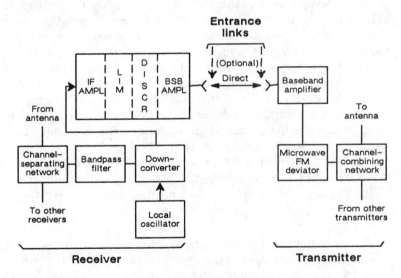

Figure 19–8. Microwave radio baseband repeater.

MHz. This signal is amplified and limited in amplitude before being applied to a discriminator, which demodulates it to baseband frequencies where it is again amplified. This portion of a baseband repeater might serve as the receiver at a terminal point in the system. In such a case, the signal is connected through a WLEL to multiplex or other terminating equipment.

In repeater applications, the baseband signal is connected directly to the transmitter portion of the repeater. After additional amplification, the baseband signal modulates the RF carrier and is combined with other channel signals for transmission by waveguide to the antenna. Normally, a frequency will be selected for the transmitted carrier that is different from that of the carrier received from the previous repeater section in order to minimize crosstalk and interference.

System Layout

System layout for baseband systems generally follows the same procedures as for heterodyne systems; however, with the frequent dropping and reinserting of circuits, baseband microwave systems usually are provided with either frequency or space diversity protection on a per-hop basis. To conserve frequency spectrum, the Federal Communications Commission will seldom authorize one-for-one frequency diversity; thus, frequency diversity arrangements typically provide one protection channel for up to 11 working channels. Crossband frequency diversity of 6/11 GHz has been used extensively on baseband systems. This arrangement has the advantage of minimizing the occupancy of the congested 6–GHz band by using an 11–GHz channel for protection. Rain attenuation effects in the 11–GHz band are minimized by using that band primarily to protect against atmospheric fading in the 6–Ghz band or when maintenance work is being done.

The service channel is applied to the baseband, which is available at each repeater. Normally, special arrangements are made to protect the diversity control channels in the event of failure of a radio channel.

19-3 FM BASEBAND/HETERODYNE SYSTEMS

A number of suppliers have designed modern FM microwave systems at 4, 6, and 11 GHz with multiple equipment module options so that they can be configured to operate, depending on requirements, in either a heterodyne or a baseband mode for each hop or switching section. Since a route may be a combination of heterodyne and baseband repeaters, tradeoffs can be made between system length and voice–channel loading in prescribing equipment options to meet message–circuit noise objectives.

Figure 19–9 is a block diagram of a typical baseband/heterodyne microwave transmitter. The signal at the transmitter input may be at baseband or intermediate frequencies. If the input signal is at baseband, it is connected to the transmitter at the input to the FM transmitter modulator. If the input signal is at IF, an IF–limiter transmitter modulator is substituted for the FM

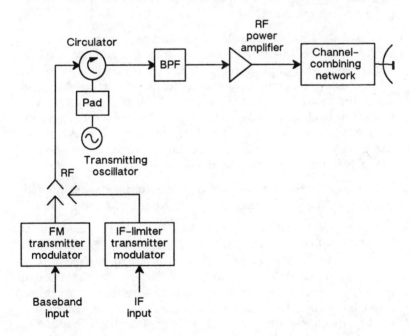

Figure 19-9. Block diagram of baseband/heterodyne microwave transmitter.

transmitter modulator. In either case, the output of the transmitter modulator is an RF signal in the desired frequency band.

The output of the transmitter local oscillator is connected to the circulator through an attenuator used to adjust the signal amplitude. The circulator directs the single–frequency signal to the FM transmitter modulator where it is combined with the IF signal and used as the RF carrier. The modulated RF signal then passes through the circulator to the bandpass filter, which removes unwanted sideband components. After amplification, the signal is combined with other channel signals and transmitted to the next repeater.

The connections between the antenna and the receiver modulator and FM transmitter modulator (including the connections between the circulators and local oscillators) are all made by waveguide. A single parabolic or horn–reflector antenna is normally used for both transmitting and receiving in one route direction. On high–capacity routes, separate transmitting and receiving antennas are used.

A block diagram of a typical baseband/heterodyne receiver is shown in Figure 19–10. Radio energy from the antenna is transmitted by waveguide through channel–separation networks (which separate horizontally and vertically polarized signals and select the desired channel signal) and through the isolator. The isolator provides an impedance match between the channel–separation network and the band–reject filter and prevents RF energy reflected by the filter from being returned to the antenna, where it would be retransmitted.

The band–reject filter is tuned to the receiver oscillator frequency and prevents oscillator energy from being transmitted.

The receiver local oscillator produces a single–frequency signal 70 MHz below the nominal carrier frequency of the desired channel. The amplitude of this signal is adjusted by the RF pad. The local oscillator signal then passes through the circulator to reach the band–reject filter at which it is reflected; it returns through the circulator to reach the receiver modulator where it is used to demodulate the received RF signal to the IF band.

Unwanted carrier and sideband energy is eliminated by the IF bandpass filter. The desired signal is equalized and amplified as

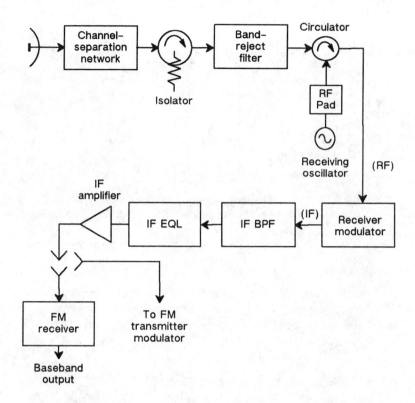

Figure 19-10. Block diagram of a typical baseband/hetero-
dyne microwave receiver.

required. If the repeater is to be used as a baseband repeater or
as a terminal repeater, the signal is applied to an FM receiver in
which the baseband signal is recovered. If the repeater is to be
used as a heterodyne repeater, the IF signal is connected to the
succeeding transmitter modulator.

Small, inexpensive, solid–state, combined transmitter–receiver
units that translate between 70–MHz IF and baseband frequencies are available and can be included in the panels at repeater
locations, as shown in Figure 19–11. This arrangement facilitates
the use of these repeaters as baseband or heterodyne (IF) according to requirements for dropping, blocking, or adding circuits. For heterodyne applications, of course, the FM terminal
units are deleted.

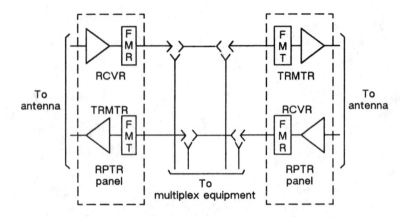

Figure 19-11. Equipment arrangements at baseband/heterodyne repeaters.

Optional diversity and protection arrangements applicable to FM heterodyne and FM baseband systems are also applicable to the hybrid systems. These arrangements are applied based on reliability requirements.

19-4 SSBAM MICROWAVE SYSTEMS

FM microwave systems are relatively immune to nonlinear distortion. However, the use of FM results in less than optimum use of the frequency spectrum. The 2400 voice–channel capacity of some 6–GHz systems is approaching the theoretical limit for FDM/FM systems in 30 MHz of bandwidth. While spectrum–efficient single–sideband techniques have been used for many years in wire–line carrier systems, they were not practical for early microwave systems because the then–available microwave power amplifiers produced unacceptable levels of nonlinear distortion. In recent years, an ultra–linear TWT has become available that, coupled with a number of other design features, made SSBAM microwave practical [6].

SSBAM microwave systems with a capacity of 6000 message circuits per RF channel have been applied in the 6–GHz frequency band. This large voice–channel capacity equates to efficient use of the limited radio frequency spectrum, allowing growth in capacity of routes that would otherwise be fully occupied.

The general features of SSBAM microwave systems closely parallel those of FM heterodyne systems. The main basic difference between the two systems is that the FM transmitter/receiver is replaced by a multimastergroup translator (MMGT–R) in the SSBAM system. Figure 9–8 in Chapter 9 shows how a typical MMGT–R translates ten 600–circuit FDM mastergroups into a 30–MHz band centered on the 74–MHz microwave system IF.

While the basic functions of the other SSBAM microwave modules are similar to their FM–system counterparts, SSBAM requires some additional equipment and some very exacting design criteria to meet the required amplitude linearity across the frequency passband in the presence of atmospheric signal fading. Special measures must also be taken to counter the effects of additional intermodulation products and inadvertent phase–modulation–to–amplitude–modulation (PM–to–AM) conversions.

The following are some of the design features of SSBAM microwave systems not normally found on FM systems: (1) use of a 74.1–MHz IF rather than 70 MHz to reduce intermodulation noise, (2) low noise–figure RF receiver preamplifiers, (3) receiver space diversity on virtually every hop, (4) adaptive amplitude equalization across the transmitted frequency band, (5) IF predistortion to compensate for amplifier nonlinearities and (6) microwave frequency synchronization with extraordinary stability.

Even though SSBAM microwave systems are very efficient from a frequency–spectrum standpoint, their initial high cost has limited their application to long systems. Because they carry analog baseband signals, they are no longer being installed even on longer routes. However, their exacting performance characteristics on routes where they have already been installed make them candidates for conversion to systems that carry high–capacity digital signals.

References

1. Friis, R. W. and A. S. May. "A New Broadband Microwave Antenna System," *Electrical Engineering* (June 1958), pp. 502–506.

2. Hamori, A. and R. M. Jensen. "The TH–3 Microwave Radio System: Microwave Transmitter and Receiver," *Bell System Tech. J.*, Vol. 50 (Sept. 1971), pp. 2117–2285.

3. Jensen, R. M., R. E. Rowe, and R. E. Sherman. "TD–3 System—Microwave Transmitter and Receiver," *Bell System Tech. J.*, Vol. 47 (Sept. 1968), pp. 1189–1225.

4. Jensen, R. M. and R. C. Prime. "The TH–3 Microwave System: System Considerations," *Bell System Tech. J.*, Vol. 50 (Sept. 1971), pp. 2085–2116.

5. Friis, R. W., J. J. Jansen, R. M. Jensen, and H. T. King. "The TM–1/TL–2 Short Haul Microwave Systems," *Bell System Tech. J.*, Vol. 45 (Jan. 1966), pp. 1–95.

6. Members of Technical Staff. *Transmission Systems for Communications*, Fifth Edition (Murray Hill, NJ: AT&T Bell Laboratories, Inc., 1982).

Chapter 20

Digital Microwave Techniques and Terrestrial Systems

Microwave radio–relay systems transmitting time–division multiplex digital signals were introduced into telecommunications networks in the early 1970s to provide an economical means for interconnecting digital transmission facilities, digital switching machines, and data networks. The continuing evolution of telecommunications networks from analog to digital increased the demand for high–capacity digital interconnections with standard interfaces. Emerging digital technology has led to new techniques and applications that have increased digital microwave's capabilities and reliability while decreasing per–channel costs. The result has been an increasing number of digital microwave systems, available from a number of suppliers, in the 2–, 4–, 6–, 11–, 18–, and 22–GHz common–carrier bands. They have generally superseded analog microwave systems. These systems have channel capacities and feature options that allow them to meet modern transmission and reliability objectives. Ongoing development activities assure the early availability of new systems with even more voice–channel capacity in the restricted frequency–band allocations. As a complement to fiber optic and satellite facilities, digital microwave will be an integral part of telecommunications networks for the foreseeable future [1]. New multistation microwave services such as digital termination systems (DTSs) are giving digital microwave yet another dimension.

At the time of the early digital–microwave system designs, analog microwave was firmly established as the dominant facility in the interexchange portion of telecommunications networks. Hence, in order to be compatible, the digital microwave systems had to meet bandwidth, spectrum–utilization, and interference criteria that had already been established for analog systems in accord with Federal Communications Commission (FCC) rules.

It is not surprising, then, that the layout of digital microwave terminals and repeaters is generally similar to the layout of the predecessor analog systems. The modulation and demodulation techniques for digital systems are much different, however, and are discussed in some detail in the following section.

20-1 DIGITAL MICROWAVE MODULATION AND DEMODULATION TECHNIQUES

Digital Modulation

Digital modulation of microwave radio relay carriers has the requirement for a high bit–rate signal within a restricted frequency bandwidth [2]. Techniques for meeting these requirements are similar to those that have previously been applied to modems transmitting high–speed data signals over voiceband telecommunications networks, as discussed in Chapter 5.

A practical means for modulating digital baseband signals onto microwave carriers involves phase shift keying (PSK). In PSK, the carrier is modulated by digital baseband pulses by way of a balanced modulator, as shown in Figure 20–1. Since the carrier amplitude in the balanced modulator is being multiplied by a "0" or "1" signal from the binary bitstream, the output is a carrier whose amplitude is constant but whose phase has two possibilities: either zero degrees (no phase shift) or 180 degrees. This provides a spectrum efficiency of one bit per second per hertz, with this bit yielding two possible states (0 or 1), and is known as 2–PSK. Figure 20–2 is a phase–plane diagram of 2–PSK with the vector at zero degrees representing 0 and the vector shifted 180 degrees representing a 1 pulse.

A spectrum efficiency almost twice that of 2–PSK comes from a process illustrated in Figure 20–3. The input serial baseband signal enters a signal processor (SP) where it is converted to two parallel digital signals, each at half the input data rate. One of the SP outputs modulates a carrier in a two–phase modulator and generates a component called the I (in–phase) rail. The other output from the SP modulates the same carrier that has been phase shifted by 90 degrees, producing a quadrature component

536

called the Q rail. The modulation process is completed by adding
the two rails. The combined output signal has four definite phase
states and is known as 4–PSK or quaternary phase shift keying
(QPSK). Figure 20–4 is a phase–plane diagram of QPSK showing
vectors representing the four possible states.

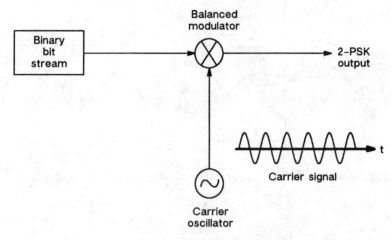

Figure 20-1. 2–PSK modulation of a binary bit stream.

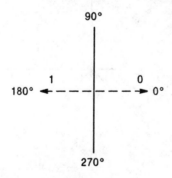

Figure 20-2. 2–PSK phase–plane diagram.

The techniques of 2–PSK and QPSK were used to apply a
digital bit stream to a 70–MHz intermediate frequency (IF)
carrier in the first generation of digital microwave systems; however, they do not provide enough spectral efficiency to be permitted by the FCC in the 4–, 6–, or 11–GHz common–carrier

bands. Subsequently, the number of possible vector positions was doubled from the QPSK design to produce 8–PSK.

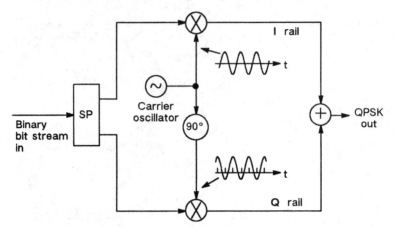

Figure 20-3. 4–PSK (QPSK) modulation of a binary bit stream.

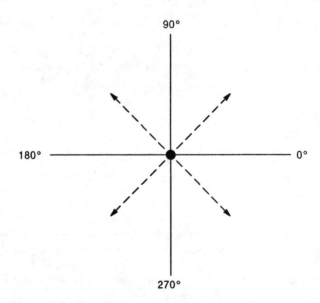

Figure 20-4. 4–PSK phase-plane diagram.

Spectral density was further improved by adding discrete amplitude levels to the quadrature rails of the basic QPSK modulator. This combination of amplitude and phase modulation is defined as M–QAM (quadrature amplitude modulation with M states of the phase vector). Figure 20–5 is a block diagram of the 16–QAM modulation process providing 16 possible vector states. The input binary bit stream is converted in the signal processor to four parallel streams, each at one quarter of the input bit rate, and fed into a digital–to–analog (D/A) converter. This device converts the bit streams to a four–level analog signal on each of two rails and then feeds each to a balanced modulator. The I rail modulates the carrier; the Q rail modulates the same carrier, which has been shifted by 90 degrees. The output of each balanced modulator has four normal states from a combination of two amplitudes and two phases. After adding the rails (which are at quadrature), the modulator output has 16 possible states as shown in the 16–QAM phase–plane diagram (Figure 20–6). This representation is also known as a signal constellation from its starlike form.

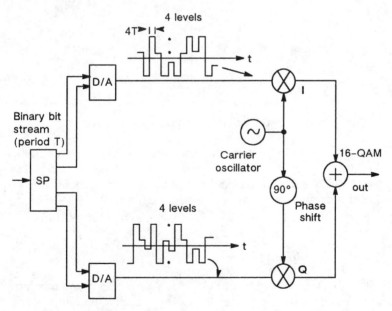

Figure 20–5. 16–QAM applied to a binary bit stream.

This concept has been extended to 64–QAM by converting the input bit stream into two eight–level signals. One is applied to the

I rail and the other to the Q rail. When the I and Q rails are added, the result is a vector that can take any of 64 states as shown in the phase–plane diagram in Figure 20–7.

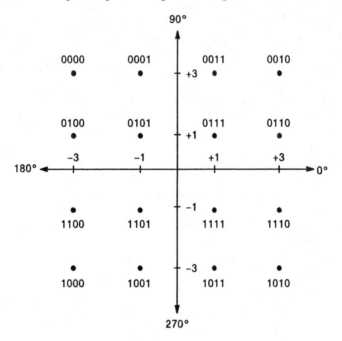

Figure 20-6. 16-QAM phase-plane diagram.

Digital microwave systems operating with 64–QAM of a 70–MHz IF are now commonplace. They provide a 135–Mb/s signal in 30 MHz of channel bandwidth. Even higher–capacity digital microwave systems are in the offing, with 256–QAM being demonstrated and even 1024–QAM being discussed [3].

Digital Demodulation

Demodulation of PSK and QAM is the reverse of modulation. In order to recognize phase shifts for the demodulation process, phase–lock arrangements are required to assure that the demodulating carrier at the receiver has the same phase as the transmitted carrier. Special data clock synchronization is also required for the baseband digital bit streams.

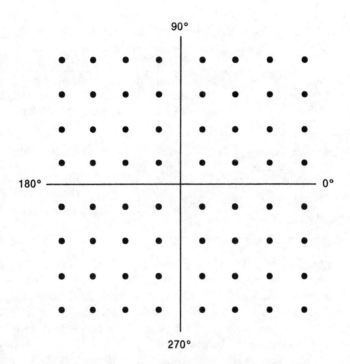

Figure 20-7. 64-QAM phase-plane diagram.

Quadrature Partial-Response Signalling

A variation of QAM is called quadrature partial-response signalling (QPRS). QPRS uses a partial-response pulse algorithm that depends on precoding to represent actual data values, and is spectrum-efficient. However, since QAM provides better error performance than QPRS for a given power level, QAM remains the modulation choice on high-capacity microwave system designs [4].

20-2 THE 4-, 6-, AND 11-GHz DIGITAL MICROWAVE SYSTEMS

Table 20-1 lists the maximum per-channel bandwidth along with the minimum voice-channel circuit requirement (using digital modulation) for various common-carrier frequency bands in order to be granted a frequency assignment by the FCC.

Table 20–1. Maximum Per–Channel Bandwidth and Minimum Voice–Channel Requirements for Digital Modulation in Common–Carrier Microwave Bands

Common–Carrier Frequency Band (GHz)	Maximum Per–Channel Bandwidth (MHz)	Minimum No. Voice Channels When Digital Modulation is Used
2	3.5	96
4	20	1152
6	30	1152
11	40	1152
18	220	No requirement
22	100	No requirement

Note that only digital microwave systems that carry 1152 circuits or more satisfy the minimum channel–loading requirements mandated by Section 21.122(a)(2) of the FCC rules for the crowded 4–, 6–, and 11–GHz frequency bands. Such high–capacity systems, type–accepted by the FCC, are available from a number of suppliers. Figure 20–8(a) diagrams the functional components of a typical high–capacity 4–, 6–, or 11–GHz digital microwave transmitter. A brief description of these functional components follows.

Coder

Depending on the channel bandwidth, the coder will accept two or three DS3 digital signals. (The 20–MHz allocation in the 4–GHz band will accommodate two DS3 signals while 30 MHz in the 6–GHz band accommodates three.) The basic function of the coder is to take baseband signals and convert them to a format that can appropriately activate a QAM modulator. This code–conversion process typically uses a number of subfunctions as shown in Figure 20–9, which is for a typical 6–GHz, 135–Mb/s digital microwave system carrying three DS3 signals. The standard 44.736–Mb/s DS3 signals enter the code converter, which is the start of the coding process. The signal format is changed at this point from a bipolar to a polar format. Any bipolar with three–zero–substitution (B3ZS) patterns are removed from the

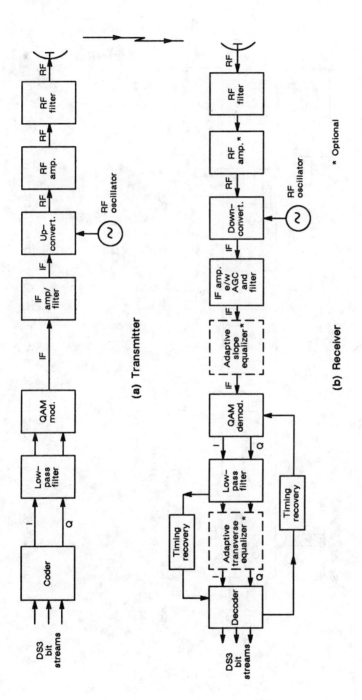

Figure 20-8. Typical high-capacity digital microwave system.

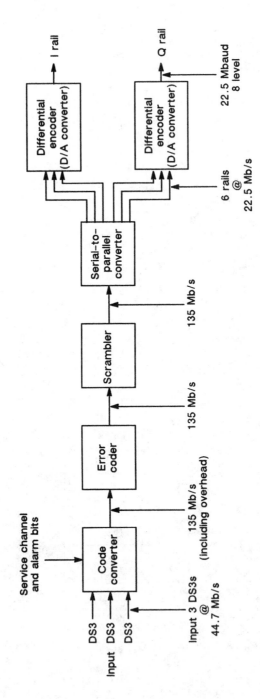

Figure 20–9. Typical coder functions for 135–Mb/s digital microwave transmitter.

signal to restore the original succession of zeros. With the aid of a buffer, the code converter introduces a new clock having a rate that is the sum of the interleaved input signals plus some proprietary (nonstandard) overhead bits for the microwave auxiliary channel. In this case, the output bit rate is approximately 135–Mb/s. From the code converter, the 135–Mb/s signal goes to an error–coder circuit that adds a parity bit to equalize the number of ones and zeros in a given block of data. (The parity is checked at the receiver for basic error–detection purposes and to initiate protection switching.) The scrambler then randomizes the data, which results in a constant power spectrum under various data sequences. This is very important since an all–ones sequence (applied in case of signal interruption) would otherwise result in loss of clock regeneration.

The scrambled signal enters a serial–to–parallel converter where the serial digital bit stream is converted to six 22.5–Mb/s parallel rails. Differential encoders then generate two eight–level modulation signals, which become the I and Q rails required for 64–QAM and complete the coding process.

Low–Pass Filter and QAM Modulator

Figure 20–8(a) then shows that after the signal leaves the coder, appropriate filtering to meet Nyquist criteria is used in both the I and Q rails to minimize intersymbol interference and thus contribute to keeping the error rate within limits [5]. These filters have a raised–cosine characteristic in order to meet the criteria with a realizable design. Half of this filtering is applied at the transmitter and the other half at the receiver. In addition to reducing intersymbol interference, these filters help to reduce out–of–band emissions. Both signals then enter the QAM modulator, where the signal on the filtered I rail modulates the 70–MHz IF in a balanced modulator while the signal on the Q rail modulates the same 70 MHz, which has been phase shifted 90 degrees as originally shown in Figure 20–5. Summation of the I and Q rails produces the 64–QAM signal.

Intermediate–Frequency Amplifier, Up–Converter, and Radio–Frequency Amplifier

Continuing with Figure 20–8(a), the IF amplifier, up–converter, and radio–frequency (RF) amplifier perform the same functions as in analog microwave systems. However, the high-level modulation associated with high-capacity digital systems carries critical amplitude values and phase relationships that require a much better linearity than in frequency-modulation (FM) systems. Therefore, special linearizing techniques are used that previously had been applied only on single-sideband amplitude modulation (SSBAM) microwave systems. These include IF amplitude and delay equalization. IF predistortion is used to compensate for the nonlinearities associated with operating the RF power amplifier close to maximum levels. Solid-state gallium arsenide (GaAs) RF power amplifiers normally have enough power output for use on the 4- and 6-GHz systems; however, 11-GHz applications may require a TWT.

Digital Microwave Receiver

The block diagram for a typical high-capacity digital microwave receiver is shown in Figure 20-8(b). The receiver and decoder generally follow the reverse of the modulation process in demodulating, decoding, and recovering the DS3 baseband signals. The IF amplifier in the receiver has automatic gain control (AGC) to compensate for 35 to 40 dB of flat fading in the transmission path.

The demodulation process requires that the receiver IF carrier and digital timing clock be in sync with their transmitter counterparts. To accomplish this, a carrier-recovery circuit detects deviations from the transmitted carrier and corrects them via a control signal to the 70-MHz local oscillator in the QAM demodulator. A timing-recovery circuit uses a phase-locked loop to maintain the synchronized receiver clock rate. At intermediate repeaters, which do not require dropping or adding circuits, regeneration of the digital signal is accomplished without dropping all the way back to the input baseband. For example, in a 135-Mb/s system using the encoding/decoding scheme shown in Figure 20-9, the regeneration at a repeater is normally done on the six 22.5-Mb/s rails with appropriate carrier and timing recovery and without returning to the input DS3 signals.

Figure 20-8(b) also shows several optional receiver components that may be used to improve system performance, and are discussed in some detail in the next section.

20-3 MEETING PERFORMANCE CRITERIA ON HIGH-CAPACITY DIGITAL SYSTEMS

Acceptable performance of digital microwave systems used in the public telecommunications network takes place during the time that the baseband bit error ratio is 10^{-7} or better. Further, this acceptable bit error ratio must be maintained for a sufficient period of time to provide reliability that conforms to very exacting network standards [6]. In general, digital microwave systems are designed to provide a bit error ratio of better than 10^{-6} under conditions of normal engineered receive signal levels. This allows for some atmospheric signal degradation before the hard-failure 10^{-3} ratio is reached. A 10^{-6} bit error ratio is attained with a carrier-to-noise (C/N) ratio in the order of 11 db with 2-PSK modulation. However, an increase in C/N is required to maintain the 10^{-6} bit error ratio as more spectrally efficient modulation schemes are applied to provide more digital capacity in the allotted bandwidth. This required increase in C/N is shown in Table 20-2 for some common modulation types. The need for additional C/N is partially offset by the fact that the high-level techniques reduce out-of-band emissions and require less bandwidth.

Table 20-2. Approximate Carrier-to-Noise Ratio to Maintain 10^{-6} Bit Error Ratio for Various Modulation Types

Modulation Type	Logic Levels	Approx. C/N Ratio for 10^{-6} Bit Error Ratio
2-PSK	2	11
QPSK	4	14
8-PSK	8	19
16-QAM	16	21
64-QAM	64	27
256-QAM	256	33

Receiver AGC circuits and the diversity techniques (frequency and space) discussed in Chapter 17 can maintain required error performance for properly engineered microwave systems with the

robust 2–PSK or QPSK signals. However, high–level QAM signals (with critical amplitude and phase relationships) require the
maintenance of a flat response across the frequency passband in
the presence of multipath fades. It is characteristic of these multipath fades to cause slope changes as well as attenuation notches
to sweep across the frequency band. These conditions cause signal degradations that lower the bit error ratio below 10^{-6}. To
compensate for these anomalies, systems using QAM generally
require adaptive equalization options in their receivers in order to
meet performance objectives.

Adaptive Frequency–Domain Equalizers

An adaptive IF slope equalizer can be used to compensate for
fades that cause a change in slope across the passband. An adaptive slope equalizer continuously monitors two bandpass filters,
each 10 MHz from the 70–MHz IF center frequency. This provides an estimate of the slope across the band and is used to
control networks that add an opposite and equal slope. Figure
20–10 shows the effects of adaptive slope equalization on a typical microwave IF band frequency response during multipath fading.

In addition to slope equalization, adaptive frequency–domain
equalizers have been designed to equalize an attenuation dip as it
moves across the frequency band. This distortion can be equalized with variable resonant filters [7]. Besides varying the position of the resonance of the filters, the equalizer can vary the
filter bandwidth as well.

Some digital microwave systems provide adaptive frequency
equalizers as standard equipment while others supply them as
designated options.

Adaptive Time–Domain Equalizers

Multipath fading can occur at such a rapid rate and take so
many forms that it is impossible for adaptive frequency equalizers
to compensate perfectly for all variations [8]. Consequently,
adaptive equalization in the time domain may be specified in

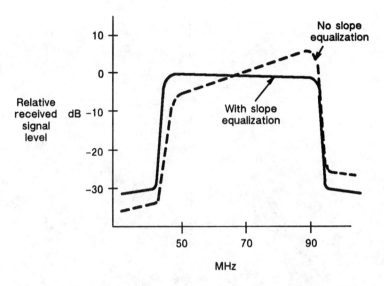

Figure 20-10. Typical digital microwave passband with and
without adaptive slope equalization during
multipath fading.

addition to or in place of adaptive frequency equalization. Time-
domain equalization is based on the fact that a digital communications system (including microwave) is designed to have its
channel impulse response satisfy Nyquist's criterion of having
regular zero amplitude crossings spaced at multiples of the symbol interval (see Volume 1, Chapter 14).

Adaptive time–domain equalizers (sometimes called adaptive
transversal equalizers) can be applied in both the digital I and Q
rails of the receiver after appropriate Nyquist filtering [9]. The
pulse–control algorithm to force the required zero crossings is
illustrated in Figure 20-11. The heavy line represents the ideal
timing of the pulse, based on the synchronized recovered timing
clock. The dotted line represents the unequalized received pulse,
which has been shifted by delay distortion caused by multipath
fading. The $\Delta a + 1$ and $\Delta a - 1$ functions, which are measures
of the deviation from the desired zero–amplitude crossings, are
detected by the equalizer and used to activate the proper delay
network to drive the timing of the received signal to have zero–
amplitude crossings at appropriate instants of time.

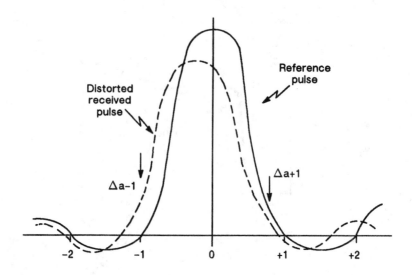

Pulse time intervals

Figure 20–11. Received digital microwave pulse, displaced from its proper position in the time domain.

The criteria to effect shift to zero crossing must consider inter-quadrature crosstalk in the decision algorithm. Figure 20–12 is a simplified diagram of the adaptive time–domain equalizer architecture. A greater number of delay networks (referred to as taps) in the transversal filters increases equalization capability.

Mathematical modeling and extensive field data have confirmed the effectiveness of adaptive frequency– and time–domain equalization in reducing intersymbol interference and meeting reliability objectives [10]. Adaptive time–domain equalization used in conjunction with several alternative diversity techniques has rendered particularly good reliability.

20–4 OTHER DIGITAL MICROWAVE SYSTEMS

While high–capacity 4–, 6–, and 11–GHz digital systems make up well over 90 percent of the new microwave installations, other digital microwave systems are used for certain applications. Frequency congestion will dictate increasing application for some of these systems in the future.

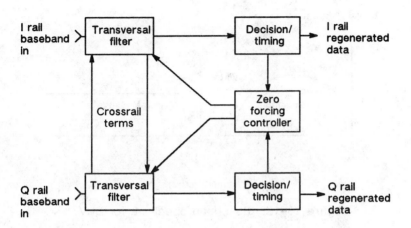

Figure 20-12. Adaptive time-domain equalizer architecture.

Hybrid Systems

Hybrid microwave systems allow limited digital-signal transmission along with the analog voice signals on existing FM analog microwave systems. Analog microwave systems generally provide voice circuits by the use of U600 frequency-division multiplex (FDM) equipment in which the lowest transmitted frequency is 564 kHz. (See Chapter 9 for a discussion of U600 mastergroups.) Thus, there is a frequency bandwidth of approximately 500 kHz within which a digital signal may be placed. Data-under-voice (DUV) systems have been developed, which allow one DS1 digital channel, using a seven-level partial-response modulation technique with a 386-kHz carrier, to be transmitted within the available 500 kHz [11]. Baseband frequency allocation for the DUV signal is shown in Figure 20-13.

Figure 20-14 is a typical hybrid microwave system carrying a DUV signal in addition to FDM. The DUV signal enters a message-data combiner for introduction to a conventional FM transmitter of any analog microwave system. Similar systems that place a DS1 digital signal in 500 kHz of spectrum above the analog signals are known as data above voice (DAV) and data above video (DAVID). Still another method for placing a DS1

551

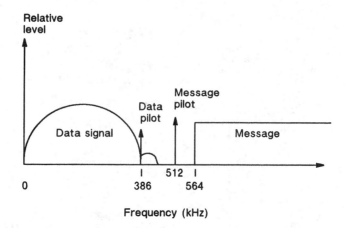

Figure 20-13. Baseband spectrum for DUV.

signal on analog digital microwave involves using a 256–QAM modem to place the 1.544–Mb/s digital signal on a 240–kHz FDM supergroup. This method uses adaptive time–domain equalizers and forward error correction to meet error perform- ance objectives.

Since typical hybrid systems can carry only one DS1 signal per RF path, they are of limited value as a digital transmission carri- er. However, they do have application where a high–speed data channel is required at a location that has existing analog micro- wave but no digital base facility.

18-GHz High- and Medium-Capacity Microwave Systems

With a maximum per–channel allocation of 220 MHz in the 18–GHz common–carrier band, very–high–capacity microwave systems have been designed using low–density modulation tech- niques, which can provide low bit error rates with a relatively low C/N ratio. Systems are available with 560–Mb/s capability (12 DS3 digital baseband signals that provide 8064 equivalent voice circuits) using QPSK modulation of an IF carrier. These systems have had relatively little application because rain attenuation lim- its repeater spacings to between 6 and 8 miles in most parts of the country. This generally makes them uneconomical when com- pared to fiber optic installations; however, they will continue to

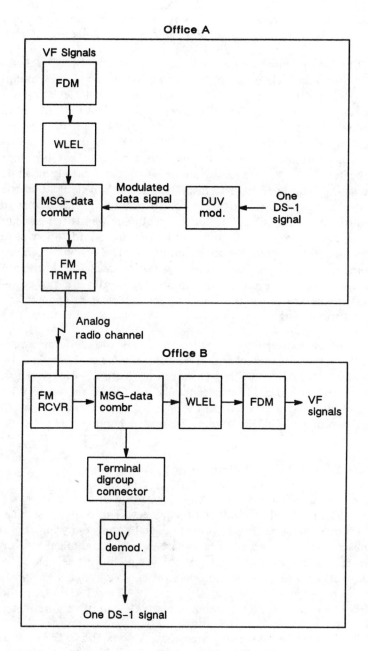

Figure 20-14. Hybrid microwave system with DUV.

be used in cases where right–of–way problems prohibit fiber, and frequency congestion makes other microwave bands impractical.

Similar medium–capacity systems that fit one DS3 baseband signal into 40 MHz of 18–GHz channel space using QPSK modulation are also available. These systems are sometimes attractive in cases where voice–circuit requirements are less than the 1152 required to get frequency allocations in the 4–, 6–, or 11–GHz common–carrier bands (see Table 20–1). While these medium-capacity systems are also plagued with a requirement for short repeater spacings, this disadvantage is partially offset by some advantages of 18–GHz systems. The shorter wavelengths of the 18–GHz frequencies can use a considerably smaller antenna to realize the same gain. The higher frequency bands use smaller waveguide components and lend themselves to microwave stripline and integrated–circuit techniques. The result is compact equipment packages that can be tower–mounted close to the antenna. Thus, waveguide runs are shortened and RF power requirements are reduced. All of this leads to low equipment and installation costs.

The basic configuration of both the high– and medium–capacity 18–GHz transmitters and receivers is similar to the typical 4–, 6–, and 11–GHz counterparts shown in Figure 20–8(a) and (b). However, 18–GHz systems generally use QPSK modulators instead of QAM and an IF in the vicinity of 140 rather than 70 MHz. Similar 22–GHz systems are also becoming available.

Low–Capacity Digital Microwave Systems

Microwave systems with a capacity of one to four DS1 signals are available from a number of suppliers. The primary application for these systems is to provide digital connectivity directly to subscribers' premises in cases where it is uneconomical to construct landline digital circuits. Such systems have been used extensively in private–user networks. Available systems to satisfy these requirements operate in the 2–, 18–, or 22–GHz bands in order to meet the FCC minimum channel–loading requirements.

While there are several systems available in the 2–GHz band, the advantages of higher frequencies (discussed in the section on medium–capacity 18–GHz systems) have resulted in a general migration to 18 and 22 GHz for these applications. These low–bit–rate systems can use relatively simple modulation schemes such as frequency shift keying (FSK), which further reduces their cost while providing a robust signal. Note that most private–user circuit requirements are for distances of 8 miles or less, which is within the transmission capabilities of 18 GHz in most localities. While 22–GHz systems are limited by atmospheric absorption to path lengths of considerably less than the 18–GHz equipment, their compactness and low cost make them a viable option where transmission conditions allow. Compactness and portability also make these systems applicable for providing temporary service very quickly and for emergency restoration.

Tropospheric Microwave Systems

Microwave radio transmission is usually considered reliable only between antennas that have an unobstructed line–of–sight path between them. However, transmission has been found to be practicable over paths longer than the line–of–sight path by taking advantage of reflection, refraction, and diffraction phenomena in the troposphere (up to between 7 and 10 miles above the earth's surface).

Systems of this type are usually called tropospheric scatter systems, but are also referred to as tropo, troposcatter, forward scatter, ultra–high–frequency scatter, over–the–horizon, or beyond–the–horizon systems. They use large highly directive antennas and high–powered transmitters. Satisfactory transmission is achieved over hops of up to 600 miles; however, because of the interference potential of the required high power, the FCC will authorize such systems only in remote areas where alternative communications are impractical. Thus, such systems may be attractive for providing service to off–shore islands where traffic is not sufficient to justify installation of an undersea cable system or a satellite system and where a line–of–sight radio system would be blocked by the curvature of the earth. They are also used in arctic regions where the maintenance of line–of–sight systems is costly and where message–channel requirements are low.

A typical terminal is made up of transmitter and receiver modules in a configuration similar to line–of–sight microwave systems. Tropospheric systems, however, require a complex arrangement of antennas. Two 30– or 60–foot diameter antennas, one for receiving only and one diplexed for transmitting, are used. The transmitters use high–powered klystron output stages and typical power of one to ten kilowatts with bandwidth accommodating the equivalent of 24 to 120 voice channels. A relay station consists of two such terminals back to back. While early tropospheric microwave systems involved analog baseband signals, virtually all current tropo systems carry digital signals in a manner similar to line–of–sight digital microwave systems.

20–5 DIGITAL TERMINATION SYSTEMS

Digital termination systems use microwave frequencies allocated by the FCC to carry digital signals to end users. While the primary use is for data communications, the customers may convert the digital information to voice or even compressed video. The FCC frequency allocation consists of a total of 130 MHz in the 10.6–GHz band. An individual carrier may generally be licensed for only one pair of 2.5– or 5–MHz bandwidth channels for distribution within a standard metropolitan statistical area (SMSA). One of these frequencies is for transmission from a central station (node) to various subscribers; the other is for transmission from subscribers back to the node.

Additional frequencies are available to interconnect nodes in order to establish a data network (the nodes may also interconnect via other facilities including satellite terminals). The DTS internodal channel is, in effect, a point–to–point microwave facility and also can be used to provide service to a single subscriber due to the commonality of nodal and subscriber radio equipment. DTS can also interface with various public data networks such as the Digital Data System and high–capacity digital service at the nodal points.

DTSs can provide various data rates from 1.2 kb/s up to 1.544 Mb/s. Service can be provided to any subscriber location that has a microwave transmission path to the DTS node location. While the narrow channel bandwidth severely limits the total amount of DTS data that can be handled by any one carrier in an SMSA, numerous subscribers can effectively share the limited capacity using time–division techniques, transmission on orthogonal polarizations, and highly directional antennas.

A number of suppliers have designed digital termination systems. These systems are basically low–capacity digital point–to–point microwave systems (used in a point–to–multipoint mode) with additional equipment units to provide frequency subchannelization and time–sharing functions. A DTS system typically uses QPSK to provide a transmission capacity of 1.8 Mb/s on 2.5 MHz of channel bandwidth. Solid–state technology, coupled with the higher microwave frequencies used, allows compact cabinet-mounted equipment.

Several system configurations take somewhat different approaches to providing DTS microwave channels. Advantages accrue to each approach depending on the location and concentration of subscribers. The most common DTS configuration is referred to as the fan–beam arrangement.

DTS Fan–Beam Arrangement

In the DTS fan–beam arrangement, a serving area is divided into cells and a node is located at the center of each cell. The node divides its cell into sectors so that each sector can be served by a fan–beam antenna, which propagates its beam over the entire sector. Figure 20–15 illustrates one sector of a fan–beam system. Subchannelization and dual polarization of the DTS microwave channel reduce interference into adjacent sectors.

Scattered throughout the sector are subscriber stations with directional parabolic antennas with a line of sight pointing at the fan–beam antenna. These subscriber antennas share the radio link over the time domain in a method referred to as time–division multiplex/time–division multiple access (TDM/TDMA). The nodal station broadcasts a continuous stream of information over the entire sector such that portions of this broadcast are addressed to particular subscriber stations. Each subscriber station receives the entire broadcast, but disregards those parts not addressed to its end users. In the return path, subscriber stations take turns sending high–speed bursts of information. The nodal station controls when the bursts may occur by assigning time slots

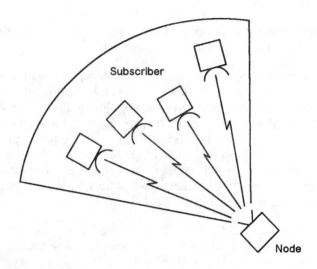

Figure 20-15. One sector of a DTS fan-beam system cell.

for the bursts, either statically with fixed duration and position or dynamically based on the subscriber stations' demands. The end user's data transmission is temporarily stored at the subscriber station in a compression buffer until a time slot becomes available. Conversely, the incoming high-speed transmission is stretched out over time in an expansion buffer to match the end user's slow data rate. For full-period service, the end user perceives only a continuous flow of information in both transmit and receive directions.

DTS Applications

In providing a DTS, the nodes are selected on the basis of sufficient antenna height to provide microwave coverage in the required geographic sectors. After permanent installations are made at the node locations, a number of portable equipment packages including small parabolic antennas are assembled for use at subscriber terminals. These portable packages can be rapidly dispatched to meet end-user needs for service. A typical equipment configuration at a DTS subscriber station in the 10.6-GHz band is shown in Figure 20-16.

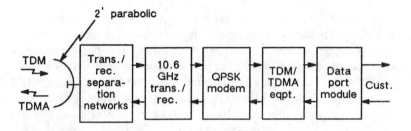

Figure 20-16. Typical DTS station equipment configuration.

While the cost of providing digital services to end users via DTS is considerably more than applying data to existing copper-pair distribution facilities, DTS provides a viable means of providing facilities when high construction costs are involved. Exchange carriers can effectively use DTS to establish temporary service rapidly during the time that it takes to condition existing facilities for higher-speed data services. DTS can also be a viable medium for emergency restoration of data services.

Other DTS Considerations

Local distribution radio (LDR), local business radio (LBR), Microwave Local Distribution System (MLDS), and Digital Electronic Message Service (DEMS) are all other names for DTSs.

20-6 TRENDS IN DIGITAL MICROWAVE SYSTEMS

Digital microwave systems will be an integral part of the digital telecommunications network in the foreseeable future. This ensures the continuing and even accelerating application of GaAs field-effect transistors (FETs), very-large-scale integration (VLSI), and monolithic microwave integrated circuits (MMICs) to the design of new generations of digital microwave systems [12].

Higher-order modulation techniques such as 256-QAM and 1024-QAM are emerging to provide increased radio system capacity and better spectrum utilization. The application of emerging automatic power control techniques will help protect these high–capacity systems from intersystem interference. Additional signal processing and forward error correction techniques are likely to be used for these high–capacity systems to meet performance objectives. The use of adaptive cross–polar interference cancellers (AXPICs) is expected to allow the simultaneous use of both vertical and horizontal polarizations to effectively double the spectrum efficiency. The large–scale integration of more system functions in VLSI will have a strong effect in reducing costs and increasing reliability. The trend toward the use of higher microwave frequencies will continue, and with the increasing use of frequencies at 18 GHz and above, sophisticated techniques such as automatic route diversity will no doubt be applied.

References

1. Lin, S. H. "Opening New Vistas for Microwave Radio," Bellcore EXCHANGE, Vol. 4, Iss. 4 (July/Aug. 1988), pp. 9–12.

2. Hartmann, P. R. and D. P. Taylor. "Telecommunications by Microwave Digital Radio," Microwave Digital Radio (New York: IEEE Press, 1988), pp. 3–9.

3. Nakamura, Y. and Y. Saito. "256 QAM Modem for High Capacity Digital Radio System," IEEE Transactions on Communications Technology, Vol. COM–34, No. 8 (Aug. 1986), pp. 799–805.

4. Daido, Y., T. Noguchi, and J. A. Nosek. "Modulation Techniques for Microwave Digital Radio," Microwave Digital Radio (New York: IEEE Press, 1988), pp. 21–30.

5. Leuenberger, K. J. "Digital Radio Systems Examined—Part II: Modulation and Transmission Characteristics," Microwave Systems News & Communications Technology (Feb. 1986), pp. 131–143.

6. Greenstein, L. J. and M. Shafi. "Outage Calculation Methods for Microwave Digital Radio," IEEE Communications Magazine, Vol. 25, No. 2 (Feb. 1987), pp. 30–37.

7. Leuenberger, K. J. "Digital Radio Systems Examined—Part I: General State of the Art," *Microwave Systems News & Communications Technology* (Jan. 1986), pp. 81–92.

8. Fenderson, G. L., M. H. Meyers, and M. A. Skinner. "Recent Advances in Multipath Propagation Countermeasures for High–Capacity Digital Radio Systems," *Conference Record*, IEEE International Conference on Communications (1985), pp. 1239–1243.

9. Chamberlain, J. K., F. M. Clayton, H. Sari, and P. Vandamme. "Receiver Techniques for Microwave Digital Radio," *Microwave Digital Radio* (New York: IEEE Press, 1988), pp. 131–141.

10. Coutts, R. P., M. Liniger, and W. D. Rummler. "Multipath Fading Channel Models for Microwave Digital Radio," *IEEE Communications Magazine*, Vol. 24, No. 11 (Nov. 1986), pp. 30–42.

11. Grady, R. R. and J. W. Knapp. "1A Radio Digital Terminals Put 'Data Under Voice," *Bell Laboratories Record*, Vol. 52 (May 1974), pp. 160–166.

12. Hart, G., K. Kohujama, O. Kurita, M. H. Meyers, V. K. Prabhu, J. A. Steinkamp, and H. Yamamoto. "Future Trends in Microwave Digital Radio," *IEEE Communications Magazine*, Vol. 25, No. 2 (Feb. 1987), pp. 40–52.

Chapter 21

Domestic Fixed Satellite Communications

While commercial international satellite communications was introduced in 1965, Domestic Fixed Satellite Service did not start in the United States until almost ten years later. Now, however, communication satellites provide a significant amount of point–to–point and especially point–to–multipoint domestic telecommunications. In effect, a domestic satellite communications circuit is a two–hop microwave system with the satellite providing the microwave repeater, which is within line of sight of any terminal located in the United States. The cost of the satellite circuit is thus insensitive to length, so obviously the facility becomes more economically viable as the distance between terminal stations increases. With all terminal stations in sight of the satellite repeater, satellite systems are particularly attractive for point–to–multipoint communications: television, radio, news distribution, paging, etc.

While satellite system components are similar in principle to their terrestrial microwave counterparts, the placing and maintaining of the satellite repeater in a hostile environment, far from the earth, provides complex and demanding engineering problems requiring the interaction of many disciplines.

Communications satellites are generally placed in a geosynchronous orbit in which the satellite is about 22,300 statute miles from the earth. The plane of this orbit must have very little inclination with respect to the equatorial plane of the earth, and the direction of rotation of the satellite about the earth's axis must be the same as that of the earth. A special case of the geosynchronous orbit is the geostationary orbit in which the inclination is zero. These terms are sometimes used interchangeably even though it is not practicable to maintain zero inclination. The advantage of the geosynchronous orbit is that the satellites appear to be stationary from any point on the earth. This provides continuous visibility, eliminates the need for tracking by earth stations with small–diameter antennas that have relatively wide beam widths, and eases the tracking requirements for even the largest narrow–beam earth station antennas. The disadvantages of the geosynchronous orbit are limited visibility to the higher latitudes and the high satellite altitude. The high altitude results in long transmission delay and high transmission loss. Furthermore, the number of geosynchronous orbital position assignments for coverage of the 50 states is limited because of interference restrictions.

In the Domestic Fixed Satellite Service, the satellites are used to interconnect fixed earth stations for the purpose of providing any of the types of service normally provided by terrestrial facilities, such as telephony, data communications, and especially television.

21-1 INTERNATIONAL AND DOMESTIC REGULATION

The design of communication satellite systems is influenced more than that of any other domestic communication system by the international Recommendations and Reports of the International Radio Consultative Committee (CCIR) and, to a lesser degree, the International Telegraph and Telephone Consultative Committee (CCITT). As with all radio systems in the United States, frequency bands for satellite services are allocated by the Federal Communications Commission (FCC) in general conformance with the allocations appearing in the Radio Regulations of the International Telecommunications Union (ITU), a specialized agency of the United Nations.

Table 21-1 lists allocated frequency bands on which United States domestic fixed telecommunications satellite services are either currently working or being considered for future applications. These satellite frequency bands are sometime referred to in terms of radar bands, shown as a letter designation noted in the left column.

The 4–GHz and 6–GHz allocated frequencies are shared with terrestrial microwave systems; therefore, it has been necessary to establish rules to allow coordinated frequency reuse in these

Table 21-1. FCC Frequency Allocations for Domestic Fixed
Public Satellite Communications

Frequency Band (GHz)	Uplink (GHz)	Downlink (GHz)	Satellite Band (MHz)
6/4 (C Band)	5.925-6.425	3.7-4.2	500
14/12 (Ku Band)	14-14.5	11.7-12.2	500
28/18 (Ka Band)	27.5-31	17.7-21.2	3500

bands. In addition to granting frequency assignments, the FCC assigns geographic slots in the geostationary orbit. To provide visibility to all of the 50 states, these assignments must be made in the geostationary orbit between 85 degrees and 135 degrees west longitude (and must be shared with other Western Hemisphere countries). Presently, the FCC strives to maintain a two-degree separation to strike a balance between interference among satellites and efficient use of the orbit and spectrum. Thus, available geographic slots in addition to frequency assignments become a limiting factor in satellite service expansion.

21-2 SPACE VEHICLE CONSIDERATIONS

Communications satellite system design can be divided into two distinct parts, the space segment and the earth stations. Although the two parts must be designed together if they are to operate as a system, certain elements of each can be considered independently.

The space segment consists of the satellite(s) and the tracking, telemetry, and control (TT&C) station located on earth. The TT&C station, as the name implies, tracks the satellite(s), receives telemetry information, and transmits signals to control their position. These stations often are designed and provided by the satellite vendor. They may be incorporated into or collocated with a communication earth station or may be operated as separate entities. The TT&C functions are not considered further here since the operation of the communication system is not affected when they are properly performed.

565

The satellites, on the other hand, are a vital part of the transmission path. Their physical as well as their electrical performance must be considered in order to realize adequate communications performance.

Satellite Stabilization

Early experimental, active, communications satellites were nongeosynchronous low–orbit space vehicles. They were spin–stabilized, as is a bullet, by rotation around an axis that maintained a fixed relation to the earth's axis. This eliminated tumbling and kept the axis properly oriented. However, communication capacity was limited because directional antennas aimed toward the earth could not be used. Since weight and therefore power are precious parameters in space, this mode of satellite operation severely limited transmission system performance. This type of spinning action for stabilization has been replaced on geosynchronous satellites by either of two methods that permit highly directional antennas to be employed. These are called the double–spin configuration and three–axis stabilization.

In the double–spin configuration, the satellite is spun at a rate of 50 to 100 revolutions per minute. The antenna platform is motor driven in the opposite direction at the same rotation rate. Depending on the mechanical design and mass distribution of the satellite, the spin rate necessary to achieve stability can be critical. Damping mechanisms are commonly employed to eliminate "wobble" or nutation. On–board earth sensors are used to control the motor speed. Thus, the antennas appear to be stationary with respect to a given point on the earth. This permits high–gain antennas to be used on the satellites. Pointing accuracies in the east–west direction (the direction of rotation) better than 0.1 degree can be obtained easily.

With three–axis stabilization, flywheels on the spacecraft rotate at high speed to provide stability in all three axes. This makes the exterior of the spacecraft appear to be fixed (within a few hundredths of a degree) with respect to a given point on the earth.

Each of these methods of stabilization has advantages and disadvantages: size and weight of the spacecraft, stability requirements during orbital maneuvers, reliability, cost, and prime power requirements are some of the items that influence the choice of the method used. Even with three-axis stabilization, rotating joints are needed on the solar panels to keep them pointing toward the sun. As long as the satellite meets specified stability requirements and the accuracy is known, the communications system design is not directly affected by the stabilization method employed.

Station-Keeping

Important items of spacecraft design include the ability to keep the satellite in orbit at its assigned longitude and in the proper inclination. The need for such control is the result of orbital perturbations that prevent satellites from maintaining perfect geostationary orbits. Corrections to counteract these perturbations, called station-keeping, are usually made by firing gas jets on board the satellite. The fuel most commonly used today for these jets is hydrazine. The life of the satellite is strongly influenced by the amount of fuel required to attain the initial assigned geosynchronous orbit and to maintain required orbital position accuracy. Earth-station antenna-positioning requirements are, of course, keyed to the station-keeping accuracy of the satellites.

Satellite Lifetime

Either of two major factors, depletion or catastrophic failure, may determine the life of a communications satellite. The probability of service outage due to catastrophic failure is minimized by careful design, redundancy, and the selection of subsystems and components by thorough testing as the satellite is assembled.

The major depletion components in a satellite are the solar cells, the control fuel, and the capacity of the batteries as reduced by repeated charge-discharge cycling. The electrical power used by present-day satellites is derived from solar cells with battery backup for periods of eclipse (i.e., when the satellite is in the earth's shadow). The solar cells deteriorate with time due to solar bombardment. Therefore, the power available from the solar cells is quoted in terms of beginning-of-life watts. The amount required for a given lifetime has an impact on the total weight of the spacecraft. These factors (solar–cell life, battery longevity, and fuel requirements) are usually balanced against each other within the overall vehicle capability to give a predicted lifetime of seven to ten years. So far, most communication satellite failures (total or partial) have been due to component failures rather than exhaustion of fuel or the decay of the power system. Costs to insure against satellite failure are a major system expense.

Launch Vehicles

All early communication satellites were placed into geosynchronous orbit by expendable vehicles launched by the National Aeronautics and Space Administration (NASA). However, with the current United States policy to phase out commercial satellite launches, a number of private firms (including several foreign companies) are now providing virtually all launch services. These services have the capability of an in–orbit payload of as much as 10,000 pounds and may carry one or two satellites per launch [1].

The cost of the launch is a major portion of the total investment in the space segment of a communication satellite system, and recent launch failures have resulted in total satellite loss. While it has been demonstrated that use of the space shuttle can reduce launch costs, current policy precludes use of the shuttle for nongovernment services.

21-3 SATELLITE TRANSMISSION EQUIPMENT

The design and development of satellites and satellite communication systems is a rapidly growing and changing field. Equipment design is subject to stringent requirements derived from the space environment and the stresses of launch and orbital adjustment.

Major Equipment Items

The earlier communication satellites operated exclusively in the 6/4 band; however, starting in 1979 a significant number of

14/12–band satellites have gone into operation. Some of the recently launched satellites operate in both bands. The frequency
separation of uplinks and downlinks as shown in Table 21–1 reduces intersystem interference. The 500–MHz radio–frequency
(RF) channel bands are normally divided into 40–MHz segments, which are composed of 36 MHz for signal transmission
plus a 4–MHz guard band. The specific equipment used to receive signals in the uplink and then to amplify, translate in frequency, and retransmit in a corresponding 40–MHz segment in
the downlink is known as a transponder. Satellites are sometimes
classified by the number of transponders they contain. Frequency band use and capacity are doubled by the use of orthogonal linear polarization or by using left– and right–hand circular
polarization. Thus, with the 40–MHz typical frequency segmen-
tation, a satellite may have as many as 48 transponders (24 in the
6/4 band and 24 in the 14/12 band).

Satellite transponders can generally retransmit multiple carriers
or signals of any type of modulation that fall within their
passbands. Depending on the linearity of the power amplifier,
transmission of some modulation types requires reduction of signal amplitudes to avoid saturation and intermodulation effects.
Communication satellite equipment must be able to operate in
the space environment. It also must be light in weight and
equipped with sufficient redundancy and protective switching so
that its design life objective can be achieved.

Satellites are equipped with antennas having sufficient gain at
microwave frequencies and appropriate beam coverage patterns
to cover the land areas of interest. The use of spot beams at the
higher 14/12–band frequencies has allowed frequency reuse,
which has increased these satellites' capacity [2]. The wideband
receivers include a low–noise solid–state RF amplifier, a frequency translator, and a driver amplifier. Lightweight filters with
phase equalization are used to separate the receiver output signal
into channels that correspond to those of the transponders. Each
transponder may have a separate output power amplifier. In addition, command and control receivers and telemetry transmitting equipment on different frequencies are also provided. Separate beacon transmitters for tracking are usually included.

Ground-controlled switching of a number of equipment units, including antenna feed horns, can be used both to increase the flexibility of a satellite system and to substitute major components in the event of equipment failure. Ground control of the gain of the satellite receiver is also desirable to balance the performance of the up- and downlinks over a wide range of earth-station antenna sizes and for single- or multiple-carrier operation of the transponders. Such control can greatly increase the capacity and efficiency of a satellite used in several different operating modes.

Redundancy is used to help ensure that a communication satellite reaches its design lifetime. However, it adds weight and cost; furthermore, the switches used can be a source of failure. In many satellite designs, redundancy is provided to protect major equipment items that are common to more than one transponder. It also may be used with equipment items whose mean time between failures would otherwise limit satellite reliability. Redundancy is particularly important to assure reliability of the TT&C system.

Typical Satellite Transponder Layout

Figure 21-1 shows a typical 6/4-band satellite transponder which receives at 6 GHz and goes through a single-stage conversion process to transmit at 4 GHz. Solid-state power amplifiers for 4 GHz have replaced traveling wave tubes (TWTs) on virtually all new satellites. This increases overall satellite reliability

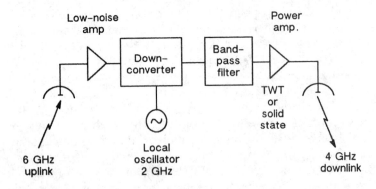

Figure 21-1. Typical transponder for 6/4-GHz band satellite.

since TWTs have been among the least reliable components. Downlink output power is limited not only by the satellite weight restrictions, but also by the need to restrict transmitted power density in order to control interference with terrestrial systems. The local oscillator is near 2 GHz to provide the frequency shift from the 6–GHz uplink frequency to the 4–GHz downlink. The bandpass filter removes unwanted modulation products and may also include an equalizer that limits phase variations across the passband.

Figure 21–2 shows the double conversion process that is normally used in 14/12–band satellite transponders to effect the conversion from the 14–GHz uplink to the 12–GHz downlink. The 13–GHz local oscillator produces a 1–GHz intermediate frequency (IF). A frequency of 1 GHz is used because it is relatively easy to build amplifiers and filters at this frequency. The IF is then up–converted to the 12–GHz downlink. TWTs are still used

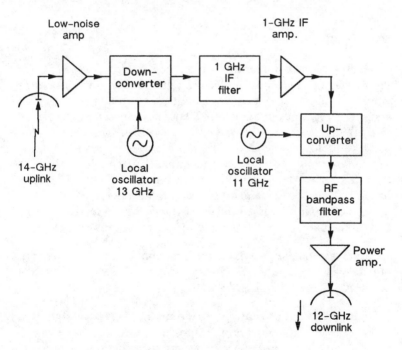

Figure 21–2. Typical   transponder   for   14/12–GHz   band satellite.

in the 12–GHz output power amplifier. Since the 14/12–GHz systems do not have the potential terrestrial–system frequency reuse that occurs on 6/4–band systems, the FCC allows higher transmitted power densities on the 12–GHz downlink. Twenty watts of output power may be authorized and two TWTs are sometimes used in tandem.

21-4 MODULATION AND SATELLITE ACCESS TECHNIQUES

Baseband signals are modulated onto satellite systems using techniques similar to those used on terrestrial microwave systems. The high path losses involved dictate special system designs and configurations to maintain transmission objectives. Since satellite systems feature access to numerous earth stations, multiple–access considerations become major factors in satellite system layouts.

Modulation Techniques

Analog Modulation. Since frequency modulation (FM) was the dominant microwave modulation at the inception of satellite communications, it is not surprising that early domestic satellite systems frequency–modulated frequency–division–multiplexed (FDM) signals onto a 70–MHz IF in a manner identical to that in FM terrestrial systems. Such FM continues on many domestic satellite systems. To increase the number of circuits within the limited transponder frequency spectrum, some analog systems have used single–sideband amplitude modulation (SSBAM) similar to terrestrial microwave SSBAM; however, these satellite systems must use voice companding to meet noise objectives.

Broadcast–quality television transmission via satellite has continued exclusively in an FM mode with each television channel using one 36–MHz transponder.

Digital Modulation. Just as terrestrial microwave has shifted to digital, satellite systems are also applying more and more digital modulation. Digital satellite systems cannot maintain the linearity to support high–density quadrature amplitude modulation (QAM) used extensively in terrestrial microwave. However, quaternary phase shift keying (QPSK) provides a robust digital signal with reasonable spectrum efficiency and is applied extensively to modulate voice, data, and video in the more recent satellite systems.

Multiple Access Techniques

There are several methods used to enable a number of earth stations to access a satellite. In frequency–division multiple access (FDMA), a satellite transponder is divided into frequency band segments where each segment is assigned for a specific user or circuit group. The frequency segments in FDMA can use either analog modulation or digital. In time–division multiple access (TDMA), each user or circuit group is assigned a specific time slot in the time domain. TDMA must use some form of digital modulation.

Frequency–Division Multiple Access. FDMA with frequency modulation of an FDM signal (FM/FDM/FDMA) is the primary method of satellite multiple access. To illustrate how FDMA can be used, consider earth station A providing circuit groups to each of three other earth stations B, C, and D. Station A transmits a carrier with normal analog supergroups (each supergroup containing five groups) to the satellite that relays the modulated carrier to all three stations. The distant stations all receive and demodulate the carrier but demultiplex only the assigned groups. In the reverse direction, station A receives the satellite signal containing groups from all three locations and, through appropriate filtering and demultiplexing, makes the proper circuit identification.

Single channel per carrier (SCPC) is another form of FDMA. In SCPC, each individual telephone channel independently modulates a separate RF carrier. Each carrier may be frequency or digitally modulated (frequently using PSK). SCPC finds its main application on low–density routes.

Time–Division Multiple Access. In TDMA, each station transmits bursts of RF energy to the satellite in a way that allows the various bursts to reach the satellite in a prescribed time sequence. TDMA transmissions are organized into time frames

573

containing reference bits that establish absolute time states for exclusive use of various stations in the network. Depending on the bandwidth of the transponder and type of digital modulation employed, bit rates of 10 to 100 Mb/s may be realized.

While TDMA requires a complex timing and control scheme, it provides a number of advantages over FDMA. Since only one carrier arrives at the transponder at any point in time, intermodulation products cannot be developed and the transponder power amplifier can thus be operated at full power. TDMA provides a straightforward interface with the emerging digital networks and easily accommodates forward error correction; it can also provide for the implementation of digital speech interpolation (DSI) and low–bit–rate coding techniques. DSI increases voice–channel capacity by using the 40–percent idle time during telephone conversations. As TDMA technology matures, these advantages assure increasing application and suggest the eventual displacement of FDMA.

Demand-Assigned Multiple Access. Demand assignment of satellite channels is sometimes used on FDMA and TDMA satellite networks to increase efficiencies where low duty–cycle traffic is involved or where the busy hours of trunk groups differ. Dynamic assignment of satellite channel capacity uses specific switching algorithms with the control provided by a hub earth station. Various schemes are sometimes used to provide random access to satellites, but these all have some inherent service–delay characteristics.

Spread-Spectrum Multiple Access. Spread–spectrum multiple access (SSMA), which is sometimes known as code–division multiple access (CDMA), modulates a combined signal onto an RF carrier that is spread across the bandwidth of the transponder. This combined signal contains the information being transmitted in the form of a coded address waveform. At the receiver, all signals are ignored except those carrying the correct SSMA code for the address. Since each SSMA signal has a unique address, the transponder can simultaneously carry overlapping signals on the same frequency spectrum without interference [3]. Thus SSMA allows multiple access; however, it has limited application because it is inferior to TDMA and FDMA in traffic–handling efficiency.

21-5 THE 6/4-GHz BAND EARTH STATIONS AND SYSTEM LAYOUT

Frequency Coordination

As previously mentioned, 6/4-band communications satellite systems share frequency allocations with terrestrial common-carrier microwave systems. This sharing of frequency bands requires careful coordination to ensure that neither service interferes with the other. The FCC rules relating to satellite communications require that, before an application for an earth station may be filed, the proposed frequency usage be coordinated with existing terrestrial stations and systems.

In the coordination process, three potential sources of interference must be investigated. First, any earth station and any terrestrial station within 100 kilometers must be coordinated in detail in a manner equivalent to a line-of-sight coordination for terrestrial microwave stations. Second, the FCC rules prescribe a method for calculating a coordination contour for the proposed earth station. The proposed frequency usage must also be coordinated with all terrestrial stations that fall beyond 100 kilometers but within the contour. The terrain of the interference path determines if a line-of-sight or an over-the-horizon study must be made. The study must include an investigation of the possibility of interference due to tropospheric scatter propagation. Third, the rules prescribe a method for calculating the potential interference caused by the scattering of energy by precipitation within the volume in space common to the beams of two antennas that intersect each other. The rules also require that proposed frequency usage in terrestrial systems be coordinated with all other users (including satellite systems) in the frequency bands involved prior to the filing of applications.

Terrestrial Connections

Unless careful coordination and shielding can be used, interference criteria usually place 6/4-band system earth stations at locations that require an interconnecting facility to the terrestrial network. These links are provided by terrestrial facilities, usually radio or fiber. They are usually short and thus contribute little impairment to the system, but they must be engineered so that intersystem interference requirements are satisfied.

6/4-Band Earth-Station Transmission Equipment

As in other communications systems, the limitations on satellite system performance are noise and interference. The factors affecting the performance are the same as those that are of concern in any microwave radio system: antenna gain, receiver noise, modulation noise, and output power. Earth–station antenna–gain requirements are determined by the transmit power of the satellite, the nature of the service being provided, and the performance objectives. Antenna size may be as much as 30 meters in diameter for large–capacity 6/4–band systems designed to meet CCITT noise objectives. Feedhorns may be designed to transmit linear–polarized or circularly polarized signals. High–capacity systems may use orthogonal linear polarizations.

Except for very–small–aperture receivers, there is usually a need to track even a stable geostationary satellite. Tracking may be automatic or manual. Large antennas with narrow beams may require automatic tracking while small broadbeam antennas, which only need to be moved occasionally, may be pointed manually.

The power transmitted by the satellite is often the most restrictive feature of a satellite system; weight limitations in the space vehicle usually limit the size of the battery that can be used. For a given satellite transmitter power, the downlink performance is a function of earth–station antenna size and receiver noise. The development of new solid–state devices for use in satellite system receivers has led to circuits having extremely low noise figures. Receivers employing such low–noise devices may be used in small or low–capacity earth stations. Where more exacting noise requirements apply, receiver noise may be reduced to a minimum by cryogenic cooling. Such techniques are used in broadband satellite systems to achieve operating noise temperatures as low as 60 kelvins.

Other earth–station equipment is typical of microwave receiving equipment in common usage. On the transmitting side, the modulators and up–converters are similar to those used in terrestrial microwave systems. The power amplifier, however, must produce higher output power than for terrestrial microwave service. Output power of several kilowatts is not unusual. Earth–station equipment may also include FM deviators, digital RF modulators, analog and digital multiplex equipment, FM deviation converters, and the terminal of a terrestrial connecting link of conventional design. Automatic polarization control of transmitted and received signals may be included to provide required on–axis cross–polarization isolation between two orthogonally polarized signals at the same frequency in either band. The stations are usually attended only for maintenance. Protection switching is normally provided for transmitting and receiving equipment.

Figure 21–3 is a block diagram of the principal transmission circuit components of a typical 6/4–band earth station involving three antennas. The deviation converter, up–converter, and high–power amplifier for each RF channel are protected by "hot standby" equipment that can protect up to six working circuits. The receiving circuits are similar to those in the transmitting direction.

The satellite and earth–station circuits provide high isolation between transmitting and receiving directions of transmission and between the two orthogonal linearly polarized signals in both the transmitting and receiving frequency bands. However, compensation must be provided for Faraday rotation effects caused by transmission of signals through the earth's magnetic field [4]. Such compensation is provided by the antenna feed system shown in Figure 21–3 and, in somewhat greater detail, in Figure 21–4.

The polarization of signals must be properly aligned with the receiving antennas at the satellite and earth stations. The feed system compensates for the Faraday rotation effects on the downlink signals and adjusts the linearly polarized uplink signals so that they arrive at the proper angles to maintain maximum discrimination.

Because of imperfections in the satellite and earth station antennas, the arriving vertical and horizontal signals are contaminated by a small cross–polarized component; i.e., they are

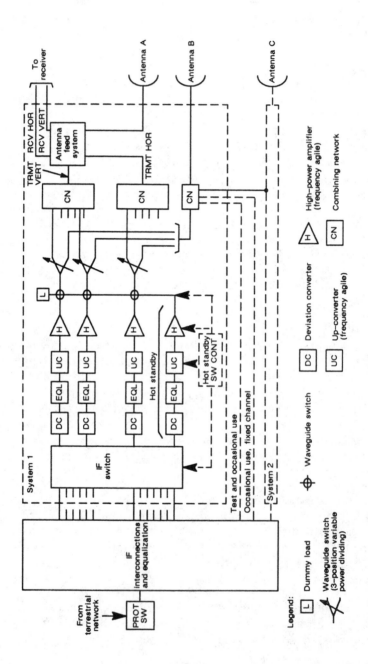

Figure 21-3. Typical earth-station transmitter arrangements.

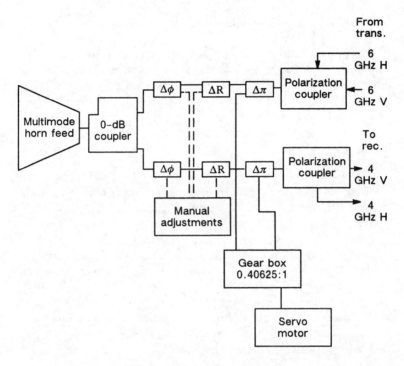

Figure 21-4. Block diagram of typical earth-station antenna feed system.

slightly elliptical in polarization. In addition, they are not quite orthogonal to each other. The $\Delta\phi$ differential phase shifters of Figure 21-4 can be adjusted to remove the ellipticity, the ΔR differential attenuators can be adjusted to make the vertical and horizontal signals orthogonal, and the $\Delta\pi$ phase shifters can be adjusted to make the vertical and horizontal signals conform to the vertical and horizontal outputs of the feed.

Changes in Faraday rotation may occur as a result of solar emission and may rotate the transmit signals as much as several degrees. Automatic tracking of $\Delta\pi$ is provided to follow the received signals and to rotate the transmitted signals in the opposite direction in expectation that they will arrive at the satellite in the proper geometrical relationship. Faraday rotation is inversely proportional to frequency squared.

579

6/4-GHz Band Transmission Design and Typical Layout

The transmission design of a satellite communication system is similar to that of terrestrial microwave radio in some respects but quite different in others. The equipment in the satellite may be regarded simply as a microwave repeater. Its functions are to provide gain to compensate for loss between transmitting and receiving earth–station antennas and to produce a frequency shift between the band used for uplink transmission and the band used for the downlink.

The great distances between earth and satellite repeaters result in high path loss and an absolute transmission delay of 240 ms in a satellite link. As a result, the control of noise and echo is unique for this type of system and has resulted in heavy use of echo cancellers for improved performance and cost. The computations outlined in the following are typical for domestic 6/4–band satellite systems employing FM [5]. The principles illustrated apply to any system, whether for heavy or light routes. In the case of a digital system, the objective is to obtain a high enough signal–to–noise ratio to give the desired error performance with a preselected margin.

The up– and downlinks to a satellite are each typically more than 22,300 miles long compared with 25 to 35 miles for terrestrial microwave radio system paths. Attenuation is about 199 dB for a 6–GHz uplink and 196 dB for a 4–GHz downlink. However, only small portions of the satellite link paths are in the earth's atmosphere and, as a result, problems due to atmospheric attenuation and multipath fading are much less than those in terrestrial systems. Tracking error must be considered for large antennas since the half–power beam widths are very narrow. This is not a major problem for smaller receptors, especially very–small-aperture terminals (VSATs).

Frequency reuse requires a high degree of cross–polarization isolation. Adaptive cross–polar interference cancellers are now available to maintain the required isolation. This procedure is not necessary with circularly polarized systems. However, it appears to be more difficult to achieve a high degree of isolation between signals at the same frequency and having opposite circular polarization.

The determination of transmission performance depends on a large number of variables that include the location of the earth station and the orbital position of the satellite. In the following discussion, the satellite system assumed is one that can serve earth stations in Puerto Rico, Hawaii, Alaska, and a number of others in the contiguous 48 states. The transmission values given are for a typical pair of links (one up at 6 GHz and one down at 4 GHz) between Los Angeles and New York City. The principles illustrated apply to any application, whether for heavy routes or light ones.

Uplink Transmission. The computation of transmission from an earth station to a satellite repeater requires a knowledge of 6–GHz gains and losses of the transmitting equipment at the earth station, the transmission path, and the receiving equipment at the satellite. The computations are made on the basis of carrier–to–thermal–noise ratios. The necessary transmitted effective isotropic radiated power (EIRP) can be calculated from the flux density needed at the receiver by considering transmission gains and losses. Full advantage is taken of the greater flexibility in design of earth–station equipment since design restrictions apply to the satellite repeater as a result of limitations on size, weight, and power.

Earth Station. Earth–station transmitters on heavy routes frequently operate at an output power in excess of 1 kW. For transmission from Los Angeles to New York, for example, the station power of +30.9 dBW, a feed–line loss of 4.5 dB, and an antenna gain of 63.3 dB result in a value of +89.7 dBW EIRP for each transmitted carrier [6]. The EIRP is not a true value of radiated power. It is rather an equivalent value stated in terms relative to the power that would be radiated for each carrier by an isotropic antenna. The above values are summarized in Table 21–2.

Transmission Loss. The path loss at 6 GHz for the Los Angeles–to–New York uplink is 199.4 dB. In addition, allowance is made for 0.3 dB loss due to earth–station tracking error and 0.1 dB for atmospheric attenuation. When these losses are combined with the 89.7 dBW EIRP for the transmitter, the isotropic received power (the power that would be received by an isotropic antenna) is found to be −110.1 dBW, as shown in Table 21–3. The gain of a one–square–meter antenna is 37.0 dB to give an

Table 21-2. Earth–Station EIRP Per Carrier for Los Angeles–to–New York Uplink Transmission

Parameter	Value
Transmitter output power	30.9 dBW
Feed–line loss	−4.5 dB
Antenna gain	63.3 dB
EIRP per carrier	89.7 dBW

Table 21-3. Isotropic Received Power for Los Angeles–to–New York Uplink Transmission

Parameter	Value
EIRP per carrier	89.7 dBW
Earth–station tracking loss	−0.3 dB
Atmospheric attenuation	−0.1 dB
Path loss	−199.4 dB
Isotropic received power	−110.1 dBW

effective satellite illumination, or flux density, of −73.1 dBW per square meter. This meets a requirement of −72.7 ± 1.5 dBW per square meter for the satellite being used.

Satellite. The signal is received at the satellite by an antenna having a gain of about 31.1 dB. With off–axis and pointing losses totaling about 2.6 dB for the Los–Angeles–to–New–York uplink and a feed–line loss of 3.8 dB, transmission from the antenna to the receiver has a gain of 24.7 dB. (For Hawaiian and Puerto Rican channels, the feed–line loss is 6.8 dB; the 3–dB added loss is due to the use of two combiners.)

Satellite signal–to–noise performance is a sensitive function of temperature. It has been found convenient to express the transmission properties of the receiving portions of the system as a gain–to–temperature ratio (G/T). The satellite receiving system operates at a noise temperature of 2140 kelvins, referred to the receiver input; it includes a receiver noise temperature of 1850 kelvins. Thus, the receiving system operates at a ratio, G/T = −8.6 dB as shown in Table 21–4. The requirement for this parameter is a minimum of −9 dB relative to 1 kelvin.

Table 21–4. Satellite Receiver Effects on Los Angeles–to–New York Uplink Transmission

Parameter	Value
Antenna gain	31.1 dB
Off–axis and pointing losses	−2.6 dB
Feed–line loss	−3.8 dB
System noise temperature	−33.3 dBK
Receive G/T	−8.6 dB

Carrier-to-Thermal-Noise Ratio. The thermal noise power at the receiver input may be computed by:

$$P = 10 \log (kTB \times 10^3) \text{ dBm}$$

where k is Boltzmann's constant (1.3805×10^{-23} joules per kelvin), $T = 2140$ is the noise temperature in kelvins, and $B = 36 \times 10^6$ is the noise bandwidth in hertz. When all these values are combined with the −110.1 dBW isotropic received power, it is found that for Los–Angeles–to–New–York transmission, the uplink carrier–to–thermal–noise ratio is 34.3 dB, as summarized in Table 21–5. Although computational details differ somewhat for other earth stations, the system is arranged to produce about the same carrier–to–thermal–noise value for all uplinks.

Table 21–5. Uplink Carrier–to–Thermal–Noise Ratio for Los Angeles–to–New York Transmission at 6 GHz

Parameter	Value
Isotropic received power from Table 21–3	−110.1 dBW
Received G/T from Table 21–4	−8.6 dB
Boltzmann's constant	228.6 dB
Noise bandwidth	−75.6 dB
Uplink carrier–to–thermal–noise ratio	34.3 dB

Downlink Transmission. Similar computations must be performed to determine the transmission over the 4–GHz downlink. The design of this path also relies on the greater flexibility in earth–station arrangements relative to those possible in the satellite. Transmitter power from the satellite is much lower than that attainable from the earth station. The design of the earth station results in an extremely low noise figure and higher antenna gain relative to those of the satellite repeater. The earth–station receiver system operates at a low noise temperature of about 60 kelvins.

Satellite. The satellite transmitter operates at +7.0 dBW (5 watts) and, with feed–line loss of 1.3 dB, produces a power at the antenna feed of +5.7 dBW (+2.7 dBW for Hawaiian and Puerto Rican transmission due to a 3–dB combiner loss). The antenna gain is 30.3 dB for Los Angeles–to–New York transmission, which is reduced to 28.1 dB by off–axis loss. Thus, the EIRP per carrier is 28.1 + 5.7 = 33.8 dBW, as shown in Table 21–6.

Table 21–6. Satellite Transmitting EIRP Per Carrier for Los Angeles–to–New York Downlink Transmission

Parameter	Value
Transmitter output power	7.0 dBW
Feed–line loss	−1.3 dB
Antenna gain	30.3 dB
Off–axis and pointing losses	−2.2 dB
EIRP per carrier	33.8 dBW

Transmission Loss. The satellite–to–earth path loss at 4 GHz for transmission from Los Angeles to New York is 196.4 dB to which 0.1 dB must be added for atmospheric attenuation. With 33.8 dBW for the EIRP value, the resulting isotropic received power is −162.7 dBW per carrier as shown in Table 21–7. The gain for an antenna of one square meter is 33.5 dB, which results in a satisfactory earth–station illumination of −129.2 dBW per square meter.

Earth Station. The gain to the receiver at the earth station is 60.3 dB, the combination of 60.9 dB antenna gain, a 0.5–dB feed–line loss, and an allowance of 0.1 dB loss for an antenna

Table 21–7. Isotropic   Received   Power   for   Los
Angeles–to–New York Downlink Transmission

Parameter	Value
EIRP per carrier	33.8 dBW
Atmospheric attenuation	0.1 dB
Path loss	−196.4 dB
Isotropic received power	−162.7 dBW

tracking inaccuracy of one tenth of the beam width. When these
values are combined with the thermal noise of the receiver (calculated for a noise temperature of 60 kelvins), the received G/T
is 41.5 dB, as summarized in Table 21–8. Finally, the receive
G/T, the isotropic received power, Boltzmann's constant, and
the noise bandwidth are combined to give the downlink carrier–
to–thermal–noise ratio of 31.8 dB, as shown in Table 21–9.

Table 21–8. Earth–Station   Receiver   Effects   on   Los
Angeles–to–New York Downlink Transmission

Parameter	Value
Antenna gain	60.9 dB
Antenna tracking loss	−0.1 dB
Feed–line loss	−0.5 dB
System noise temperature	−18.8 dBK
Receive G/T	41.5 dB

Table 21–9. Downlink   Carrier–to–Thermal–Noise   Ratio   for
Los Angeles–to–New York Transmission at 4 GHz

Parameter	Value
Isotropic received power	−162.7 dBW
Receive G/T	41.5 dB
Boltzmann's constant	228.6 dB
Noise bandwidth	−75.6 dB
Downlink carrier–to–thermal–noise ratio	31.8 dB

Overall Transmission. The carrier–to–thermal–noise ratios for uplink and downlink transmission may be combined to yield the overall carrier–to–thermal–noise ratio for the two links. For the Los–Angeles–to–New–York example, the overall carrier–to–thermal–noise ratio is found, by combining the uplink and downlink values, to be 29.9 dB. Typical values involving transmission between an earth station in the contiguous 48 states and outlying earth stations are 30.1 dB for Alaska, 29.8 dB for Hawaii, and 29.4 dB for Puerto Rico.

21-6 THE 14/12-GHz BAND SATELLITE SYSTEMS

Transmission Design

The transmission design of 14/12–band systems involves elements and considerations similar to those in the previous section on 6/4–band systems. In contrast to 6/4–band systems, 14/12–band systems are involved in only very minor sharing of frequencies with terrestrial systems. Consequently, 14/12–band systems require virtually no frequency coordination, and also allow earth stations for 14/12–band systems to be located in highly congested metropolitan areas. While the free–space loss at the 14– and 11–GHz frequencies is somewhat higher than at 4 and 6 GHz, the additional loss is entirely offset by the additional gain for similar–sized antennas. The narrower antenna beams associated with the higher frequency make it easier for these systems to meet interference criteria.

While the 14/12–band frequencies are noticeably attenuated by rain, the effects are not as serious as on terrestrial systems because the satellite beam traverses the earth's atmosphere for a relatively short distance. For example, at an antenna elevation angle of 10 degrees, the path distance that would be affected by rain would be in the order of 10 km [7].

Since the 14/12–band frequencies are relatively uninvolved with terrestrial systems, more transponder radiated power is allowed for the 14/12–band systems than for the 6/4 band. Thus EIRPs of 14/12–band transponders are typically 20 dB more than their 6/4–band counterparts. While a portion of this additional power is required to combat rain attenuation, a majority is allocated so that smaller, lower–gain antennas can be used for earth stations.

14/12–Band Earth Stations

The ability to effectively use small antennas in congested metropolitan areas for 14/12–band earth stations coupled with the availability of low–cost, low–noise receiver amplifiers has led to extensive application of 14/12–GHz VSATs with antennas as small as eighteen inches. VSATs are generally applied to private networks where low–circuit requirements can use robust modulation techniques, which keep the cost of the overall terminal low. Since these systems are predominantly digital, they readily interconnect with computer networks and digital terrestrial facilities. Portable VSAT stations provide an effective means for network service restoration.

21-7 TRANSMISSION IMPAIRMENTS

System engineering to meet appropriate carrier–to–thermal–nose ratios as outlined in Part 5 of this chapter can assure satellite circuit transmission compatible with various networks. Where digital services are applied, the carrier–to–thermal–nose ratios can be related to bit error ratios. Forward error correction is sometimes applied to meet digital performance criteria.

Noise Considerations

Noise accumulates from thermal sources, intermodulation, gain/delay distortion, and end–link connections. In addition, noise may be added from various interfering sources. These include internal multipath coupling through adjacent satellite filters, adjacent channels in the satellite or earth stations, nearby satellites, and terrestrial radio systems. Intersatellite interference must consider not only antenna patterns, but also spacing between satellites. Allowable system noise is normally allocated between the various sources in accord with recommendations of the CCIR.

Sun Transit

For a few minutes during each of several days about the time of the spring and fall equinoxes, the sun appears behind the satellite. Emissions from the sun into earth–station antennas make analog satellite circuits in the 4– and 6–GHz bands very noisy; the effect is much smaller in the 12/14–GHz bands. This predictable phenomenon can be avoided by switching to a protection satellite at a different longitude. A second antenna continuously tracking the protection satellite and appropriate switching equipment are provided to ensure service continuity where necessary.

Transmission Delay

With one important exception, the transmission characteristics of satellite facilities can be superior to those of analog terrestrial facilities that require many repeaters. The exception is the round–trip transmission delay. The overall delay can exceed 0.5 second when the 240 ms transit delay is added to the delay associated with common digital error–correction schemes. This requires the use of echo cancellation to control echo that would otherwise be intolerable. On voice circuits, digital echo cancellers have almost completely replaced echo suppressors to provide effective echo control. With echo cancellation, the delay is perceptible; however, a majority of users do not find it annoying. The CCITT recommends that only one satellite circuit be used in a telephone connection to avoid excessive impairment, and domestic interexchange carriers provide safeguards to prevent tandem satellite connections.

The long delay on satellite circuits may also result in problems with some types of bulk data transmission. These problems can normally be resolved by either changing the modes of operation or making appropriate modifications to the data sets. Most VSAT applications are for data use; with suitable data protocols, they operate quite satisfactorily.

21-8 INTERNATIONAL SATELLITE COMMUNICATIONS

International satellite telecommunication systems involve the same technologies, basic system components, access techniques, design considerations, and transmission impairments that this chapter has already covered in some detail for domestic satellite systems. However, international systems have some characteristics that differ from domestic systems and will be touched on very briefly.

A great majority of international satellite telecommunications is provided by the International Telecommunications Satellite Organization (Intelsat), which is a consortium of 112 member nations. Intelsat provides service to 159 countries via 15 satellites and almost 700 earth stations [1]. Intelsat satellites are stationed in the geosynchronous orbit in three general areas over the Atlantic, Pacific, and Indian Oceans to provide essentially global coverage. While domestic satellites use antenna beam patterns centered on the country being served, international satellites may need to cover over 40 percent of the earth's surface in order to reach widely separated locations. This requirement has led to very complex multibeam zone coverage antenna systems on international satellites. The positioning of Intelsat satellites creates an angular separation of about 10 degrees between the beams that span oceans; thus, separate antennas with properly shaped beams reuse the same frequency band in communicating with earth stations on different continents.

The long distances between terminations for international circuits increase the economic advantage of satellites over other facilities and, along with the rapid growth in international traffic, supports the large investment to incorporate the latest technologies to maximize the circuit capacity of new satellites as they are designed. The result has been a steady progression of new satellites with new features and more capacity. The latest satellite (Intelsat VI), will use 48 transponders in the 6/4 and 14/12 bands. This will provide a total capacity of 35,000 two–way voice channels plus two TV channels. High transmitted power levels of the Intelsat VI satellite will allow the use of relatively smaller earth–station antennas to provide high–quality service.

In addition to providing circuits for the international public switched network, Intelsat provides a number of satellites for providing digital communication networks to link the various locations of multinational corporations. Spot–beam antennas are used on these satellites to allow smaller earth–station antennas.

Recently, private international communication system operators have been allowed to compete with Intelsat for these services. In some cases, these operators lease facilities from Intelsat while their satellite systems are becoming operational.

Because of the perceived long distances involved (and the un-availability of alternate facilities to remote areas), the public generally accepts the real–time satellite transmission delay on international circuits.

21-9 TRENDS IN COMMUNICATIONS SATELLITE TECHNOLOGY AND APPLICATIONS

Technology advances in areas such as monolithic microwave integrated circuits (MMICs), very–large–scale integration (VLSI), on–board satellite baseband processing, satellite–switched TDMA, and multibeam switchable antennas will continue to increase satellite communication capacity and reduce system costs [8]. This will lead to increasing VSAT applications for multiterminal, wide–area, thin–route networks. International network satellite circuits to remote and sparsely settled countries will also continue to increase.

The continuing construction of long–haul optical fiber inter-exchange cables is resulting in an abundance of domestic facilities that do not have the absolute delay inherent in satellite circuits. This has resulted in a near–disappearance of satellite circuits from the domestic public switched network. The same is likely to occur on some of the high–density international routes as undersea optical fiber cables are completed. Portable earth stations will continue to make satellite systems applicable for temporary and emergency transmission facilities.

References

1. Long, M. *World Satellite Almanac*, Second Edition (Indianapolis, IN: Howard W. Sams and Company, Inc., 1987).

2. Bostian, C. W. and T. Pratt. *Satellite Communications* (New York: John Wiley and Sons, Inc., 1986).

3. Joseph, K. and D. Raychanduri. "Channel Access Protocols for Ku–Band VSAT Networks: A Competitive Evaluation," *IEEE Communications Magazine*, Vol. 26, No. 5 (May 1988), pp. 34–51.

4. Panofsky, W. K. H. and M. Phillips. *Classical Electricity and Magnetism* (Reading, MA: Addison–Wesley Publishing Company, Inc., 1955).

5. "Application for a Domestic Communications Satellite System," Attachment A of the American Telephone and Telegraph Company submission to the Federal Communications Commission (Mar. 29, 1973).

6. Gould, R. G. and Y. F. Lum. *Communication Satellite Systems: An Overview of the Technology* (New York: IEEE Press, 1976), pp. 113–115.

7. Chakraborty, D. "Constraints in Ku–Band Continental Satellite Network Design," *IEEE Communications Magazine*, Vol. 24, No. 8 (Aug. 1986), pp. 33–43.

8. Hyde, D., T. Inukai, and C. E. Mahle. "Satellite Scenarios and Technology for the 1990s," *IEEE Journal on Selected Areas in Communications*, Vol. SAC-5, No. 4 (May 1987), pp. 556–570.

Chapter 22

Mobile Radio Communications

While microwave radio systems provide only one of a number of alternative facilities for fixed point–to–point telecommunications, radio remains the only viable medium for providing communications to portable and mobile stations that cannot be physically tethered to the network. While the initial conventional radio–telephone systems provide service to vehicles, service limitations have restricted their application. However, high–capacity cellular mobile radio systems that provide service equivalent to land–based telephones are fostering a rapid and increasing demand for vehicular mobile telephones in urban areas. Emerging domestic satellite mobile services may well provide the means for also economically providing high–quality service in sparsely populated regions.

The availability of low–cost, light–weight mobile units is stimulating use of mobile radio technology for personal portable communications. New technologies that are rapidly becoming available can provide ubiquitous digital portable communication interconnection to the public switched network. It may even become economical to apply these systems in lieu of inside wire at users' premises.

22–1 CONVENTIONAL LAND–MOBILE COMMUNICATIONS

Wire–line common carriers started providing domestic public land mobile service to moving vehicles from the public switched network in 1946. These conventional mobile services continue to provide service in the 150–MHz and 450–MHz bands. Public service is also provided by other common carriers that operate competitively in the same bands. These competitive services are interconnected to the public network by arrangements provided by the wire–line carriers. There are also many private mobile services relating to police, fire–fighting, utility maintenance, transportation dispatching, and other activities.

Until the early 1960s, essentially all land–mobile network communications service required a mobile service operator to assist on calls, and push–to–talk operation was always required at the mobile stations. With push–to–talk operation, the mobile set user listens with the telephone handset held to the ear as usual. However, to talk over the connection, it is necessary to depress a push–to–talk button on the handset.

Improved Mobile Telephone Service (IMTS) was introduced during the 1960s with the development of two new mobile telephone systems: the MJ system operating in the 150–MHz band and the MK system operating at 450 MHz. Except for the frequency bands, these systems are similar and operate compatibly with central–office switching systems.

With IMTS, it is possible to dial directly, without operator assistance, from a mobile unit when it is in its home service area. Similarly, incoming calls to the mobile unit are on a direct–dial basis. Each mobile unit is assigned a normal ten–digit telephone number distinct from any other number in the switched message network. Features available on IMTS include automatic channel access and automatic number identification. The system can also be arranged to provide dial service to roamers, i.e., to those mobile units that left their home areas and desire to operate with systems in the areas in which they are temporarily located.

Channel Frequencies

Table 22–1 shows the channel designations and frequency assignments traditionally used by wire–line carriers in providing mobile service in the 150– and 450–MHz bands. Up to eleven 150–MHz and twelve 450–MHz channels could thus be assigned in a service area. More recently, the Federal Communication Commission (FCC) has opened all channels to both wire–line and non–wire–line common carriers, adding 21 base–station frequencies of 152.03 to 152.21 MHz in 30–kHz steps and 454.025 to 454.350 MHz in 25–kHz steps. The corresponding mobile frequencies are 158.49 to 158.67 and 459.025 to 459.350 MHz.

Four–wire duplex transmission is provided between base and mobile stations. Signals carried in these channels are phase–modulated radio–frequency (RF) carriers with a maximum frequency modulation (FM) deviation of 5 kHz. The characteristics of the mobile equipment and the applicable performance requirements are explicitly specified. Interference patterns that affect transmission have been studied and much of the system engineering and applications have been related to the results of those studies [1].

Table 22–1. Traditional Wire–Line Carrier Assignments for 150–MHz and 450–MHz Service

(a)   150–MHz band (MJ)

Channel	Transmit Freq. (MHz)	
	Base	Mobile
JL	152.51	157.77
YL	152.54	157.80
JP	152.57	157.83
YP	152.60	157.86
YJ	152.63	157.89
YK	152.66	157.92
JS	152.69	157.95
YS	152.72	157.98
YR	152.75	158.01
JK	152.78	158.04
JR	152.81	158.07

(b)   450–MHz band (MK)

Channel	Transmit Freq. (MHz)	
	Base	Mobile
QC	454.375	459.375
QJ	454.400	459.400
QD	454.425	459.425
QA	454.450	459.450
QE	454.475	459.475
QP	454.500	459.500
QK	454.525	459.525
QB	454.550	459.550
QO	454.575	459.575
QR	454.600	459.600
QY	454.625	459.625
QF	454.650	459.650

System Layout

The principal elements of a conventional land–mobile radio communications system (either manual or IMTS) are a control terminal with connections to the switched message network, base–station radio transmitter and receivers, and mobile station equipment. The mobile station includes an antenna, transmitter and receiver circuits, supervisory and control circuits, and a telephone set. The basic system elements, essentially the same for all conventional mobile systems, are illustrated in Figure 22–1. The

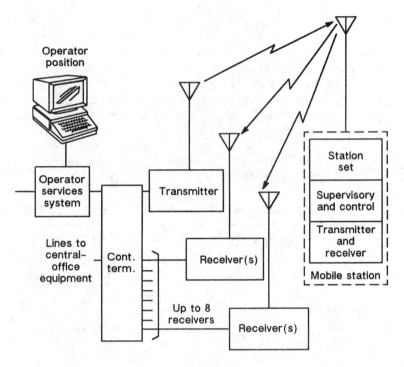

Figure 22-1. Typical layout for conventional mobile radio service.

figure shows radio equipment for one channel; transmitters and receivers for additional channels are added in accordance with traffic demands and the availability of frequencies in the area, up to a theoretical total of 18 (150–MHz band) or 26 (450–MHz band).

The area covered by the arrangement of Figure 22–1 is typically 30 to 40 miles in diameter. The base–station transmitting equipment may be located some distance from the control terminal and is usually connected by private–line facilities. Each channel is equipped with a 50– to 250–watt transmitter at the transmitting antenna site with the output power depending on the area to be covered and FCC radiation restrictions. Base–station receivers may be located about the area as required to compensate for the lower output power of the mobile–station transmitters, nominally 20 watts.

IMTS Operation

In IMTS operation, the control terminal automatically selects and marks an idle channel (when available) to be used for the next call, whether incoming or outgoing. The control terminal marks the channel by applying a 2000–Hz idle tone. Under the control of their supervisory and control circuits, all idle mobile sets within transmitter range hunt automatically for this marked channel and camp on it until a call is established. The first mobile user to go off–hook then seizes this channel, and all other mobile sets again hunt for a newly marked idle channel. This feature makes it unnecessary to monitor channels manually at a mobile set and affords a degree of privacy when in the automatic mode.

The control terminal circuits are responsible for most of the call–handling processes in IMTS, although there are some logic circuits at the mobile sets as well. The control terminal provides a transmission, signalling, and switching interface with the central office.

Transmission Features. Two–wire voice circuits from the central–office equipment are transformed into four–wire circuits for transmission between the base and mobile stations. A voice–operated gain–adjusting device (VOGAD) is used in the transmission path from the base to the mobile station to regulate outgoing speech volume. In the receiving path from the mobile station, a speech–operated noise–adjusting device (SONAD) provides noise suppression during silent intervals.

Equipment Features. The IMTS mobile set consists of a radio receiver and transmitter, a control unit, and a telephone with push–to–talk feature. The control unit includes appropriate selector switches labeled to correspond to the 11 system channels. Normally, since mobile units may roam into other serving areas, all authorized channels are equipped.

Any of three modes of operation designated H (home), R (roam), and M (manual) can be selected. When the mobile unit is operating in the home area, the H button is depressed. This conditions the station equipment for IMTS operation and causes the equipment to hunt automatically over only the locally provided channels to find the one marked with idle tone.

Operation Beyond the Home Area. If this mobile unit moves into another area equipped for IMTS system operation, the R button is depressed as are the channel selection buttons for channels provided in that area. The set then hunts automatically over only those channels that have been selected.

Other Conventional Mobile Radio Applications

Service to Ships and Planes. FCC rules provide separate frequencies for mobile systems with special characteristics for providing service to ships and airplanes. Various common carriers provide a number of separate systems to serve these and other specialized needs: very–high–frequency (VHF) coastal and Great Lakes service, using manual–operator or dial techniques; service to ships on the high seas via either satellites (dial) or high frequency radio (manual); service from private aircraft and airliners, etc. Their general configuration and operation is similar to those of the conventional land mobile systems already discussed. It is necessary to provide additional channels on maritime systems, and continuous monitoring, for safety and calling.

Special Mobile Radio Service. While operators of special mobile radio systems are not classified as common carriers, the FCC authorizes them to sell service on Special Mobile Radio Service (SMRS) trunked facilities in the 800–MHz band. These services, which operate through IMTS–type terminals, afford interconnection to the public switched network; thus they are essentially equivalent to the domestic public service provided by common carriers.

Mobile Dispatch Service. Private systems involving a dispatcher and mobile units can be adapted to provide interconnected switched network traffic. This has limited application since large dispatch users (taxi, police, etc.) have high channel usage that justifies their own private systems.

Telephone Maintenance Radio Service. Four VHF and six ultra–high–frequency (UHF) frequency pairs are allocated exclusively to provide common carriers with two–way mobile communications to improve field operations and customer service. These systems may be operated in either a manual or dial mode;

however, they may not be used to provide customers with service except in an emergency.

22-2 CELLULAR LAND-MOBILE COMMUNICATIONS

With only 3 MHz of total allocated bandwidth, overcrowded channels with relatively poor transmission had been the norm for conventional domestic public land–mobile services prior to 1984. Private land–mobile channels were also congested and interference–laden. The result was long waiting lists for inferior service. In response, the AT&T Company proposed in the early 1960s that a wide band of frequencies be allocated to support a cellular mobile development to provide high–quality service to a large number of subscribers in a spectrum–efficient manner. After years of competing development, field experiments, petitions, comments, preliminary rule making, hearings, and reconsideration, the FCC formalized rules for commercial operation of cellular mobile systems in 1982. A total of 40 MHz of bandwidth was allocated in the band between 825 and 890 MHz for cellular mobile radio applications. This allocation is divided evenly between two competing carriers in each market area. The allocation has since been expanded to 70 MHz in the 824–894 MHz band.

At the end of 1988, all of the 305 larger metropolitan areas had full cellular coverage by two competing companies; applications are being granted and systems are being installed in over 400 smaller market areas as well. It is estimated that the number of cellular subscribers will be in the two million range in the early 1990s [2].

Cellular Concept

Conventional mobile radio systems usually use high–power transmitters at an advantageous site and tower height to provide coverage over a large geographic area. Such application provides effective communication to mobile units within 20 to 30 miles of the base, but can cause harmful interference to adjacent systems operating on the same frequency. Hence co–channel operation can seldom be tolerated for systems with less than a 100–mile spacing between base stations.

Cellular mobile radio systems, on the other hand, use short antenna towers and low power transmitters in order to reuse frequencies without co–channel interference [3]. This frequency reuse allows the geographic service area to be divided into many small areas (cells). Such a configuration allows spectrum–efficient operation and allows traffic growth within the service area by further reducing transmitter power and splitting cells into still smaller geographic segments. Geographic growth can be accommodated in a spectrum–efficient manner by adding additional cells at the boundaries of the initial system.

System Layout

Figure 22–2 shows the basic layout of the cellular mobile radio communications system. The area to be served is divided into small geographic cells. Cells are initially laid out with centers spaced about 4 to 8 miles apart. The basic system components

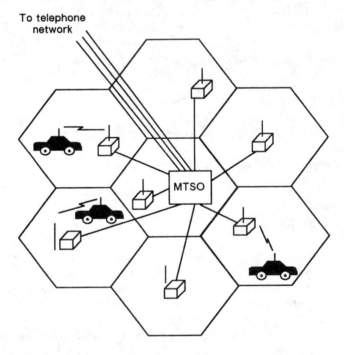

Figure 22–2. Basic cellular mobile system layout.

are the cell sites, a mobile telephone switching office (which incorporates most system design elements), and the mobile units.

Cell Sites. Each cell includes a site with a building that houses base radio equipment that can connect and control any mobile unit within that cell's geographic area. Radio transmitters located at the cell site have a maximum effective radiated power of 100 watts. Combiners are used to connect multiple transmitters to a common antenna on a radio tower that is usually between 100 and 300 feet high. Base receivers use a separate antenna system on the same tower; this is usually arranged in a space–diversity configuration.

Mobile Telephone Switching Office. The cell sites are interconnected to and controlled by a mobile telephone switching office (MTSO). This switching office is an electronic switching machine with substantial central processing capability to control communications to and from mobile units as they move between cells, as well as to make connections to and from the public network. The MTSO not only makes the connection between public land telephones and the cellular mobile units, but also controls cell site activities and mobile actions through commands relayed via data channels. The channels connecting the MTSO and cell sites may be dedicated landline (often DS1) or microwave facilities. The FCC has allowed digital termination system (DTS) frequencies (see Chapter 16, Part 5) to be used for these microwave applications.

Mobile Units. Each mobile unit consists of a control unit, a combined transceiver/logic unit, and the mobile antenna. The control unit includes a handset to provide acoustical interface, a pushbutton keypad to enter commands into the telephone network, and audible and visual indications to provide customer alerting. The transceiver provides duplex transmission and reception between mobile and cell sites. It normally has an effective radiated power on the order of 6 watts. It must be capable of transmitting and receiving on any of the assigned channels. Services provided to mobile units are roughly equivalent to those provided to landline public telephone subscribers.

System Frequencies

Figure 22–3 shows the original total common–carrier cellular frequency allocations. The 20–MHz band between 825 and 845 was for mobile transmission to the base while the band between 870 and 890 was for transmission from base to mobile; these are split into bands so that two competing systems can be made available in each area. In 1987 new allocations extended each of these bands 25 MHz, from 824 to 849 MHz and 869 to 894 MHz.

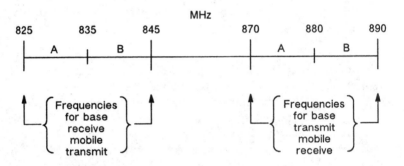

A represents the original wire–line common–carrier allocations

B represents the similar non–wire–line common–carrier allocations

Figure 22–3. Cellular mobile frequency allocations.

Present cellular system design specifications call for FM channels spaced at 30 kHz with a peak frequency deviation of 12 kHz. The 12.5 MHz of frequency spectrum with a 30–kHz spacing yields 416 channels. With 21 channels used for control purposes, each carrier still has 395 channels available for subscriber communications.

In a typical system, a set of 10 to 50 channel frequencies is assigned to carry the mobile traffic within a cell; the number used depends on the traffic load and the blocking objective. The power of the base transmitters within the cell is maintained at a relatively low level with just enough antenna height to cover the limited cell geography. This allows reuse of the 20 channels in nonadjacent cells within the same market area, by controlling co-channel interference. A coordinated frequency reuse methodology enables tens of thousands of simultaneous calls in a market area [4].

This method is illustrated in Figure 22-4, where four sets of channel frequencies are assigned in a way that avoids the same set being used in adjacent cells. While this plan could be applied with uniform terrain contours, actual conditions dictate further geographic separation of the cells that use the same frequencies. Plans with 7 or 12 sets of channel frequencies obviously provide more physical separation and are often used depending on the shape of the antenna pattern employed.

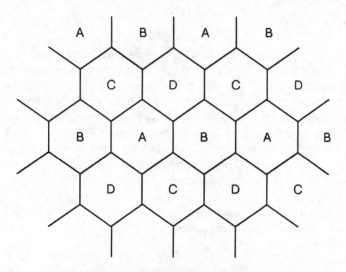

Cells with the same designation share the same channel
set and potential co-channel interference.

Figure 22-4. Geographic separation of cells with four different
sets of frequencies.

Cell Splitting

When systems are initially placed in service, the channels assigned to the cells will adequately carry the traffic load. As mobile units are added to the system, the available channels in some cells may become overloaded. In these cases, the congested cells can be subdivided into smaller cells, each with its own base station. The smaller cells may use lower transmitting power with appropriate antennas and reuse frequencies in an efficient way that ties in with the overall system reuse pattern. Similarly, the subdivided cells can be further subdivided as necessary. While, theoretically, cell splitting could continue indefinitely, a one—mile cell radius is generally a practical lower limit. While omnidirectional antennas are normally used at startup, 60—degree or 120—degree directional antennas may be used as cells are split in order to alleviate interference caused by the increased channel reuse.

Radio Propagation

To make cellular service similar to what customers experience on their regular telephones, cellular system design must keep transmission impairments within prescribed limits. While line—of—sight radio propagation from a transmitter to a receiver can be calculated easily, propagation from a fixed base station to a moving mobile unit does not usually involve line—of—sight conditions. Rather, the propagation mode is most likely to be multipath scattering, reflections, or diffraction by obstructions and buildings in the general vicinity of the moving mobile unit. The resulting received signal, then, varies randomly as the sum of many individual waves with changing amplitude, phase, and direction of arrival. The statistical autocorrelation distance is of the order of one—half wavelength.

These signal variations can severely impair transmission quality. The same diversity techniques that are applied to alleviate the effects of fading on microwave paths can also be applied to mobile systems. Space diversity is most applicable to cellular systems and is generally applied to base receive antenna systems.

System Operation

In Figure 22-3, the MTSO is connected to each cell site by a voice trunk for each of the radio channels installed at the site. Two data links are also installed from the MTSO to each cell site in order to transmit information for processing calls and controlling the mobile units. In addition to housing the base radio equipment carrying voice traffic, each cell site contains signal monitoring equipment and a "setup" radio to establish calls. (This is the same concept as the common–channel signalling used to set up interoffice calls in the public switched network.)

Whenever a mobile unit has power applied, it automatically selects and moves to the setup channel with the highest signal strength. In monitoring the selected setup channel, it interprets the data stream emanating from the base station, which includes identification numbers of mobile units to which calls are currently being addressed. When a mobile unit detects that it is being called, it again samples the signal strengths of all the standard setup channels so that it can respond through the cell site offering the strongest signal. It quickly tunes to the strongest setup channel before relaying a response. The system, via the MTSO, transmits a voice channel assignment. The mobile unit switches to the assigned correspondence channel and alerts the subscriber that he or she is receiving a call. A similar sequence of events takes place when the mobile unit originates the call.

While a call is in progress, the system examines the signal strength at the serving cell site every few seconds. If the signal level drops, the system seeks another cell to handle the call. When it finds a suitable cell site, the system transmits a command to the mobile unit to reset to an available frequency at the new location. While the mobile unit is changing channels, the MTSO reswitches the land party to the voice trunk associated with the new channel. The periodic monitoring of mobile unit signals is known as "locating" and the act of changing channels has come to be called "handover." The purpose of the locating and handover functions is to provide satisfactory transmission quality on telephone calls as mobile units move from cell to cell. Handovers become frequent as cells become smaller.

Signalling and Supervision

Normal system operation along with the locating and handover functions requires complex signalling and supervision functions to take place on the setup and voice radio channels.

Setup Channel. A 10–kb/s data stream on the setup radio channel sends paging, voice channel designation, and overhead messages to mobile units. The mobile unit returns page responses, origination messages, and order confirmations.

Voice Channel. Both digital messages and continuous supervision tones are transmitted on the voice radio channel. The digital messages are sent as a discontinuous blank–and–burst inband data stream at 10 kb/s and include order and handover messages. The mobile unit returns order confirmations and messages that contain the dialed digits. Continuous positive supervision is provided by an out–of–band 6–kHz audio tone, which is modulated onto the carrier along with the speech transmission.

Additional Applications

In addition to providing service to vehicles, cellular systems provide communications to trains in the northeastern United States and to ferry boats in the state of Washington. Cellular systems also provide service to portable hand–carried units equipped with battery power packs. Some vehicular mobile units include arrangements so that they can be temporarily removed for portable use. All cellular systems accommodate data and facsimile transmission through appropriate modems.

As cellular radio expands, a single MTSO is sometimes used to control a number of cellular systems, which facilitates roaming within the connected systems. Arrangements are also being made to accommodate roaming between systems in different localities and with different owners. The industry is moving toward cellular networking, which will allow a subscriber to make a call immediately from any cellular location.

Digital Systems

While terrestrial network facilities are evolving toward end–to–end digital transmission, radio transmission for cellular systems has remained analog. With emerging digital and very–large–scale–integration (VLSI) technologies, digital cellular mobile radio transmission could realize a number of advantages over the existing analog systems such as:

(1) Better spectrum efficiency by using spectrum–efficient modulation and differential coding techniques

(2) Better signal quality in an environment subject to radio fading by using forward error correction

(3) Higher usable data transmission rates to mobile subscribers, which is a feature inherent in digital systems

(4) Direct connectivity to integrated services digital network (ISDN) and other emerging terrestrial digital networks

(5) Possible lower subscriber radio–set costs consistent with the proliferation of inexpensive digital components.

In spite of these apparent advantages, the large capital investment in analog cellular systems and mobile equipment precludes the displacement of analog–by–digital systems in the near future. On the other hand, the push for network standardization has fostered proposals for incorporating digital channels into existing analog cellular systems [5]. This is likely to take the form of digital channels (to communicate with digital mobiles) added to existing cell sites; thus, such systems could serve both analog and digital mobiles. This type of application requires development of and agreement on standards.

22–3 PERSONAL PAGING SERVICES

Services are available to provide one–way radio communication to a subscriber carrying a small pocket receiver. The communication originates from a telephone in the public switched network and alerts the subscriber via a coded radio signal that he or she is being paged, and may include a short message. The service is used extensively by people who rely heavily on communications for their usual activities, but who are frequently moving about and have no ready access to a telephone. Personal paging service continues to grow rapidly and is furnished competitively by various common carriers.

Types of Service

Tone–Only Service. For tone–only service, the coded signal activates the receiver, which alerts the subscriber by audible, tactile, or visible means. The subscriber then must find a telephone to place a call to a previously agreed number. A significant proportion of customers subscribe to two numbers, each with a distinctive alerting signal. This permits them to distinguish between routine and priority calls, between group or individual calls, or between sources such as their offices or an answering service.

Tone/Display Service. Tone/display service provides for the same alert as tone–only service, but offers, in addition, a short message that appears on an LCD (liquid crystal display) in the paging receiver. A numeric display service shows only numbers, while an alphanumeric display provides for text as well. Twelve to 16 characters can be seen at one time and the display receiver can store up to 1000 characters in memory.

Numeric display service requires only the use of a conventional dual–tone multifrequency (DTMF) telephone to key in the message. On the other hand, alphanumeric display requires a special data terminal from which to originate the message; this somewhat restricts its application. The transmission of the display information takes little time, hence, it has a negligible effect on radio channel loading.

Tone–Plus–Voice Service. Tone–plus–voice service provides the conventional tone alert followed by a preset time (such as 20 seconds) for an audible voice message received via a small speaker in the paging receiver. Tone–plus–voice service uses a significant amount of transmission time for the audible message, which severely limits the number of pagers that can be assigned to the radio paging channel. It is also easy for the message to be misunderstood if the subscriber is in a noisy location. In spite of these disadvantages, some customers prefer tone–plus–voice service.

Nationwide Paging Service. Some service vendors provide for paging a subscriber simultaneously in a large number of different metropolitan areas by interconnecting systems via landline or satellite circuits.

System Operation

Most personal paging services operate on allocated channels near 150 MHz. However, frequency congestion at 150 MHz has resulted in new systems being installed at available frequencies in the 930–MHz band. A few systems are using subcarriers leased from commercial FM broadcast stations.

The principal system components are a control terminal, radio transmission equipment, and pocket receivers in a configuration shown in Figure 22–5. A number of different suppliers provide system components. Designs are continually updated with state-of-the-art advances.

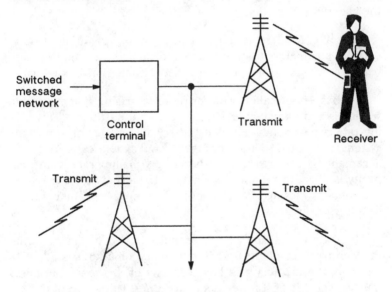

Figure 22–5. Personal paging system layout.

In modern paging systems, the caller dials a conventional telephone number via the public switched network for the person being paged. The control terminal accepts the call, generates the appropriate radio transmission code, activates the transmitters, and returns a signal to the caller that the page is being made. For display or voice–message services and for many tone–only systems, the terminal also sends a distinctive signal back so that the caller can input the message or other identification.

Control Terminal

The caller–dialed telephone numbers generally reach connecting circuits that outpulse digits to the control terminal much as if it were a private branch exchange with direct–inward–dialing. In some small installations, the interconnection logic that determines the flow of address signals to the radio transmitters is built directly into the terminal circuitry, but in most cases, the terminal is controlled by a programmed minicomputer. These computer functions include the assigning of subscriber numbers, activating multiple transmitters, queueing paging requests, and accumulating usage data. Some control terminals can simultaneously accommodate multiple service types and more than one radio paging channel.

Capacity. Modern terminals can assign up to 100,000 numbers per channel, but holding time and calling rate limit the number of receivers on a system to a figure somewhat below that.

The busy–hour calling rate for personal paging systems now in service is approximately 0.1 to 0.2 calls per customer. This calling rate, when combined with the signalling rate for which the system is designed, determines the overall system capacity for an acceptable grade of service. Where the signalling rate is fast, capacity is likely to be address–limited. However, where it is slow (or contains message information), capacity is more likely to be calling–rate–limited.

The code format must be large and flexible enough to permit the construction of the required number of address codes. In addition, the memory and logic capacity of the control terminal must be capable of storing such coded information and of retrieving it quickly and accurately. This information is stored at the same time as the queued addresses and any caller–originated messages are transmitted to the receivers. Finally, the time required to broadcast the addresses influences the overall system capacity.

A system feature that affects the total addressing time significantly is the number of times the address is transmitted. In early system designs, the address was transmitted three times on the theory that the probability of successful transmission would thus, be significantly enhanced. However, studies have shown that the enhancement is slight and now the address is generally broadcast only once.

Address Formats. Original personal paging systems used a combination of single–frequency tones to signal receivers; however, these have almost all been converted to a digital format. Digitally encoded addresses use carefully chosen sequences of *1*s and *0*s to which digital logic circuits in the addressed receiver can respond. With a digital format, these receivers are not vulnerable to intermodulation and usually incorporate error detection and correction features.

Transmitter

Address signals are transmitted by frequency or phase modulation of an RF carrier. The maximum deviation for the modulated carrier is 5 kHz. The transmitted output power is expressed as an effective radiated power of 500 watts and must be less if the antenna is higher than 500 feet above average terrain. Most systems are arranged so that signals are transmitted from the control terminal to several transmitters strategically located throughout the serving area. Thus as the receiver is moved from place to place, the received signal is maintained within a range consistent with the receiver sensitivity. The several transmitters are operated simultaneously in most systems. In–building coverage is clearly important for pocket receivers; building penetration losses may be 20 to 40 dB. With simultaneous operation, the interconnecting facilities from the control terminal to the transmitters may have to be equalized to the same absolute delay to provide efficient operation in areas where the transmitter coverage overlaps.

Receiver

The range of operation of a personal paging system depends heavily on the sensitivity of the pocket receivers, the nature and size of surrounding buildings, and the power output and placement of the radio transmitters. Typically, a range of 4 to 5 miles has been found feasible in city business districts; this may be reduced to as little as 1 to 1.5 miles around each transmitter since

611

reception is desired inside buildings that use large amounts of metal.

The receiver sensitivity is a design parameter controlled by the manufacturer. Its value must be known when a new paging system is being engineered for service. Sensitivity specifications must include the method of holding the receiver, an allowance for body effects and temperature variations, and other detailed requirements. Measurements with transmitter frequency tolerances appropriate to normal operation must be made.

The receiver must be highly selective in order to function properly in an environment of strong RF signals from other services. The selectivity must be maintained over a wide range of environmental temperatures.

Radiation of RF energy from the local oscillator in the receiver must meet FCC requirements. In addition, two receivers should not interfere with one another when separated by a distance of two feet.

A number of receiver features are offered by manufacturers including numeric and alphanumeric display options. A receiver may respond immediately to a paging signal or may store the signal until interrogated by the called person. This feature is valuable to people who may not want the alerting signal to disturb them or others at certain times.

22-4 OTHER DOMESTIC MOBILE COMMUNICATION SERVICES AND APPLICATIONS

In addition to conventional mobile, cellular mobile, and personal paging services, a number of additional mobile radio applications are either in use or proposed. These will not be given detailed coverage in this volume; however, some of them may well become major network communications media.

Mobile Satellite Service

Communication satellites have been providing effective mobile service to ships on the high seas for some time. The technology now appears to be available in the form of higher power satellites, low–noise receivers, and sophisticated, low–cost mobile antennas to allow economically viable domestic mobile satellite service.

After extensive hearings, the FCC has proposed that a consortium of various applicants provide a domestic mobile satellite system to cover the entire United States. The system is to operate on a pair of frequency bands near 1.5 GHz. It is not anticipated that the system will compete with cellular systems, but rather supplement cellular by providing service in vast, sparsely populated geographic areas.

The technical configuration will allow a mobile station to communicate with other mobile users, the public switched network, or a dispatcher [6]. Since Mobile Satellite Service (MSS) will be weather– and terrain–resistant, it can provide emergency communications whenever a disaster renders parts of the terrestrial network inoperative. Once the system is in place, it may be able to provide long rural loops to remote areas more economically than terrestrial facilities.

Mobile data services are also proposed using existing Ku–band satellite transponders with VSAT–type terminals mounted on vehicles. This type of service will be particularly applicable to vehicle position reporting.

Cordless Telephones

A cordless telephone uses radio frequencies to provide a wireless link to a "base" unit that provides for network interface via a connection to the inside wiring of a normal telephone installation. Since output power of the cordless–telephone transmitter is low, the customer does not need to obtain an FCC license; however, reliable coverage does not extend much over 100 feet from the "base" unit. Cordless phones are manufactured and marketed widely. While cordless sets have been generally well accepted, privacy concerns and co–channel interference limit their application.

The FCC currently allows cordless phones to operate on any one of ten duplex channels near 46 and 49 MHz on an interim basis. As cordless–telephone usage continues to increase, the limited number of channels will lead to more and more co–channel interference in urban areas. Cordless–phone users are also subject to interference from the primary users of the frequencies (U.S. Government mobile radio). The FCC is being petitioned to provide additional frequencies for cordless–telephone usage on a permanent basis. Digital techniques are being introduced to provide privacy.

Considerable effort is underway to expand the scope of cordless telephones to provide person–to–person and person–to–network communications within an office complex or in a large building environment. Such "expanded cordless phones" use digital techniques with higher power transmitters (about one watt) and require an FCC license to operate on allocated frequencies in the 900–MHz band. Spread–spectrum modulation techniques to ensure privacy and improve noise performance have been proposed for these systems.

Infrared radiation (requiring no FCC authorization) can also be used for interconnecting various types of terminal within a range of about 30 meters in a large room.

Universal Digital Portable Communications

A system configuration within the capability of current digital and network technologies has been proposed that can provide universal digital portable communications (UDPC) [7]. Such a configuration could eliminate many of the shortcomings of the current methods for providing portable communications and lead to a truly universal service connecting to the public switched network. In addition to providing personal communications to a highly mobile society, UDPC has the potential for replacing the capital– and maintenance–intensive end–portion of the local terrestrial distribution plant with portable telephone units.

While frequencies have not been allocated or system designs completed for UDPC, considerable and increasing research effort by various organizations demonstrates growing interest and feasibility.

22-5 MOBILE RADIO SYSTEMS FOR BASIC TELEPHONE EXCHANGE SERVICE

In addition to their basic mobile application, almost all of the two-way mobile radio systems that have been described have been used to provide basic telephone service to remote rural subscribers.

The FCC has for some time made conventional 150-MHz and 450-MHz domestic public mobile frequencies available on a secondary, noninterfering basis so that these mobile systems can be operated in a fixed mode to provide exchange service to individual rural customers. This application has been quite limited since it requires considerable capital investment.

The FCC has recently authorized a more efficient and cost-effective means of providing rural exchange facilities by radio: the Basic Exchange Telecommunications Radio Service (BETRS). This approach, based on service tests already underway in several locations, would share conventional or cellular mobile frequencies on a noninterfering co-primary basis [8].

References

1. Douglas, V. A. "The MJ Mobile Radio Telephone System," *Bell Laboratories Record*, Vol. 42 (Dec. 1964), pp. 382-389.

2. Shostick, H. "Can Cellular Be Sold?," *Telephone Engineer and Management* (July 15, 1987), pp. 72-77.

3. "Advanced Mobile Phone Services," *Bell System Tech. J.*, Vol. 58, No. 1 (Jan. 1979).

4. Oetting, J. "Cellular Mobile Radio—An Emerging Technology," *IEEE Communications Magazine*, Vol. 21, No. 11 (Nov. 1983), pp. 10-15.

5. Calhoun, G. "The Digital Future for Mobile Radio," *Telecommunications* (Aug. 1986), pp. 51-64.

6. Morley, N. "Mobile-Satellite Service: An Update," *Telecommunications* (June 1987), pp. 57-58.

7. Arnold, H. W., D. C. Cox, and P. T. Porter. "Personal Digital Portable Communications: A System Perspective," *IEEE Journal on Selected Areas in Communications*, Vol. SAC–5, No. 5 (June 1987), pp. 764–773.

8. Clements, P. E. "Wireless Digital Carrier for the Rural Local Loop," *Telephone Engineer and Management* (May 15, 1987), pp. 82–86.

Telecommunications Transmission Engineering

Section 6

Transmission Maintenance

Transmission maintenance is made up of those operations that are concerned with keeping transmission facilities operating so that service objectives are met. This section classifies maintenance into three major functions: surveillance, analysis, and repair, all of which must be carried out quickly, efficiently, and economically.

Chapter 23 shows how network growth and complexity have made necessary new approaches to transmission maintenance. Two major trends are noted. One is toward centralization of maintenance and operations control; the other is toward mechanization through the use of computers. Centralized maintenance systems that illustrate these trends are described and the way maintenance capability is designed into some transmission systems is also discussed.

In spite of these trends toward centralization and mechanization, a large number of mobile, independently mounted, fixed and portable test sets are still required for use by maintenance personnel. Chapter 24 describes selected examples of modern test sets in these classifications.

Chapter 23
Maintenance Systems

Transmission maintenance in the broadest sense includes the testing and adjustment of circuits during installation and preparation for service as well as during active service. Maintenance activities are designed to prepare a facility for initial operation, to locate sources of trouble, and to repair the troubles so that transmission performance is held to high standards. Maintenance activities also include the ability to remove failed circuits from service, to make them appear busy (unavailable) to switching machines, to apply restoration and temporary repairs, to support trouble reporting, and to perform record–keeping and administration procedures. These procedures must provide a range of accurate information about circuits and facilities. When systems and circuits are installed, adjusted, and tested properly before they are put into service, the incidence of trouble is significantly lower and, as a result, maintenance costs are reduced.

Maintenance equipment, systems, and methods have undergone the same patterns of innovation that have accompanied the growth of the entire telecommunications network. Factors that have influenced these changes include the necessity of keeping pace with network growth and of applying new technology in order to keep maintenance economical and compatible with the technical advances in facility and circuit design. These effects have been felt in the maintenance of trunks and special–services circuits as well as in facilities.

The changes that have taken place in maintenance systems reflect two notable trends: centralization of maintenance control and mechanization through computers. These trends have produced major changes in methods of operation, have led to new training requirements, and have resulted in computer software applications throughout the industry.

In many cases, a transmission facility is monitored and tested by equipment that is an integral part of the facility. In other cases, maintenance systems are shared by a number of different types of transmission facility. For both, centralization is notable. Modern maintenance systems are capable of remote testing, analysis, and control of transmission systems over unlimited miles from a central point.

Loops, trunks, and special–services circuits are dispersed over wide areas and use a variety of facilities. Furthermore, their maintenance is more directly related to the satisfactory operation of traffic networks than to the maintenance of a specific transmission system or facility. When an individual circuit fails, it is not necessarily the result of a facility failure. However, if it is a trunk or special–services circuit, it may seriously affect the network in which it is used. Thus, circuit maintenance systems are not designed as integral parts of specific transmission systems, but are designed to fit the broad classes of message and special circuitry.

Maintenance activities cannot be carried out efficiently without support equipment. This equipment includes arrangements for gaining access to the transmission facilities to be maintained, order–wire and alarm systems, record keeping, and provisions for remote control and telemetry.

23–1 NETWORK EFFECTS ON MAINTENANCE

Network growth and the need to control costs have had remarkable effects on the methods and procedures used to maintain the telecommunications plant. Increasing demands for service have brought about an impressive growth in the number of trunks. At the same time, the simplicity of digital facilities and the rising cost of labor have brought the near–elimination of manual testing and a great increase in centralization and mechanization of trunk testing.

Surveillance

Transmission facilities are subjected to continuous surveillance in a number of ways. In the newer digital systems, monitoring circuits make continual checks of error performance. When the error rate is excessive, protection switching may be activated and alarms are initiated. Power fuses and circuit breakers are equipped with alarm features that alert maintenance personnel in the event of power system troubles. Modern switching machines test for loop continuity, insulation quality, and return loss each time they set up a call.

To supplement these and other built–in surveillance systems, routine tests are made periodically to verify the satisfactory operation of both facilities and circuits. In the past, such testing was performed manually. However, the factors discussed earlier that are leading toward the mechanization of maintenance procedures have modernized surveillance testing as well. Loops, trunks, and special–services circuits are normally tested by automatic means and by remote control. Output data usually include a printout of only those circuits that fail to meet requirements.

Test Procedures

Initially, testing involved the coordination and cooperation of two testers, one to transmit test signals and the other to measure the results at the other end of the circuit. Such procedures are time–consuming and difficult to schedule efficiently because the testers must be available simultaneously.

The problems of coordinating maintenance work have been greatly mitigated by the development of arrangements that can be controlled remotely and thus permit one–person or automated testing. With such remote control, a single tester, or the test system itself, makes many measurements of overall performance and sectionalizes the circuit to assist with trouble isolation. Test systems have been made available to facilitate testing in both directions of transmission automatically; a wide range of transmission and operational tests can be performed. Access to these test lines is provided by dialing through the switched message or private network, with appropriate security provisions. Single–person testing with remote control and loop–back circuit arrangements have proven to be efficient and economical.

Test Equipment

A wide variety of test equipment is required in the maintenance of circuits and facilities. Measurements must be made to determine gains, losses, noise, delay and attenuation/frequency distortion, return loss, error ratio, error–free seconds, and other parameters. The test equipment that is now available for these tasks has risen in sophistication with the advance of technology.

Although portable test sets are still available for manual testing, maintenance equipment has become more centralized and less mobile as techniques for testing by one person have been introduced. Loop–back circuits, test lines, and computer–controlled test equipment are all mounted in equipment bays, in consoles permanently located in areas of central offices most convenient to the circuits under test, or at a centralized location that provides convenient access. The shift to computer control of maintenance activities has introduced an emphasis on the development and enhancement of computer software.

Preventive Maintenance

In the past, considerable effort was placed on preventive maintenance. In such activities, adjusting electronic equipment, cleaning and adjusting mechanical parts, and replacing electronic components were accomplished at specified intervals in an attempt to prevent trouble conditions and to anticipate failure.

These activities were costly and sometimes introduced troubles that otherwise would not have occurred. Since solid–state and digital facilities tend to be highly stable over extended periods of time, there is now little need for this type of preventive maintenance. The need still exists, of course, for such routine activities as adding water to batteries, pruning tree limbs, and other routines that must be followed to keep equipment in proper working order and to prevent damage. However, the emphasis has shifted to timely detection and repair of incipient failure.

Trouble Identification and Location

Automated test facilities for identifying and locating service–affecting troubles are now common. Even when a trouble has been identified with a specific system, it is expensive and difficult to locate the source of trouble without adequate fault–locating facilities. Many of these fault–locating facilities can be operated remotely under the control of a maintenance center. The accuracy of fault location has a strong impact on the cost of repairs since maintenance crews can be dispatched more efficiently when troubles are accurately located.

Effective trouble location, down to circuit–pack level, reduces exposure to system outage caused by electrostatic discharge. Because a growing amount of electronic equipment uses such integrated–circuit technology as CMOS (complementary metal–oxide semiconductor), it is undesirable to handle circuitry that can be damaged by incidental static charges in the work area. Control measures (wrist straps, conductive floors, etc.) are of value, but definite trouble location to a specific circuit board is a further sizable aid.

Operating Centers

The centralization of maintenance activities mentioned previously can be seen in nearly all the maintenance systems and procedures in common use. Loops from many different central offices are now tested from a single, centralized automated repair service bureau (ARSB), often statewide in scope. Trunks serving the intertandem portion of the network over hundreds of square miles can be tested by a single center. Similarly, most special–services circuits undergo mechanized testing from a central location.

The centralization of maintenance activities can also be seen in carrier system operation. The present systems can be tested, monitored, and controlled over hundreds of miles by remote control from a centralized point. This capability has also been extended to the remote control of transmission terminals and multiplex equipment. However, as maintenance functions are centralized they become vulnerable to catastrophic outages. Periodic reviews of disaster routines lessen the likelihood of such occurrences.

23–2 FACILITY MAINTENANCE SYSTEMS

The maintenance of transmission facilities (media, line equipment, and terminals) is administered and controlled by systems and equipment of two general classifications. In the first group, maintenance capability is designed as an integral function of a transmission system. In the second classification, maintenance systems are designed as independent entities with functions that may be used by a number of different transmission systems. The functions in both classifications include surveillance, identifying and locating troubles, and alerting personnel to the existence of troubles. The remote control of certain operations (e.g., protection switching) is also provided in some systems.

System-Integrated Maintenance Arrangements

All carrier systems have some built-in maintenance equipment. Some of this equipment provides little more than a form of surveillance. In other systems, the equipment is quite extensive and includes many operational and maintenance features.

Analog Transmission Systems. Maintenance of analog transmission systems is based primarily on the transmission and measurement of single-frequency pilot signals applied to the system at controlled frequencies and amplitudes. Variations in amplitude are used at the receiving end of a line section or system to adjust regulating equalizers automatically. Circuits are also provided at the receivers to detect variations of the received signal beyond set limits. These circuits actuate visual and audible alarms and initiate the switching of service to protection facilities.

N-Type Carrier Systems. The single-frequency signals that are used in N-type systems for regulation are the real or reinserted channel carriers. In the double-sideband N2 terminals, these carriers are modulated by channel signals but, even with this modulation, the total power of these transmitted carriers is sufficiently constant that system regulators operate on the basis of this power. In the N4 terminals, the operating mode is single-sideband suppressed carrier with 12 of the carriers reinserted after suppression. They are transmitted with the complex message signal at amplitudes and frequencies equal to those in N2.

When system failure is indicated by the loss of carrier power, detection circuits initiate carrier failure alarms and a trunk processing sequence as described in Chapter 11. The affected trunks are then held out of use until the system is restored.

Other forms of maintenance in N–type systems are performed by the use of portable test equipment. This includes transmission and noise measurements, location of troubles, equalizer adjustments, etc.

Analog Multiplex Equipment. Multiplex equipment has maintenance features that include the transmission of pilot signals, the use of regulators, alarms, and protection switching. These features, described in Chapter 9, are summarized here.

Group and supergroup multiplex equipment uses pilot–controlled regulators to maintain transmission loss to within 0.1 dB of the nominal value. The alarm feature associated directly with transmission is end–of–range and loss–of–pilots alarms, which scan pilots and report deviations from normal level. In most large offices, the scanning function is performed by the carrier transmission maintenance system described later in this chapter.

Equipment that operates at mastergroup or multimastergroup levels of the multiplex hierarchy usually has automatic protection switching and patching facilities that permit flexible use of spare equipment for maintenance and broadband restoration.

Analog Coaxial Systems. Like the "N" family, coaxial transmission systems use pilot–controlled regulators to maintain line transmission characteristics within acceptable limits. Each system also has an automatic protection switch to protect against equipment or cable failure. In addition, these systems have specialized equipment for equalizer adjustment, trouble analysis, and fault location.

In the L5E system, a centralized and automated transmission surveillance system, with remote auxiliary stations controlled from a transmission surveillance center, is an integral part of the system [1]. Digitally operated test equipment makes desired measurements under local or remote control on a programmed or manual basis. Data are collected and analyzed at the surveillance center where all operations, including repeater fault location, are controlled by a minicomputer.

Microwave Radio Systems. The maintenance facilities that are integrated with microwave radio systems are those of

625

surveillance, protection switching, and alarms. The digital radio systems use violation or parity monitors and restorers. When violations exceed established limits, these circuits also trigger protection switching. In the analog systems, surveillance takes the form of single–frequency pilot signals, which control flat–gain regulators. The regulators correct the system gains to compensate for changes due to atmospheric fading or other causes. Together with noise–slot monitors, which sample the noise level in an otherwise unused part of the baseband spectrum, they initiate protection switching when limits are exceeded.

All radio systems are equipped with alarm arrangements that indicate signal loss and deteriorated performance. These alarms are displayed locally and usually extend to a Facilities Maintenance and Administration Center (FMAC).

Digital Systems. A comprehensive maintenance plan is available for the digital transmission network. In some cases, maintenance features and functions are incorporated in the transmission systems; in other cases, maintenance is provided by external systems that include record keeping and operational features as well.

Terminology. To facilitate discussion of digital system maintenance, it is desirable to define several commonly–used terms: *red alarm, yellow alarm, upstream, downstream,* and *alarm indication signal (AIS).* When failure occurs in one direction of transmission, a loss–of–service alarm is initiated at the affected receiving terminal. Since loss of service is involved, a red alarm lights and an audible alarm is sounded; the alarm is called red alarm. When such an alarm is present, the distant transmitting terminal is signalled automatically to indicate the failure. At the distant (transmitting) end, a yellow diode lights and the alarm is called a yellow alarm. The red and yellow convention is maintained throughout the digital network.

Upstream and *downstream* describe transmission phenomena relative to a reference point in a transmission path. Points downstream are those to which signals are being transmitted from the reference point and points upstream are those from which signals are being received at the reference point.

An alarm indication signal (also called a "blue signal") is substituted for a failed signal to minimize unnecessary protection switching or the sounding of alarms in equipment located downstream from a failed link or piece of equipment [2]. An AIS satisfies line format specifications at the hierarchy level at which it is inserted, but carries no message or framing information for lower hierarchy levels.

Digital Terminals and Switches. The principal maintenance feature of digital channel banks or terminals is a circuit that recognizes a loss of framing in the receiving equipment. When such a failure occurs, this circuit initiates a red alarm and transmits a yellow alarm to the other end of the system.

The presence of these alarm conditions also initiates trunk processing carrier group alarm functions similar to those in analog carrier.

Maintenance and surveillance of multiplex units are controlled in much the same manner as that used for terminals. Circuits are provided to monitor the received signal. These circuits register an out–of–service alarm when the incoming signal is lost or when the multiplex unit goes out–of–frame.

To prevent a loss of signal or framing from affecting downstream multiplex equipment and terminals, an AIS is substituted for the regular signal in most multiplex units. Thus a failure at, for example, a DS3 facility does not force protection of a healthy DS3 facility that is connected in tandem with it, but the DS1 facilities that use those DS3s are driven into an alarm state to remove service from the affected trunks.

Digital switches monitor the above parameters, with the additional ability to collect data on timing slips and errored seconds. They report minor or major alarms based on the number of occurrences per day.

Digital Lines. Surveillance of repeatered–line performance and location of faulty repeaters on digital transmission facilities are performed from central offices at the ends of or along the route of each system. Performance is evaluated by violation monitors that examine the signal for code violations while ignoring valid bipolar violations such as those introduced by bipolar with eight–zero substitution (B8ZS), B6ZS, or B3ZS formats. Signals are also generally monitored for violations of successive–zeros restrictions and outright loss of signal. Equipment that uses the extended superframe format can monitor cyclic redundancy check (CRC) codes along with related performance parameters. Appropriate alarms indicate the nature of any detected impairment. As in multiplex units, most fiber and radio span lines provide an AIS in case of total failure.

The repeatered lines of all digital systems have fault location circuitry so that a defective repeater can be identified from the central office before maintenance personnel are dispatched. The fault location arrangements used on T1, T1C, and T2 lines involve the transmission of a specially coded bipolar–violation signal from the central office. This digital signal contains a high concentration of energy at one of 12 specific voice frequencies that are assigned to correspond to specific repeater locations. At each remote repeater, a bandpass filter selects the frequency associated with that location; circuits are provided to transmit the voice–frequency signal back to the central office over a separate wire pair. Missing or weak signals identify faulty repeaters. Comparable test signals are used for fault location on optical–fiber regenerators.

Regenerator frames for fiber systems offer, in addition to the above measures, monitoring of such parameters as laser diode current to detect an approaching failure.

Digital Cross–Connect Frames. Equipment frames containing jack panels serve as cross–connection points in the central office for the interconnection of digital channel banks, other terminals, digital switches, multiplex equipment, and transmission facilities [3]. These cross–connect frames also serve as access points for service restoration, testing, and trouble location.

Cross–connect frames are designated separately (DSX–0, DSX–1, DSX–1C, DSX–2, DSX–3, and DSX–4) for each of six digital rates. Each frame is used to interconnect equipment that operates at that rate. The six frames can be grouped into three types, each with different features.

The DSX–0 is the only frame of the first type. It is used only for interconnecting terminal and multiplex equipment as part of the Digital Data System (DDS). Quad terminals on the cross-connect panels are interconnected by four–wire jumpers equipped with quad connectors.

The second type includes the DSX–1, DSX–1C, and DSX–2 frames. These feature monitoring and patching jacks, and accept normal telephone–type plugs. They are equipped with tracer lamps for convenient identification of the two ends of a cross-connection. They include order–wire terminations and multiple outputs from a quasi–random signal source for testing. DSX–1s are often divided into "loop" and "trunk" sections in offices having a large amount of digital loop carrier (DLC).

The DSX–3 and DSX–4 make up the third type of frame. The jacks, plugs, and cross–connect cords are of a 75–ohm coaxial type. A tracer lamp feature is included as with the DSX–1.

Testing Complete Systems

There is a need to document a standard method and equipment functions for testing a link section and the multiplex equipment (via cross–connection equipment at either side) that make up a digital circuit. Such a standard [4] is being currently drafted by the IEEE Project P1007 Measurements Group. It covers digital multiplex testing, including the basic tests containing analog–to–digital conversion, the parameters to be measured, the test-equipment functions that are needed and the test configurations to be used. The North American digital levels that are covered are DS1, DS1C, DS2, and DS3.

System–Independent Maintenance

The complexity of modern transmission systems and of the network itself has caused maintenance by manual methods to become obsolete. As a result, computer–automated maintenance systems are used routinely.

Analog Carrier Maintenance. Automatic, in–service testing of analog broadband systems and terminals may be provided by a system that has access to carrier test points via a broadband switching and control network using coaxial switches. The central installation may contain a minicomputer, a cassette–tape or disk memory unit, switch control circuits, and a teleprinter.

The system monitors pilot amplitudes and noise. It scans the transmission band of the facility under test for unwanted high–amplitude signals (a hot–tone scan). The system may be used to identify and isolate troubles and to determine whether they are inside or outside the central office.

Measurements may be made automatically on a programmed basis, or may be initiated by operator command from a remote control and display unit or from distant offices via a data set. The remote control and display unit may be plugged into access connectors at convenient bay locations in the office. Test results may be displayed on a numerical readout [5].

Alarm Surveillance and Control. A general–purpose alarm surveillance and control system provides mechanized and centralized alarm reporting, status surveillance, and remote control of a large variety of telecommunications equipment. This system may analyze failures and present processed information to a central operator. It may log all operating events, provide for selective log retrieval, and administer trouble tickets and other tasks.

Data channels are used to connect the central location with remote control terminals and computers for monitoring and control. These features permit this system to function simultaneously as an independent alarm center and an integral component of a multisystem control center. A computer connection may be linked to minicomputers to support an electromechanical switching control center.

T–Carrier Administration and Maintenance Systems. The universal use of digital carrier systems in metropolitan areas led to an early need for centralized and automated facilities for the administration and maintenance of the digital network [6]. A large metro network may include 10,000 T1 systems made up of 50,000 DS1 facility sections using microwave radio, wire span lines, and fiber. The complexities of operation and interconnections in such a network can be solved only by a centralized administration system.

Maintenance and operation activities in a network of digital systems are controlled from the FMAC [7]. Such activities may be augmented in large networks by the use of a system to provide surveillance of performance and analysis of system failures. This surveillance system may also provide automatic trouble isolation to a faulty terminal or a specific span, report on the current status of the network, periodically monitor the performance of each working system, and maintain a log of the status and use of maintenance lines. A feature of growing importance is patterning: tracing the simultaneous failure of a group of DS1 facilities to a DS3 that carries them all, even though the DS1s rarely terminate in the same offices.

A minicomputer is used at the maintenance center for control of surveillance system operations. Connections are made from the maintenance center to remote offices by data links.

Network Monitoring

An improvement over segmented maintenance and surveillance systems is a system that correlates surveillance indications from many network elements into an "overall" evaluation of network performance. The network can be protected more effectively by centralized switching, interoffice, and loop surveillance rather than by individual systems [8]. This provides a useful complement to the network management efforts involved in traffic—network operations [9].

The electronic, stored—program—controlled switches introduced in the 1960s and early 1970s gave exchange carriers their first opportunity to centralize maintenance efforts. This new equipment, coupled to remote data—communications capabilities, made centralized surveillance effective. The result was the creation of switching control centers for maintenance surveillance of these stored—program—controlled switches.

Similarly, maintenance centers were created to control and maintain interoffice facilities. The digital carrier systems introduced in the 1960s made it possible to monitor for transmission failures on an ongoing basis. Since the early 1970s, indications of failure, or alarms, have been sent to a central location.

Outside plant maintenance centers are responsible for the network's outside plant. The centers had depended on customer trouble reports to direct their maintenance efforts. The use of DLC systems in the outside plant network enables these centers to benefit from network surveillance indications generated from carrier systems and switches.

The application of digital technology throughout the network and the merging of maintenance support into a uniform set of capabilities in network equipment has led to an integrated application of supporting surveillance systems. Centralizing switching, interoffice, and loop surveillance into a common analysis effort brings to light many service problems that might otherwise go unrecognized.

Nonintrusive Single-Point Measurement System. The national telecommunications network has migrated from its original unified topology into an entirely different transmission and signalling hierarchy. At present, the methods of measuring the network and the parameters measured are based to some degree on predivestiture methods and measurements. These methods are predicated on the measurement of an analog network with concern for parameters such as loss and noise. The rapidly evolving digital network changes the parameters of prime concern from loss and noise to echo and delay.

Therefore, a new method of measurement is needed to deal with the digital network. A nonintrusive single-point method of measurement will access the network at a digital point (e.g., DS1) and measure groups of connections to the calling- and called-party terminations. This will assess transmission quality of the total trunking network and local loops. Initially, this measurement method will supplement existing measurement systems. As standards are developed and confidence is built in the new technique, traditional connection-appraisal measurements and maintenance systems would be phased out, with attendant cost savings. This fits in with the future digital maintenance systems that monitor the digital bit stream and make no repetitive tests over idle channels. The system operates by sampling the data internal to an echo canceller inserted into a digroup that contains the trunk group to be assessed [10,11]. The canceller coefficients can then be processed into transmission measurements.

Level measurements are determined only during the time that a signal is present, and are not influenced by silent intervals. In order to preserve the privacy of information, the sampling period cannot be long enough to preserve the intelligence of the signal but must be long enough to determine that a signal is present. The measurement of signal power requires some restriction of the range expected to avoid measuring noise and silent periods as signal power or signal power as noise. The noise measurement is made after the called party answers but prior to conversation over the channel. The measurement system will provide the ability to measure echo path loss (EPL) and absolute delay in the network. Digital parameters such as error rates and error–free seconds can potentially be included. In addition, the system will be capable of measuring traffic data such as dial–tone delay and post–dialing delay.

The system envisioned to date, using available hardware, is a single–point nonintrusive monitoring system that collects transmission and signalling data on each connection selected in a sampling plan. The system would collect the following data.

(1) Active signal level

(2) Noise during pre–signal quiet periods, equivalent to C–message noise

(3) C–notched noise equivalent to analog measurements of the C–notched noise on analog carrier systems, and currently measured by analog means on digital carrier systems

(4) 3–kHz flat–weighted noise, equivalent to analog measurements of the same parameter

(5) Data level

(6) Absolute echo path delay (in milliseconds) of the signal (either voice or data) from its source

(7) EPL

(8) Multiple EPLs

(9) Origin and terminus of the call

(10) Dial–tone delay and post–dialing delay encountered on complete calls and on unsuccessful attempts.

633

Mathematically combining the real–time delay results, the noise data, the EPL measurements, and the voice power results will map into a measure of customer opinion of the transmission within a wire center's serving area, within the local switching area, or for the access services offered to interexchange carriers. An output from the measurement system can provide weak–spot indications for quality–assurance functions. Focused reports will point out specific loops that exhibit high loss, noise, or echo. Additional quality–assurance outputs can be made available for managerial and executive level reports of customer satisfaction with transmission. A further refinement of the system would be an artificial–intelligence program to analyze the data collected and direct corrective action.

Cable Pressure–Monitoring Systems. Although not devoted to transmission measurements, cable pressure–monitoring systems are important to transmission maintenance. The quality of transmission deteriorates quickly when moisture enters pulp–insulated cables. Many cables are maintained under gas pressure to impede the entrance of water through small holes or breaks in the cable sheath and to provide indications of such breaks by changes in gas pressure.

Pressure transducers or contactors usually are installed in cable sheaths, status indicators are installed on air dryers and air–feed pipes, and monitoring devices are used to measure gas flow. These devices may be all monitored using telemetry systems to transmit status information to terminals in each wire center. A central computer may collect this data by automatically polling wire–center terminals via switched network connections. The system generates alarm messages that are printed out at a central terminal and transmitted to the maintenance center. Special measurements and data may be requested from the central location by data links.

23–3 CIRCUIT MAINTENANCE SYSTEMS

Message network loops and trunks and most special–services circuits are maintained on the basis of measurements made by computer–controlled test equipment and maintenance systems. Many of these systems also incorporate large–scale data bases that replace manual records.

Loop Maintenance

The high rate of station movement and the complexities of feeder and distribution cable layouts make loop maintenance difficult and encourage paperless record keeping. Loop operations are centered in an ARSB, which is responsible for maintaining loops.

A large part of loop maintenance work pertains to cable testing and cable maintenance. Most of this type of work, once performed manually, is now via automatic testing and analysis of results. Since outside plant cables terminate in the central office at a main distributing frame (MDF), testing and other loop operations must be carried out with adequate concern for the complexities that exist at the MDF.

Where loops are provided by DLC, system alarms are usually telemetered to a maintenance center analogous to an FMAC. Protection switching of span lines (for example, one–for–four protection of T1 lines) is usually included. The carrier systems include a pair–gain test controller for remote testing, which lets the loop testing system check pair–gain loops as if they were copper.

Cable Testing. Some cable testing is still performed manually using portable sets that can be carried into the outside environment [12]. However, remotely controlled automatic testing and trouble logging are now routine.

A simple measure of cable–pair quality is the line insulation resistance. Thus, tests are made in which the resistance between the conductors of a pair or from conductor to ground is measured and compared with expected values. Automatic test equipment makes such tests economical. A computer program may be used for the analysis of automatic line tests. Systems such as this have made possible effective methods for improving plant quality and avoiding customer complaints. Complementing the line insulation test, particularly in rural areas where premises visits are expensive, maintenance terminating units (MTUs) can be used to sectionalize a problem as being in the loop or in the customer–premises equipment (CPE). The MTU can be ordered remotely to disconnect the CPE briefly and make similar tests.

635

Automated Repair Service Bureau. Loop maintenance activities are centered at the ARSB where records of station locations, cable assignments, and customer services are available in a data base such as the Facilities Assignment and Control System (FACS) or Computer System for Mainframe Operations (COSMOS) and where personnel and data terminals are located. Repair service attendants are stationed at the bureau to receive customer trouble reports. At one time, activities at these bureaus were manual; many test procedures required coordination between test–desk personnel and other maintenance personnel responsible for activities at the MDF, at customer premises, or along the cable. Most of this work is now mechanized under computer control [13].

As repair service bureau (RSB) functions were mechanized, the bureau became an ARSB. The major objectives in mechanizing operations were: to improve efficiency and reduce the cost of repair operations; to improve customer service by reducing the time required for detecting, locating, and repairing troubles; and to improve the handling of customer contacts by RSB attendants.

An important component of an ARSB is a computer system that mechanizes customer line records by storing them in a data base and that can produce a variety of management reports. Among its functions are customer trouble report processing, control of mechanized testing, analysis of past trouble reports, and the provision of equipment use reports.

This system may also provide a portable data terminal so that a maintenance technician in the field may dial in to a controller. The controller has access to information on pending trouble cases and trouble histories. Thus, the remote technician can command the test system to perform tests, receive the results of those tests, and pick up dispatches without outside assistance [14,15].

Trunk Maintenance

Two major functions are provided by most network trunks. They provide transmission paths between switching entities; in addition, trunk circuits in a pre–common–channel signalling environment provide address and signalling functions associated with setting up connections. Thus, trunk maintenance must include tests to evaluate both transmission and operating performance.

The message telecommunications network has grown to such a degree that the maintenance of trunks numbering in the millions had to be mechanized in order to provide satisfactory service economically. As trunk testing progressed from manual to computer–assisted methods, intermediate stages of development produced semiautomatic equipment with limited capabilities. Most of these intermediate maintenance systems have vanished with the electromechanical switches that they supported.

A typical transmission measuring set provides rack–mounted test equipment and several types of digital display capable of being viewed from various distances. The system is arranged to measure and display noise in dBrnc, frequency in kHz, and power in dBm.

Outgoing trunk test frames are found in older electromechanical switching offices. These frames provide jack access and test facilities for outgoing trunks. They may operate manually or in conjunction with automatic or semiautomatic systems, some of which are maintenance support systems for specific switching systems. Several vintages of semiautomatic test frame have been employed. These arrangements are being replaced by newer mechanized test arrangements.

Versatile systems for testing network trunks usually use a computer–operated controller, remote office responders or remote trunk–test units, remote office test lines for use with most types of switching equipment, and miscellaneous other test lines [16].

A system, with its central controller, may combine features in such a way that tests can be performed on trunks between any two offices in the controlled area. The central controller may be located at a minicomputer center within or near that area. From the central location, a controller can use remote trunk–test units to perform transmission–loss and noise tests and operational tests on trunks between surrounding central offices. If measured values fall outside established limits, a trunk may be considered impaired and test results are presented in a form suitable for troubleshooting. Trunks that test marginal are reported separately from those that are unacceptable. With the current versions, tests are available of 1000–Hz loss, three–tone slope, terminal balance, and C–message noise (both with and without holding tone).

Tests are controlled by a minicomputer. Trunks within the served area are identified and their designations entered into disk files that are updated regularly to reflect changes in the network. Trunks are tested in regular sequence during nonbusy hours, at the rate of 10,000 to 15,000 trunks per night. During more active periods of the day, the system may be used, on demand, to test trunks that are being investigated because of troubles indicated during the routine tests.

The advent of digital switching led to the need for further mechanization in operation and administration services to operations, clerical, and management personnel. Work centers are provided with interfaces to the systems through interactive keyboard and cathode ray tube displays [17]. The systems mechanize much of the work distribution, circuit–order administration, and reporting functions. The systems have very large capability, which can be exercised through interactive connections with the switch processor and other maintenance and administration systems. As switching evolves toward predominantly digital, full-digital trunks lose the need for individual tests. The maintenance system then evolves toward surveillance–based maintenance based on monitoring the performance of complete digroups via error counts [18].

Special-Services Maintenance

With the great diversity of functions and the wide range of circuit types involved, centralized and mechanized testing of special–services circuits developed somewhat more slowly than that for network trunks. There had been specialized test centers for each major classification of special services.

Most of these test centers have been merged into a special-services center (SSC) or digital SSC to provide centralized and mechanized control of special–services operations. Maintenance systems have mechanized much of the administration and record keeping of the centralized operations control centers, to the point that paper records are now rare.

Most actual testing of special–services circuits is via a system that allows circuits to be tested from a remote location. One such common system is the remote test access placer and the circuit access point is called the remote test access point.

Self–Adjustment of Channel Banks. The current generation of digital channel banks incorporates the ability to set or reset options on channel units that are used for special–services circuits solely via software. Gain, equalization, hybrid balance, and signalling features are controlled from a keyboard at the system controller in the central office, or via a data link from a distant point. Transmission adjustments on most circuits can also be made automatically via a transponder at the end user's location, as described in Chapter 24, Part 1.

Switched–Access Remote Testing. A system for remote testing by means of switched access must combine two functions to provide one–person testing of special–services circuits from the SSC. The first function, switched access, uses a test system controller/remote test unit (TSC/RTU) at locations remote from the SSC [19,20]. The second function is remote transmission and operational tests on a wide variety of specials. Remote operation of the TSC/RTU is controlled from the SSC over data links that also transmit test results from the remote location to the SSC.

Access and test commands are initiated at the SSC by use of test positions equipped with cathode ray tube displays to guide the test processes and to indicate test results.

Systems are available from a variety of makers. Some of them are designed to be economical in smaller sizes. Modern systems can gain test access to switched special–services circuits via the "no–test" trunks in a central office (so–named because they make no test for a busy condition). Access is also available through a test digroup associated with a digital cross–connect system (DCS) or the test features of a "smart" channel bank system as well as via voice–frequency access points.

The network channel terminating equipment on most four–wire special services, upon receipt of a 2713–Hz tone from the remote test system, will loop the transmit and receive paths on an equal–level basis for testing. The same applies to DDS and Basic Dedicated Digital Service (BDDS) private lines, which loop back upon receipt of a digital channel service unit loop–back code. Likewise, DS1 high–capacity services of the current type include a "smart jack" that loops back on receipt of a test code.

Circuit Maintenance Information System

This multiprocessor maintenance system mechanizes administrative and record–keeping functions to provide convenient and interactive person–machine interfaces for operations personnel. It is a *subsystem* of a large sophisticated software system that issues work orders for the construction and installation of circuits and various communications systems. This large system, a basic tool of circuit provisioners, accepts orders for anything from a residential burglar alarm to a high–capacity corporate data network. The system automatically designs the circuits that will make up a new communications system. It selects and assigns inventory and produces a work order to be implemented by craftspeople or by stored–program network elements. This system includes components to help engineers and planners who must forecast what facilities will be needed several years in the future. Other components assist operations personnel in carrying out the work orders produced by the circuit provisioners. The maintenance component tracks the installation and maintenance process of circuits and communications systems to provide for rapid circuit information retrieval on demand.

23-4 MAINTENANCE SUPPORT

The trend toward computer control of operations and maintenance has not lessened the need for many items of support equipment. Some of these facilities provide efficient access to circuits for test. In other cases, the support is via equipment to enable maintenance personnel to communicate with one another efficiently or to permit remote control and surveillance of transmission systems and circuits. Some support items, such as protection channels, are needed for service protection and for the temporary restoration of failed facilities.

Access for Maintenance

All electronic equipment must be designed so that the equipment can be tested. In some cases, the necessary test access is provided by pin jacks. In some systems that employ plug–in equipment, "extenders" are used to permit the circuit cards or boards to remain in the operating environment and yet to make all the components available for test and adjustment. Often, jacks are mounted conveniently so that test equipment can be plugged in for maintenance testing. Increasingly, switching crosspoints provide test access from a central local or distant location: access contacts are built into the circuit components and brought out to a switching stage and distribution system.

Distributing frames provide access for maintenance testing when necessary as well as for circuit installation and rearrangement work. Connectors, called shoes, may be used to make contact with selected cable pairs and to extend the connection by test cords to jacks that carry the circuit test connection to an automatic test system.

Communications for Maintenance

Three general types of communications facility are used for operations and maintenance work. Order wires provide voice communications for maintenance personnel. Mobile radio and pagers play an important role in efficient operation of maintenance forces. Data links extend alarms and other status indicators from unmanned and remote locations to centralized points where maintenance and operations are controlled. They pass control information in the other direction.

Order Wires. Voice communications facilities permit maintenance personnel to communicate with one another between remote locations or between a remote location and a centralized location. The facilities may be no more than a connection to the message network, a point–to–point connection with direct and

641

uncomplicated signalling arrangements, or a complex communication system with selective signalling. Order wires may be routed over facilities separate from those with which they are associated for maintenance, or they may gain a transmission path by use of overhead bits in the high–capacity path between fiber or digital–radio multiplexers. In some cases, fiber routes have been laid out with an extra fiber pair dedicated to the order wire; otherwise, the circuit uses a metallic pair in the fiber cable.

Order–wire appearances are provided where needed. Such appearances, in the form of telephone headset jacks, are commonly found at all remote repeater points along transmission routes. Jack or station–set appearances may also be found in a central office at distributing frames, transmission bays, multiplex bays, etc.

Telephone Maintenance Radio Service. As discussed in Chapter 22, there is substantial use of mobile radio frequencies in the Telephone Maintenance Radio Service (TMRS) for dispatching repair crews to remote locations. Radio repeaters, multiple dispatch points, and involved switching arrangements contribute to an effective system. Widespread use of radio paging similarly assists the operation of maintenance groups.

Data Communications. It is often desirable to extend alarm and other status indications from remote to central locations. Data transmission for alarm, status, and control of many of the systems previously discussed may be provided by *E–type telemetry systems* [21]. Status inputs at remote locations are represented by two–state (binary) information from alarm circuits or relays; commands from a central location are similarly coded in a binary form. Thus, the system transmits binary coded signals to and from the central location.

Considerable flexibility has been designed into the E–type systems. They operate over a wide range of facilities and are intended for computer control and interaction. Four–wire data transmission facilities and medium–speed data sets are used for communication between E2 central and remote locations.

Service Protection

Many transmission systems and most multiplex equipment are provided with protection switching and transmission facilities. These protection systems are described with the systems with which they are associated. Generally, they protect service by switching from a working to a protection facility when there is an equipment failure or loss of transmission for some other reason such as multipath fading of microwave radio systems.

In addition to their service protection functions, these arrangements also facilitate maintenance. When maintenance of a working system is required, service may be transferred by manual control of the switching system (or by patching) to the protection facility. When maintenance work is completed, service is restored to the regular facility.

Protection facilities are also used for emergency restoration. Service interruption due to a major route failure can often be made good by rerouting channels over protection facilities of other systems. After repairs have been made, service is restored to the regular facilities. There is growing application of ring–and–spoke network layouts in which failure of a fiber link can be made good by DCSs and diversely routed spare facilities.

Service restoral is sometimes accomplished by temporary repairs. Emergency equipment is stored for this purpose. For example, a microwave radio route might fail due to the destruction of a repeater tower. A temporary tower might be delivered by truck and erected near the original tower to carry service while a permanent tower is being constructed. Spare reels of fiber cable are similarly stored and may be used to effect a temporary repair while a major cable break is being restored. Many other examples of such temporary service restoral can be cited.

References

1. Anderson, R. E., P. J. Baun, and J. L. Thomas. "L5 System: Centralized Transmission Surveillance," *Bell System Tech. J.*, Vol. 53 (Dec. 1974), pp. 2035–2064.

2. *Alarm Indication Signals—Requirements and Objectives*, Technical Reference TR–TSY–000191, Bellcore (Iss. 1, May 1986).

3. Kovac, E. J. and H. K. Penberthy. "The DSX—A Key to the Emerging Digital Network," Bellcore EXCHANGE, Vol. 3, Iss. 1 (Jan./Feb. 1987), pp. 14–18.

4. IEEE Draft, *Standards Project P1007*, "Methods and Equipment Standard for Measuring the Transmission Characteristics of PCM Telecommunications Circuits and Systems" (New York: Institute of Electrical and Electronics Engineers, Inc., Jan. 1989).

5. Anderson, T. C. "Testing Long–Haul Carrier Systems Automatically," *Bell Laboratories Record*, Vol. 52 (July/Aug. 1974), pp. 212–216.

6. Buus, R. G., D. L. Rechtenbaugh, and R. B. Whipp. "T–Carrier Administration System Speeds Service Restoration," *Bell Laboratories Record*, Vol. 53 (May 1975), pp. 217–225.

7. Bergmann, H. J. "Taking the Pulse of Digital Facilities," Bellcore EXCHANGE, Vol. 2, Iss. 3 (May/June 1986), pp. 13–17.

8. Koblentz, M. E., M. R. Nash, and M. Seldner. "Seeing the Big Picture: Network Monitoring and Analysis," Bellcore EXCHANGE, Vol. 3, Iss. 5 (Sept./Oct. 1987), pp. 28–32.

9. Tow, D. M. "Back to the Future: Advances and Trends in Network Management," Bellcore EXCHANGE, Vol. 4, Iss. 1 (Jan./Feb. 1988), pp. 14–19.

10. Sutton, R. A. et al. "Tracing Quality with Live Calls," *Telephone Engineer and Management* (Nov. 15, 1986), pp. 88–94.

11. Avery, R. "The Live–Call Test System Does a Variety of Jobs," *Telephone Engineer and Management* (Nov. 15, 1986), pp. 94–96.

12. Bowker, M. W. "Testing Cable Pairs—Fast," *Bell Laboratories Record*, Vol. 50 (Mar. 1972), pp. 87–92.

13. "MLT–2: Advanced System for Interactive Loop Testing," *Bell Laboratories Record*, Vol. 62 (Aug. 1984), pp. 16–17.

14. *Generic Requirements for Craft Technician Handsets/Terminals to Provide Access to Technician Access Network (TAN)*, Technical Advisory TA–TSY–000363, Bellcore (Iss. 2, Jan. 1988).

15. Hodges, V. and L. Kinlaw. "The Anatomy of a Line Test System," *Telephone Engineer and Management* (Nov. 15, 1986), pp. 97–99.

16. Plato, J. J. and B. S. Robb. "CAROT's New Features Expand Maintenance and Administrative Functions," *Bell Laboratories Record*, Vol. 61 (Jul./Aug. 1983), pp. 18–24.

17. Giunta, J. A. "Linking People and Systems for Better Trunk Maintenance," *Bell Laboratories Record*, Vol. 54 (May 1976), pp. 127–133.

18. *Extended Superframe Format (ESF) Interface Specification*, Technical Reference TR–TSY–000194, Bellcore (Iss. 1, Dec. 1987).

19. Helsing, D. V., L. V. Pannone, and T. K. Srinivas. "Reach Out and Test Something Special," *Bell Laboratories Record*, Vol. 62 (Nov. 1984), pp. 10–14.

20. Feuster, I. R. and D. C. Radeschi. "Speeding Up the 'Service' in Special Services Circuits," *Bell Laboratories Record*, Vol. 62 (May 1984), pp. 8–12.

21. Sanferrare, R. J. "E–Telemetry: Inside Story of Centralized Maintenance," *Bell Laboratories Record*, Vol. 52 (Dec. 1974), pp. 345–350.

Chapter 24

Test Equipment

Testing of circuits and facilities for transmission evaluation and trouble location requires test equipment in fixed locations and in the form of portable test sets. For example, a specific type of set may be essential for occasional use but too expensive to be provided in many central offices, only to lie idle most of the time. Other sets are hand–carried for use in field locations. Some sets are arranged so that they may be conveniently mounted in a fixed or mobile bay. Some sets are designed to operate on commercial power only, some on batteries only, and others on either. Such equipment complements the capabilities of the switched–access test systems that are routinely used for remote testing of trunks and special services.

Microprocessors have reduced the size and weight of test sets and added a myriad of capabilities. They process and store information and, on demand, show the results in the form of readouts on a display. Some sets display instructional menus to guide the user through successive test procedures.

Essentially, the types of measurement made are those of digital performance, loss, gain, return loss, longitudinal balance, impedance, background noise, impulse noise, phase jitter, phase hits, gain hits, dropouts, and intermodulation distortion. Voiceband data transmission systems require that peak–to–average ratio (PAR), envelope delay distortion (EDD), bandwidth, and phase jitter be measured. In fiber systems, optical power meters, optical loss test sets, and time–domain reflectometers measure the transmission losses in fiber systems. The reflectometer is capable of displaying the locations of poor splices or actual breaks.

A comprehensive discussion of test equipment is made difficult because of the large number of parameters that must be measured and the wide variety of circuits, systems, and facilities to be evaluated. Transmission parameters are measured on voiceband and wideband circuits and on analog and digital transmission systems. In addition, requirements differ for the measurements of loops, trunks, the many types of special–services circuits, and the type of facility that is being measured. As a result of these factors, there are many types of test set.

The continuing growth of the message telecommunications service network, the variety of services, and the division of service into local access and transport area (LATA) access and inter-LATA segments has had a major impact on transmission maintenance. The increase in data transmission and in types of data service has had the greatest single influence. The emphasis on digital data transmission has made it necessary to examine the capabilities of the message network to transmit data signals and to specify a consistent set of requirements for maintenance equipment [1].

Test equipment for transmission maintenance must meet electrical and physical requirements. Electrical requirements include the transmission parameters to be measured and the method of measurement. Accuracy, range, displays of testing results, programmability and other features and characteristics are specified. Physical features such as size, weight, portability, mounting arrangements, identification, and other requirements are also specified. The degree to which these electrical and physical requirements are met determines the usefulness and cost of the equipment. Thus, these factors must be known in order to provide maintenance test equipment that will be used efficiently.

24-1 VOICEBAND LOSS AND NOISE–MEASURING EQUIPMENT

The most significant parameters that determine the quality of a voiceband channel are attenuation/frequency and noise. Thus, many test sets are designed to measure transmission loss (or gain) at specific frequencies or over certain frequency bands and to measure the noise in the channel.

Oscillators and detectors, usually combined into a single instrument, are the fundamental types for measuring circuit losses, gains, or noise. Within the frequency range for which an oscillator is designed, the important characteristics are the output impedance, the accuracy and stability of output frequency and amplitude, amplitude range, and the purity of output signal wave shape [2]. Important characteristics of a detector are input impedance, frequency range, amplitude measuring range, resolution, and accuracy. Longitudinal balance, stability, high–voltage protection, and other parameters must also be specified.

Test signal amplitudes are typically between −40 and +10 dBm at the points of measurement. Circuits that normally carry speech or voiceband data are measured from 300 Hz to 3200 Hz. The frequency range of interest in program circuit measurements is from 50 Hz to 15 kHz. Measurements to determine slope across the voice–frequency (VF) band are normally made at 404, 1004, and 2804 Hz. Noise is measured using selectable weighting networks, which condition the frequency response of the detector to determine the degree of interference to a particular service.

Often the functions of a full variety of test sets are combined into a single instrument. They are also provided by a remote-controlled automated circuit–maintenance system with switched access to special–services circuits. For application by end users in their own networks, in–service measuring equipment is available. These perform signal–processing analysis on a known digital signal, deriving the normal channel–parameter measurements on a circuit that is carrying normal traffic [3].

Signal Generators

Sine–wave signals are provided at 404, 1004, and 2804 Hz by typical precision tone generators to perform gain–slope measurements over the VF band. In addition, such generators may be used as a replacement for the older types, usually called *milliwatt supplies*. The output needs to be stable at a variety of selectable output powers and output impedances. The output frequencies are all offset from 400, 1000, and 2800 Hz in order to fit transmission testing of digital facilities. A test signal close to an integral submultiple of the 8–kHz sampling frequency used in digital channel banks and switches can cause harmonically related interferences to fall back into the VF band. These can result in variations, or "beats," of the measured signal amplitude or of noise measurements that depend on the use of a signal as a "holding tone." In addition, integral submultiples like 1000 Hz can simulate the framing pattern of the D4 superframe format and cause false framing. When the holding–tone frequency is a rational submultiple of the 8–kHz sampling rate, the quantizing noise power is concentrated at a few frequencies rather than spread over the VF band.

The actual tone may be synthesized from a crystal–controlled frequency standard (typical in general–purpose multifrequency sets), may be obtained from a dedicated frequency divider driven by a crystal–controlled source, or may come from a look–up table in a read–only memory as part of a digital system. The latter approach is particularly applicable to digital–reference–signal sources in digital switches.

Because of the variety of instrument suppliers furnishing transmission test equipment, standardization is necessary. Required performance criteria for oscillators and signal generators include output level range, frequency stability, level stability, distortion, background noise, frequency accuracy, and spurious noise [4].

Signal–Measuring Equipment

Signal power must often be measured with great accuracy in order to calibrate signal sources. Many types of meter and analyzer are available for such measurements. Some are frequency-selective, some are wideband, and some are designed for specialized measurement functions.

As with signal generators, there are required performance criteria for signal–measuring instruments. These include range, accuracy, terminating and bridging impedances, low– and high–frequency noise protection, type of detector, display response time, and crosstalk (oscillator into detector and input signal into oscillator) [4].

Noise–Measuring Equipment

Any interference in a communication channel may be considered noise. Some types of noise arise in channels as a result of physical phenomena (e.g., flat or Gaussian noise). Some are generated by mechanisms within the channel (e.g., quantizing noise) and may depend on the signals transmitted as well as on the channel characteristics. Other types are introduced in the channel from outside sources by induction (e.g., a spectrum of harmonics of 60 Hz).

The measurement of noise in telecommunication circuits is expressed in terms of relative interfering effect. Measuring equipment must account for the subjective effects of noise on human listeners as well as objective effects on inanimate receivers such as data terminals. For telephone noise measurement, the test equipment response must be frequency-dependent because human hearing is similarly dependent and also to allow for loss-frequency distortion between the point of electrical measurement and the acoustic output at the telephone receiver. The equipment must allow for inertia in the human hearing system, which does not sense the full intensities of sounds until they have persisted for about 0.2 second. A burst that does not last 0.2 second is evaluated in proportion to its intensity and duration. For impulse noise, the measuring set registers all noise impulses strong enough to be accepted as data signal elements. Such impulses are typically too short in duration to be sensed by ear and cannot be evaluated by means of message noise measurements; a separate measuring technique is needed to evaluate impulse noise.

Any specific pattern and intensity of voiceband noise has different interfering effects on different persons and for various amplitudes of the speech with which it is interfering. Thus, the objective measurement of telephone noise with a noise-measuring set gives only a rough average of the interfering effect of that noise under various conditions. Interfering effects under specific conditions can vary by several decibels. Variability in the types and amplitudes of noise may render short-period measurements of little value in trouble detection. On the other hand, since the variability among data transmitting and receiving sets is comparatively small and since the data transmission levels are comparatively well controlled, the meaning of impulse noise measurements is more definite.

Noise measurements on most VF channels used for data transmission are valid only if a holding tone is present. The signal used

651

for such measurements is 1004 or 1010 Hz. Beyond the point in the transmission path where it is needed but before it reaches the noise–measuring circuitry, this signal is suppressed by a sharp band–elimination filter in the weighting filter known as a C–notched network. The probability of significant noise components falling in the eliminated band is low, and the effect of the filter in measurements of flat Gaussian noise is to reduce the reading by less than 0.5 dB.

Impulse–Noise–Measuring Equipment

Impulse–noise–measuring equipment is designed to measure the amplitude or the distribution of noise impulse amplitudes in voiceband data circuits. As with message noise, several weighting networks are used for C–notched and flat measurements.

The distribution of impulse amplitudes in a channel is determined by counters that register all impulse peaks that exceed specific threshold settings. A multilevel distribution is helpful to determine the error performance in data signal transmission as a statistical function of the interference.

Performance criteria for impulse measuring equipment include counting rate, counting interval, the effects of dropouts or phase/gain hits on impulse counting, range of threshold settings, threshold accuracy, count capacity, overload characteristics, operation without holding tone, and indication of a loss of holding tone [4].

Phase Hits, Gain Hits, and Dropouts. It is quite common to design impulse–noise–measuring equipment to measure phase hits, gain hits, and dropouts along with impulse noise. The performance criteria of each section of the combined measuring set are also specified, similar to those described for impulse noise alone [3].

Envelope–Delay–Distortion–Measuring Equipment

There are occasions when it is necessary to measure the degree of EDD in voiceband circuits, particularly those for which data conditioning is ordered, even though digital carrier facilities are

relatively good in this regard. The required performance criteria
for the transmitter of envelope–delay–measuring equipment include the percent modulation, modulation frequency, distortion,
frequency range, frequency accuracy, output level range, and
flatness. The performance criteria for the receiver include accuracy and resolution, envelope–delay range, input power range,
display response time, indicated frequency accuracy, envelope-
delay stability with amplitude variations, transmitter–to–receiver
crosstalk, and accuracy of the indicated envelope delay versus
the signal–to–noise of the measured signal. Other parameters are
self–checking capability, output for X–Y recording, drift of envelope delay and level readings, capability of transferring the received envelope delay signal to a new carrier for transmission
back to the originating end, display of sending and receiving frequency and level, and forward and return reference modes [4].

PAR–Measuring Equipment

The PAR system is designed to measure the simultaneous effects of EDD, bandwidth reduction, and poor return loss (producing gain and phase distortion), which cause intersymbol interference in voiceband data signals. The PAR measurement is
largely insensitive to noise, phase jitter, intermodulation distortion, or transient phenomena.

The PAR technique consists of transmitting a train of precisely
shaped pulses having a known ratio of peak–to–average full-
wave rectified voltage into one end of a channel and observing at
the other end the extent to which that ratio has changed. Thus, a
rapid, weighted, straightaway measurement is made of some
channel impairments.

The PAR receiver displays the PAR rating. A rating of 100
means that the ratio in the received pulses is the same as that in
the transmitted pulses, while a rating of zero means that the ratio
in received pulses is only half of that in the transmitted ones.
Intermediate ratings and ratios are linearly related. The performance criteria for the transmitter of PAR–measuring equipment
include the test spectrum, spectrum distortion, signal period stability, output level range, and output level resolution. Receiver
criteria include accuracy, capability of accuracy check, PAR

range, resolution, input level range, input response, type of detector, display response time, out–of–range indicator, self–check capability, and transmitter–to–receiver crosstalk [4].

Smart–Bank Transponders

For use with the D5 and enhanced–D4 channel bank systems described in Chapter 15, a test transponder (transmitter–responder) is used to give automatic circuit lineup from the customer's location. The transponder usually eliminates the need for coordinated measurement and adjustment work between an installer and a central–office technician, substantially reducing circuit turn–up effort and cost.

The transponder is a portable microprocessor–controlled set that is used by circuit installers. It is attached to the network interface at the customer's location. The channel–bank system detects the transponder's presence and measures loop loss and three–tone slope. The system then automatically adjusts gain and equalization on either a two–wire or a four–wire channel unit as well as the automatic balance network of a two–wire channel.

Using the transponder to adjust a channel unit can provide transmission performance superior to that obtained from prescription settings derived from loop–makeup records and entered directly into the channel bank system. The transponder also reduces time and effort when prescription settings must be readjusted to satisfy transmission requirements.

The transponder and system controller communicate through the channel unit and loop under test. When the transponder is connected to the loop at the customer's location, the transponder sends dc current over the loop. On detecting this current, the channel unit notifies the system controller of the transponder's signal. The controller then connects an internal automatic test unit to verify the presence of the transponder and measure loop loss near 404, 1004, and 2804 Hz. The automatic balance unit in a two–wire channel unit is adjusted for maximum transhybrid loss. Gain and equalization are then adjusted in the channel unit to provide the correct circuit loss and frequency response.

The results of the test process are indicated at the customer's location by diode lamps in the transponder (pass–conditional–

fail) and to the special–services center by output messages from the system controller.

24-2 IMPEDANCE-RELATED MEASURING EQUIPMENT

The effect on transmission performance of noise and echoes is significantly influenced by circuit impedances. This is critical where circuit interfaces may introduce impedance discontinuity or longitudinal unbalance. In addition, impedance discontinuities may be introduced along a VF cable circuit by cable damage or by omission or improper placement of load coils. Such discontinuities produce transmission echoes that impair transmission.

A large variety of test equipment is available for the measurement of impedance–related parameters. These include sets to measure return loss and longitudinal balance and to evaluate the impedance of a transmission line by simulation.

Return-Loss Measurement

Control of echoes, essential to good transmission, depends on maintenance of adequate return loss within the circuit at points of transition between four–wire and two–wire facilities. Return loss includes a measure of the composite reflections from irregularities within a medium. It is generally a function of frequency, but its effective value within a specific frequency band can be obtained in a single measurement by using appropriately weighted thermal noise as test power and a power–sum detector as a measuring device.

Return-Loss Measuring Equipment. The functions of evaluating echo and singing return losses on either two–wire or four–wire circuits usually are combined in return–loss measuring sets. They generate a wide band of noise that may be passed through any one of three weighting networks and used for return–loss measurements. These sets are used primarily for making through– and terminal–balance tests.

The echo return loss (ERL) weighting network has 3–dB points at 560 and 1965 Hz, representing the mid–voiceband spectrum.

On the other hand, the singing return loss–low (SRL–LO) weighting, having 3–dB points at 260 and 500 Hz, emphasizes the influence of frequencies in the lower part of the voiceband. The singing return loss–high (SRL–HI) weighting, having 3–dB points at 2200 and 3400 Hz, measures the influence of frequencies in the upper part of the voiceband. The high and low frequencies are important from the standpoint of repeater stability rather than echoes.

Longitudinal Balance Testing

The degree of impedance balance between each conductor of a wire pair or of an equipment unit and ground is a measure of immunity to noise induced from extraneous sources such as power lines and power conductors of electric railroads. A measure of this balance can be approximated by using a noise–measuring set to obtain separate readings of noise to ground and metallic noise on the same facility. The longitudinal balance is calculated as the difference between the two readings. Such determinations depend on the frequency spectrum of the noise induced in the facility at the time of measurement. Single–frequency measurements of longitudinal balance can also be made by energizing the longitudinal circuit at the desired frequency and measuring metallic noise with a frequency analyzer having a tunable narrowband filter [5]. As with other test equipment, performance criteria are also specified for equipment manufactured to measure longitudinal balance [4].

Level Tracers

A test set for measuring electrical characteristics of facilities and equipment as functions of frequency and for displaying them graphically on a video display is called a level tracer. It may supply a swept–frequency signal internally or, for measuring characteristics such as attenuation, may receive a sweeping signal from the far end of a transmission facility. In either case, it continuously monitors the frequency of the signal and places the horizontal sweep of the display in proportion to frequency while placing the vertical coordinate in proportion to the measured characteristic. Level tracers are commonly used in displaying loss, return loss, and impedance magnitude.

In early level tracers, the cathode ray tube (CRT) beam was controlled directly by the measured X (frequency) and Y (magnitude) coordinates and produced a trace that faded out gradually within a sweep cycle. In later designs, the measured coordinates are stored in memories that are swept rapidly to produce nonfading traces that change only as the coordinates are updated in the memories as a result of adjustment of the circuit being measured. Some of the latter designs can generate in turn, and update alternately, two traces comparing the same or different circuits. That ability is useful in locating and diagnosing impedance irregularities in cable pairs by using simulation with artificial cable modules. Some level tracers provide auxiliary dc outputs, proportional to horizontal and vertical coordinates of the graph, for driving X–Y plotters when a permanent record is wanted. For such use, means are also provided for slowing the sweep and reducing the plotting errors caused by inertia of the plotter.

Measurement of Line Impedance

A major use of impedance measurements is to diagnose and locate impedance irregularities in cable pairs. A commonly used technique is to terminate the pair under investigation with a precision network having the characteristic impedance of the line at the far end and to obtain a graph of impedance magnitude versus frequency at the near end by using a level tracer. The tracer applies a constant level to the pair, through a fixed source impedance, as the frequency range is swept and uses the voltage across the pair at each frequency as a measure of the impedance magnitude. Amplification of the voltage, coordinated with the choice of the impedance scale on the CRT display, results in a direct indication of impedance magnitude. Deviations in the graph provide data for deducing the nature of the irregularity (e.g., an omitted loading coil) and computing its distance from the measuring end.

A different empirical procedure after the graph has been obtained involves simulation of the real pair, including the irregularity, by means of an artificial cable kit. A group of graphs of simple irregularities at various distances from the measuring end provides initial guidance for setting up the artificial layout. Successful imitation of the irregularity is indicated by close agreement of

657

the graphs of the real and artificial pairs as shown simultaneously by the level tracer.

Typical artificial line equipment permits simulation of the transmission characteristics of cable circuits at voice frequencies. It consists of a number of cable modules and loading coils, packaged in small plastic cases equipped with jacks and plugs for interconnection. The modules simulate the impedance and propagation characteristics of 19–, 22–, 24–, 25–, and 26–gauge cable pairs in lengths of 6000, 3000, 1500, 750, and 250 feet. Loading coils of 88, 66, 44, and 22 mH are available.

The typical kit simulates a cable circuit from 10 to 7000 Hz with errors no greater than ±2 percent in either impedance or propagation constant; it is thus well within the performance range of actual cable. When ground resistance, which is too variable in the field to be included in the kit, is added externally in series with the ground line, the kit simulates the longitudinal circuit (pair–to–ground) up to about 300 Hz, a range that is of interest for signalling purposes. In the laboratory, the kit provides means for measuring the transmission performance of proposed layouts in advance; for example, the possible transmission penalty that may come from a cost reduction. In the field, the kit provides means for identifying and locating irregularities in cable pairs by adjusting the simulated layout to exhibit the same shortcomings as those of the real cable.

Computer software that calculates the performance of a particular cable layout has largely displaced the use of artificial cables; however, there are still many tests where an "actual" (simulated) pair is required or is easier to use.

24–3 CARRIER–MEASURING EQUIPMENT

Many transmission measurements must be made on broadband analog channels and high–capacity digital systems in order to determine performance quality and to carry out maintenance. In some cases, test equipment available for these purposes is designed for use with specific systems or channels. In other cases, the equipment is general–purpose and can be used for measurements on a wide variety of channels and systems.

The parameters of interest in broadband channels and systems are similar to those in voiceband channels. Loss/frequency characteristics and noise of all types are the most important impairments to be considered.

Test Sets for Analog Carrier Systems

A variety of high–frequency test sets are required for analog maintenance of analog systems. These sets cover a wide range of frequencies and bandwidths as required by the various systems. They can pick out a single voice channel for testing from a mastergroup or multimastergroup spectrum.

General Purpose Test Equipment. Some testing equipment has a wide range of capabilities and may be regarded as a test and maintenance system. Others are designed on a modular basis with individual units having specialized functions but capable of being incorporated into maintenance systems under manual or automatic control.

Test Sets for Digital Carrier Systems

Test equipment for these systems must be capable of detecting deformations or displacements of pulses that would prevent correct interpretation by receiving equipment. Portable test sets for T1 digital system lineup and maintenance include a line–error detector and an error–rate test set.

Error Detector for the T1 System. A portable line–error detector is used for monitoring T1 signals at repeater points. The set recognizes a violation of the bipolar signal as an error and stores this information in a counter. Isolation of an error–producing section or repeater can be achieved by using test access points along the transmission path, usually test jacks at DSX frames. With modifications to disregard bipolar with eight–zero substitution (B8ZS) coding patterns, the same technique can be used on B8ZS lines where some violations are intentional.

General Error–Measurement Sets. Numerous test sets are available for measuring the performance of digital facilities at the

DS1, −1C, −2, or −3 levels. They typically measure and store counts of bit errors, errored seconds, and severely errored seconds [6]. Options are available to let them test the facility on an out–of–service basis by sending a pseudorandom code word (typically $2^{20} - 1$, or 1,048,575 bits long), or by monitoring in–service by counting cyclic redundancy check (CRC) errors. They may be relatively simple, dedicated to digital facility maintenance, or may operate as part of a general–purpose data protocol analyzer [7]. They may also measure timing jitter and wander, and record the occurrence of timing slips. Connected to more involved personal–computer–based monitoring systems, they can be used for special studies [8].

Byte–Interceptor Test Sets. A class of test set in current use is able to gain test access to an individual voice or data channel in a DS1 bit stream without affecting the 23 others. By intercepting just the eight–bit bytes for the selected channel, it can monitor the states of the A and B signalling bits and force them to the *0* or *1* state. It is able to send and receive test tones, measure levels, and provide voiceband access for more specialized testing. In short, this type of test set allows for all the usual VF transmission and signalling tests at a point where only DS1 signals are available.

Time–Domain Reflectometer for Fiber Spans. The installation and maintenance of fiber transmission systems requires test sets for verifying that the losses of fibers, cross–connections, and splices are satisfactory [9], and for locating breaks if they occur. A general–purpose instrument for these uses is the optical time–domain reflectometer (OTDR) [7]. This is a radar–like test set that sends a pulse of light in the same wavelength band that the transmission system uses. The pulse travels down the fiber and is scattered back to the test set by small irregularities in the fiber, the larger discontinuities at splices, and, especially, the gross disruptions at fiber breaks. The results are displayed on a cathode–ray screen showing light intensity on the vertical axis versus distance on the horizontal axis. Comparison of the intensity shown on the trace before and after a splice allows measurement of the loss in the splice itself. The distance to the splice, and especially to a break, can be read from a multidigit display, typically with a resolution of three feet or better. A typical OTDR can measure through 20 to 100 or more kilometers of fiber, locating most faults from one end. Digitized records of the loss–distance profile of a fiber can be stored on disk for later reuse.

24–4 DATA TEST EQUIPMENT

Analog voiceband circuits are most conveniently evaluated for digital transmission by test instruments specifically designed for that purpose. In addition to circuit evaluation, it is also often necessary to evaluate the performance of data sets used as terminal equipment at the ends of analog data circuits (particularly for circuits for internal use by the exchange carrier where it is supplying and maintaining the modems).

Data Test Sets

General–purpose serial data test capability for installation and maintenance testing at data stations is provided by a variety of data test sets. They provide the convenience of luggage–type packaging since they must often be carried to test sites by public transportation.

Usually a microprocessor converts the input to the set into easily read information, administering overall system control, and setting up required interconnections for the desired measurements under control of the operator. These sets make use of a 32–character alphanumeric display or liquid–crystal screen to show processed data and to communicate with the operator. Through its capability of setting up preprogrammed tests and of processing input data, the microprocessor minimizes setup and adjustment time and reduces operator errors. A memory–based controller and plug–in interface modules provide flexibility for adding new test features.

These sets are usable for end–to–end and station–to–serving–test–center tests. Synchronous and nonsynchronous data sets and data service units (DSUs), used in the Digital Data System (DDS), can be tested. They may be used with data test sets of other types for end–to–end testing.

Plug–in modules are provided to meet *EIA Standard EIA–232D* and a number of other interface standards. The status of interface leads is monitored and shown by light–emitting diodes. Access to 37 interface leads is provided to accommodate existing data sets. A bridging mode can be used for on–line tests. Data rates up to 56 kb/s for synchronous applications and a choice of bit rates for asynchronous applications are usually available. Operation may be either duplex or half–duplex.

With the microprocessor, these sets have been preprogrammed to carry out a number of tests automatically. Steady–state synchronous services may be tested for bit and block error rates and for proper start–up and synchronization functions. Start–stop distortion measurements for data set operation, parity error measurements, and specially coded test messages may be selected for asynchronous services. Isochronous distortion measurements may be made on DDS circuits. In addition, these sets can perform a number of general–purpose tests including verification of their own performance.

DDS Test Sets

A transmitter–receiver pair of portable test sets is used to test 64–kb/s signals in digital services. The transmitting test set provides either balanced bipolar or logic–level signals at the 64–kb/s DS0 level, as timed from the composite clock signal in the associated equipment. The set produces signals at the four basic data rates: 2.4, 4.8, 9.6, or 56 kb/s. Output data words of either 511 or 2047 bits are provided, singly or repeatedly. The set is designed to generate signals toward either an office channel unit (OCU) or a multiplexer. It furnishes discrete control codes to which DSUs and OCUs respond. It also generates loop–back test patterns for those units.

The receiving test set is designed to monitor signals at the 64–kb/s level. It can perform error tests between a hub office and loop terminations and can provide loop–back at a DSU and OCU. The receiver demultiplexes signals at any of the DDS subrates and can accommodate "stuffed" signals at any of those rates. It accepts either 511– or 2047–bit test–word lengths. Lighted diodes display the detected control codes and the byte patterns. The bit–error or block–error count is displayed on a three–digit readout. The receiver accepts signals originating from the companion transmitter or any of several other data test sets after those signals are processed by the DDS.

ISDN Test Equipment

Test equipment for integrated services digital network (ISDN) may evaluate bit integrity, bipolar violations, and service performance. Remote testing to a network interface may be accomplished with loop–back methods in the NT1 terminator. A test set for use toward the central office emulates the customer–premises equipment, sending test signals or digitized voice on the B channels and sending/receiving signalling on the D channel. The major control of ISDN quality is accomplished by in–service evaluations on the 16–kb/s embedded maintenance channel for basic–rate access, and on the CRC bits in the framing pattern for primary–rate access. Performance measurements are in the form of errored seconds, severely errored seconds, unavailable time, and degraded minutes. The storage of error history is at the ISDN switch, which detects errors to and from a termination. The network termination equipment automatically transmits an error indication with any received errors so that the entire transmission path is monitored. Figure 24–1 is a block diagram of these features.

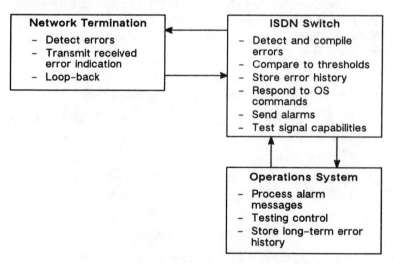

Figure 24–1. ISDN performance monitoring.

References

1. Bell System Technical Reference PUB 41008, *Analog Parameters Affecting Voiceband Data Transmission—Description of Parameters*, American Telephone and Telegraph Company (July 1974).

2. *Tone Generator Test Sets*, Technical Reference TR-TSY-000197, Bellcore (Iss. 1, Feb. 1985).

3. Sturgeon, A. "In-Service Tests Let Circuits Keep Working," *Telephone Engineer and Management* (Nov. 1, 1987), pp. 58-61.

4. *IEEE Std. 743-1984*, "IEEE Standard Methods and Equipment for Measuring the Transmission Characteristics of Analog Voice-Frequency Circuits" (New York: Institute of Electrical and Electronics Engineers, Inc., 1984).

5. *IEEE Std. 455-1985*, "IEEE Standard Test Procedure for Measuring Longitudinal Balance of Telephone Equipment Operating in the Voice Band" (New York: Institute of Electrical and Electronics Engineers, Inc., 1985).

6. IEEE Draft, *Standards Project P1007*, "Methods and Equipment Standard for Measuring the Transmission Characteristics of PCM Telecommunications Circuits and Systems" (New York: Institute of Electrical and Electronics Engineers, Inc., Jan. 1989).

7. *Optical Time Domain Reflectometers*, Technical Reference TR-TSY-000196, Bellcore (Iss. 1, Oct. 1986).

8. *Basic Testing Functions for Digital Networks and Services*, Technical Advisory TA-TSY-000055, Bellcore (Iss. 3, Apr. 1987).

9. *Optical Loss Test Equipment*, Technical Reference TR-TSY-000198, Bellcore (Iss. 1, Nov. 1986).

Additional Reading

IEEE Stds. 488-1978 and *488.1-1987*, "Standard Digital Interface for Programmable Instrumentation" (including Supplement)

(New York: Institute of Electrical and Electronics Engineers, Inc., 1987).

IEEE Std. 752–1986, "Standard for Functional Requirements for Methods and Equipment for Measuring the Performance of Tone Address Signalling Systems" (New York: Institute of Electrical and Electronics Engineers, Inc., 1986).

IEEE Std. 753–1983, "Functional Methods and Equipment for Measuring the Performance of Dial–Pulse (DP) Address Signalling Systems" (New York: Institute of Electrical and Electronics Engineers, Inc., 1983).

Telecommunications Transmission Engineering

Section 7

Transmission System Integration

In the previous sections of this volume, circuits, systems, and equipment of various types have been described as elements of the telecommunications facility network. Only modest attention has been given to the way these elements interact when they are connected or used in proximity to one another. This section discusses the limitations on certain types of simultaneous operation. It covers the way systems and circuits are connected to show how network facilities are integrated to form a working telecommunications system.

Chapter 25 considers system compatibility and coordination. Some systems and circuits do not work well together because of interferences induced by one into another. In other cases, coordination is satisfactory, with few constraints on system operation over the same or nearby facilities. Where problems exist, there are methods of mitigating the interference; the chapter describes these methods.

Chapter 26 shows how systems with different characteristics are interconnected to provide a flexible network, one that can grow and be rearranged quickly and economically. Certain aspects of network operation involve the use of equipment that is common to many systems. Outstanding in this respect is the network of equipment and circuits that synchronize the repetition rates of most of the carrier systems used in the public as well as private switched networks. Additional areas of interaction and commonality are discussed also.

Chapter 25

System Compatibility and Coordination

The design and application of transmission systems and circuits that use the same or proximate facilities must be coordinated in order to prevent excessive cross–coupled interference. The interferences that must be controlled include crosstalk (analog or digital), inductive interference (fundamental–frequency or harmonic interference from power lines), and radio–frequency (RF) disturbances.

Basically, coordination consists of understanding and controlling interference couplings. The elements of these phenomena are *influence, coupling,* and *susceptibility.* A thorough understanding of these elements requires definitions of (1) signals transmitted in disturbing channels, (2) disturbing–channel characteristics, (3) coupling–path characteristics, (4) disturbed–channel characteristics, and (5) susceptibility of signals in the disturbed channel to the interferences.

Interference problems in the loop and trunk areas are similar, but with differing emphases. Common to both is the interaction with other utilities, especially with power transmission and distribution facilities. Control of interferences from power lines into communications circuits is referred to as inductive coordination.

25–1 COUPLING CONSIDERATIONS

Coordination and crosstalk coupling are two aspects of the same problem. When crosstalk coupling is under consideration, specific channels and signals, interfering and impaired, are of primary concern, as in the case of intelligible crosstalk between voice circuits. When inductive interference is under consideration, a variety of disturbed channels must be considered together with a number of coupling paths. The challenge is to consider the relevant combinations and to determine which is limiting. A review of the controlling parameters is desirable in order to visualize them in relation to one another and to show how they interact.

Where interference between transmission systems or circuits is a problem, it is essential that the characteristics of signals in the disturbing system or circuit be well defined. The important characteristics are the amplitude, power spectral density, and the nature of single–frequency components (frequencies, amplitudes, consistency, duty cycle, etc.) of the signal. The statistical occupancy of the disturbed and disturbing channels may be significant. All of these parameters are established by the nature of the signals transmitted and by the design of the circuits or systems being used. Little control can be exercised in the operating environment except to be sure that application limits imposed on the signals and channels are met.

The characteristics of the disturbing channel have less effect on coordination problems than the nature of the transmitted signal, but they cannot be ignored. The normal power spectral density of the signal at different points in the channel may be modified significantly by the channel. The low– and high–frequency cutoff characteristics of the channel must also be taken into consideration.

The coupling paths between disturbing and disturbed systems and circuits have a major effect on the magnitude of the coordination problem. The transfer function (loss/frequency characteristic) of the coupling path, together with the magnitude and spectrum of the disturbing signal, determine the effect of the interference in the disturbed channel.

Finally, the signals and channel characteristics of the disturbed systems or circuits must also be considered in terms of coordination. The susceptibility of these signals to the types of interference introduced and the manner in which the channel may change the characteristics of signals and interferences must be evaluated. Susceptibility of signals varies widely. For example, if the interference has high–amplitude impulse components and the disturbed channel carries data signals, the desired signals are

670

more subject to impairment than would be the case with voice signals.

In some cases, interference problems can be solved by limiting the use of facilities. For example, one type of system produces excessive interference in another type of system when an excessive number of the disturbing systems are carried in the same cable or in the same binder group. Satisfactory operation can be achieved by limiting the number of systems of the disturbing type in the cable or binder group. Physical separation of transmission facilities (e.g., by use of nonadjacent binder groups) is sometimes necessary to solve such problems.

25-2 COORDINATION IN THE LOOP PLANT

Transmission in the distribution portion of the loop plant, as opposed to the feeder part, is primarily on wire–pair cables that have been engineered and installed to satisfy voice and data transmission requirements. However, many other types of signal are transmitted. Each time a new signal type is added, coordinating the new service or system with the existing loop plant and the environment within which it will operate must be considered carefully (i.e., loop signals need "spectrum management"). T1 carrier spans used in the feeder part of the plant also require coordination to ensure low error rate, typically by controlling level differences in the numerous route junctions found in loop facilities.

In many locations, loops and trunks are intermixed in the same cable sheath. Thus, particularly where carrier techniques are employed, more combinations of systems and circuits may coexist. Pole–line and underground facilities are shared by communications and power distribution circuits to a greater extent in the loop plant than in the trunk plant. There is greater use of ground return signals in the loop area for such purposes as ground–start, party identification, multiparty ringing, and coin control, all of which aggravate the exposure to induced interference. As a result, intercompany coordination of these situations is more intensive in the loop plant.

671

Inductive Coordination

The problems of inductive interference are classified as those of influence, coupling, and susceptibility. These problems all relate to the introduction of interference in communications circuits from electric power systems [1]. A number of techniques are used to control interferences. These include the careful balancing and shielding of communications circuits to reduce susceptibility, the physical separation of power and communications circuits to reduce coupling, and the transposition and load–balancing of power conductors to reduce influence. Generally, the transposition of power–line conductors is undertaken only as a last resort.

The longitudinal voltage induced on long rural loops occasionally exceeds 50 volts at 60 Hz. Equipment may be added to telecommunications circuits to reduce excessive longitudinal noise or voltage, which cause interference to voiceband transmission (for example, noise occurring at the "odd–triple" harmonics such as 180, 900, and 1500 Hz) or impairment of out–of–band functions such as ground–start signalling [2,3]. Four classes of mitigation are possible: (1) reduction of longitudinal current, (2) reduction of longitudinal voltage, (3) reduction of both voltage and current, and (4) reduction of susceptibility. In all cases, care must be taken to ensure that such action does not introduce new transmission problems.

The susceptibility of individual circuits to inductive interferences is greatly aggravated when terminations are poorly balanced with respect to ground. Thus, an effective and permanent form of interference reduction is the improvement of circuit balance where required. Such improvements may be effected by the application of modern circuit components especially designed to achieve balance, for example, ringer isolators that disconnect a ground–return bell except during ringing.

Individual voice–frequency (VF) circuits that exhibit an excessive amount of power interference can sometimes be improved by the use of longitudinal choke coils. These devices are inserted in series with the line to increase the longitudinal impedance of the line at the interference frequencies while presenting a low metallic impedance to the desired signals. The impedance increase reduces longitudinal currents that make up the interference. At frequencies as low as 60 Hz, this method may be of little benefit. Resonance of the inductor and the capacitance to ground may exist and actually increase the longitudinal current at the resonant frequency. The choke coil can also have an adverse effect on the transmission of 20–Hz ringing current on party lines. However, in some cases, longitudinal choke coils can be advantageously used for the reduction of VF noise; each case is analyzed separately. Usually this form of treatment is practical on only a small percentage of coordination problems.

Another method of reducing longitudinal currents is by the use of neutralizing transformers. These are roughly comparable to longitudinal chokes but provide an active offset to the induced current. A neutralizing transformer is constructed by winding a telephone cable, sometimes several hundred feet long, on a ferromagnetic core. The cable may consist of 6 to more than 100 pairs, one or two of which are designated as the primary winding. The pairs of this primary winding are connected in parallel and inserted in a cable pair that is grounded at each end of the induction exposure. Longitudinal current induced in the primary winding is coupled into the secondary windings. The coupled voltages and the voltages of induced currents in the secondary windings are oppositely phased and tend to cancel. Substantial improvement can be realized but there are major limitations. As a result, the use of such transformers is often only a temporary solution until coordination efforts to reduce influence satisfactorily are completed.

Longitudinal currents can be eliminated as sources of interference by the use of isolation transformers. However, dc continuity is interrupted, so this method cannot be used where dc transmission is required for transmitter current or for signalling. Even where it can operate satisfactorily, such as on carrier spans, complications relating to testing, maintenance, and the application of sealing current may be introduced.

Longitudinal voltages can sometimes be controlled by the use of a well–balanced two–winding coil, called a drainage reactor, with closely coupled windings. The two windings are connected in series across the line and the center tap is grounded. The windings are poled so the equal and opposite currents cause cancellation of the longitudinal inductance. The windings provide a low–impedance path from each side of the line to ground for the drainage of longitudinal currents. The effect of the shunt impedance is small because of the series–aiding inductance across the line. Balanced capacitors are frequently used in series with each winding to avoid placing a dc path across the line. As with other forms of line–by–line control of induced interference, drainage reactors have limitations and can be used only with care.

A unique coordination issue arises in regard to communications facilities terminating at large power–generating plants or substations. The power system is normally protected by an extensive ground mat comprising a network of interconnected ground rods. However, during a power system fault the current flowing in the station ground may be enough to bring the local ground potential several hundred or thousand volts above remote ground [4]. This induces large transient currents in the multigrounded sheath of the telecommunications cable, and produces large longitudinal potentials on the cable pairs. This problem is treated as a special coordination case.

The increasing use of digital loop carrier (DLC) has the highly beneficial effect of breaking up long exposures to power induction in the loop plant. It is not a universal cure, however, since in low–growth rural areas the existing metallic cables may have adequate spare pairs to make added facilities unjustifiable. DLC systems on metallic facilities may have a susceptibility to fundamental frequency power induction because of the effect of excessive longitudinal current on regulator diodes in regenerators. Fiber spans are inherently immune to induction, but induced voltages and currents in paralleling order–wire pairs or strength members in the cable may be troublesome.

Broadcast Radio Interference

Amplitude–modulated (AM) radio stations with up to 50 kilowatts transmitter output are usually located in remote areas, but site relocation or real–estate development may bring telecommunications plant close to them. Sizable longitudinal RF voltages may be induced into loop cable, especially aerial, and may interfere with customer–premises equipment (CPE) or exchange carrier facilities. The problem may show itself as demodulation ("radio") in the customer's telephone set. It may also appear as tones generated in channels of a DLC system or lines in a customer's private branch exchange (PBX). The tones are generated as beats between the AM radio carrier signal and a multiple of the 8–kHz sampling frequency in the DLC terminal or PBX. For example, a 570–kHz radio signal will mix with the 71st harmonic of 8 kHz to produce a 2–kHz tone. Survey results are available [5] describing typical RF voltages on exposed loop pairs.

Interference to CPE results from RF pickup in the exchange carrier's facilities, the customer's premises wire, or both. Mitigation of this interference into CPE is ultimately the responsibility of the customer via such measures as bypassing the RF to ground and the use of longitudinal choke coils, but an understanding of the problem is necessary for productive interaction. Correction of problems involving network facilities is, of course, an exchange carrier issue. While the primary exposure is to high–powered AM broadcast stations, other radio transmitters occasionally produce similar effects.

Transmission Level Point Coordination

VF circuits that provide similar services coordinate best when they are laid out so that transmission level points (TLPs) are equal at the same physical points along the common route. When this is done, crosstalk effects are minimized because there is no high TLP producing crosstalk by coupling into a low TLP of another circuit. Such an ideal layout is often not achievable. Different directions of transmission usually result in different TLPs at the same point in a two–wire circuit and at highly correlated points in a four–wire circuit. Furthermore, the signal amplitudes at a given TLP may vary considerably according to the type of signal transmitted. Nevertheless, crosstalk can be controlled by making the TLPs in different circuits as much alike as possible.

In all cases, signal levels in disturbed and disturbing circuits at the point of coupling determine to a large extent the seriousness of any coordination problems. If the circuits involved are voiceband and if the coupling characteristics are known, the TLP concept is useful in establishing coordination relationships. Where grossly unlike signals are involved, other criteria must be used to judge the interactions that may exist.

Data Loops

Loops are used for the transmission of voiceband data, local area data channel (LADC) signals, Public Switched Digital Service (PSDS) 56–kb traffic, data–above–voice, integrated services digital network (ISDN) signals, DS1 high–capacity services, ISDN primary–rate access, and the customer data speeds (2.4, 4.8, 9.6, 19.2, or 56 kb/s) in the Digital Data System (DDS). It has been found that data loops for most of these services coordinate satisfactorily with each other, with voiceband circuits, and with the T1 carrier systems found in the loop plant. However, these data signals may cause excessive interference in 15–kHz program circuits. Single–channel analog loop carrier systems are uniquely exposed to 56–kb/s data when a 28–kHz carrier frequency is used. When such a difficulty is encountered, it is considered a special coordination problem. The disturbing signal amplitude may have to be reduced, coupling losses increased, or disturbed–circuit signal amplitude increased. It may be necessary to reassign service to different cable pairs or use DLC facilities. The use of a 2B1Q line–code standard for ISDN basic–rate access is intended to reduce the effects of ISDN–to–ISDN near–end crosstalk, which would be more severe if a code with greater high–frequency content were used.

There are a wide variety of proprietary formats for data–above–voice systems. ISDN basic–rate access involves the 2B1Q standard, and at least two prestandard line formats. These signals are capable of reducing each other's error margins. Coordination studies have been made, and spectrum–management tables are available showing the reduction in maximum loop range necessary to coordinate combinations of these systems.

Customer–Generated Signals

To prevent harmful interference via crosstalk, the power spectra of signals generated in terminal equipment are limited in

676

terms of their inband and out–of–band power. Federal Communications (FCC) rules [6] define the permissible power levels for voice and voiceband data, PBX systems, LADC terminals, and 1.5–Mb terminations. They also set requirements for longitudinal balance. Technical References are also available covering terminal output signals for a variety of services, for example, PSDS [7], DDS [8], voiceband data [9], and LADC circuits [10].

Loop Carrier Systems

Loop transmission needs are being served increasingly by digital carrier systems. Coordination problems have been studied extensively and such systems have been found to coordinate satisfactorily with preexisting analog systems in loop cables provided that certain restrictions are observed. Any number of analog loop carrier lines may be used with up to five T1–type lines in 6–, 11–, 16–, and 25–pair polyethylene–insulated conductor (PIC) cables and in 8–, 9–, 12–, 13–, and 25–pair binder units of larger PIC cables. For different binder units in PIC cables and in all types of pulp–insulated cable, there are no interference constraints and regular engineering rules apply. Span lines for 1.5–Mb/s high–capacity services and ISDN primary–rate access are designed similarly to T1 DLC spans, but require coordination of levels with DLC facilities at "Y" junctions.

25–3 COORDINATION IN THE TRUNK PLANT

As previous mentioned, coordination problems are basically crosstalk between carrier systems, between large numbers of circuits carried in the same or nearby facilities, or between combinations of such systems and circuits. In addition, there are a number of intrasystem phenomena that may be regarded as coordination problems to solve in the application of each system type.

Carrier Systems

The systems most commonly used are the T–types. These systems must be considered from the point of view of their coordination with systems of similar types. Some problems of coordination have grown out of methods of cable plant administration; engineering rules have been written in some cases to account for those methods of administration.

Generally, any type of interference in a digital transmission system results in a deterioration of the error margin. This may result in excessive errors in data transmission, an increase in impulse noise in pulse code modulation speech transmission, or, when framing is grossly affected, a temporary loss of service. Interference from one analog system into another is most likely to be evidenced by tones or intelligible crosstalk; interference from a digital system to an analog system is most likely to result in excessive noise in the disturbed circuits.

N–Type Carrier Systems. When early N–type carrier systems were installed, cable splicing methods, called random splicing, were such that the integrity of the binder groups was not maintained. As a result, most of these cables have limited usefulness for the application of T1 digital systems and essentially do not coordinate when both N– and T–type systems are required. The interference of T–type signals into N–type systems is likely to be excessive even where the cables have been spliced with binder group integrity maintained. The level of interference is hard to predict in advance. However, in a few cases working N cables have been converted to T1 spans without excessively degrading the remaining N systems.

T–Type Digital Systems. Coordination of T–type systems is primarily a problem of meeting crosstalk requirements between combinations of systems. For the most part, the T–type systems do not coordinate well with other systems such as the N–type or with circuits such as 15–kHz program. Such circuits should be segregated (e.g., by using a different binder group) from T–type systems. Where alternate facilities are not available, special engineering is usually necessary to make transmission satisfactory.

Upgrades of T1 span lines to higher capacity (e.g., to T1C, T1D, T148, or T1G) have often been carried out, but have required analysis of the potential for crosstalk within the cable or within the apparatus cases. In some instances, resplicing or upgraded cases were necessary.

Engineering rules specify the way T–type spans may be assigned to pairs in cables. The rules vary according to type of system, type of cable and apparatus case, mode of operation (i.e., one–cable, screened–cable, or two–cable), and other parameters. These rules are designed to permit a maximum number of systems to be assigned to a cable within the constraints of crosstalk and other interference criteria. The rules are dynamic: in some cases, further study of crosstalk effects and the performance of specific equipment items has led to the relaxation of previous limits, for example, permitting full–fill operation of the middle–ring pairs of large cables in single–cable spans.

Central–Office Cabling. In many cases, the routing of cables through central offices is carefully specified to control crosstalk between systems and circuits. Separate cables are specified for different types of systems and, in some cases, spacing between cables is specified as well. Sometimes the spacing requires different cable racks. Wiring to DSX–1, –1C, and –2 bays uses multipair cable with a shield overall; wiring to DSX–3 and –4 bays uses coaxial cable with its good shielding properties. Shielded frame jumpers have sometimes been required, despite their large size and relative inflexibility.

Frequency Coordination

The engineering of microwave radio systems and routes always involves careful consideration of frequency coordination. In the design of such systems, frequency allocations and the achievability of appropriate band–edge cutoff characteristics must optimize performance within the system and, simultaneously, must satisfy the rules and regulations of the FCC regarding occupied bandwidths, spectrum–usage efficiency, and frequency stability.

The layout of radio system routes must satisfy intrasystem requirements. Consideration must also be given to intersystem interferences between exchange carrier radio routes and between exchange carrier and other carrier routes using the same or similar microwave frequencies. Occasional special cases, like interference from radar, also occur.

Such coordination problems tend to be trivial where potential interference is between two systems using widely different frequency bands, but become most significant where the same frequency bands are involved. Such problems multiplied when satellite systems came into service because they originally used the 4– and 6–GHz bands predominantly. Interferences between satellite and terrestrial systems must be avoided. The problems become more complex because of the wide areas covered by microwave antenna patterns in satellite systems, but are relieved sizably by use of the 12– and 14–GHz bands.

References

1. *IEEE Std. 776–1987*, "IEEE Guide for Inductive Coordination of Electric Supply and Communication Lines" (New York: Institute of Electrical and Electronics Engineers, Inc., 1987).

2. *ANSI/IEEE Std. 820–1984*, "IEEE Standard Telephone Loop Performance Characteristics" (New York: Institute of Electrical and Electronics Engineers, Inc., 1984).

3. Batorsky, D. V. and M. E. Burke. "1980 Bell System Noise Survey of the Loop Plant," *AT&T Bell Laboratories Technical Journal*, Vol. 63, No. 3 (May/June 1984).

4. *ANSI/IEEE Std. 367–1979*, "Guide for Determining the Maximum Electric Power Station Ground Potential Rise and Induced Voltage from a Power Fault" (New York: Institute of Electrical and Electronics Engineers, Inc., 1979).

5. *Lightning, Radio Frequency, and 60–Hz Disturbances at the Bell Operating Company Network Interface*, Technical Reference TR–EOP–000001, Bellcore (Iss. 2, June 1987), pp. 23–27.

6. Federal Communications Commission. *Rules and Regulations, Title 47, Code of Federal Regulations, Part 68* (Washington, DC: U.S. Government Printing Office, Oct. 1987), Sections 68.308(b) and (e).

7. *Circuit Switched Digital Capability Network Access Interface Specifications*, Technical Reference TR–880–22135–84–01, Bellcore (Iss. 1, July 1984).

8. Bell System Technical Reference PUB 62310, *Digital Data System—Channel Interface Specification*, American Telephone and Telegraph Company (Sept. 1983).

9. Bell System Technical Reference PUB 41004, *Transmission Specifications for Voice Grade Private Line Data Channels*, American Telephone and Telegraph Company (Oct. 1973), pp. 19–20.

10. Bell System Technical Reference PUB 41028, *Data Communications Using Local Area Data Channels*, American Telephone and Telegraph Company (Iss. 1, June 1979), pp. 2–5.

Chapter 26

Common System Facilities

To function as an integrated network, the many types of transmission system, with different circuits and media, must interconnect flexibly. Each network element must operate compatibly with all the others to provide a full range of communications services economically and with satisfactory performance. The requirement for interconnection and compatibility necessitates special equipment units and creates a need for circuits and equipment common to a number of systems.

Among the most important features of the network regarding interconnection and compatibility are hierarchical multiplex arrangements. The resulting relationships among frequency bands in analog equipment and among transmission speeds in digital equipment make possible relatively simple translation between multiplex levels, provide standard interfaces, and facilitate maintenance and administration.

In addition to the need for interconnection, there are a number of other ways in which systems tie together through common equipment. In this category of equipment, the most significant is the signal sources and distribution facilities that synchronize analog and digital systems. Of similar importance is the equipment for emergency restoration of service that is required in the event of major route failure.

26-1 CIRCUIT AND SYSTEM INTERCONNECTION

Interconnections between various parts of the facility network may take place directly, where full compatibility exists, or through interface equipment that may modify signals only slightly or significantly. The various types of interconnection equipment may be grouped conveniently into categories that relate them to the frequency bands or to the types of carrier system involved. There are interconnections of voice–frequency (VF) circuits; of group, supergroup, and mastergroup channels of the frequency-division multiplex (FDM) hierarchy; of digital channels transmitting signals at defined bit speeds; and of mixed digital–analog channels.

Voice–Frequency Interconnections

Since the largest number of circuits in the telecommunications plant are currently VF, the largest number of interconnections are also at VF. These include cable–to–cable connections and connections between VF circuits and the channel banks of carrier systems. Interconnection points must provide signalling compatibility and maintenance access to each circuit.

Switching Systems. VF circuits are interconnected flexibly by switching systems that are organized into public or private switched networks or that provide business communications systems in the form of private branch exchanges (PBXs) and key telephone systems. These interconnections are made in switching networks according to the needs of the user, which are indicated by address signal–generated dial or dual–tone multifrequency (DTMF) pulsing and are extended through the networks by signalling systems. Most of the line equipments, and some of the trunk circuits, of these switches terminate on a VF basis.

Distributing Frames. There are several types of distributing frame. The older ones are arranged with cable pairs connected to terminals in vertical rows on one side of the frame and in horizontal rows on the other. Connections are made between pairs of terminals by jumper wires between the vertical and horizontal sides of the frame. The newer designs are single–sided and use insulation–displacement terminal blocks in only one orientation. To prevent jumper congestion, these later frames use a highly structured layout that interleaves terminations of loop pairs, line equipment, and tie cable pairs. With computer–controlled assignment to minimize jumper length, the result is a sizably improved frame system.

The most common of these frames is the main distributing frame (MDF). Trunk or loop cable pairs terminate on the vertical side of the MDF; equipment cables terminate on the horizontal side. The distant ends of the equipment cables are connected to line or trunk circuits at switching machines or to other equipment in the office. Jumper wires, called cross–connections, connect a specific loop or trunk to the assigned switch termination or other type of equipment. Other frames, for example, the intermediate distributing frame (IDF), terminate other equipment and the cables within the office.

Interconnections can be made at the MDF with nearly as much flexibility as those made by switching machines. However, the intended operations are relatively slow and semipermanent. Although these connections are soldered on older frame designs, most are made by wire–wrapping techniques or by forked terminals that cut through the insulation of the jumper.

Voice–Frequency Patch Bays. Jacks are provided in limited quantities for test access or patch–cord connections between VF circuits. Loops and special–services circuits may be connected to such patch facilities by cross–connection at the MDF. The patch–cord method provides great flexibility in the way circuits may be interconnected, but has declined in the face of automated test access and digital interfaces to switches.

Facility Terminals. All the features required to terminate a transmission circuit are consolidated into a facility terminal, as discussed in Chapter 4. Plug–in units that provide transmission and signalling functions are mounted in uniform bay arrangements. In addition to providing these functions for circuits operating exclusively at voice frequencies, facility terminal designs provide interfaces between VF and digital carrier systems with switched test access. Thus, they may be regarded as another type of equipment designed for interconnecting VF loops, trunks, and special–services circuits.

Analog Carrier Systems

The broadband analog carrier systems use equipment based on the group, supergroup, and mastergroup frequency assignments of the FDM hierarchy.

To satisfy service requirements along facility routes, blocks of channels must be dropped, blocked, and added. These functions, collectively called branching, are fulfilled by combinations of filters that pass or suppress those portions of the spectrum involved.

Where transmission systems are interconnected, the signals of all circuits of one system could be demultiplexed to VF and then reassembled for transmission over the other route or system. However, this would be unacceptably complex and expensive. Thus, connecting filters are provided at group, supergroup, and mastergroup levels of the hierarchy in the form of equipment units called connectors. Another unit, the N3–to–L junction, connects between N3 systems and the group band of the FDM hierarchy. For a discussion on branching, connectors, and the N3–L junction see Chapter 9.

Undersea Cable System Interconnections. A unique feature of most analog undersea cables is that they use 3–kHz channelization instead of the 4–kHz channels that are otherwise universal. Broadband facilities carrying a mixture of 3–kHz and 4–kHz channels would produce undesirable intermodulation products and other interferences. Therefore, undersea cable VF channels are transformed to 4–kHz channels at the first office location encountered in the United States.

Digital Systems

As new digital transmission and switching systems are added and as new digital services are introduced, provision must be made for the same flexibility, synchronization, and interconnection as in the analog portions of the network. Indeed, one reason for the success of digital facilities is their flexible interconnection without expensive filters, signal converters, high/low frequency plans, etc. The principal interconnection elements of the digital network are the multiplex units used to translate signals between the levels of the hierarchy, DSX–coded cross–connect frames, lightguide interconnection frames, digital cross–connect systems (DCSs), and interface units used for the direct interconnection of digital transmission and switching systems.

Digital Cross–Connect Frames. Digital cross–connections are made at the same hierarchical level (e.g., DSX–1 or DSX–3), which are also the designations for manual metallic cross–connect frames [1,2]. These frames, in addition to cross–connection terminations, include patch and monitor jacks along with tracer lamps to identify the two ends of a jumper. They are used for network rearrangement, patching, and test purposes. Interconnection standards describing the electrical characteristics at DSX–1, DSX–1C, DSX–2, DSX–3, and DSX–4NA interfaces have been produced by American National Standards Institute (ANSI) committee T1X1.4 [3]. The standard includes specifications on line rates, codes, and formats (including zero–code suppression), timing tolerances (jitter and wander), power levels, pulse shapes, and other characteristics, most of which are covered in Chapter 15. The tolerances on line rates are quoted here, in Table 26–1.

Table 26–1. Digital Line Rates and Tolerances

Signal	Line Rate (Mb/s)	Tolerance (ppm)
DS1	1.544	$\pm$ 32* (self–timed)
DS1C	3.152	$\pm$ 30
DS2	6.312	$\pm$ 33
DS3	44.736	$\pm$ 20
DS4NA	139.264	(Not available)

*DS1 receivers should tolerate $\pm$ 130 ppm.

Table 15–2 in Chapter 15 gives the maximum permissible levels of output jitter at DSX–1, DSX–1C, DSX–2, and DSX–3 interfaces within a digital network. These limits include jitter accumulated from transmission source to sink.

The DSX–1, –1C, and –2 are 110–ohm balanced points; higher DSXs are 75–ohm coaxial interfaces. A given office may have separate DSX–1s for loop and interoffice use, with tie cables or short span lines between them. Limits exist on the length of office cabling that can be accommodated between a terminal and a DSX bay while preserving standard signal levels. Greater lengths, as with long inter–DSX tie cables, may require repeatered intraoffice span lines.

Cross–Connect	Cable	Max. Length
DSX–1 or –1C	22 ga.	655 ft.
DSX–2	22 ga.	1000 ft.
DSX–3	RG–59	450 ft.

Fiber Distributing Frames. Where fiber facilities enter a building, it is common practice to use a special distributing frame with plug–and–jack connections for cross–connections between fiber pairs and optical regenerators. The jacks provide access for fault location via time–division reflectometers and other test sets, and for emergency restoration. The frames may provide mounting locations for wavelength–division multiplexing filters. They are carefully designed to protect the fiber patch cords and to guarantee that the minimum bending radius of a fiber is observed.

Digital Cross–Connect Systems. All–electronic (software controlled) cross–connect equipment is designated DCS. Some of the capabilities of a DCS are the integration of the basic DS0 or DS1 signals within or between higher level signals, multipoint bridging, one–way broadcasting, and test access [4]. These units use time–slot interchanges to transfer channels among terminations. They thus allow interconnection of, for example, channel 3 of termination 7 to channel 18 of termination 126. They eliminate channel banks at points where channels are transferred between carrier systems. This eliminates a decoding/recoding step with its transmission penalties, at the cost of about one millisecond of added round–trip delay. DS1 DCSs, originally available with only 127 ports (plus a test port), are now obtainable down to 16 ports and up to 1000 ports.

A DCS can be controlled remotely via a data link. This forms the basis of a service [5], whereby the exchange carrier's customer may control the cross–connections of rented circuit segments. This gives the user flexibility to reconfigure an existing network conveniently and almost instantaneously. Security partitioning is included to protect other customers whose circuits pass through the same DCS.

A DCS that can rearrange DS0 or DS1 signals within a DS3 has applications in avoiding back–to–back multiplexers. Termed a DCS 3/0 or DCS 3/1, it can be used for such purposes as handling integrated DLC systems and special services on the same DS3 signal, separating the two at the central office for routing to their respective destinations.

Performance considerations for multipoint bridging or conferencing of DS0 channels [6] when using a DCS include avoiding distortion caused by the summation of two legs, controlling level contrast between legs, overload protection, and noise and echo control.

A DCS may be equipped to handle digital data signals [7], providing DS0 cross–connection, subrate multiplexing, and test access for 2.4–, 4.8–, 9.6–, 19.2–, and 56–kb/s signals.

Digital–Analog Interfaces. At the time when long–haul transmission facilities were predominantly the broadband analog FDM type but digital switches were coming into the network, there was a pressing need for ways to connect analog channel groups to DS1 switch terminations without the expense of back–to–back channel banks [8]. There will remain some need for these devices during replacement of the remaining analog facilities. Two general devices are used for this purpose.

The first approach, termed an L[MX]–to–T connector, is basically a quad of analog channel banks integrated with a D4–type digital bank [9]. It thus accepts four 12–channel two–way channel groups (single–sideband, 60–108 kHz each), converts to voice frequency, then codes them (using pulse code modulation) into a pair of two–way DS1 signals (1.544 Mb/s each). Depending on the specific unit, it optionally provides for conversion of single–frequency signalling on the analog side to A– and B–bit signalling on the digital side, echo cancellation, compandoring for satellite facilities, and a DS1C signal in place of two DS1s. Analog carrier supplies and conversion of carrier–group–alarm signals between the analog and digital sides are included.

The second approach is to obtain a nearly all–digital design using finite–impulse–response digital filter banks [10]. The use of digital signal processing techniques avoids analog and per–channel components. The all–digital transmultiplexer connects two channel groups to a single DS1, including processing of the signalling paths.

Restoration. Most of the equipment and facilities used to restore service that has been lost due to a route failure consist of protection lines on other routes that have not been cut. Restoration procedures involve the use of such facilities by direct interconnection when the failed and restoration facilities are of the same type. Where the facilities are incompatible, the failed systems are often connected to maintenance multiplex equipment; the signals are demultiplexed and restored DS3–by–DS3 or mastergroup–by–mastergroup to the extent possible. DCSs and SONET*–based multiplexers afford the capability for switched restoration of high–capacity digital facilities.

Synchronous Optical Network. The need for SONET [11] has become evident as fiber optic systems materialize with ever–increasing bit–rate capacity and incompatible line codes. When several DS3 bit streams are multiplexed together, the timing similarity of each stream to the other streams becomes critical. Without SONET, a fragmented optical network would result. A standard signal format, with an extremely accurate synchronization network, ensures compatibility and flexibility with a variety of optical interfaces, as described in Chapter 15.

26-2 SYNCHRONIZATION

To avoid timing slips, there is an urgent need for accurate and stable timing signals for digital transmission and switching systems. Timing slips would cause clicks in speech signals and serious deterioration of digital signal transmission. The frequencies of pilots and carriers used in FDM equipment must be precise and stable. If they were not, serious transmission impairment would result. Signals might drift out of the passbands of filters and signal components might be significantly distorted.

In the United States, the needs for such accurate frequency and timing signals were filled for some years by the basic synchronization reference frequency (BSRF) and a nationwide carrier synchronization network. Individual subnetworks either draw from this synchronization network, or operate plesiochronously

---

* Synchronous optical network.

with high–quality clocks of their own. In addition to the stringent requirements on accuracy and stability, the BSRF and the distribution network must be highly reliable. Further details on analog synchronization are given in Chapter 9.

Digital Synchronization

In most digital transmission systems, the signal formats are designed so that a timing signal can be derived from the line signal at regenerators and terminals. The timing signal recovery circuits are designed to operate within the normal range of frequency shift expected. In a stand–alone digital system with only two terminals, one at each end, obtaining the timing signal from one of the terminal clocks for this purpose is satisfactory. However, fewer and fewer digital systems stand alone today. To have the flexibility needed to use digital transmission economically, it is necessary to interconnect digital signals between systems through digital switching and cross–connect systems. Therefore, a regional clock–synchronization network ensures that the timing of all interconnected digital signals are synchronized, as shown in Figure 26–1.

Small differences between the rate of a received signal and that of the master clocking network can be detected and compensated for by buffer stores and bit stuffing. However, if the frequency difference persists, a buffer may overflow or underflow and cause a timing slip. The system is designed to reset the buffer when this occurs, thus causing deletion or repetition of bits in the output signal. The overflow or underflow and the resulting reset cycle of the buffer continue until the frequency offset is corrected.

Digital timing is derived from and controlled by clocks of extremely high accuracy and stability. The outputs of these clocks are transmitted in a variety of ways to all parts of the region. At each location where synchronization is needed, a control signal derived from these clocks is used as a master.

The distribution and transmission of clock signals involve many intermediate links and pieces of apparatus. Each dependent office has a clock or synchronizing signal source of its own. These

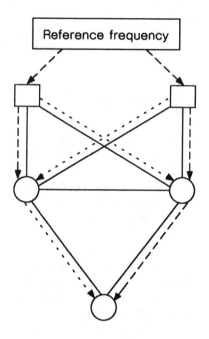

Digital switching system with reference frequency

Other digital switching system

Digital transmission facility

Primary frequency reference

Secondary frequency reference

Figure 26-1. Typical synchronization network.

local signal sources are controlled by a master clock as long as a master clock signal is available. Failure of intermediate transmission links or apparatus, however, can make a master clock signal unavailable. In such a case, the local clock becomes free–running, and its frequency may deviate enough from that of the master to be a source of synchronization impairments.

A variety of hardware items—the building integrated timing supply (BITS), the synchronization distribution expander (SDE), the composite clock generator (CCG), the Digital Data System

(DDS) timing supplies described in Volume 3, and the clock sources in digital switches—make up the timing network. As the name implies, the BITS concept ties all digital equipment in the building—switches, DDS equipment, DCSs, channel banks—to a common clock. This principle unifies formerly separate synchronization networks. The SDE is a multi–output source of timing outputs for use with multiple equipment bays. The CCG produces DDS composite clock signals, that is, with 8–kHz byte clock and 64–kHz bit clock on the same leads.

Synchronization Hierarchy

An ubiquitous synchronization network is required to prevent slips as the telecommunications network evolves toward all–digital operation. This requires that a hierarchical synchronization plan be adhered to for a systematic supply of timing signals. One of the dangers of not following a hierarchy system is the possibility of creating a loop within the synchronization network where a clock is being timed by its own output via other clocks in the loop. This would result in timing instability. Clocks must derive synchronization reference from other clocks that are higher in the synchronization hierarchy, never from one lower in the hierarchy.

Separate transmission facilities are not needed for hierarchical synchronization since existing digital transmission facilities are used between switching nodes. To enhance reliability, a backup link is furnished between each level of the network and high facility reliability criteria are established when choosing the facilities to be used for both the primary and alternate link [12].

References

1. Kovac, E. J. and H. K. Penberthy. "The DSX—A Key to the Emerging Digital Network," Bellcore EXCHANGE, Vol. 3, Iss. 1 (Jan./Feb. 1987), pp. 14–18.

2. *Fundamental Generic Requirements and Design Considerations for Metallic Digital Signal Cross–Connect Systems DSX–1, –1C, –2, –3*, Technical Advisory TA–NPL–000320, Bellcore (Iss. 2, Sept. 1986).

3. *ANSI T1.102–1987*, "American National Standard for Telecommunications—Digital Hierarchy—Electrical Interfaces" (New York: American National Standards Institute, 1987).

4. *Digital Cross-Connect System (DCS)—Requirements and Objectives*, Technical Reference TR–TSY–000170, Bellcore (Iss. 1, Nov. 1985).

5. Matthews, R. L. "Network Control in the Hands of the Customer," Bellcore EXCHANGE, Vol. 2, Iss. 2 (Mar./Apr. 1986), pp. 24–27.

6. *Digital Cross-Connect System—Requirements and Objectives for the Digital Multipoint Bridging Feature*, Technical Advisory TA–TSY–000281, Bellcore (Iss. 2, June 1986).

7. *Digital Cross-Connect System—Requirements and Objectives for the Sub-Rate Data Cross-Connect Feature*, Technical Advisory TA–TSY–000280, Bellcore (Iss. 2, May 1986).

8. *LT–1B Facility Connector Requirements and Specifications*, Compatibility Bulletin CB–119, American Telephone and Telegraph Company (1980).

9. Mitchell, W. J. "The LT–1 Connector—A Conventional Transmultiplexer," *IEEE Transactions on Communications Technology*, Vol. COM–27, No. 4 (Feb. 1979), pp. 355–360.

10. Narasimha, M. J. et al. "The TM7400–M2: An Improved Digital Transmultiplexer with Universal Signalling," *Conference Record*, IEEE International Conference on Communications (1981), Paper 7–2.

11. *Wideband Digital Cross-Connect System (W–DCS)—Generic Requirements and Objectives*, Technical Advisory TA–TSY–000233, Bellcore (Iss. 3, Dec. 1987).

12. *Digital Network Synchronization Plan*, Technical Advisory TA–NPL–000436, Bellcore (Iss. 1, Nov. 1986).

Acronyms

The acronyms listed here reflect usage in this book. They may be used differently in other contexts.

ABBH	Average Bouncing Busy Hour	**AIS**	Automatic Intercept System
ABS	Average Busy Season	**AL**	Acceptance Limit
ABSBH	Average Busy–Season Busy Hour	**ALBO**	Automatic Line Build–Out
		AM	Amplitude Modulation
ACD	Automatic Call Distributor	**AMI**	Alternate Mark Inversion
ACRS	Accelerated Cost Recovery System	**AML**	Actual Measured Loss
ACXT	Apparatus Case Crosstalk	**ANSI**	American National Standards Institute
ADM	Adaptive Delta Modulation	**AOS**	Alternate Operator Services
ADPCM	Adaptive Differential Pulse Code Modulation	**APC**	Automatic Power Control
ADR	Asset Depreciation Range	**APD**	Avalanche Photodetector Diode
ADTS	Automated Digital Termination System	**ARSB**	Automated Repair Service Bureau
AGC	Automatic Gain Control	**ASK**	Amplitude Shift Keying
AIOD	Automatically Identified Outward Dialing	**AT**	Access Tandem
		AT&T	American Telephone and Telegraph Company
AIS	Alarm Indication Signal (or)		

AUTOVON	Automatic Voice Network	CAC	Compandored Analog Carrier
AWG	American Wire Gauge	CAMA	Centralized Automatic Message Accounting
AXPIC	Adaptive Cross–Polar Interference Canceller		
		CARL	Computerized Administrative Route Layouts
		CAROT	Centralized Automatic Reporting on Trunks
B3ZS	Bipolar Format with Three–Zero Substitution		
B6ZS	Bipolar Format with Six–Zero Substitution	CATV	Cable Television
		CCC	Clear–Channel Capability
B8ZS	Bipolar Format with Eight–Zero Substitution	CCG	Composite Clock Generator
		CCIR	International Radio Consultative Committee
BDDS	Basic Dedicated Digital Service		
BER	Bit Error Ratio	CCIS	Common–Channel Interoffice Signalling
BETRS	Basic Exchange Telecommunications Radio Service		
		CCITT	International Telegraph and Telephone Consultative Committee
BITS	Building Integrated Timing Supply		
BLER	Block Error Ratio		
BOC	Bell Operating Company (or)	CCS	Common–Channel Signalling (or)
BOC	Build–Out Capacitor		
BOL	Build–Out Lattice	CCS	Hundred Call Seconds (Per Hour)
BOR	Build–Out Resistor		
BPF	Bandpass Filter		
BRI	Basic Rate Interface	CCSA	Common–Control Switching Arrangement
BSRF	Basic Synchronization Reference Frequency	CDCF	Cumulative Discounted Cash Flow

CDMA	Code–Division Multiple Access	**CREG**	Concentrated Range Extension with Gain
CEPT	European Conference of Posts and Telecommunications	**CS**	Channel Switching
		CSA	Carrier Serving Area
CFA	Carrier Failure Alarm	**CSDC**	Circuit Switched Digital Capability
CGA	Carrier Group Alarm	**CSP**	Control Switching Point
CHILL	CCITT High–Level Language	**CSU**	Channel Service Unit
CL	Carrier Liaison	**CTX**	Centrex
CLRC	Circuit Layout Record Card	**CUCRIT**	Capital Utilization Criteria
CMC	Cellular Mobile Carrier	**CX**	Composite (Circuit)
CMD	Circuit–Mode Data		
CMOS	Complementary Metal–Oxide Semiconductor	**DA**	Directory Assistance
		DART	Distribution Area Rehabilitation Tool
CMTT	Joint CCIR–CCITT Study Group on Transmission of Sound Broadcasting and Television Systems Over Long Distances	**DAVID**	Data Above Video
		DBOC	Drop Build–Out Capacitor
		DCE	Data Circuit–Terminating Equipment
		DCF	Discounted Cash Flow
CMV	Joint CCIR–CCITT Study Group for Vocabulary	**DCMS**	Digital Circuit Multiplication System
CO	Central Office	**DCS**	Digital Cross–Connect System
COD	Central–Office District		
COT	Central–Office Terminal	**DCT**	Digital Carrier Terminal (or)
CPE	Customer–Premises Equipment	**DCT**	Digital Carrier Trunk
CRC	Cyclic Redundancy Check	**DDB**	Digital Data Bank

DDD	Direct Distance Dialing	**DSBTC**	Double Sideband with Transmitted Carrier
DDS	Digital Data System		
DEMS	Digital Electronic Message Service	**DSI**	Digital Speech Interpolation
DFB	Distributed Feedback	**DSL**	Digital Subscriber Line
DFSG	Direct–Formed Supergroup	**DSN**	Defense Switched Network
DIC	Direct InterLATA Connecting	**DSS**	Data Station Selector
DILEP	Digital Line Engineering Program	**DSU**	Data Service Unit
		DSX	Digital Signal Cross–Connect
DLC	Digital Loop Carrier	**DTA**	Digitally Terminated Analog
DLP	Decode Level Point	**DTE**	Data Terminal Equipment
DM	Digital Multiplex		
DNHR	Dynamic Nonhierarchical Routing	**DTMF**	Dual–Tone Multifrequency
		DTS	Digital Termination System
DP	Dial Pulse		
DPP	Discounted Payback Period	**DUV**	Data Under Voice
		DX	Duplex (Signalling)
DRS	Digital Reference Signal		
DS	Digital Signal		
DS0	Digital Signal Level 0 (64 kb/s)	**EA**	Equal Access
		EAEO	Equal–Access End Office
DS1	Digital Signal Level 1 (1.544 Mb/s)	**EAS**	Extended Area Service
DS2	Digital Signal Level 2 (6.312 Mb/s)	**ECSA**	Exchange Carriers Standards Association
DS3	Digital Signal Level 3 (44.736 Mb/s)		
		EDD	Envelope Delay Distortion
DS4	Digital Signal Level 4 (274.176 Mb/s)	**EFS**	Error–Free Seconds
DSB	Double Sideband	**EHD**	Expected High Day
DSBSC	Double–Sideband Suppressed Carrier	**EIA**	Electronic Industries Association

EIRP	Effective Isotropic Radiated Power	FCC	Federal Communications Commission
ELCL	Equal Level Coupling Loss	FCOD	Foreign Central–Office District
ELEPL	Equal Level Echo Path Loss		
ELERL	Equal Level Echo Return Loss	FDM	Frequency–Division Multiplexing
ELP	Encode Level Point	FDMA	Frequency–Division Multiple Access
ELSRL	Equal Level Singing Return Loss	FET	Field–Effect Transistor
EML	Expected Measured Loss	FEXT	Far–End Crosstalk
EO	End Office	FFM	First Failure to Match
EPL	Echo Path Loss (or)	FFT	Fast Fourier Transform
EPL	Equivalent Peak Level	FG	Feature Group
ERL	Echo Return Loss	FM	Frequency Modulation
ES	Errored Seconds		
ESD	Electrostatic Discharge	FMAC	Facilities Maintenance and Administration Center
ESF	Extended Superframe Format		
ESM	Economic Study Module	FSK	Frequency Shift Keying
ET	Exchange Termination	FSL	Free Space Loss
ETL	Equipment Test List	FX	Foreign Exchange
		FXS	Foreign Exchange Station
ETN	Electronic Tandem Network	GDF	Group Distributing Frame
ETV	Educational Television	GoB	Good or Better
EU	End User	GOSCAL	Grade–of–Service Calculation
EVE	Extreme Value Engineering	GS	Ground Start
		HAIS	Host Automatic Intercept System
FAX	Facsimile Communication	HC	High Capacity

HCDS	High–Capacity Digital Service	**ISC**	Intercompany Service Coordination
HDBH	High–Day Busy Hour	**ISDN**	Integrated Services Digital Network
HDTV	High–Definition Television	**ISMX**	Integrated Subrate Multiplexer
HF	High Frequency		
HU	High Usage	**ITC**	International Teletraffic Congress
		ITT	Intertandem Trunk
		ITU	International Telecommunications Union
IAL	Immediate Action Limit		
IC	Interexchange Carrier	**ITV**	Industrial Television
		IXT	Interaction Crosstalk
ICCF	Industry Carriers Compatibility Forum	**JEG**	Joint Expert Group
		JFS	Jumbogroup Frequency Supply
ICL	Inserted Connection Loss	**JIS**	Jurisdictionally Interstate Service
IDF	Intermediate Distributing Frame	**JMX**	Jumbogroup Multiplex
IDLC	Integrated Digital Loop Carrier		
IEEE	Institute of Electrical and Electronics Engineers	**KEMAR**	Knowles Electronic Manikin for Acoustic Research
IEOT	Inter–End–Office Trunk	**KSI**	Key Service Indicator
IF	Intermediate Frequency	**KTS**	Key Telephone System
IMTS	Improved Mobile Telephone Service	**KTU**	Key Telephone Unit
INA	Integrated Network Access	**LAD**	Loop Activity Data
INMD	In–Service Nonintrusive Measurement Device	**LAMA**	Local Automatic Message Accounting
		LAN	Local Area Network
IROR	Internal Rate of Return	**LATA**	Local Access and Transport Area

LATIS	Loop Activity Tracking Information System	**MAN**	Metropolitan Area Network
LBO	Line Build-Out	**MARR**	Minimum Attractive Rate of Return
LBR	Local Business Radio	**MAT**	Metropolitan Area Trunk
LBRV	Low-Bit-Rate Voice	**MCVD**	Modified Chemical Vapor Deposition
LCD	Liquid Crystal Display	**MDF**	Main Distributing Frame
LD	Long Distance		
LDR	Local Distribution Radio	**MF**	Multifrequency
		MFD	Mode Field Diameter
LEAD	Loop Engineering Assignment Data	**MFT**	Metallic Facility Terminal
LED	Light-Emitting Diode	**MG**	Mastergroup
LEIM	Loop Electronics Inventory Module	**MGDF**	Mastergroup Distributing Frame
LFACS	Loop Facility Assignment and Control System	**MGT**	Mastergroup Translator
LIU	Line Interface Unit	**M-JCP**	Multiplexer Jack and Connector Panel
LMX	L-Type Multiplex		
LOCAP	Low Capacitance	**MJU**	Multipoint Junction Unit
LPC	Linear Predictive Coding	**ML**	Maintenance Limit
LPF	Low-Pass Filter	**MLDS**	Microwave Local Distribution System
LRD	Long-Route Design		
LRE	Loop Range Extender	**MLRD**	Modified Long-Route Design
LSB	Lower Sideband	**MMGT**	Multimastergroup Translator
LSSGR	LATA Switching Systems Generic Requirements	**MMIC**	Monolithic Microwave Integrated Circuit
LT	LATA Tandem		
LTEE	Long-Term Economic Evaluator	**MML**	Man-Machine Language
		MMX	Mastergroup Multiplex
MAC	Multiplexed Analog Component	**MNRU**	Modulated Noise Reference Unit

701

MRSELS	Microwave Radio and Satellite Engineering and Licensing System	**NMDG**	Network Management Development Group
MSS	Mobile Satellite Service	**NOF**	Network Operations Forum
MTBF	Mean Time Between Failures	**NOTE**	Network Office Terminal Equipment
MTS	Message Telecommunications Service	**NPA**	Numbering Plan Area
		NPV	Net Present Value
MTSO	Mobile Telephone Switching Office	**NPWE**	Net Present Worth of Expenditures
MTU	Maintenance Terminating Unit	**NRZ**	Non-Return to Zero
		NT	Network Termination
		NT1	Network Termination Type 1
		NTC	Network Transmission Committee
NA	Numerical Aperture		
NANP	North American Numbering Plan	**NTIA**	National Telecommunications & Information Administration
NAS	North American Standard		
NBOC	Network Building-Out Capacitor	**NTS**	Network Technical Support
NCAC	Noncompandored Analog Carrier	**NTSC**	National Television System Committee
NCF	Net Cash Flow	**NTT**	Nippon Telegraph and Telephone
NCTE	Network Channel Terminating Equipment	**NTTMP**	Network Trunk Transmission Measurements Plan
NE	Network Element		
NEBS	Network Equipment Building System	**NXX**	End-Office Code
NEXT	Near-End Crosstalk		
NI	Network Interface		
NIC	Nearly Instantaneously Compandored	**OAM**	Once A Month
		OBF	Ordering and Billing Forum

702

OCL	Overall Connection Loss	PBX	Private Branch Exchange
OCU	Office Channel Unit	PC	Personal Computer (or)
OCUDP	Office Channel Unit Dataport	PC	Primary Center
OCVD	Outside Chemical Vapor Deposition	PCM	Pulse Code Modulation
OGT	Outgoing Trunk	PDM	Pulse Duration Modulation
OMFS	Office Master Frequency Supply	PEVL	Polyethylene Video Line (16–gauge cable)
ONAL	Off–Network Access Line		
ONI	Operator Number Identification	PFM	Pulse Frequency Modulation
ONS	On–Premises Station	PFS	Primary Frequency Supply
OPS	Off–Premises Station		
OPX	Off–Premises Extension	PIC	Polyethylene– Insulated Conductor
ORB	Office Repeater Bay		
OS	Operations System	PIN	Positive Intrinsic Negative
OSHA	Occupational Safety and Health Administration	PLAR	Private–Line Automatic Ringdown
OSI	Open Switch Interval	PLL	Phase–Locked Loop
OSS	Operations Support System (or)	PM	Phase Modulation
		PMD	Packet–Mode Data
		POT	Point of Termination
OSS	Operator Services System	POTS	Plain Old Telephone Service
OSSGR	Operator Services Systems Generic Requirements	PoW	Poor or Worse
		PPM	Pulse Position Modulation
OTDR	Optical Time– Domain Reflector	PPSN	Public Packet–Switched Network
		PPSNGR	Public Packet–Switched Network Generic Requirements
PAM	Pulse Amplitude Modulation		
PAR	Peak–to–Average Ratio	PR	Protective Relaying

PRR	Project Rate of Return	**REG**	Range Extender with Gain
PSAP	Public Safety Answering Point	**RF**	Radio Frequency
		RG	Ringing Generator
PSDS	Public Switched Digital Service	**RHC**	Regional Holding Company
PSK	Phase Shift Keying	**RL**	Return Loss
PSN	Public Switched Network	**ROH**	Receiver Off Hook
		ROLR	Receive Objective Loudness Rating
PSS	Packet Switching System	**RRD**	Revised Resistance Design
PT	Principal Tandem		
PVN	Private Virtual Network	**RSB**	Repair Service Bureau
PWAC	Present Worth of Annual Charges	**RSM**	Remote Switching Module
PWE	Present Worth of Expenditures	**RSU**	Remote Switch Unit
		RT	Remote Terminal
		RTA	Remote Trunk Arrangement
QAM	Quadrature Amplitude Modulation	**RTU**	Remote Test Unit
		RZ	Return to Zero
QPRS	Quadrature Partial-Response Signalling	**SAGM**	Separated Absorption, Grating, and Multiplication
QSDG	Quality of Service Development Group		
		SAI	Serving Area Interface
RAIS	Remote Automatic Intercept System	**SAS**	Switched Access Service
RC	Regional Center (or)	**SB**	Sideband
RC	Resistor–Capacitor	**SC**	Sectional Center
RD	Resistance Design	**SCA**	Subsidiary Communications Authorization
RDS	Radio Digital System		
RDSN	Region Digital Switched Network	**SCPC**	Single Channel Per Carrier
RDT	Remote Digital Terminal	**SDE**	Synchronization Distribution Expander
REA	Rural Electrification Administration		

SDL	Specification and Descriptive Language	SRL	Singing Return Loss
		SSB	Single Sideband
		SSBAM	Single–Sideband Amplitude Modulation
SDM	Standard Error of Mean		
SDN	Switched Digital Network	SSC	Special–Services Center
SES	Severely Errored Seconds	SSMA	Spread–Spectrum Multiple Access
SF	Single Frequency	SSN	Switched Services Network
SG	Study Group		
SGDF	Supergroup Distributing Frame	ST	Sector Tandem
		STC	Serving Test Center
SL	System Level	STDM	Statistical Time–Division Multiplexer
SMDR	Station Message Detail Recording		
		STD–RL	Standard Return Loss
SMDS	Switched Multi–Megabit Data Service	STE	Signalling Terminal Equipment
SMRS	Special Mobile Radio Service	STL	Studio–to–Transmitter Link
SMSA	Standard Metropolitan Statistical Area	SW	Sync Word
		SX	Simplex
		SYNTRAN	Synchronous Transmission
SOLR	Sidetone Objective Loudness Rating		
SONAD	Speech–Operated Noise–Adjusting Device	T1	Carrier System or Standards Committee
SONET	Synchronous Optical Network	T1DM	T1 Data Multiplexer
		T1OS	T1 Outstate
SP	Signal Processor	TAS	Telephone Answering Service
SPC	Stored Program Control		
		TASI	Time–Assignment Speech Interpolation
SPCS	Stored Program Controlled System		
SR	Sidetone Response	TC	Time Consistent (or)
SRDM	Subrate Data Multiplexer		
		TC	Toll Center
SRE	Signalling Range Extender	TCM	Time–Compression Multiplexing

TCT	Tandem–Connecting Trunk	TSPS	Traffic Service Position System
TD	Terminal Digit (or)	TT&C	Tracking, Telemetry, and Control
TD	Test Distributor	TWT	Traveling Wave
TDM	Time–Division Multiplexing		Tube
TDMA	Time–Division Multiple Access	UDPC	Universal Digital Portable
TE	Transverse Electric		Communications
TEM	Transverse Electromagnetic	UHF	Ultra High Frequency
THDBH	Ten High–Day Busy Hour	UI	Unit Interval
TIC	Tandem InterLATA Connecting	UNICCAP	Universal Cable Circuit Analysis Program
TL	Transducer Loss (or)	USB	Upper Sideband
TL	Transmission Level	USOA	Uniform System of Accounts
TLP	Transmission Level Point		
TM	Transverse Magnetic	VBD	Voiceband Data
TMRS	Telephone Maintenance Radio Service	VF	Voice Frequency
		VG	Voice Grade
		VHF	Very High Frequency
TOC	Television Operating Center	VITS	Vertical Interval Test Signal
TOLR	Transmit Objective Loudness Rating	VLSI	Very–Large–Scale Integration
TRA	Tax Reform Act	VNL	Via Net Loss
TSA	Transmission Surveillance Auxiliary	VNLF	Via Net Loss Factor
		VOGAD	Voice–Operated Gain–Adjusting Device
TSC	Transmission Surveillance Center	VSA	Voice–Switched Attenuator
TSGR	Transport Systems Generic Requirements	VSAT	Very–Small– Aperture Terminal
TSI	Time–Slot Interchange	VSB	Vestigial Sideband

VSWR	Voltage Standing Wave Ratio	**WEPL**	Weighted Echo Path Loss
VT	Virtual Tributary	**WLEL**	Wire–Line Entrance Link
VU	Volume Unit	**WORD**	Work Order Record and Details
WAL	WATS Access Line		
WAN	Wide Area Network	**WP**	Working Party
WATS	Wide Area Telecommunications Service	**ZBTSI**	Zero–Byte Time–Slot Interchange
WDM	Wavelength–Division Multiplexing		

Index

A

A and B leads, 179
A2 video transmission system, 156
A4 video transmission system, 158
Absolute delay, 590, 611, 633
Absorption,
  fiber, 63
  microwave rain, 51, 475
ac signalling, 131
Access, primary rate, 145
Access facilities, data, 136
Active equalizer, 127
Activity factor, 243
Adaptive cross-polarization
  interference canceller, 560, 580
Adaptive differential pulse code
  modulation (ADPCM), 322
Adaptive equalizer, 50, 140, 254,
  548
Add/drop multiplexer (ADM), 404
Add-on channel, 103
Add-on service, 199
Adding, channel, 497, 685
Addition,
  laws of, 244, 248
  voltage, 248
Address signal, 611
Administration,
  line, 298
  main-station, 297
Aircraft services, 598
Alarm,
  carrier failure (CFA), 237
  carrier frequency, 228, 492, 625
  carrier group (CGA), 237, 272,
    625
  red, 626
  yellow, 327, 626
Alarm arrangement, 340, 620
Alarm indication signal (AIS), 626
Alarm polling, 301
Alarm services, 103
Alarm surveillance and control,
  630

Alerting signal, 186
Allocation area, 602
Alternate mark inversion, 111, 146
Alternate routing, 480
American National Standards
  Institute, 112
Amplifier,
  intermediate-frequency, 545,
  radio-frequency, 545
Amplifier stability, 129, 457
Amplitude modulation, 5, 311, 532,
  572
Analog carrier interconnection,
  683
Analog carrier system, 6, 103, 239
  coaxial, 283, 625
  maintenance, 237, 256, 624
  short-haul, 7, 259
Analog data signal, 135
Analog entrance link, 481
Analog interface, data station, 142
Analog load capacity, 241
Analog loop-back testing, 279
Analog loop carrier, 103
Analog microwave system, 517
Analog multiplex hierarchy, 230
Analog system design, 240
Analog system reliability, 298
Analog transmission system
  maintenance, 237, 624
Analog trunk interface, 191
Analysis, transmission, 16, 240,
  301, 617
Angle diversity, 489
Answering service, telephone, 198,
  208
Antenna,
  diversity, 487
  fan-beam, 557
  horn-reflector, 54, 476, 518
  microwave, 52
  mobile radio, 595, 600
  parabolic, 53, 476
Antenna gain, 47, 52, 566, 576, 581
Antenna polarization, 52, 475, 576
Apparatus-case crosstalk, 444

G

N

O

P